Second Custom Edition for Jefferson Community and Technical College

ELEMENTARY AND INTERMEDIATE ALGEBRA

CONCEPTS AND APPLICATIONS

MT 065 Basic Algebra

MARVIN L. BITTINGER
DAVID J. ELLENBOGEN
BARBARA L. JOHNSON

D1317103

Taken from:
Elementary and Intermediate Algebra: Concepts and Applications, Fifth Edition
by Marvin L. Bittinger, David J. Ellenbogen, and Barbara L. Johnson

Custom Publishing

New York Boston San Francisco
London Toronto Sydney Tokyo Singapore Madrid
Mexico City Munich Paris Cape Town Hong Kong Montreal

Cover photos courtesy of Jefferson Community and Technical College

Taken from:

Elementary and Intermediate Algebra: Concepts and Applications, Fifth Edition
by Marvin L. Bittinger, David J. Ellenbogen, and Barbara L. Johnson
Copyright © 2010 by Pearson Education, Inc.
Published by Addison-Wesley
Boston, Massachusetts 02116

Printed in the United States of America

10 9 8 7 6 5 4 3 2

2009361009

JM/LD

**Pearson
Custom Publishing**
is a division of

www.pearsonhighered.com

ISBN 10: 0-558-30605-5
ISBN 13: 978-0-558-30605-2

Jefferson Community & Technical College

MT065 Basic Algebra with Measurement

Supplemental Material

Table of Contents

Acknowledgements

The Developmental Mathematics Department extends much deserved thanks and sincere appreciation to the following faculty and college administration members for their contribution toward creation of this customized Pre-algebra book for the Jefferson Community and Technical College and the University of Louisville Pathways Program's students:

Mrs. Shari Bennett

Mrs. Lisa Brosky

Mrs. Venita Dobson

Dr. Dennis Guagliardo

Mrs. Linda Hook

Mrs. Monica Jones

Mr. Dan Kesterson

Mr. Paul Klein

Mrs. Karen Klingenfus

Mrs. Caroline Martinson

Mr. Bob Olsen

Dr. Frank Pecchioni

Mrs. Donna Riedel

Hamid Attarzadeh
Associate Professor, Mathematics
Developmental Mathematics Department Head
Jefferson Community and Technical College Downtown
(502) 213 – 5038
Hamid.attarzadeh@kctcs.edu

MT065 Basic-Algebra

Important Information

Class Information	Instructor Information
Section	Name
Class Number	Office Location
Meeting Days	Phone Number
Meeting Time	Email Address
Classroom Location	Office Hours

The Natural Sciences/Mathematics Division office is located in HFD 1111. The phone number for the Division office is 213-5012 or 213-5013.

This course is part of the Developmental Mathematics Department. Please contact Developmental Mathematics Department Head Hamid Attarzadeh at 213-5038 for further information.

Natural Sciences/Mathematics Learning Lab is Located in HFD 505. Call 213-5086 for hours of operation.

Natural Sciences/Mathematics Computer Lab is Located in HFD 1110. Call 213-5083 for hours of operation.

Natural Sciences/Mathematics Computer Classroom is Located in HFD 607A. Call 213-5012 or 213- 5013 for hours of operation.

Steps for Registering as a new student with MyMathLab®

1) Go to www.coursecompass.com.
2) Click on REGISTER button for Students.
3) Make sure that the button for Get access to a new course is selected and click Next.
4) Enter the course ID provided by your teacher and click FIND THE COURSE button.
5) Select Access Code.
6) Enter your code in the space below (using tab to move between the fields) and Click on NEXT.
7) Create a login name and a password that you will use in the future.
8) Retype the password and record them for future use with MyMathLab®.
9) Put in the School's zip code, which is 40202.
10) Select United States as the country.
11) Select Your College (Jefferson Community College).
12) Select a security question and enter your answer, then select NEXT.
13) Enter first name, last name, email address.
13) Click NEXT button.
14) If your information is complete you will now be on the confirmation screen.
15) Click on the button to LOGIN with MyMathLab®.
16) You will be returned to the main login screen.
17) Enter the login name and password you just created to enter MyMathLab®.
18) Click on your course.
19) Click on your Homework, Quizzes, or Tests.
20) Click on your questions.
21) Submit or save after you finish all the questions.
22) If you have problem with your login, call 1-800-677-6337.

Organization of 3-Ring Binder

Some of your instructors may require that you organize your work in a 3-ring binder. You will use this to keep important materials that you will receive in class. **Much of your success in college is based on your ability to organize information so that you can use it easily.**

<u>Please buy dividers with tabs and organize your 3-ring binder.</u>   Your instructor may give you specific titles for the dividers in your notebook. If you are not directed to use specific titles, you might want to organize your binder as follows:

1st Divider Tab - Syllabus, etc.

Remember your syllabus is an important document that you may need to reference regarding class requirements and policies regarding attendance, exams, and grading. Other important papers might include the class calendar, assignment sheet and/or grade sheet to record quiz and exam grades.

2nd Divider Tab   Current Book and Class Notes

Before you attend class you should always read the section that will be covered and take notes. Write down important vocabulary words and definitions. Write down examples of problems that will be covered in class.   When you attend class you will be prepared to listen and add to your notes any notes from the class lecture or discussion. It is a good idea to review notes and reorganize any that are unclear. Use a highlighter to mark vocabulary or examples that your instructor emphasizes in class.

3rd Divider Tab   Documentation of Homework

Homework may be from your math textbook or MyMathLab. Label each section and number each problem. If you are doing homework from the textbook be sure to check your answers in the back of the textbook. This will help you prepare for quizzes and exams.

4th Divider Tab   Returned Quizzes and Exams

These will help you study for the comprehensive final exam.

5th Divider Tab...Handouts and Study Aids

You will receive many important handouts from your instructor during the semester. Now when you need one of those important papers in class, you will not have to turn your backpack upside down to find it!

Better Math Study Techniques

Good study strategies are the foundation of being a successful student in mathematics courses. The following are study habits that are specifically geared for use in your math class. If you make it a priority to do them, soon they will become a part of your life.

Before Class

- Review your previous class notes.
- Be sure you have worked all assigned problems from the previous class. Write down all questions exactly where you ran into trouble.
- Go to the math lab or seek help from other resources if you are having trouble.
- Read over the material that will be covered in the next class lecture. Don't worry if you don't understand. This will give you a general idea of what the lecture will cover and help you formulate possible questions for class.
- Bring a pencil, textbook, notebook, and a calculator ready to class.

During Class

- Attend class regularly.
- Be on time to class.
- Participate in class. Ask questions and answer questions posed by the teacher.
- Take good notes. Make sure your notes can be read and understood weeks later.
- Sit near the front of class
- Don't space out during lecture. Try to stay focused at all times during class.
- Don't compare your progress in class with that of you class mates. Everyone's mathematical background is different.

Studying for a test

- Don't cram. Make a study schedule. Work on math everyday.
- Review your notes, homework, and the textbook sections that will be covered on the test. If you missed a class, get the notes from a classmate or the teacher.
- Make a list of all concepts, formulas, and rules that will be covered on the test.

- Get help if you need assistance with the material or if you have test anxiety.
- Make a sample test.
- Review and relax the night before the test. Get a good night's sleep.

The Test
- Arrive early
- Ignore what other students have to say right before the test. Often they are confused and anxiously searching for solutions at the last minute.
- Bring pencils, paper, and a calculator to class.
- Write down all memorized formulas on your test paper before you begin working the test.
- Read all directions. If you don't understand the directions, ask the teacher for clarification.
- Look over the test and do what you know first.
- Show all your steps in a neat and orderly fashion.
- Check your work. Careless errors can make you lose points.
- Keep track of the time. If you get stuck, move on. Come back to that problem later. Do not spend 20 minutes on a problem that will give you few or no points.
- Try all problems. You may be able to get partial credit by just writing the formula or for setting up the problem.
- Watch out for math anxiety. Don't fool yourself into thinking you won't do well on the test before you have given your best effort.

The Returned Test
- Don't throw the test away.
- Read all the teacher comments and suggestions.
- Correct your test. Write the corrections on a separate piece of paper.
- Go see your teacher if you have questions about your grade or if you don't understand a problem.
- See if your mistakes have a common pattern.
- Use the returned test as a review for the final exam.

Effectively Using Your Resources

Tutors should be coaches, not crutches. They should not be expected to completely do the problem for you. Tutors are there to encourage you, give you hints, and sometimes show you how to do the problems. They are there to help you discover how to learn math for yourself.   To effectively use your resources, you should remember the following:

1. Don't get behind. Get help before a test is near or you fail a test.

2. Read your textbook and notes on the material that is confusing you and try to do some problems before you ask for help.

3. If you get stuck on a problem, do not erase your work. The tutor or teacher can look at your steps and see where you are going wrong.

4. Ask questions. Don't pretend to understand.

5. Do not become dependent on a tutor or your teacher constantly giving you hints or working problems for you. You are the one that has to take the test.

6. Tell your teacher or tutor how you feel about math and your math history. This can help them relate to your situation.

Check Yourself

Many students say that Math is difficult for them or that they are not "good" in Math. The reality may be that they are not putting the effort into the subject or using the support services available. Here is a list of behaviors that are necessary to succeed in Math at the college level.

Check the boxes that apply to you.

- ❑ I go to all classes.
- ❑ I know what's on the syllabus and have marked it in my day-planner
- ❑ I take notes in class.
- ❑ I read the textbook before class (and after if necessary.)
- ❑ I do the practice problems.
- ❑ I get help from the instructor – office hours or e-mail
- ❑ I use the study guide.
- ❑ I use the publisher's computer program.
- ❑ I go to the NS/Math Learning Lab – HFD 505.
- ❑ I belong to a Study group.
- ❑ I talk to other students.
- ❑ I have a private tutor.
- ❑ I get help from math oriented family or friends.

What can you add to your math study plan that can make you more successful?

_____

_____

_____

_____

_____

_____

_____

_____

_____

JCTC's Mathematics Courses

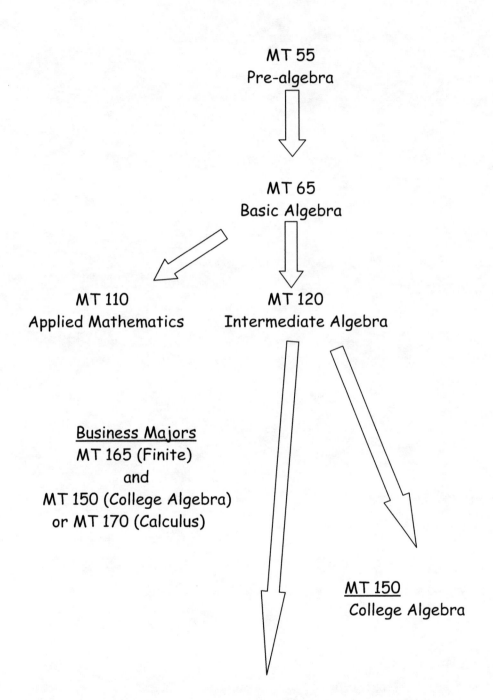

MT 55
Pre-algebra

MT 65
Basic Algebra

MT 110
Applied Mathematics

MT 120
Intermediate Algebra

Business Majors
MT 165 (Finite)
and
MT 150 (College Algebra)
or MT 170 (Calculus)

MT 150
College Algebra

If you don't need a particular Math
MT 145
(Contemporary College Mathematics)

Double Entry Organizer

FROM THE TEXT CONCEPTS/FACTS/INFORMATION	FROM THE READER QUESTIONS/IDEAS/OPINIONS

Discovering the Rules for the X-Game (Factoring Activity)

What patterns can you find? Think Critically. Write the rule that you discovered for each game.

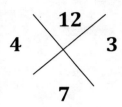

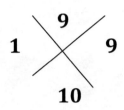

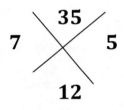

Complete each X-game below.

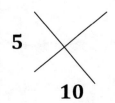

More X –Game Problems

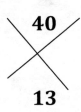

28
4

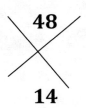

40

13

9   8

24
3

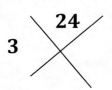

48

14

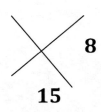

8

15

Evaluating Square and Cube Roots

Fill in the following chart by squaring each number.

x	x^2	x	x^2	x	x^2
1		6		11	
2		7		12	
3		8		13	
4		9		14	
5		10		15	

Evaluate the following square roots to the nearest hundredth where appropriate.

1. $\sqrt{16}$ _____

2. $\sqrt{25}$ _____

3. $\sqrt{9}$ _____

4. $\sqrt{81}$ _____

5. $\sqrt{49}$ _____

6. $\sqrt{144}$ _____

7. $\sqrt{200}$ _____

8. $\sqrt{225}$ _____

9. $\sqrt{289}$ _____

10. $\sqrt{345}$ _____

11. $\sqrt{75}$ _____

12. $\sqrt{89}$ _____

13. $\sqrt{167}$ _____

14. $\sqrt{654}$ _____

15. $\sqrt{987}$ _____

16. $\sqrt{37}$ _____

17. $\sqrt{35}$ _____

18. $\sqrt{27}$ _____

19. $\sqrt{245}$ _____

20. $\sqrt{880}$ _____

21. $\sqrt{12}$ _____

Fill in the following chart by cubing each number.

x	x^3	x	x^3	x	x^3
1		6		11	
2		7		12	
3		8		13	
4		9		14	
5		10		15	

Evaluate the following cube roots to the nearest hundredth where appropriate.

25. $\sqrt[3]{8}$ _____

26. $\sqrt[3]{64}$ _____

27. $\sqrt[3]{27}$ _____

28. $\sqrt[3]{125}$ _____

29. $\sqrt[3]{343}$ _____

30. $\sqrt[3]{512}$ _____

31. $\sqrt[3]{50}$ _____

32. $\sqrt[3]{72}$ _____

33. $\sqrt[3]{324}$ _____

34. $\sqrt[3]{16}$ _____

35. $\sqrt[3]{81}$ _____

36. $\sqrt[3]{144}$ _____

37. $\sqrt[3]{216}$ _____

38. $\sqrt[3]{200}$ _____

39. $\sqrt[3]{64}$ _____

40. $\sqrt[3]{256}$ _____

41. $\sqrt[3]{729}$ _____

42. $\sqrt[3]{54}$ _____

Finding the Third Side of a Right Triangle using the Pythagorean Theorem

In a right triangle, find the length of the side not given. Sides a and b are legs of the right triangle. Side c is the hypotenuse of the right triangle. Give your answers to the nearest hundredth where appropriate.

Pythagorean Theorem: $a^2 + b^2 = c^2$

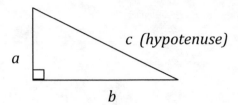

Example 1
A right triangle has legs of lengths 9cm and 12 cm. What is the length of the hypotenuse?

$$a^2 + b^2 = c^2$$
$$9^2 + 12^2 = c^2$$
$$81 + 144 = c^2$$
$$225 = c^2$$
$$\sqrt{225} = \sqrt{c^2}$$
$$c = 15$$

The hypotenuse has a length of 15cm.

Example 2
A right triangle has a leg that is 16ft long and a hypotenuse that is 30ft long. What is the length of the other leg?

$$a^2 + b^2 = c^2$$
$$16^2 + b^2 = 30^2$$
$$256 + b^2 = 900$$
$$b^2 = 644$$
$$\sqrt{b^2} = \sqrt{644}$$
$$b = 25.38$$

The length of the other leg is approximately 25.38 ft.

In a right triangle, find the length of the side not given. Sides a and b are legs of the right triangle. Side c is the hypotenuse of the right triangle. Give your answers to the nearest hundredth where appropriate.

1. $a = 3$, $b = 4$, $c =$ _____

2. $a = 6$, $b = 8$, $c =$ _____

3. $a = 7$, $b =$ _____, $c = 18$

4. $a = 9$, $b =$ _____, $c = 15$

5. $a = 24$, $b =$ _____, $c = 26$

6. $a =$ _____, $b = 4$, $c = 9$

7. $a = 8$, $b = 24$, $c =$ _____

8. $a = 1$, $b = 2$, $c =$ _____

9. $a =$ _____, $b = 7$, $c = 10$

10. $a =$ _____, $b = 12$, $c = 13$

11. $a = 4$, $b = 4$, $c =$ _____

12. $a = 13$, $b = 2$, $c =$ _____

13. $a = 15$, $b =$ _____, $c = 25$

14. $a =$ _____, $b = 10$, $c = 15$

15. $a = 75$, $b =$ _____, $c = 100$

16. $a =$ _____, $b = 12$, $c = 18$

Simplifying Square and Cube Roots

Simplify the following square roots.

43. $\sqrt{27}$ _____

44. $\sqrt{45}$ _____

45. $\sqrt{8}$ _____

46. $\sqrt{50}$ _____

47. $\sqrt{325}$ _____

48. $\sqrt{18}$ _____

49. $\sqrt{28}$ _____

50. $\sqrt{198}$ _____

51. $\sqrt{75}$ _____

52. $\sqrt{200}$ _____

53. $\sqrt{48}$ _____

54. $\sqrt{245}$ _____

55. $\sqrt{880}$ _____

56. $\sqrt{12}$ _____

57. $\sqrt{32}$ _____

58. $\sqrt{108}$ _____

59. $\sqrt{80}$ _____

60. $\sqrt{98}$ _____

Simplify the following cube roots.

61. $\sqrt[3]{16}$ _____

62. $\sqrt[3]{81}$ _____

63. $\sqrt[3]{40}$ _____

64. $\sqrt[3]{250}$ _____

65. $\sqrt[3]{320}$ _____

66. $\sqrt[3]{72}$ _____

67. $\sqrt[3]{324}$ _____

68. $\sqrt[3]{144}$ _____

69. $\sqrt[3]{200}$ _____

70. $\sqrt[3]{256}$ _____

71. $\sqrt[3]{54}$ _____

72. $\sqrt[3]{128}$ _____

THE METRIC SYSTEM

The metric system is based on powers of ten. This makes conversion between units much easier than with the English system. The basic metric units are the meter, the gram, and the liter. Meters, grams, and liters have smaller units and larger units than themselves. We will only study three larger units and three smaller units. Prefixes are used to talk about larger or smaller units. (Refer to page 8 of this handout.)

To convert from one metric unit to another, we can use dimensional analysis or a method of moving decimal points. Suppose you want to convert 52 dekameters to centimeters. Using dimensional analysis, we have

$$\frac{52 \text{ dam}}{1} \cdot \frac{10 \text{ m}}{1 \text{ dam}} \cdot \frac{100 \text{ cm}}{1 \text{ m}} = 52,000 \text{ cm}$$

A much easier method of converting in the metric system uses the number line below:

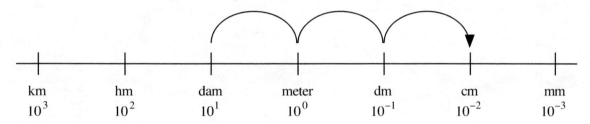

km	hm	dam	meter	dm	cm	mm
10^3	10^2	10^1	10^0	10^{-1}	10^{-2}	10^{-3}

To convert 52 dam to cm:

1. Locate dam (10^1) on the number line above.
2. Count the number of steps you have to take to get to cm (10^{-2}).
3. Move the decimal point that same number of steps (and in the same direction) to arrive at the conversion.

52.000

(Move decimal point 3 places to the right)

52 dam = 52,000 cm

Example 2:
Convert 32.6 millimeters to decimeters.
Referring to the number line above, to get from mm to dm, you must take two steps to the left.
Therefore,   32.6 mm = 0.326 dm

Example 3:
Convert 4.8 liters to kiloliters.
Again using the number line, to get from liters to kiloliters, you must take three steps to the left.
Therefore,   4.8 L = 0.0048 kL

METRIC/ENGLISH CONVERSIONS

There are times when you will need to convert English to metric measurements or metric to English measurements. Suppose you want to convert 16 feet to meters. Use dimensional analysis.

$$\frac{16 \text{ ft}}{1} \cdot \frac{12 \text{ in}}{1 \text{ ft}} \cdot \frac{2.54 \text{ cm}}{1 \text{ in}} \cdot \frac{1 \text{ m}}{100 \text{ cm}} = 4.8768 \text{ m}$$

$$16 \text{ ft} = 4.88 \text{ m}$$

Example 2:
Convert 52 ounces to kilograms.

$$\frac{52 \text{ oz}}{1} \cdot \frac{1 \text{ lb}}{16 \text{ oz}} \cdot \frac{0.454 \text{ kg}}{1 \text{ lb}} = 1.4755 \text{ kg}$$

$$52 \text{ oz} = 1.476 \text{ kg}$$

TEMPERATURE

In the metric system, temperatures are measured on the Celsius scale. You may also hear this called the Centigrade scale. The freezing point of water is 0 degrees. The boiling point of water is 100 degrees.

To convert 7° F to ° C, use the formula on page 8 of this handout.

$$C = \frac{5}{9}(F - 32)$$

$$C = \frac{5}{9}(7 - 32)$$

$$C = \frac{5}{9}(-25)$$

$$C = -13\frac{8}{9}\,^{\circ}$$

To convert 50° C to ° F:

$$F = \frac{9}{5}C + 32$$

$$F = \frac{9}{5}(50) + 32$$

$$F = 90 + 32$$

$$F = 122°$$

MEASUREMENT AND CONVERSIONS

To be successful in this section, you must memorize the following tables and formulas:

English System

Length

12 inches (in)	=	1 foot (ft)
3 feet	=	1 yard (yd)
5280 feet	=	1 mile (mi)

Weight

16 ounces (oz)	=	1 pound (lb)
2000 pounds	=	1 ton

Volume (liquid)

16 ounces	=	1 pint (pt)
2 pints	=	1 quart (qt)
4 quarts	=	1 gallon (gal)
8 ounces	=	1 cup

Volume (dry)

and

2 pints	=	1 quart (qt)
8 quarts	=	1 peck (pk)
4 pecks	=	1 bushel (bu)

Metric System

Length

1 kilometer (km)	=	1000 meters
1 hectometer (hm)	=	100 meters
1 dekameter (dam)	=	10 meters
1 meter (m)	=	10 decimeters (dm)
1 meter	=	100 centimeters (cm)
1 meter	=	1000 millimeters (mm)

Weight

gram (g)

Volume

# liter (L) or litre		
1 mL	=	1 cm^3

\# The same prefixes are used in weight

volume as are used in length.

English-to-Metric Conversions

Length

1 in	=	2.54 cm
1 mi	=	1.61 km
1 yd	=	0.91 m

Weight

1 oz	=	28.3 g
1 lb	=	0.454 kg

Volume

1 gal	=	3.78 L
1 qt	=	0.946 L

Temperature

$$C = \frac{5}{9}(F - 32)$$

$$F = \frac{9}{5}C + 32$$

C represents Celsius temperature and F represents Fahrenheit temperature.

CONVERTING UNITS – USING DIMENSIONAL ANALYSIS

You'll often need to convert from one measurement unit to another. For example, you may measure length with a measuring tape that reads in inches, but building materials are often supplied by the foot. Suppose you need 150 inches of wire but wire is sold by the foot. How many feet will you need?

To solve this problem, you must convert inches to feet. As you know, there 12 inches to a foot. This is called a **conversion factor**.

A conversion factor is a ratio. You can write a conversion factor as a fraction that is equal to one. For example,

$$\frac{12 \text{ inches}}{1 \text{ foot}} = 1 \qquad\qquad \frac{1 \text{ foot}}{12 \text{ inches}} = 1$$

Both fractions are equal to one. Multiplying by one leaves a value unchanged. You can multiply by a conversion factor without changing the original value.

In the wire example, you want to select a fraction that will end up with the correct units (feet). Set up the fraction so that you can cancel the units you do not want (inches).

$$\frac{150 \text{ i\!n.}}{1} \cdot \frac{1 \text{ ft.}}{12 \text{ i\!n.}} = 12.5 \text{ ft.}$$

Sometimes you may need to use more than one conversion factor. What if you needed to find the number of inches in 2 miles? You don't have a conversion factor for changing miles to inches. However, you do have a conversion factor for miles to feet and one for changing feet to inches. If you use both of these factors, you can change miles to inches.

$$\frac{2 \text{ m\!i.}}{1} \cdot \frac{5280 \text{ f\!t.}}{1 \text{ m\!i.}} \cdot \frac{12 \text{ in.}}{1 \text{ f\!t.}} = 126,720 \text{ in.}$$

The procedure for converting measurement units is shown below.

Converting Measurement Units

1. Select the appropriate conversion factor(s).
2. Write each conversion factor as a fraction that is equivalent to 1.
3. Set up a multiplication problem. Write the conversion factor(s) so that the units you wish to eliminate are in cross positions.
4. Eliminate (cancel) the units.
5. Complete the calculations. Your answer should be in the desired unit.

CONVERSION WORKSHEET

1. 650 m   =   _____ km

2. 6.1 kg   =   _____ g

3. 5.2 mm   =   _____ dm

4. 315 ft   _____ yd

5. 72° F   =   _____ ° C

6. 12 cups   =   _____ qt

7. 5 dL   =   _____ mL

8. 750 mL   =   _____ L

9. –25° C   =   _____ ° F

10. 8 pk   =   _____ pt

11. 5 km   =   _____ dam

12. 14 yd   =   _____ in

13. 380 cg   =   _____ hg

14. 2.64 hg   =   _____ cg

15. 8 oz   =   _____ g

16. 1500 yd   =   _____ km

17. 10 pt   =   _____ L

18. 56 dg   =   _____ oz

19. 1.5 mi   =   _____ km

20. 2 km   =   _____ ft

21. 15 cm   =   _____ ft

22. 4 cups   =   _____ cL

23. 2 1/4 mi   =   _____ yd

24. 746 in   =   _____ yd

25. 14 L   =   _____ pt

26. 2050 cg   =   _____ dag

ANSWERS

1.   0.65 km
2.   6100 g
3.   0.052 dm
4.   105 yd
5.   22.2° C
6.   3 qt
7.   500 mL
8.   0.75 L
9.   −13° F
10.   128 pt
11.   500 dam
12.   504 in
13.   0.038 hg
14.   26,400 cg
15.   226.4 g
16.   1.37 km
17.   4.73 L
18.   0.198 oz
19.   2.42 km
20.   6,559 ft
21.   0.49 ft
22.   94.6 cL
23.   3,960 yd
24.   20 13/18 yd ≈ 20.7 s yd
25.   29.6 pt
26.   2.05 dag

Electronics Technology
Engineering Notation

When working in electronics, you will encounter some very large and very small numbers. A coulomb, for example, represents the quantity of electrical charge carried by 6,250,000,000,000,000,000 electrons. We can use an extremely small number as another example. Some radios are set to break squelch at about 0.000003 volts. Numbers expressed in this fashion are often difficult for technicians to use. What range would you set a meter on to read 0.000003 volts? How many voltmeters have a 0.000001 volt range? If you were told that a computer's hard drive could hold 8,000,000,000 bytes, how would you convert that number to one that someone could understand?

The answer to the above questions can be answered by converting these numbers to engineering notation. Engineering notation is a term that refers to the application of scientific notation in which the powers of ten are limited to multiples of three. In **scientific notation**, a quantity is expressed as a product of a positive number between 1 and 10 and a power of 10. For example, the quantity 250,000 would be expressed in scientific notation as 2.5×10^5. The number 0.015 could be expressed as 1.5×10^{-2}.

To express a large number as a power of 10, move the decimal point to the left and count the number of places the decimal point is moved. The number of places counted indicates the power of 10. As an example let's convert 81,337 to scientific notation. We would start out by changing the number to 8.1337. Count the number of places the decimal moved to the left. Since it moved to the left 4 places, the number becomes 8.1337×10^4. Here are some more examples:

$$320,000 \text{ becomes } 3.2 \times 10^5$$
$$425,050,000 \text{ becomes } 4.2505 \times 10^8$$

To express a decimal fraction in scientific notation, express the fraction as a whole number times a power of 10. Move the decimal point to the right and count the number of places it has been moved. The number of places moved will be the negative power of 10. Consider the number 0.032. First change the number to 3.2. Count the number of places the decimal moved to the right. We moved the decimal 2 places, thus the number is 3.2×10^{-2}. Here are some more examples:

$$0.0000045 \text{ becomes } 4.5 \times 10^{-6}$$
$$0.000306 \text{ becomes } 3.06 \times 10^{-5}$$

Numbers can be more easily understood by using **engineering notation**. As mentioned above, engineering notation refers to the application of scientific notation in which the powers of ten are limited to multiples of three. Electronic multimeters are set up in ranges that accommodate engineering notation. If the above example were amperes, we would have a hard time finding out what range to put the amp meter on. We would quickly discover that there is no range for 10^{-5} amperes. There would, however, be a range for

10^{-6} amperes. It is more sensible to convert large and small numbers using engineering notation rather than simple scientific notation. How would we convert 0.0000306 (or 3.06×10^{-5}) to engineering notation? Remember, we want a multiple of three. This means that we want to convert the number to something $\times 10^{-6}$. If we move the decimal one more place to the right, our number will become 30.6×10^{-6} amperes or 30.6 microamps. Let's convert some of the other previous examples to engineering notation. Remember, 320,000 was 3.2×10^{5}. In order to express it as engineering notation, we would want it to be 10^{3} or 10^{6}. If we move our decimal to the left three places, the number becomes 320×10^{3} or 320 kilo.

The prefixes associated with engineering notation are shown in the table below.

Power of 10	Prefix	Symbol
10^{12}	Tera	T
10^{9}	Giga	G
10^{6}	Mega	M
10^{3}	Kilo	k
10^{-3}	Milli	m
10^{-6}	Micro	μ
10^{-9}	Nano	n
10^{-12}	Pico	p
10^{-15}	Femto	f
10^{-18}	Atto	a

Now let's use this notation on the numbers we saw in the introduction.

For the number 6,250,000,000,000,000,000 we would move the decimal point to the left 18 places. Our number would become 6.25×10^{18}. That's right! A coulomb represents the quantity of electrical charge carried by 6.25×10^{18} electrons. It's been said that if electrons were houseflies, a "coulomb" of dead flies would cover the state of New York to a depth of several feet!

To convert 0.000003, we would move the decimal point to the right 6 places. The number would then become 3×10^{-6}. According to our list, this number would have a "Micro" prefix. Thus our radio would break squelch at 3 microvolts or, using the symbol 3 μ volts.

What about the number 3.06×10^{-5}? This number is express in scientific notation not engineering notation. If you told some one that you wanted to measure 3.06×10^{-5} amperes, you would probably get a strange look at the very least. This answer is impractical and inappropriate. If we move the decimal point to the right one position, the exponent will decrease by one (remember that −6 is less than −5). Our number becomes

30.6×10^{-6} or 30.6 microamps (μ amps). A technician would have no trouble determining what scale to use to measure this quantity.

Convert the following quantities to engineering notation:

1. 0.00001204 amps = _____ m amps = _____ μ amps

2. 3,000,000,000 Hz = _____ MHz = _____ GHz

3. 47,500 W = _____ kW = _____ MW

4. 0.000000012 seconds = _____ μ sec = _____ n sec

5. 1.2×10^2 volts = _____ volts = _____ k volts

6. 1.2×10^{-2} volts = _____ volts = _____ m volts

7. 4.276×10^5 W = _____ kW = _____ MW

Complete the following:

8. 5 seconds = _____ m sec = _____ μ sec

9. 6.25 kW = _____ W = _____ MW

10. 3.25 m volts = _____ volts

11. 20 n seconds = _____ seconds

12. 8 G bytes = _____ bytes

Record the answer to each of the questions below in the space provided.

13. A certain technician calculated that **12 volts / 1250 W = 0.0096 amperes**. The ammeter s/he intends to use has a 1 amp range, a 1 m amp range, a 10 m amp range, a 100 m amp range, and a 1 μ amp range. Which range would s/he use to measure this quantity?

14. When reading the specifications for a computer, you discover that the bus frequency is 66 MHz. You decide to calculate the access time by performing the reciprocal of the frequency (T = 1/F). **1/66 MHZ = 0.000000015 seconds**. What is the access time in nanoseconds?

15. The wavelength of a certain frequency is 1 foot. By manipulating the formula $\lambda = v/f$ (where λ represents wavelength, v represents the velocity of the wave, and f represents the frequency), we determine that the frequency is 982,080,000 Hz. What is this frequency in MHz?

16. Bill's computer reports that his hard drive's capacity is 7,516 M bytes. How many G bytes is this? (Round off to the nearest ½ G byte.)

ANSWERS

1. 0.01204 m amps = 12.04 μ amps

2. 3,000 MHz = 3 GHz

3. 47.5 KW = 0.0475 MW

4. 0.012 μ sec = 12 n sec

5. 120 volts = 0.12 k volts

6. 0.012 volts = 12 m volts

7. 427.6 kW = 0.4276 MW

8. 5,000 m sec = 5,000,000 μ sec

9. 6,250 W = 0.00625 MW

10. 0.00325 volts

11. 0.00000002 seconds = 2×10^{-8} seconds

12. 8,000,000,000 bytes = 8×10^{9} bytes

13. 0.0096 amps = 9.6 m amps, so use the 10 m amp range

14. 15 nanoseconds

15. 982.08 MHz

16. 7.5 GB

Final Exam Practice   **MT 065**

Multiple Choice Practice: <u>Write the letter</u> **of the correct answer in the blank** <u>and circle the correct letter.</u>

_____1.   Simplify: $3 + 6 \div 3 * 2 + 7$

a) 10   b)   11   c) 12   d) 14

_____2.   Simplify: $4m - 9n - 3(2m - n)$

a) $4m - 10n$ b) $-2m - 6n$ c) $-2m - 12n$ d) $4m - 10n - 3$

_____3.   Evaluate: $-x^2 - x + 4$ when $x = -2$.

a) 10   b) -2   c) 4   d) 2

_____4.   Solve for c: $A = \dfrac{a + b + c}{3}$

a) $c = \dfrac{A + 3}{a + b}$ b) $c = \dfrac{A + 3}{-a - b}$ c) $c = 3A - a - b$ d) $c = 3A + a + b$

_____5.   Multiply: $(4x + 3)(4x - 3)$

a) $16x - 9$ b) $16x^2$ c) $16x^2 - 9$ d) $16x^2 - 12x - 9$

6.   When you factor: $x^2 - 3x - 10,$ which of the following is one of the factors?

a) $x + 5$ b) $x + 2$ c) $x - 10$ d) $x - 2$

_____7.   Simplify: 2^{-2}

a) -2 b) -4 c) $\dfrac{1}{2}$ d) $\dfrac{1}{4}$

_____8.   Translate into an algebraic expression and simplify:
Five less than three times the difference between a number and two.

a) $3x - 11$ b) $5 - 3x$ c) $3x - 2$ d) $3x - 7$

_____9.　　Simplify:　　$\left(-3x^5y^3\right)^4$

    a) $81x^{20}y^{12}$　　　　b) $12x^{20}y^{12}$　　　　c) $81x^9y^7$　　d) $12x^9y^7$

_____10.　　Evaluate:　　54 is 24% of what number?

    a) 12.96　　　　b) 225　　　　c) 29　　　　d) 20

_____11.　　Solve for m:　　$\dfrac{3m}{5} - 3 = \dfrac{m}{2}$

    a) $m = -30$　　　　b) $m = -4$　　　　c) $m = 1$　　d) $m = 30$

_____12.　　Solve the inequality and give the solution set:　$-2x + 3 > -7$

    a) $x > 5$　　　　b) $x < \dfrac{2}{3}$　　　　c) $x < 5$　　d) $x > \dfrac{2}{3}$

_____13.　　Factor Completely:　$9y^2 - 4$

    a) $(3y - 2)(3y - 2)$　　b) $(3y - 2)(3y + 2)$　　c) $(4y - 3)(4y + 3)$　　d) Not Factorable

_____14.　　Simplify:　　$(3x^2 - 4x + 1) - (2x^2 + x - 1)$

    a) $x^2 + 2$　　　　b) $x^2 - 3x$　　c) $x^2 - 5x + 2$　　　　d) $3x^2 + 1$

_____15.　　Divide:　　$\dfrac{6m^5 + 9m^3 - 3m}{3m}$

    a) $2m^4 + 3m^2 - 1$　　b) $2m^4 + 3m^2 + 1$　　c) $2m^4 + 3m^2$　　d) $2m^4$

_____16.　　The perimeter of a rectangular piece of land is 52 ft. The length is 8 ft. more than the width. Find the length.

    a)　　34 ft　　　　b) 19 ft　　　　c) 17 ft　　　　d) 9 ft

_____17.   What is the degree of this polynomial and the leading coefficient?
$2x^3 - 3x^5 + 3x^2 - 7$

   a) 5, –3   b) 3, 2   c) 5, –7   d) 3, –3

_____18.   Simplify: $-3x^0$

   a) $-3x$ b) 0   c) 1   d) –3

_____19.   Multiply: $(2x + 3)(2x - 3)$

   a) $4x - 6$ b) $4x^2 - 9$ c) $4x^2 + 9$ d) $4x^2 - 12x - 9$

_____20.   Find the y-intercept of the line whose equation is: $2x - 3y = 6$?

   a) $(0, -3)$ b) $(0, -2)$ c) $(0, 3)$ d) $(-2, 0)$

_____21.   What is the slope of the line containing these points: $(4, -7)$ and $(-2, 3)$

   a) $-\dfrac{5}{3}$ b) $-\dfrac{3}{2}$ c) $\dfrac{1}{3}$ d) $\dfrac{5}{2}$

_____22.   Convert to scientific notation: 123,000,000,000

   a) 123×10^{12} b) 123×10^{-9} c) 123×10^9 d) 1.23×10^{11}

_____23.   Factor $25x^4 - 5x^3$ completely.
   Which of the following is one of the factors in your factorization?

   a) $5x^4$ b) $5x - x^2$ c) $5x - 1$ d) $5x + 5$

_____24.   Solve for y: $\dfrac{y}{4} + \dfrac{3}{2} = \dfrac{y}{3}$

   a) $y = -9$ b) $y = 18$ c) $y = 6$ d) $y = \dfrac{4}{3}$

_____25.   Factor: $x^2 + 4x - 12$
   Which of the following is one of the factors?

   a) $x - 12$ b) $x + 3$ c) $x + 6$ d) $x + 2$

_____26. Multiply: $-2x^3(x^4 - 3x^2 + 1)$

   a) $-2x^{12} + 6x^6 - 2x^3$

   b) $-12x^6 - 6x^3 + 2x^2$

   c) $-12x^6 + 6x^3 - 2x^2$

   d) $-2x^7 + 6x^5 - 2x^3$

_____27. Solve for x: $5 - 3(2x - 4) = 5$

   a) $x = -6$

   b) $x = 2$

   c) $x = \dfrac{7}{10}$

   d) No solution

_____28. Multiply: $(2x - 3)^2$

   a) $4x^2 - 9$

   b) $4x^2 + 9$

   c) $4x^2 + 6x - 9$

   d) $4x^2 - 12x + 9$

_____29. Solve for x: $\dfrac{2}{3}(3x - 9) = 8$

   a) $x = 7$

   b) $x = 6$

   c) $x = 3$

   d) $x = 2$

_____30. Lucinda has a budget of $390 for her birthday party at a local restaurant. If the restaurant charges a $45 set up fee plus $15 per person, how many people can she invite to the party and stay within her budget.

   a)   23

   b) 26

   c) 27

   d) 36

_____31. Mike has been offered a promotion, which will mean moving from Louisville to Los Angeles. To have a comparable standard of living Jay must earn 42% more than he is currently. Currently he is making $27,000. How much would Jay have to make in Los Angeles to have a similar standard of living.

   a) $11,340

   b) $15,660

   c) $38,340

   d) $69,000

_____32. Norma's checkbook shows that she wrote a check for $736.70 for building materials, which included cost of materials and a 6% sales tax. What was the original price of the materials before the sales tax was added?

   a) $692.50

   b) $695

   c) $700

   d) $780.90

33.   The second angle of a triangle is 3 times as large as the first. The third angle is 40 degrees more than the first. Find the measure of each angle.

a) 66, 264, 106   b) 30, 90, 60   c) 28, 84, 68   d) 36, 198, 96

_____34 y varies directly as x. y is 23 when x is equal to 46. Find y when x is equal to 75.

a) 150   b) 75   c) 111.5   d) 37.5

Answers:

1). D
2). B
3). D
4). C
5). C
6). B
7). D
8). A
9). A
10). B
11). D
12). C
13). B
14). C
15). A
16). C
17). A
18). D
19). B
20). B
21). A
22). D
23). C
24). B
25). C
26). D
27). B
28). D
29). A
30). A
31). C
32). B
33). C
34). D

Dear Faculty,

Below is the new Advising Recommendation form for the current students. Students need to have one before his or her advising appointment.

Advising Recommendation

Student's Name:_____

Student's ID# : _____

Is currently taking:
- **MT 055**
- **MT065**
- **MT120**

And should enroll in:
- **MT055**
- **MT065**
- **MT120 or MT110 or MT105***
- **MT150 or MT145 or MT 151***

Faculty Signature: _____

Note to students: give this recommendation to your advisor during early advising/advanced registration (EA/AR). However, you must still complete this course. Your final grade in this course may require you to go through drop/add next semester.

* Choice of course depends on the requirements for your major.

You may re-take the Compass test, if you wish. If the test places you in a higher class, you may enroll in that class. Take a copy of Compass score with you when you register.

Contents

3 Introduction to Graphing   14

4 Polynomials   227

Tables   1003

Preface

1t is with great pleasure that we introduce you to the fifth edition of *Elementary and Intermediate Algebra: Concepts and Applications*. Our goal, as always, is to present content that is easy to understand and has the depth required for success in this and future courses. In this edition, faculty will recognize features, applications, and explanations that they have come to rely on and expect. Students and faculty will also find many changes resulting from our own ideas for improvement as well as insights from faculty and students throughout North America. Thus this new edition contains exciting new features and applications, along with updates and refinements to those from previous editions.

Appropriate for a course, or courses, combining the study of elementary and intermediate algebra, this text covers both elementary and intermediate algebra topics without the repetition of instruction necessary in two separate texts. It is one of three texts in an algebra series that also includes *Elementary Algebra: Concepts and Applications*, Eighth Edition, by Bittinger/Ellenbogen, and *Intermediate Algebra: Concepts and Applications*, Eighth Edition, by Bittinger/Ellenbogen.

Approach

Our goal, quite simply, is to help today's students both learn and retain mathematical concepts. To achieve this goal, we feel that we must prepare developmental-mathematics students for the transition from "skills-oriented" elementary and intermediate algebra courses to more "concept-oriented" college-level mathematics courses. This requires that we teach these same students critical thinking skills: to reason mathematically, to communicate mathematically, and to identify and solve mathematical problems. Following are three aspects of our approach that we use to help meet the challenges we all face when teaching developmental mathematics.

Problem Solving

One distinguishing feature of our approach is our treatment of and emphasis on problem solving. We use problem solving and applications to motivate the material wherever possible, and we include real-life applications and problem-solving techniques throughout the text. Problem solving not only encourages students to think about how mathematics can be used, it helps to prepare them for more advanced material in future courses.

In Chapter 2, we introduce our five-step process for solving problems: (1) Familiarize, (2) Translate, (3) Carry out, (4) Check, and (5) State the answer. These steps are then used consistently throughout the text when encountering a problem-solving situation. Repeated use of this problem-solving strategy helps provide students with a starting point for any type of problem they encounter, and frees them to focus on the unique aspects of the particular problem situation. We often use estimation and carefully checked guesses to help with the *Familiarize* and *Check* steps (see pp. 110 and 422–423).

Applications

Interesting applications of mathematics help motivate both students and instructors. Solving applied problems gives students the opportunity to see their conceptual understanding put to use in a real way. In the fifth edition of *Elementary and Intermediate Algebra: Concepts and Applications*, we have increased the number of applications, the number of real-data problems, and the number of reference lines that specify the sources of the real-world data. As in the past, art is integrated into the applications and exercises to aid the student in visualizing the mathematics. (See pp. 111, 190, 260, 364.)

Pedagogy

New!

TRY EXERCISES

Try Exercises. This icon concludes nearly every example by pointing students to one or more parallel exercises from the corresponding exercise set so that they can immediately reinforce the concepts and skills presented in the examples. For easy identification in the exercise sets, the "Try" exercises have a shaded block on the exercise number. (See pp. 56, 256, 415.)

New!

Translating for Success and **Visualizing for Success.** These matching exercises help students learn to associate word problems (through translation) and graphs (through visualization) with their appropriate mathematical equations. (See pp. 134, 361 (Translating); pp. 212, 753 (Visualizing).) Each feature contains a corresponding activity in MyMathLab.

Revised!

Connecting the Concepts. Revised and expanded to include new Mixed Review exercises, this midchapter review helps students understand the big picture and prepare for chapter tests and cumulative reviews by relating the concept at hand to previously learned and upcoming concepts. (See pp. 206, 279, 739.)

Revised!

Study Summary. Found at the end of each chapter and now presented in a two-column format organized by section, this synopsis gives students a fast and effective review of key chapter terms and concepts paired with accompanying examples. (See pp. 139, 218, 367.)

Revised!

Cumulative Review. This review now appears after every chapter to help students retain and apply their knowledge from previous chapters. (See pp. 145, 300, 574.)

Algebraic–Graphical Connections. This feature provides students with a way to visualize concepts that might otherwise prove elusive. (See pp. 350, 416, 704.)

Study Skills. This feature in the margin provides tips for successful study habits that even experienced students will appreciate. Ranging from time management to test preparation, these study skills can be applied in any college course. (See pp. 86, 229, 597.)

Student Notes. These notes in the margin give students extra explanation of the mathematics appearing on that page. These comments are more casual in format than the typical exposition and range from suggestions for avoiding common mistakes to how to best read new notation. (See pp. 79, 312, 728.)

Technology Connection. These optional boxes in each chapter help students use a graphing calculator to better visualize a concept that they have just learned. To connect this optional instruction to the exercise sets, certain exercises are marked with a graphing calculator icon 📷 to indicate the optional use of technology. (See pp. 164, 351, 791.)

Revised!

Concept Reinforcement Exercises. Now with all answers listed in the answer section at the back of the book, these section and review exercises build students' confidence and comprehension through true/false, matching, and fill-in-the-blank exercises at the start of most exercise sets. To help further student understanding, emphasis is given to new vocabulary and notation developed in the section. (See pp. 10, 165, 760.)

Aha!

Aha! Exercises. These exercises are not more difficult than their neighboring exercises and can be solved quickly, without going through a lengthy computation, if the student has the proper insight. Designed to reward students who "look before they leap," the icon indicates the first time a new insight applies, and then it is up to the student to determine when to use the Aha! method on subsequent exercises. (See pp. 213, 285, 730.)

Revised!

Skill Review Exercises. These exercises, included in Section 1.2 and every section thereafter, review skills and concepts from preceding sections of the text. In most cases, these exercises prepare students for the next section. An introduction to each set directs students to the appropriate sections to review if necessary. On occasion, Skill Review exercises focus on a single topic in greater depth and from multiple perspectives. (See pp. 166, 243, 594.)

Synthesis Exercises. Synthesis exercises follow the Skill Review exercises at the end of each exercise set. Generally more challenging, these exercises synthesize skills and concepts from earlier sections with the present material, often providing students with deeper insight into the current topic. Aha! exercises are sometimes included as Synthesis exercises. (See pp. 99, 365, 714.)

Writing Exercises. These appear just before the Skill Review exercises (two basic writing exercises) and also in the Synthesis exercises (at least two more challenging exercises). Writing exercises aid student comprehension by requiring students to use critical thinking to provide explanations of concepts in one or more complete sentences. Because some instructors may collect answers to writing exercises and because more than one answer can be correct, only answers to writing exercises in the review section are included at the back of the text. (See pp. 58, 473, 686.)

Collaborative Corner. These optional activities for students to explore together usually appear two to three times per chapter at the end of an exercise set. Studies show that students who study in groups generally outperform those who do not, so these exercises are for students who want to solve mathematical problems together. Additional collaborative activities and suggestions for directing collaborative learning appear in the *Instructor and Adjunct Support Manual*. (See pp. 158, 537, 766.)

What's New in the fth Edition?

We have rewritten many key topics in response to user and reviewer feedback and have made significant improvements in design, art, pedagogy, and an expanded supplements package. Detailed information about the content changes is available in the form of a conversion guide. Please ask your local Pearson sales consultant for more information. Following is a list of the major changes in this edition.

NEW DESIGN

While incorporating a new layout, a fresh palette of colors, and new features, we have a larger page dimension for an open look and a typeface that is easy to read. As always, it is our goal to make the text look mature without being intimidating. In addition, we continue to pay close attention to the pedagogical use of color to make sure that it is used to present concepts in the clearest possible manner.

CONTENT CHANGES

A variety of content changes have been made throughout the text. Some of the more significant changes are listed below.

What's New in Combined

- Examples and exercises that use real data are updated or replaced with current applications.
- Over 35% of the exercises are new or updated.
- Quick-glance reminders for multistep process are included next to examples. These appear by one multistep example of each type. (See pp. 197, 333, 519.)
- Chapter 2 now includes increased practice of solving for y in a formula.
- Interval notation is introduced when students first solve inequalities in Section 2.6.
- Inequalities are now graphed on number lines using brackets and parentheses. Interval notation can thus be read directly from the graph of an inequality.
- Chapter 3 now gives increased emphasis to units when finding a rate of change.

- Discussion of negative exponents (Section 4.2) now immediately follows the introduction to the rules for manipulating exponents.
- Chapter 5 now makes greater use of prime factorizations as a tool for finding the largest common factor.
- Domains of radical functions are now discussed in Section 9.1, separately from domains of rational functions in Section 9.2.
- The distance formula is now presented in Section 10.7 as one application of the Pythagorean theorem.
- In Chapter 11, the discussion of the discriminant now directly follows the quadratic formula.

ANCILLARIES

The following ancillaries are available to help both instructors and students use this text more effectively.

STUDENT SUPPLEMENTS

New! Chapter Test Prep Video CD

- Watch instructors work through step-by-step solutions to all the chapter test exercises from the textbook. The Chapter Test Prep Video CD is included with each new student text.

New! Worksheets for Classroom or Lab Practice

by Carrie Green
These lab- and classroom-friendly workbooks offer the following resources for every section of the text:

- A list of learning objectives;
- Vocabulary practice problems;
- Extra practice exercises with ample work space.

ISBNs: 0-321-59933-0 and 978-0-321-59933-9

Student's Solutions Manual

by Christine S. Verity

- Contains completely worked-out solutions with step-by-step annotations for all the odd-numbered exercises in the text, with the exception of the writing exercises.
- New! Now contains all solutions to Chapter Review, Chapter Test, and Connecting the Concepts exercises.

ISBNs: 0-321-58623-9 and 978-0-321-58623-0

INSTRUCTOR SUPPLEMENTS

Annotated Instructor's Edition

- Provides answers to all text exercises in color next to the corresponding problems.
- Includes Teaching Tips.
- Icons identify writing and graphing calculator exercises.

ISBNs: 0-321-56726-9 and 978-0-321-56726-0

Instructor's Solutions Manual

by Christine S. Verity

- Contains fully worked-out solutions to the odd-numbered exercises and brief solutions to the even-numbered exercises in the exercise sets.
- Available for download at www.pearsonhighered.com

ISBNs: 0-321-58620-4 and 978-0-321-58620-9

Instructor and Adjunct Support Manual

- Includes resources designed to help both new and adjunct faculty with course preparation and classroom management.
- Offers helpful teaching tips correlated to the sections of the text.

ISBNs: 0-321-58624-7 and 978-0-321-58624-7

Videos on DVD

- A complete set of digitized videos on DVD for use at home or on campus.
- Includes a full lecture for each section of the text, many presented by author team members David J. Ellenbogen and Barbara Johnson.
- Optional subtitles in English are available.

ISBNs: 0-321-59935-7 and 978-0-321-59935-3

InterAct Math® Tutorial Website

www.interactmath.com

- Online practice and tutorial help.
- Retry an exercise with new values each time for unlimited practice and mastery.
- Every exercise is accompanied by an interactive guided solution that gives helpful feedback when an incorrect answer is entered.
- View the steps of a worked-out sample problem similar to those in the text.

Printable Test Bank

by Laurie Hurley

- Contains two multiple-choice tests per chapter, six free-response tests per chapter, and eight final exams.
- Available for download at www.pearsonhighered.com

PowerPoint® Lecture Slides

- Present key concepts and definitions from the text.
- Available for download at www.pearsonhighered.com

TestGen

www.pearsonhighered.com/testgen

- Enables instructors to build, edit, print, and administer tests using a computerized bank of questions developed to cover all text objectives.
- Algorithmically based, TestGen allows instructors to create multiple but equivalent versions of the same question or test with the click of a button.
- Instructors can also modify test bank questions or add new questions.
- Tests can be printed or administered online.

Pearson Math Adjunct Support Center

http://www.pearsontutorservices.com/math-adjunct.html

Staffed by qualified instructors with more than 50 years of combined experience at both the community college and university levels, this center provides assistance for faculty in the following areas:

- Suggested syllabus consultation;
- Tips on using materials packed with the text;
- Book-specific content assistance;
- Teaching suggestions, including advice on classroom strategies.

AVAILABLE FOR STUDENTS AND INSTRUCTORS

MyMathLab® Online Course (access code required)

MyMathLab is a series of text-specific, easily customizable online courses for Pearson Education's textbooks in mathematics and statistics. Powered by CourseCompass™ (our online teaching and learning environment) and MathXL® (our online homework, tutorial, and assessment system), MyMathLab gives you the tools you need to deliver all or a portion of your course online, whether your students are in a lab setting or working from home. MyMathLab provides a rich and flexible set of course materials, featuring free-response exercises that are algorithmically generated for unlimited practice and mastery. Students can also use online tools, such as video lectures, animations, and a multimedia textbook, to independently improve their understanding and performance. Instructors can use MyMathLab's homework and test managers to select and assign online exercises correlated directly to the textbook, and they can also create and assign their own online exercises and import TestGen tests for added flexibility. MyMathLab's online gradebook—designed specifically for mathematics and statistics—automatically tracks students' homework and test results and gives the instructor control over how to calculate final grades. Instructors can also add offline (paper-and-pencil) grades to the gradebook. MyMathLab also includes access to the **Pearson Tutor Center** (www.pearsontutorservices.com). The Tutor Center is staffed by qualified mathematics instructors who provide textbook-specific tutoring for students via toll-free phone, fax, e-mail, and interactive Web sessions. MyMathLab is available to qualified adopters. For more information, visit our website at www.mymathlab.com or contact your sales representative.

MathXL® Online Course (access code required)

MathXL® is a powerful online homework, tutorial, and assessment system that accompanies Pearson Education's textbooks in mathematics or statistics. With MathXL, instructors can create, edit, and assign online homework and tests using algorithmically generated exercises correlated at the objective level to the textbook. They can also create and assign their own online exercises and import TestGen tests for added flexibility. All student work is tracked in MathXL's online gradebook. Students can take chapter tests in MathXL and receive personalized study plans based on their test results. The study plan diagnoses weaknesses and links students directly to tutorial exercises for the objectives they need to study and retest. Students can also access supplemental animations and video clips directly from selected exercises. MathXL is available to qualified adopters. For more information, visit our website at www.mathxl.com, or contact your Pearson sales representative.

MathXL® Tutorials on CD

This interactive tutorial CD-ROM provides algorithmically generated practice exercises that are correlated at the objective level to the exercises in the textbook. Every practice exercise is accompanied by an example and a guided solution designed to involve students in the solution process. Selected exercises may also include a video clip to help students visualize concepts. The software provides helpful feedback for incorrect answers and can generate printed summaries of students' progress.

Acknowledgments

No book can be produced without a team of professionals who take pride in their work and are willing to put in long hours. Laurie Hurley, in particular, deserves extra thanks for her work as developmental editor. Rebecca Hubiak, Laurie Hurley, Holly Martinez, Ann Ostberg, and Christine Verity also deserve special thanks for their careful accuracy checks, well-thought-out suggestions, and uncanny eye for detail. Thanks to Carrie Green, Laurie Hurley, and Christine Verity for their outstanding work in preparing supplements.

We are also indebted to Chris Burditt and Jann MacInnes for their many fine ideas that appear in our Collaborative Corners and Vince McGarry and Janet Wyatt for their recommendations for Teaching Tips featured in the Annotated Instructor's Edition.

Geri Davis, of the Davis Group, Inc., performed superb work as designer, art editor, and photo researcher, and is always a pleasure to work with. Tracy Duff and her colleagues at Pre-Press PMG provided excellent composition and editorial support throughout the production process. Network Graphics generated the graphs, charts, and many of the illustrations. Not only are the people at Network reliable, but they clearly take pride in their work. The many illustrations appear thanks to Bill Melvin—an artist with insight and creativity.

Our team at Pearson deserves special thanks. Acquisitions Editor Randy Welch provided many fine suggestions, remaining involved and accessible throughout the project. Executive Project Manager Kari Heen carefully coordinated tasks and schedules, keeping a widely spread team working together. Associate Editor Joanna Doxey coordinated reviews and assisted in a variety of tasks with patience and creativity. Editorial Assistant Jonathan Wooding responded quickly to all requests, always in a pleasant manner. Production Manager Ron Hampton's attention to detail, willingness to listen, and creative responses helped result in a book that is beautiful to look at. Marketing Manager Marlana Voerster and Marketing Assistant Nathaniel Koven skillfully kept us in touch with the needs of faculty. Our Editor in Chief, Maureen O'Connor, and Editorial Director, Chris Hoag, deserve credit for assembling this fine team.

We also thank the students at Indiana University Purdue University Indianapolis and the Community College of Vermont and the following professors for their thoughtful reviews and insightful comments.

Elementary Algebra: Concepts and Applications, Eighth Edition

Roberta Abarca, *Centralia College*
Darla J. Aguilar, *Pima Community College, Desert Vista Campus*
Bonnie Alcorn, *Waubonsee College*
Eugene Alderman, *South University*
Joseph Berland, *Chabot College*
Paul Blankenship, *Lexington Community College*
Susan Caldiero, *Cosumnes River College*
David Casey, *Citrus College*
Emmett Dennis, *Southern Connecticut State University*
Henri Feiner, *Coastline Community College*
Gary Glaze, *Spokane Falls Community College*
Janet Hansen, *Dixie State College*
Elizabeth Hodes, *Santa Barbara City College*
Weilin Jang, *Austin Community College*
Paulette Kirkpatrick, *Wharton County Junior College*
Susan Knights, *Boise State University*
Jeff Koleno, *Lorain County Community College*
Julianne Labbiento, *Lehigh Carbon Community College*
Kathryn Lavelle, *Westchester Community College*
Amy Marolt, *Northeastern Mississippi Community College*
Rogers Martin, *Louisiana State University, Shreveport*
Ben Mayo, *Yakima Valley Community College*
Laurie McManus, *St. Louis Community College–Meramac*
Carol Metz, *Westchester Community College*
Anne Marie Mosher, *St. Louis Community College–Florissant Valley*
Pedro Mota, *Austin Community College, South Austin Campus*
Brenda M. Norman, *Tidewater Community College*
Kim Nunn, *Northeast State Technical College*
Michael Oppedisano, *Morrisville College SUNY*
Zaddock B. Reid, *San Bernardino Valley College*
Terry Reeves, *Red Rocks Community College*
Terri Seiver, *San Jacinto College–Central*
Timothy Thompson, *Oregon Institute of Technology*
Diane Trimble, *Tulsa Community College, West Campus*
Jennifer Vanden Eynden, *Grossmont College*
Beverly Vredevelt, *Spokane Falls Community College*
Michael Yarbrough, *Cosumnes River College*

Intermediate Algebra: Concepts and Applications, Eighth Edition

Marie Aratari, *Oakland Community College–Orange Ridge Campus*
Barbara Armenta, *Pima Community College*
Douglas Brozovic, *University of North Texas*
Barbara Burke, *Hawaii Pacific University*
Laura Burris, *Sam Houston State University*
Lisa Carnell, *High Point University*
Sharon Edgmon, *Bakersfield College*
Karen Ernst, *Hawkeye College*
Kathy Garrison, *Clayton College and State University*
Cynthia Harrison, *Baton Rouge Community College*
Tracey L. Johnson, *University of Georgia*
Joanne Kawczenski, *Luzerne County Community College*
Rachel Lamp, *North Iowa Area Community College*
Kevin J. Leith, *Central New Mexico Community College*
Stephanie Lochbaum, *Austin Community College*

Debi McCandrew, *Florence-Darlington Technical College*
Bob McCarthy, *Community College of Allegheny County—South Campus*
Doug Mace, *Kirtland Community College*
Timothy McKenna, *University of Michigan–Dearborn*
Rhea Meyerholtz, *Indiana State University*
Bronte Miller, *Patrick Henry Community College*
Kausha Miller, *Lexington Community College*
Rebecca Parrish, *Ohio University*
Kay Petrash, *Sam Houston State University*
Debra Pharo, *Northwestern Michigan College*
Terry Reeves, *Red Rocks Community College*
Kathy Rod, *Wharton County Junior College*
Nicole Saporito, *Luzerne Community College*
Elgin Schilhab, *Austin Community College*
M. Terry Simon, *University of Toledo*
Fran Smith, *Oakland Community College*
Donald Soloman, *University of Wisconsin–Milwaukee*

***Elementary and Intermediate Algebra: Concepts and Applications,* Fifth Edition**

Michael Anzzolin, *Waubonsee Community College*
Jan Archibald, *Ventura College*
Don Brown, *Macon State College*
Gary Carpenter, *Pima Community College, Northwest Campus*
Tim Chappell, *Penn Valley Community College*
Ola Disu, *Tarrant County College*
Anissa Florence, *University of Louisville*
Sandy Gordon, *Central Carolina Technical College*
Sharon Hamsa, *Longview Community College*
Geoffrey Hirsch, *Ohlone College*
Pat Horacek, *Pensacola Junior College*
Sally Keely, *Clark College*
Ana Leon, *Louisville Community College*
Linda Lohman, *Jefferson Community College*
Bob Martin, *Tarrant County College*
Amy Petty, *South Suburban College*
Thomas Pulver, *Waubonsee Community College*
Angela Redmon, *Wenatchee Valley College*
Richard Rupp, *Del Mar College*
Mehdi Sadatmousavi, *Pima Community College*
Ann Thrower, *Kilgore College*

Finally, a special thank-you to all those who so generously agreed to discuss their professional use of mathematics in our chapter openers. These dedicated people all share a desire to make math more meaningful to students. We cannot imagine a finer set of role models.

M.L.B.
D.J.E.
B.L.J.

Introduction to Algebraic Expressions

BRIAN BUSBY
CHIEF METEOROLOGIST
Kansas City, Missouri

...ll weather measurements are a series of numbers and values. Temperature, relative humidity, ...d speed and direction, precip-...ation amount, and air pressure ...e all expressed in various num-bers and percentages. Because ...ather systems move north and south, east and west, up and ...own, *and* over time, high-level ...th like calculus is the only way ...represent that movement. But ...before you study calculus, you must begin with algebra.

AN APPLICATION

On December 10, Jenna notes that the temperature is −3°F at 6:00 A.M. She predicts that the temperature will rise at a rate of 2° per hour for 3 hr, and then rise at a rate of 3° per hour for 6 hr. She also predicts that the temperature will then fall at a rate of 2° per hour for 3 hr, and then fall at a rate of 5° per hour for 2 hr. What is Jenna's temperature forecast for 8:00 P.M.?

This problem appears as Exercise 135 in Section 1.7.

Problem solving is the focus of this text. Chapter 1 presents important preliminaries that are needed for the problem-solving approach that is developed in Chapter 2 and used throughout the rest of the book. These preliminaries include a review of arithmetic, a discussion of real numbers and their properties, and an examination of how real numbers are added, subtracted, multiplied, divided, and raised to powers.

1.1 Introduction to Algebra

Algebraic Expressions ■ Translating to Algebraic Expressions ■ Translating to Equations

This section introduces some basic concepts and expressions used in algebra. Solving real-world problems is an important part of algebra, so we will focus on the wordings and mathematical expressions that often arise in applications.

Algebraic Expressions

Probably the greatest difference between arithmetic and algebra is the use of *variables* in algebra. When a letter can be any one of a set of numbers, that letter is a **variable**. For example, if n represents the number of tickets purchased for a Maroon 5 concert, then n will vary, depending on factors like price and day of the week. This makes n a variable. If each ticket costs \$40, then 3 tickets cost $40 \cdot 3$ dollars, 4 tickets cost $40 \cdot 4$ dollars, and n tickets cost $40 \cdot n$, or $40n$ dollars. Note that both $40 \cdot n$ and $40n$ mean 40 *times n*. The number 40 is an example of a **constant** because it does not change.

Price per Ticket (in dollars)	Number of Tickets Purchased	Total Paid (in dollars)
40	n	$40n$

The expression $40n$ is a **variable expression** because its value varies with the replacement for n. In this case, the total amount paid, $40n$, will change with the number of tickets purchased. In the following chart, we replace n with a variety of values and compute the total amount paid. In doing so, we are **evaluating the expression** $40n$.

Price per Ticket (in dollars), 40	Number of Tickets Purchased, n	Total Paid (in dollars), $40n$
40	400	$16,000
40	500	20,000
40	600	24,000

Variable expressions are examples of *algebraic expressions*. An **algebraic expression** consists of variables and/or numerals, often with operation signs and grouping symbols. Examples are

$$t + 97, \quad 5 \cdot x, \quad 3a - b, \quad 18 \div y, \quad \frac{9}{7}, \quad \text{and} \quad 4r(s + t).$$

Recall that a fraction bar is a division symbol: $\frac{9}{7}$, or 9/7, means $9 \div 7$. Similarly, multiplication can be written in several ways. For example, "5 times x" can be written as $5 \cdot x, 5 \times x, 5(x)$, or simply $5x$. On many calculators, this appears as $5 * x$.

To **evaluate** an algebraic expression, we substitute a number for each variable in the expression. We then calculate the result.

EXAMPLE **1**

Evaluate each expression for the given values.

a) $x + y$ for $x = 37$ and $y = 28$

b) $5ab$ for $a = 2$ and $b = 3$

SOLUTION

a) We substitute 37 for x and 28 for y and carry out the addition:

$$x + y = 37 + 28 = 65.$$

The number 65 is called the **value** of the expression.

b) We substitute 2 for a and 3 for b and multiply:

$$5ab = 5 \cdot 2 \cdot 3 = 10 \cdot 3 = 30. \qquad 5ab \text{ means 5 times } a \text{ times } b.$$

TRY EXERCISE 17

EXAMPLE **2**

The area A of a rectangle of length l and width w is given by the formula $A = lw$. Find the area when l is 17 in. and w is 10 in.

SOLUTION   We evaluate, using 17 in. for l and 10 in. for w, and carry out the multiplication:

$$A = lw$$
$$A = (17\,\text{in.})(10\,\text{in.})$$
$$A = (17)(10)(\text{in.})(\text{in.})$$
$$A = 170\,\text{in}^2, \text{ or 170 square inches.}$$

Note that we always use square units for area and $(\text{in.})(\text{in.}) = \text{in}^2$. Exponents like the 2 within the expression in^2 are discussed further in Section 1.8.

TRY EXERCISE 25

EXAMPLE   3   The area of a triangle with a base of length b and a height of length h is given by the formula $A = \frac{1}{2}bh$. Find the area when b is 8 m (meters) and h is 6.4 m.

SOLUTION   We substitute 8 m for b and 6.4 m for h and then multiply:

$$A = \tfrac{1}{2}bh$$
$$A = \tfrac{1}{2}(8\,\text{m})(6.4\,\text{m})$$
$$A = \tfrac{1}{2}(8)(6.4)(\text{m})(\text{m})$$
$$A = 4(6.4)\,\text{m}^2$$
$$A = 25.6\,\text{m}^2, \text{ or } 25.6 \text{ square meters.}$$

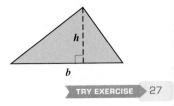

TRY EXERCISE   27

Translating to Algebraic Expressions

Before attempting to translate problems to equations, we need to be able to translate certain phrases to algebraic expressions.

Important Words	Sample Phrase or Sentence	Translation
Addition (+)		
added to	700 pounds was added to the car's weight.	$w + 700$
sum of	The sum of a number and 12	$n + 12$
plus	53 plus some number	$53 + x$
more than	800 more than Biloxi's population	$p + 800$
increased by	Ty's original estimate, increased by 4	$n + 4$
Subtraction (−)		
subtracted from	2 ounces was subtracted from the bag's weight.	$w - 2$
difference of	The difference of two scores	$m - n$
minus	A team of size s, minus 2 injured players	$s - 2$
less than	9 less than the number of volunteers last month	$v - 9$
decreased by	The car's speed, decreased by 8 mph	$s - 8$
Multiplication (·)		
multiplied by	The number of reservations, multiplied by 3	$r \cdot 3$
product of	The product of two numbers	$m \cdot n$
times	5 times the dog's weight	$5w$
twice	Twice the wholesale cost	$2c$
of	$\frac{1}{2}$ of Amelia's salary	$\frac{1}{2}s$
Division (÷)		
divided by	A 2-pound coffee cake, divided by 3	$2 \div 3$
quotient of	The quotient of 14 and 7	$14 \div 7$
divided into	4 divided into the delivery fee	$f \div 4$
ratio of	The ratio of $500 to the price of a new car	$500/p$
per	There were 18 computers per class of size s.	$18/s$

Any variable can be used to represent an unknown quantity; however, it is helpful to choose a descriptive letter. For example, w suggests weight and p suggests population or price. It is important to write down what the chosen variable represents.

EXAMPLE 4   Translate each phrase to an algebraic expression.

a) Four less than Ava's height, in inches

b) Eighteen more than a number

c) A day's pay, in dollars, divided by eight

SOLUTION   To help think through a translation, we sometimes begin with a specific number in place of a variable.

a) If the height were 60, then 4 less than 60 would mean $60 - 4$. If the height were 65, the translation would be $65 - 4$. If we use h to represent "Ava's height, in inches," the translation of "Four less than Ava's height, in inches" is $h - 4$.

b) If we knew the number to be 10, the translation would be $10 + 18$, or $18 + 10$. If we use t to represent "a number," the translation of "Eighteen more than a number" is

$$t + 18, \quad \text{or} \quad 18 + t.$$

c) We let d represent "a day's pay, in dollars." If the pay were $78, the translation would be $78 \div 8$, or $\frac{78}{8}$. Thus our translation of "A day's pay, in dollars, divided by eight" is

$$d \div 8, \quad \text{or} \quad \frac{d}{8}.$$

 TRY EXERCISE 31

CAUTION!   The order in which we subtract and divide affects the answer! Answering $4 - h$ or $8 \div d$ in Examples 4(a) and 4(c) is incorrect.

EXAMPLE 5   Translate each phrase to an algebraic expression.

a) Half of some number

b) Seven more than twice the weight

c) Six less than the product of two numbers

d) Nine times the difference of a number and 10

e) Eighty-two percent of last year's enrollment

SOLUTION

Phrase	*Variable(s)*	*Algebraic Expression*
a) Half of some number	Let n represent the number.	$\frac{1}{2}n$, or $\frac{n}{2}$, or $n \div 2$
b) Seven more than twice the weight	Let w represent the weight.	$2w + 7$, or $7 + 2w$
c) Six less than the product of two numbers	Let m and n represent the numbers.	$mn - 6$
d) Nine times the difference of a number and 10	Let a represent the number.	$9(a - 10)$
e) Eighty-two percent of last year's enrollment	Let r represent last year's enrollment.	82% of r, or $0.82r$

TRY EXERCISE 45

Translating to Equations

The symbol = ("equals") indicates that the expressions on either side of the equals sign represent the same number. An **equation** is a number sentence with the verb =. Equations may be true, false, or neither true nor false.

EXAMPLE **6**

Determine whether each equation is true, false, or neither.

a) $8 \cdot 4 = 32$ **b)** $7 - 2 = 4$ **c)** $x + 6 = 13$

SOLUTION

a) $8 \cdot 4 = 32$ The equation is *true*.

b) $7 - 2 = 4$ The equation is *false*.

c) $x + 6 = 13$ The equation is *neither* true nor false, because we do not know what number x represents.

> ### Solution
> A replacement or substitution that makes an equation true is called a *solution*. Some equations have more than one solution, and some have no solution. When all solutions have been found, we have *solved* the equation.

To see if a number is a solution, we evaluate all expressions in the equation. If the values on both sides of the equation are the same, the number is a solution.

EXAMPLE **7**

Determine whether 7 is a solution of $x + 6 = 13$.

SOLUTION   We evaluate $x + 6$ and compare both sides of the equation.

$$x + 6 = 13 \qquad \text{Writing the equation}$$
$$7 + 6 \mid 13 \qquad \text{Substituting 7 for } x$$
$$13 \overset{?}{=} 13 \qquad 13 = 13 \text{ is TRUE.}$$

Since the left-hand side and the right-hand side are the same, 7 is a solution.

TRY EXERCISE 57

Although we do not study solving equations until Chapter 2, we can translate certain problem situations to equations now. The words "is the same as," "equal," "is," and "are" often translate to "=."

> **Words indicating equality, =** : "is the same as," "equal," "is," "are"

When translating a problem to an equation, we translate phrases to algebraic expressions, and the entire statement to an equation containing those expressions.

EXAMPLE 8   Translate the following problem to an equation.

What number plus 478 is 1019?

SOLUTION   We let y represent the unknown number. The translation then comes almost directly from the English sentence.

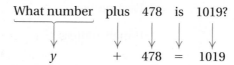

What number   plus   478   is   1019?

$$y \qquad + \qquad 478 \quad = \quad 1019$$

Note that "what number plus 478" translates to "$y + 478$" and "is" translates to "=."

TRY EXERCISE ▶ 63

Sometimes it helps to reword a problem before translating.

EXAMPLE 9   Translate the following problem to an equation.

The Taipei Financial Center, or Taipei 101, in Taiwan is the world's tallest building. At 1666 ft, it is 183 ft taller than the Petronas Twin Towers in Kuala Lumpur. How tall are the Petronas Twin Towers?

Source: *Guinness World Records* 2007

SOLUTION   We let h represent the height, in feet, of the Petronas Towers. A rewording and translation follow:

Rewording: The height of   183 ft more than the height
                Taipei 101   is   of the Petronas Towers

Translating: 1666   = $h + 183$

TRY EXERCISE ▶ 69

TECHNOLOGY CONNECTION

Technology Connections are activities that make use of features that are common to most graphing calculators. In some cases, students may find the user's manual for their particular calculator helpful for exact keystrokes.

Although all graphing calculators are not the same, most share the following characteristics.

Screen.   The large screen can show graphs and tables as well as the expressions entered. The screen has a different layout for different functions. Computations are performed in the **home screen**. On many calculators, the home screen is accessed by pressing **2ND** (QUIT). The **cursor** shows location on the screen, and the **contrast** (set by **2ND** ⌃ or **2ND** ⌄) determines how dark the characters appear.

Keypad.   There are options written above the keys as well as on them. To access those above the keys, we press

2ND or **ALPHA** and then the key. Expressions are usually entered as they would appear in print. For example, to evaluate $3xy + x$ for $x = 65$ and $y = 92$, we press 3 (×) 65 (×) 92 (+) 65 and then **ENTER**. The value of the expression, 18005, will appear at the right of the screen.

```
3*65*92+65
                        18005
```

Evaluate each of the following.

1. $27a - 18b$, for $a = 136$ and $b = 13$
2. $19xy - 9x + 13y$, for $x = 87$ and $y = 29$

STUDY SKILLS

Get the Facts

Throughout this textbook, you will find a feature called Study Skills. These tips are intended to help improve your math study skills. On the first day of class, you should complete this chart.

Instructor: Name _____

Office hours and location _____

Phone number _____

Fax number _____

E-mail address _____

Find the names of two students whom you could contact for information or study questions:

    1. Name _____

        Phone number _____

        E-mail address _____

    2. Name _____

        Phone number _____

        E-mail address _____

Math lab on campus:

    Location _____

    Hours _____

    Phone _____

Tutoring:

    Campus location _____

    Hours _____

Important supplements:

(See the preface for a complete list of available supplements.)

    Supplements recommended by the instructor.

_____

_____

Translating for Success

1. Twice the difference of a number and 11

2. The product of a number and 11 is 2.

3. Twice the difference of two numbers is 11.

. The quotient of twice a number and 11

. The quotient of 11 and the product of two numbers

Translate to an expression or an equation and match that translation with one of the choices A–O below. Do not solve.

A. $x = 0.2(11)$

B. $\dfrac{2x}{11}$

C. $2x + 2 = 11$

D. $2(11x + 2)$

E. $11x = 2$

F. $0.2x = 11$

G. $11(2x - y)$

H. $2(x - 11)$

I. $11 + 2x = 2$

J. $2x + y = 11$

K. $2(x - y) = 11$

L. $11(x + 2x)$

M. $2(x + y) = 11$

N. $2 + \dfrac{x}{11}$

O. $\dfrac{11}{xy}$

Answers on page A-1

6. Eleven times the sum of a number and twice the number

7. Twice the sum of two numbers is 11.

8. Two more than twice a number is 11.

9. Twice the sum of 11 times a number and 2

10. Twenty percent of some number is 11.

1.1   EXERCISE SET

↪ *Concept Reinforcement*   *Classify each of the following as either an expression or an equation.*

1. $10n - 1$
2. $3x = 21$
3. $2x - 5 = 9$
4. $5(x + 2)$
5. $38 = 2t$
6. $45 = a - 1$
7. $4a - 5b$
8. $3s + 4t = 19$
9. $2x - 3y = 8$
10. $12 - 4xy$
11. $r(t + 7) + 5$
12. $9a + b$

To the student and the instructor: *The* TRY EXERCISES *for examples are indicated by a shaded block* ▮ *on the exercise number. Complete step-by-step solutions for these exercises appear online at www.pearsonhighered.com/ bittingerellenbogen.*

Evaluate.

13. $5a$, for $a = 9$
14. $11y$, for $y = 7$
15. $12 - r$, for $r = 4$
16. $t + 8$, for $t = 2$
17. $\dfrac{a}{b}$, for $a = 45$ and $b = 9$
18. $\dfrac{c + d}{3}$, for $c = 14$ and $d = 13$
19. $\dfrac{x + y}{4}$, for $x = 2$ and $y = 14$
20. $\dfrac{m}{n}$, for $m = 54$ and $n = 9$
21. $\dfrac{p - q}{7}$, for $p = 55$ and $q = 20$
22. $\dfrac{9m}{q}$, for $m = 6$ and $q = 18$
23. $\dfrac{5z}{y}$, for $z = 9$ and $y = 15$
24. $\dfrac{m - n}{2}$, for $m = 20$ and $n = 8$

Substitute to find the value of each expression.

25. *Hockey.*   The area of a rectangle with base b and height h is bh. A regulation hockey goal is 6 ft wide and 4 ft high. Find the area of the opening.

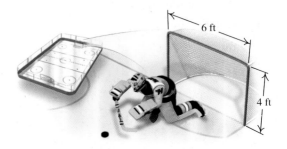

6 ft
4 ft

26. *Orbit time.*   A communications satellite orbiting 300 mi above the earth travels about 27,000 mi in one orbit. The time, in hours, for an orbit is

$$\frac{27,000}{v},$$

where v is the velocity, in miles per hour. How long will an orbit take at a velocity of 1125 mph?

27. *Zoology.*   A great white shark has triangular teeth. Each tooth measures about 5 cm across the base and has a height of 6 cm. Find the surface area of the front side of one such tooth. (See Example 3.)

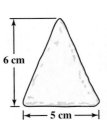

6 cm
5 cm

28. *Work time.*   Javier takes three times as long to do a job as Luis does. Suppose t represents the time it takes Luis to do the job. Then $3t$ represents the time it takes Javier. How long does it take Javier if Luis takes **(a)** 30 sec? **(b)** 90 sec? **(c)** 2 min?

29. *Women's softball.*   A softball player's batting average is h/a, where h is the number of hits and a is the number of "at bats." In the 2007 Women's College World Series, Caitlin Lowe of the Arizona Wildcats had 10 hits in 29 at bats. What was her batting average? Round to the nearest thousandth.

30. *Area of a parallelogram.* The area of a parallelogram with base b and height h is bh. Find the area of the parallelogram when the height is 6 cm (centimeters) and the base is 7.5 cm.

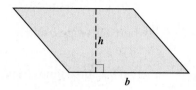

Translate to an algebraic expression.

31. 5 more than Ron's age

32. The product of 4 and a

33. 6 times b

34. 7 more than Lori's weight

35. 9 less than c

36. 4 less than d

37. 6 increased by q

38. 11 increased by z

39. 8 times Mai's speed

40. m subtracted from n

41. x less than y

42. 2 less than Than's age

43. x divided by w

44. The quotient of two numbers

45. The sum of the box's length and height

46. The sum of d and f

47. The product of 9 and twice m

48. Pemba's speed minus twice the wind speed

49. Thirteen less than one quarter of some number

50. Four less than ten times a number

51. Five times the difference of two numbers

52. One third of the sum of two numbers

53. 64% of the women attending

54. 38% of a number

Determine whether the given number is a solution of the given equation.

55. 25; $x + 17 = 42$

56. 75; $93 - y = 28$

57. 93; $a - 28 = 75$

58. 12; $8t = 96$

59. 63; $\dfrac{t}{7} = 9$

60. 52; $\dfrac{x}{8} = 6$

61. 3; $\dfrac{108}{x} = 36$

62. 7; $\dfrac{94}{y} = 12$

Translate each problem to an equation. Do not solve.

63. What number added to 73 is 201?

64. Seven times what number is 1596?

65. When 42 is multiplied by a number, the result is 2352. Find the number.

66. When 345 is added to a number, the result is 987. Find the number.

67. *Chess.* A chess board has 64 squares. If pieces occupy 19 squares, how many squares are unoccupied?

68. *Hours worked.* A carpenter charges \$35 an hour. How many hours did she work if she billed a total of \$3640?

69. *Recycling.* Currently, Americans recycle or compost 32% of all municipal solid waste. This is the same as recycling or composting 79 million tons. What is the total amount of waste generated?
Source: U.S. EPA, Municipal Solid Waste Department

70. *Travel to work.* In 2005, the average commuting time to work in New York was 31.2 min. The average commuting time in North Dakota was 14.9 min shorter. How long was the average commute in North Dakota?
Source: American Community Survey

In each of Exercises 71–78, match the phrase or sentence with the appropriate expression or equation from the column on the right.

71. _____ Twice the sum of two numbers

a) $\dfrac{x}{y} + 6$

72. _____ Five less than a number is twelve.

b) $2(x + y) = 48$

73. _____ Twelve more than a number is five.

c) $\dfrac{1}{2} \cdot a \cdot b$

74. _____ Half of the product of two numbers

d) $t + 12 = 5$

75. _____ Three times the sum of a number and five

e) $ab - 1 = 48$

76. _____ Twice the sum of two numbers is 48.

f) $2(m + n)$

77. _____ One less than the product of two numbers is 48.

g) $3(t + 5)$

78. _____ Six more than the quotient of two numbers

h) $x - 5 = 12$

To the student and the instructor: Writing exercises, denoted by 🖎 , *should be answered using one or more English sentences. Because answers to many writing exercises will vary, solutions are not listed in the answers at the back of the book.*

🖎 **79.** What is the difference between a variable, a variable expression, and an equation?

🖎 **80.** What does it mean to evaluate an algebraic expression?

Synthesis

To the student and the instructor: Synthesis exercises *are designed to challenge students to extend the concepts or skills studied in each section. Many synthesis exercises will require the assimilation of skills and concepts from several sections.*

🖎 **81.** If the lengths of the sides of a square are doubled, is the area doubled? Why or why not?

🖎 **82.** Write a problem that translates to $1998 + t = 2006$.

83. Signs of Distinction charges \$120 per square foot for handpainted signs. The town of Belmar commissioned a triangular sign with a base of 3 ft and a height of 2.5 ft. How much will the sign cost?

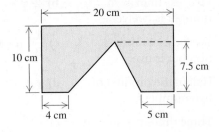

84. Find the area that is shaded.

85. Evaluate $\dfrac{x - y}{3}$ when x is twice y and $x = 12$.

86. Evaluate $\dfrac{x + y}{2}$ when y is twice x and $x = 6$.

87. Evaluate $\dfrac{a + b}{4}$ when a is twice b and $a = 16$.

88. Evaluate $\dfrac{a - b}{3}$ when a is three times b and $a = 18$.

Answer each question with an algebraic expression.

89. If $w + 3$ is a whole number, what is the next whole number after it?

90. If $d + 2$ is an odd number, what is the preceding odd number?

Translate to an algebraic expression.

91. The perimeter of a rectangle with length l and width u (perimeter means distance around)

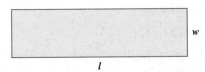

92. The perimeter of a square with side s (perimeter means distance around)

93. Ellie's race time, assuming she took 5 sec longer than Joe and Joe took 3 sec longer than Molly. Assume that Molly's time was t seconds.

94. Ray's age 7 yr from now if he is 2 yr older than Monique and Monique is a years old

🖎 **95.** If the length of the height of a triangle is doubled, is its area also doubled? Why or why not?

CORNER

Teamwork

Focus: Group problem solving; working collaboratively

Time: 15 minutes

Group size: 2

Working and studying as a team often enables students to solve problems that are difficult to solve alone.

ACTIVITY

1. The left-hand column below contains the names of 12 colleges. A scrambled list of the names of their sports teams is on the right. As a group, match the names of the colleges to the teams.

1. University of Texas	**a)** Antelopes
2. Western State College of Colorado	**b)** Banana Slugs
3. University of North Carolina	**c)** Sea Warriors
4. University of Massachusetts	**d)** Gators
5. Hawaii Pacific University	**e)** Mountaineers
6. University of Nebraska	**f)** Sailfish
7. University of California, Santa Cruz	**g)** Longhorns
8. University of Louisiana at Lafayette	**h)** Tar Heels
9. Grand Canyon University	**i)** Seawolves
10. Palm Beach Atlantic University	**j)** Ragin' Cajuns
11. University of Alaska, Anchorage	**k)** Cornhuskers
12. University of Florida	**l)** Minutemen

2. After working for 5 min, confer with another group and reach mutual agreement.

3. Does the class agree on all 12 pairs?

4. Do you agree that group collaboration enhances our ability to solve problems?

1.2   The Commutative, Associative, and Distributive Laws

Equivalent Expressions ▪ The Commutative Laws ▪ The Associative Laws ▪ The Distributive Law ▪ The Distributive Law and Factoring

In order to solve equations, we must be able to manipulate algebraic expressions. The commutative, associative, and distributive laws discussed in this section enable us to write *equivalent expressions* that will simplify our work. Indeed, much of this text is devoted to finding equivalent expressions.

Equivalent Expressions

The expressions $4 + 4 + 4, 3 \cdot 4$, and $4 \cdot 3$ all represent the same number, 12. Expressions that represent the same number are said to be **equivalent**. The equivalent expressions $t + 18$ and $18 + t$ were used on p. 5 when we translated "eighteen more than a number." These expressions are equivalent because they

STUDY SKILLS

Learn by Example

The examples in each section are designed to prepare you for success with the exercise set. Study the step-by-step solutions of the examples, noting that color is used to indicate substitutions and to call attention to the new steps in multistep examples. The time you spend studying the examples will save you valuable time when you do your assignment.

represent the same number for any value of t. We can illustrate this by making some choices for t.

$$\text{When } t = 3, \quad t + 18 = 3 + 18 = 21$$
$$\text{and} \quad 18 + t = 18 + 3 = 21.$$
$$\text{When } t = 40, \quad t + 18 = 40 + 18 = 58$$
$$\text{and} \quad 18 + t = 18 + 40 = 58.$$

The Commutative Laws

Recall that changing the order in addition or multiplication does not change the result. Equations like $3 + 78 = 78 + 3$ and $5 \cdot 14 = 14 \cdot 5$ illustrate this idea and show that addition and multiplication are **commutative**.

The Commutative Laws

For Addition.   For any numbers a and b,

$$a + b = b + a.$$

(Changing the order of addition does not affect the answer.)

For Multiplication.   For any numbers a and b,

$$ab = ba.$$

(Changing the order of multiplication does not affect the answer.)

EXAMPLE   1   Use the commutative laws to write an expression equivalent to each of the following: **(a)** $y + 5$; **(b)** $9x$; **(c)** $7 + ab$.

SOLUTION

a) $y + 5$ is equivalent to $5 + y$ by the commutative law of addition.

b) $9x$ is equivalent to $x \cdot 9$ by the commutative law of multiplication.

c) $7 + ab$ is equivalent to $ab + 7$ by the commutative law of *addition*.

$7 + ab$ is also equivalent to $7 + ba$ by the commutative law of *multiplication*.

$7 + ab$ is also equivalent to $ba + 7$ by the two commutative laws, used together.

TRY EXERCISE ❯ 11

The Associative Laws

Parentheses are used to indicate groupings. We generally simplify within the parentheses first. For example,

$$3 + (8 + 4) = 3 + 12 = 15$$

and

$$(3 + 8) + 4 = 11 + 4 = 15.$$

Similarly,

$$4 \cdot (2 \cdot 3) = 4 \cdot 6 = 24$$

and

$$(4 \cdot 2) \cdot 3 = 8 \cdot 3 = 24.$$

Note that, so long as only addition or only multiplication appears in an expression, changing the grouping does not change the result. Equations such as $3 + (7 + 5) = (3 + 7) + 5$ and $4(5 \cdot 3) = (4 \cdot 5)3$ illustrate that addition and multiplication are **associative**.

The Associative Laws

For Addition.   For any numbers a, b, and c,

$$a + (b + c) = (a + b) + c.$$

(Numbers can be grouped in any manner for addition.)

For Multiplication.   For any numbers a, b, and c,

$$a \cdot (b \cdot c) = (a \cdot b) \cdot c.$$

(Numbers can be grouped in any manner for multiplication.)

EXAMPLE **2**   Use an associative law to write an expression equivalent to each of the following:
(a) $y + (z + 3)$; **(b)** $(8x)y$.

SOLUTION

a) $y + (z + 3)$ is equivalent to $(y + z) + 3$ by the associative law of addition.

b) $(8x)y$ is equivalent to $8(xy)$ by the associative law of multiplication.

> TRY EXERCISE 27

When only addition or only multiplication is involved, parentheses do not change the result. For that reason, we sometimes omit them altogether. Thus,

$$x + (y + 7) = x + y + 7 \quad \text{and} \quad l(wh) = lwh.$$

A sum such as $(5 + 1) + (3 + 5) + 9$ can be simplified by pairing numbers that add to 10. The associative and commutative laws allow us to do this:

$$(5 + 1) + (3 + 5) + 9 = 5 + 5 + 9 + 1 + 3$$
$$= 10 + 10 + 3 = 23.$$

EXAMPLE **3**   Use the commutative and/or associative laws of addition to write two expressions equivalent to $(7 + x) + 3$. Then simplify.

SOLUTION

$$(7 + x) + 3 = (x + 7) + 3 \qquad \text{Using the commutative law;}$$
$$(x + 7) + 3 \text{ is one equivalent expression.}$$

$$= x + (7 + 3) \qquad \text{Using the associative law; } x + (7 + 3)$$
$$\text{is another equivalent expression.}$$

$$= x + 10 \qquad \text{Simplifying} \qquad \text{> TRY EXERCISE 39}$$

EXAMPLE **4** Use the commutative and/or associative laws of multiplication to write two expressions equivalent to $2(x \cdot 3)$.

SOLUTION

$$2(x \cdot 3) = 2(3x)$$ Using the commutative law; $2(3x)$ is one equivalent expression.

$$= (2 \cdot 3)x$$ Using the associative law; $(2 \cdot 3)x$ is another equivalent expression.

$$= 6x$$ Simplifying   **TRY EXERCISE** 41

The Distributive Law

The *distributive law* is probably the single most important law for manipulating algebraic expressions. Unlike the commutative and associative laws, the distributive law uses multiplication together with addition.

You have already used the distributive law although you may not have realized it at the time. To illustrate, try to multiply $3 \cdot 21$ mentally. Many people find the product, 63, by thinking of 21 as $20 + 1$ and then multiplying 20 by 3 and 1 by 3. The sum of the two products, $60 + 3$, is 63. Note that if the 3 does not multiply *both* 20 and 1, the result will not be correct.

EXAMPLE **5** Compute in two ways: $4(7 + 2)$.

SOLUTION

a) As in the discussion of $3(20 + 1)$ above, to compute $4(7 + 2)$, we can multiply both 7 and 2 by 4 and add the results:

$$4(7 + 2) = 4 \cdot 7 + 4 \cdot 2$$ Multiplying both 7 and 2 by 4

$$= 28 + 8 = 36.$$ Adding

b) By first adding inside the parentheses, we get the same result in a different way:

$$4(7 + 2) = 4(9)$$ Adding; $7 + 2 = 9$

$$= 36.$$ Multiplying

STUDENT NOTES ————

To remember the names *commutative, associative,* and *distributive,* first understand the concept. Next, use everyday life to link each word to the concept. For example, think of commuting to and from college as changing the order of appearance.

> ### The Distributive Law
> For any numbers a, b, and c,
> $$a(b + c) = ab + ac.$$
> (The product of a number and a sum can be written as the sum of two products.)

EXAMPLE **6** Multiply: $3(x + 2)$.

SOLUTION Since $x + 2$ cannot be simplified unless a value for x is given, we use the distributive law:

$$3(x + 2) = 3 \cdot x + 3 \cdot 2$$ Using the distributive law

$$= 3x + 6.$$ Note that $3 \cdot x$ is the same as $3x$.

     TRY EXERCISE 47

The expression $3x + 6$ has two *terms*, $3x$ and 6. In general, a **term** is a number, a variable, or a product or a quotient of numbers and/or variables. Thus, t, 29, $5ab$, and $2x/y$ are terms in $t + 29 + 5ab + 2x/y$. Note that terms are separated by plus signs.

EXAMPLE **7**   List the terms in the expression $7s + st + \dfrac{3}{t}$.

SOLUTION   Terms are separated by plus signs, so the terms in $7s + st + \dfrac{3}{t}$ are

$7s$, st, and $\dfrac{3}{t}$.

TRY EXERCISE 61

The distributive law can also be used when more than two terms are inside the parentheses.

EXAMPLE **8**   Multiply: $6(s + 2 + 5w)$.

SOLUTION

$$6(s + 2 + 5w) = 6 \cdot s + 6 \cdot 2 + 6 \cdot 5w \qquad \text{Using the distributive law}$$
$$= 6s + 12 + (6 \cdot 5)w \qquad \text{Using the associative law for multiplication}$$
$$= 6s + 12 + 30w$$

TRY EXERCISE 55

Because of the commutative law of multiplication, the distributive law can be used on the "right": $(b + c)a = ba + ca$.

EXAMPLE **9**   Multiply: $(c + 4)5$.

SOLUTION

$$(c + 4)5 = c \cdot 5 + 4 \cdot 5 \qquad \text{Using the distributive law on the right}$$
$$= 5c + 20 \qquad \text{Using the commutative law; } c \cdot 5 = 5c$$

TRY EXERCISE 57

CAUTION!   To use the distributive law for removing parentheses, be sure to multiply *each* term inside the parentheses by the multiplier outside. Thus,

$\cancel{a(b + c) = ab + c}$ but $a(b + c) = ab + ac$.

The Distributive Law and Factoring

If we use the distributive law in reverse, we have the basis of a process called **factoring**: $ab + ac = a(b + c)$. To **factor** an expression means to write an equivalent expression that is a product. The parts of the product are called **factors**. Note that "factor" can be used as either a verb or a noun. Thus in the expression $5t$, the factors are 5 and t. In the expression $4(m + n)$, the factors are 4 and $(m + n)$. A **common factor** is a factor that appears in every term in an expression.

EXAMPLE **10**   Use the distributive law to factor each of the following.

a) $3x + 3y$

b) $7x + 21y + 7$

SOLUTION

a) By the distributive law,

$$3x + 3y = 3(x + y).$$ The common factor for $3x$ and $3y$ is 3.

b) $7x + 21y + 7 = 7 \cdot x + 7 \cdot 3y + 7 \cdot 1$ The common factor is 7.

$$= 7(x + 3y + 1)$$ Using the distributive law. Be sure to include both the 1 and the common factor, 7.

TRY EXERCISE 69

To check our factoring, we multiply to see if the original expression is obtained. For example, to check the **factorization** in Example 10(b), note that

$$7(x + 3y + 1) = 7 \cdot x + 7 \cdot 3y + 7 \cdot 1$$
$$= 7x + 21y + 7.$$

Since $7x + 21y + 7$ is what we started with in Example 10(b), we have a check.

CAUTION! Do not confuse **terms** with **factors**. Terms are separated by plus signs, and factors are parts of products. The distributive law is used when there are two or more terms inside parentheses. For example, in the expression $a(b \cdot c)$, b and c are factors, not terms. We can use the commutative and associative laws to reorder and regroup the factors, but the distributive law does not apply here. Thus,

$$\cancel{a(b \cdot c) = a \cdot b \cdot a \cdot c} \quad \text{but} \quad a(b \cdot c) = (a \cdot b) \cdot c.$$

1.2   **EXERCISE SET**

For Extra Help
MyMathLab   Math XL   PRACTICE   WATCH   DOWNLOAD

Concept Reinforcement   *Complete each sentence using one of these terms:* commutative, associative, *or* distributive.

1. $8 + t$ is equivalent to $t + 8$ by the _____ law for addition.

2. $3(xy)$ is equivalent to $(3x)y$ by the _____ law for multiplication.

3. $(5b)c$ is equivalent to $5(bc)$ by the _____ law for multiplication.

4. mn is equivalent to nm by the _____ law for multiplication.

5. $x(y + z)$ is equivalent to $xy + xz$ by the _____ law.

6. $(9 + a) + b$ is equivalent to $9 + (a + b)$ by the _____ law for addition.

7. $a + (6 + d)$ is equivalent to $(a + 6) + d$ by the _____ law for addition.

8. $3(t + 4)$ is equivalent to $3(4 + t)$ by the _____ law for addition.

9. $5(x + 2)$ is equivalent to $(x + 2)5$ by the _____ law for multiplication.

10. $2(a + b)$ is equivalent to $2 \cdot a + 2 \cdot b$ by the _____ law.

Use the commutative law of addition to write an equivalent expression.

11. $11 + t$

12. $a + 2$

13. $4 + 8x$

14. $ab + c$

15. $9x + 3y$

16. $3a + 7b$

17. $5(a + 1)$

18. $9(x + 5)$

Use the commutative law of multiplication to write an equivalent expression.

19. $7x$

20. xy

21. st

22. $13m$

23. $5 + ab$

24. $x + 3y$

25. $5(a + 1)$

26. $9(x + 5)$

Use the associative law of addition to write an equivalent expression.

27. $(x + 8) + y$

28. $(5 + m) + r$

29. $u + (v + 7)$

30. $x + (2 + y)$

31. $(ab + c) + d$

32. $(m + np) + r$

Use the associative law of multiplication to write an equivalent expression.

33. $(8x)y$

34. $(4u)v$

35. $2(ab)$

36. $9(7r)$

37. $3[2(a + b)]$

38. $5[x(2 + y)]$

Use the commutative and/or associative laws to write two equivalent expressions. Answers may vary.

39. $s + (t + 6)$

40. $7 + (v + w)$

41. $(17a)b$

42. $x(3y)$

Use the commutative and/or associative laws to show why the expression on the left is equivalent to the expression on the right. Write a series of steps with labels, as in Example 4.

43. $(1 + x) + 2$ is equivalent to $x + 3$

44. $(2a)4$ is equivalent to $8a$

45. $(m \cdot 3)7$ is equivalent to $21m$

46. $4 + (9 + x)$ is equivalent to $x + 13$

Multiply.

47. $2(x + 15)$

48. $3(x + 5)$

49. $4(1 + a)$

50. $6(v + 4)$

51. $8(3 + y)$

52. $7(s + 1)$

53. $10(9x + 6)$

54. $9(6m + 7)$

55. $5(r + 2 + 3t)$

56. $4(5x + 8 + 3p)$

57. $(a + b)2$

58. $(x + 2)7$

59. $(x + y + 2)5$

60. $(2 + a + b)6$

List the terms in each expression.

61. $x + xyz + 1$

62. $9 + 17a + abc$

63. $2a + \dfrac{a}{3b} + 5b$

64. $3xy + 20 + \dfrac{4a}{b}$

65. $4(x + y)$

66. $(7 + y)2$

67. $4x + 4y$

68. $14 + 2y$

Use the distributive law to factor each of the following. Check by multiplying.

69. $2a + 2b$

70. $5y + 5z$

71. $7 + 7y$

72. $13 + 13x$

73. $32x + 4$

74. $20a + 5$

75. $5x + 10 + 15y$

76. $3 + 27b + 6c$

77. $7a + 35b$

78. $8x + 24y$

79. $44x + 11y + 22z$

80. $14a + 56b + 7$

List the factors in each expression.

81. $5n$

82. uv

83. $3(x + y)$

84. $(a + b)12$

85. $7 \cdot a \cdot b$

86. $m \cdot n \cdot 2$

87. $(a - b)(x - y)$

88. $(3 - a)(b + c)$

89. Is subtraction commutative? Why or why not?

90. Is division associative? Why or why not?

Skill Review

To the student and the instructor: Exercises included for Skill Review include skills previously studied in the text. Often these exercises provide preparation for the next section of the text. The numbers in brackets immediately following the directions or exercise indicate the section in which the skill was introduced. The answers to all Skill Review exercises appear at the back of the book. If a Skill Review exercise gives you difficulty, review the material in the indicated section of the text.

Translate to an algebraic expression. [1.1]

91. Half of Kara's salary

92. Twice the sum of m and 3

Synthesis

93. Give an example illustrating the distributive law, and identify the terms and the factors in your example. Explain how you can determine terms and factors in an expression.

94. Explain how the distributive, commutative, and associative laws can be used to show that $2(3x + 4y)$ is equivalent to $6x + 8y$.

Tell whether the expressions in each pairing are equivalent. Then explain why or why not.

95. $8 + 4(a + b)$ and $4(2 + a + b)$

96. $5(a \cdot b)$ and $5 \cdot a \cdot 5 \cdot b$

97. $7 \div 3m$ and $m \cdot 3 \div 7$

98. $(rt + st)5$ and $5t(r + s)$

99. $30y + x \cdot 15$ and $5[2(x + 3y)]$

100. $[c(2 + 3b)]5$ and $10c + 15bc$

101. Evaluate the expressions $3(2 + x)$ and $6 + x$ for $x = 0$. Do your results indicate that $3(2 + x)$ and $6 + x$ are equivalent? Why or why not?

102. Factor $15x + 40$. Then evaluate both $15x + 40$ and the factorization for $x = 4$. Do your results *guarantee* that the factorization is correct? Why or why not? (*Hint:* See Exercise 101.)

COLLABORATIVE CORNER

Mental Addition

Focus: Application of commutative and associative laws

Time: 10 minutes

Group size: 2–3

Legend has it that while still in grade school, the mathematician Carl Friedrich Gauss (1777–1855) was able to add the numbers from 1 to 100 mentally. Gauss did not add them sequentially, but rather paired 1 with 99, 2 with 98, and so on.

ACTIVITY

1. Use a method similar to Gauss's to simplify the following:

$$1 + 2 + 3 + 4 + 5 + 6 + 7 + 8 + 9 + 10.$$

One group member should add from left to right as a check.

2. Use Gauss's method to find the sum of the first 25 counting numbers:

$$1 + 2 + 3 + \cdots + 23 + 24 + 25.$$

Again, one student should add from left to right as a check.

3. How were the associative and commutative laws applied in parts (1) and (2) above?

4. Now use a similar approach involving both addition and division to find the sum of the first 10 counting numbers:

$$\begin{array}{r} 1 + 2 + 3 + \cdots + 10 \\ + 10 + 9 + 8 + \cdots + 1 \\ \hline \end{array}$$

5. Use the approach in step (4) to find the sum of the first 100 counting numbers. Are the associative and commutative laws applied in this method, too? How is the distributive law used in this approach?

1.3 Fraction Notation

Factors and Prime Factorizations ▪ Fraction Notation ▪ Multiplication, Division, and Simplification ▪ More Simplifying ▪ Addition and Subtraction

This section covers multiplication, addition, subtraction, and division with fractions. Although much of this may be review, note that fraction expressions that contain variables are also included.

Factors and Prime Factorizations

In preparation for work with fraction notation, we first review how *natural numbers* are factored. **Natural numbers** can be thought of as the counting numbers:

$$1, 2, 3, 4, 5, \ldots .*$$

(The dots indicate that the established pattern continues without ending.)

Since factors are parts of products, to factor a number, we express it as a product of two or more numbers.

Several factorizations of 12 are

$$1 \cdot 12, \quad 2 \cdot 6, \quad 3 \cdot 4, \quad 2 \cdot 2 \cdot 3.$$

It is easy to miss a factor of a number if the factorizations are not written methodically.

EXAMPLE **1**   List all factors of 18.

SOLUTION   Beginning at 1, we check all natural numbers to see if they are factors of 18. If they are, we write the factorization. We stop when we have already included the next natural number in a factorization.

1 is a factor of every number. $1 \cdot 18$

2 is a factor of 18. $2 \cdot 9$

3 is a factor of 18. $3 \cdot 6$

4 is *not* a factor of 18.

5 is *not* a factor of 18.

6 is the next natural number, but we have already listed 6 as a factor in the product $3 \cdot 6$.

We need check no additional numbers, because any natural number greater than 6 must be paired with a factor less than 6.

We now write the factors of 18 beginning with 1, going down the list of factorizations writing the first factor, then up the list of factorizations writing the second factor:

$$1, \quad 2, \quad 3, \quad 6, \quad 9, \quad 18.$$

> TRY EXERCISE ▸ 15

Some numbers have only two different factors, the number itself and 1. Such numbers are called **prime**.

---

*A similar collection of numbers, the **whole numbers,** includes 0: 0, 1, 2, 3, ...

> ### Prime Number
>
> A *prime number* is a natural number that has exactly two different factors: the number itself and 1. The first several primes are 2, 3, 5, 7, 11, 13, 17, 19, and 23.

If a natural number other than 1 is not prime, we call it **composite**.

EXAMPLE **2**   Label each number as prime, composite, or neither: 29, 4, 1.

SOLUTION

29 is prime. It has exactly two different factors, 29 and 1.

4 is not prime. It has three different factors, 1, 2, and 4. It is composite.

1 is not prime. It does not have two *different* factors. The number 1 is not considered composite. It is neither prime nor composite.

TRY EXERCISE 5

Every composite number can be factored into a product of prime numbers. Such a factorization is called the **prime factorization** of that composite number.

EXAMPLE **3**   Find the prime factorization of 36.

SOLUTION   We first factor 36 in any way that we can. One way is like this:

$$36 = 4 \cdot 9.$$

The factors 4 and 9 are not prime, so we factor them:

$$36 = 4 \cdot 9$$
$$= 2 \cdot 2 \cdot 3 \cdot 3. \quad \text{2 and 3 are both prime.}$$

The prime factorization of 36 is $2 \cdot 2 \cdot 3 \cdot 3$.

TRY EXERCISE 25

Fraction Notation

An example of **fraction notation** for a number is

$$\frac{2}{3}. \quad \begin{array}{l} \leftarrow \text{Numerator} \\ \leftarrow \text{Denominator} \end{array}$$

The top number is called the **numerator**, and the bottom number is called the **denominator**. When the numerator and the denominator are the same nonzero number, we have fraction notation for the number 1.

> ### Fraction Notation for 1
>
> For any number a, except 0,
>
> $$\frac{a}{a} = 1.$$
>
> (Any nonzero number divided by itself is 1.)

STUDENT NOTES

When writing a factorization, you are writing an equivalent expression for the original number. Some students do this with a tree diagram:

$$
\begin{array}{c}
36 \\
36 = 4 \quad \cdot \quad 9 \\
36 = \underbrace{2 \cdot 2 \cdot 3 \cdot 3} \\
\text{All prime}
\end{array}
$$

Note that in the definition for fraction notation for the number 1, we have excluded 0. In fact, 0 cannot be the denominator of *any* fraction. In this section, we limit our discussion to natural numbers, so this situation does not arise. Later in this chapter, we will discuss why denominators cannot be 0.

Multiplication, Division, and Simplification

Recall from arithmetic that fractions are multiplied as follows.

Multiplication of Fractions

For any two fractions a/b and c/d,

$$\frac{a}{b} \cdot \frac{c}{d} = \frac{ac}{bd}.$$

(The numerator of the product is the product of the two numerators. The denominator of the product is the product of the two denominators.)

EXAMPLE 4   Multiply: (a) $\dfrac{2}{3} \cdot \dfrac{5}{7}$; (b) $\dfrac{4}{x} \cdot \dfrac{8}{y}$.

SOLUTION   We multiply numerators as well as denominators.

a) $\dfrac{2}{3} \cdot \dfrac{5}{7} = \dfrac{2 \cdot 5}{3 \cdot 7} = \dfrac{10}{21}$

b) $\dfrac{4}{x} \cdot \dfrac{8}{y} = \dfrac{4 \cdot 8}{x \cdot y} = \dfrac{32}{xy}$

TRY EXERCISE 53

Two numbers whose product is 1 are **reciprocals**, or **multiplicative inverses**, of each other. All numbers, except zero, have reciprocals. For example,

the reciprocal of $\dfrac{2}{3}$ is $\dfrac{3}{2}$ because $\dfrac{2}{3} \cdot \dfrac{3}{2} = \dfrac{6}{6} = 1$;

the reciprocal of 9 is $\dfrac{1}{9}$ because $9 \cdot \dfrac{1}{9} = \dfrac{9}{9} = 1$; and

the reciprocal of $\dfrac{1}{4}$ is 4 because $\dfrac{1}{4} \cdot 4 = 1$.

Reciprocals are used to rewrite division in an equivalent form that uses multiplication.

Division of Fractions

To divide two fractions, multiply by the reciprocal of the divisor:

$$\frac{a}{b} \div \frac{c}{d} = \frac{a}{b} \cdot \frac{d}{c}.$$

EXAMPLE **5**   Divide: $\dfrac{1}{2} \div \dfrac{3}{5}$.

SOLUTION

$$\dfrac{1}{2} \div \dfrac{3}{5} = \dfrac{1}{2} \cdot \dfrac{5}{3} \qquad \dfrac{5}{3} \text{ is the reciprocal of } \dfrac{3}{5}.$$

$$= \dfrac{5}{6}$$

TRY EXERCISE 73

When one of the fractions being multiplied is 1, multiplying yields an equivalent expression because of the *identity property of* 1. A similar property could be stated for division, but there is no need to do so here.

> ## The Identity Property of 1
>
> For any number a,
>
> $$a \cdot 1 = 1 \cdot a = a.$$
>
> (Multiplying a number by 1 gives that same number.) The number 1 is called the *multiplicative identity*.

EXAMPLE **6**   Multiply $\dfrac{4}{5} \cdot \dfrac{6}{6}$ to find an expression equivalent to $\dfrac{4}{5}$.

SOLUTION   Since $\frac{6}{6} = 1$, the expression $\frac{4}{5} \cdot \frac{6}{6}$ is equivalent to $\frac{4}{5} \cdot 1$, or simply $\frac{4}{5}$. We have

$$\dfrac{4}{5} \cdot \dfrac{6}{6} = \dfrac{4 \cdot 6}{5 \cdot 6} = \dfrac{24}{30}.$$

Thus, $\frac{24}{30}$ is equivalent to $\frac{4}{5}$.

The steps of Example 6 are reversed by "removing a factor equal to 1"—in this case, $\frac{6}{6}$. By removing a factor that equals 1, we can *simplify* an expression like $\frac{24}{30}$ to an equivalent expression like $\frac{4}{5}$.

To simplify, we factor the numerator and the denominator, looking for the largest factor common to both. This is sometimes made easier by writing prime factorizations. After identifying common factors, we can express the fraction as a product of two fractions, one of which is in the form a/a.

EXAMPLE **7**   Simplify: **(a)** $\dfrac{15}{40}$; **(b)** $\dfrac{36}{24}$.

SOLUTION

a) Note that 5 is a factor of both 15 and 40:

$$\dfrac{15}{40} = \dfrac{3 \cdot 5}{8 \cdot 5} \qquad \text{Factoring the numerator and the denominator, using the common factor, 5}$$

$$= \dfrac{3}{8} \cdot \dfrac{5}{5} \qquad \text{Rewriting as a product of two fractions; } \dfrac{5}{5} = 1$$

$$= \dfrac{3}{8} \cdot 1 = \dfrac{3}{8}. \qquad \text{Using the identity property of 1 (removing a factor equal to 1)}$$

b) $\dfrac{36}{24} = \dfrac{2 \cdot 2 \cdot 3 \cdot 3}{2 \cdot 2 \cdot 2 \cdot 3}$ Writing the prime factorizations and identifying common factors; 12/12 could also be used.

$= \dfrac{3}{2} \cdot \dfrac{2 \cdot 2 \cdot 3}{2 \cdot 2 \cdot 3}$ Rewriting as a product of two fractions; $\dfrac{2 \cdot 2 \cdot 3}{2 \cdot 2 \cdot 3} = 1$

$= \dfrac{3}{2} \cdot 1 = \dfrac{3}{2}$ Using the identity property of 1   **TRY EXERCISE** ▸ 35

It is always wise to check your result to see if any common factors of the numerator and the denominator remain. (This will never happen if prime factorizations are used correctly.) If common factors remain, repeat the process by removing another factor equal to 1 to simplify your result.

More Simplifying

"Canceling" is a shortcut that you may have used for removing a factor equal to 1 when working with fraction notation. With *great* concern, we mention it as a possible way to speed up your work. Canceling can be used only when removing common factors in numerators and denominators. Canceling *cannot* be used in sums or differences. Our concern is that "canceling" be used with understanding. Example 7(b) might have been done faster as follows:

$$\frac{36}{24} = \frac{\cancel{2} \cdot \cancel{2} \cdot 3 \cdot \cancel{3}}{\cancel{2} \cdot \cancel{2} \cdot 2 \cdot \cancel{3}} = \frac{3}{2}, \quad \text{or} \quad \frac{36}{24} = \frac{3 \cdot \cancel{12}}{2 \cdot \cancel{12}} = \frac{3}{2}, \quad \text{or} \quad \frac{\overset{3}{\cancel{\overset{18}{\cancel{36}}}}}{\underset{2}{\cancel{\underset{12}{\cancel{24}}}}} = \frac{3}{2}.$$

> **CAUTION!** Unfortunately, canceling is often performed incorrectly:
>
> $$\frac{\cancel{2} + 3}{\cancel{2}} = 3, \qquad \frac{\cancel{4} - 1}{\cancel{4} - 2} = \frac{1}{2}, \qquad \frac{1\cancel{5}}{\cancel{5}4} = \frac{1}{4}.$$
>
> The above cancellations are incorrect because the expressions canceled are *not* factors. For example, in $2 + 3$, the 2 and the 3 are not factors. Correct simplifications are as follows:
>
> $$\frac{2 + 3}{2} = \frac{5}{2}, \qquad \frac{4 - 1}{4 - 2} = \frac{3}{2}, \qquad \frac{15}{54} = \frac{5 \cdot \cancel{3}}{18 \cdot \cancel{3}} = \frac{5}{18}.$$
>
> *Remember*: **If you can't factor, you can't cancel! If in doubt, don't cancel!**

Sometimes it is helpful to use 1 as a factor in the numerator or the denominator when simplifying.

EXAMPLE   **8**   Simplify: $\dfrac{9}{72}$.

SOLUTION

$$\frac{9}{72} = \frac{1 \cdot 9}{8 \cdot 9}$$ Factoring and using the identity property of 1 to write 9 as $1 \cdot 9$

$$= \frac{1 \cdot \cancel{9}}{8 \cdot \cancel{9}} = \frac{1}{8}$$ Simplifying by removing a factor equal to 1: $\dfrac{9}{9} = 1$ **TRY EXERCISE** ▸ 39

Addition and Subtraction

When denominators are the same, fractions are added or subtracted by adding or subtracting numerators and keeping the same denominator.

Addition and Subtraction of Fractions

For any two fractions a/d and b/d,

$$\frac{a}{d} + \frac{b}{d} = \frac{a+b}{d} \quad \text{and} \quad \frac{a}{d} - \frac{b}{d} = \frac{a-b}{d}.$$

EXAMPLE **9**   Add and simplify: $\dfrac{4}{8} + \dfrac{5}{8}$.

SOLUTION   The common denominator is 8. We add the numerators and keep the common denominator:

$$\frac{4}{8} + \frac{5}{8} = \frac{4+5}{8} = \frac{9}{8}.$$

You can think of this as
$$4 \cdot \frac{1}{8} + 5 \cdot \frac{1}{8} = 9 \cdot \frac{1}{8}, \text{ or } \frac{9}{8}.$$

> **TRY EXERCISE** 63

In arithmetic, we often write $1\frac{1}{8}$ rather than the "improper" fraction $\frac{9}{8}$. In algebra, $\frac{9}{8}$ is generally more useful and is quite "proper" for our purposes.

When denominators are different, we use the identity property of 1 and multiply to find a common denominator. Then we add, as in Example 9.

EXAMPLE **10**   Add or subtract as indicated: **(a)** $\dfrac{7}{8} + \dfrac{5}{12}$; **(b)** $\dfrac{9}{8} - \dfrac{4}{5}$.

SOLUTION

a) The number 24 is divisible by both 8 and 12. We multiply both $\frac{7}{8}$ and $\frac{5}{12}$ by suitable forms of 1 to obtain two fractions with denominators of 24:

$$\frac{7}{8} + \frac{5}{12} = \frac{7}{8} \cdot \frac{3}{3} + \frac{5}{12} \cdot \frac{2}{2}$$

Multiplying by 1. Since $8 \cdot 3 = 24$, we multiply $\frac{7}{8}$ by $\frac{3}{3}$. Since $12 \cdot 2 = 24$, we multiply $\frac{5}{12}$ by $\frac{2}{2}$.

$$= \frac{21}{24} + \frac{10}{24}$$

Performing the multiplication

$$= \frac{31}{24}.$$

Adding fractions

b)
$$\frac{9}{8} - \frac{4}{5} = \frac{9}{8} \cdot \frac{5}{5} - \frac{4}{5} \cdot \frac{8}{8}$$

Using 40 as a common denominator

$$= \frac{45}{40} - \frac{32}{40} = \frac{13}{40}$$

Subtracting fractions

> **TRY EXERCISE** 69

After adding, subtracting, multiplying, or dividing, we may still need to simplify the answer.

EXAMPLE 11   Perform the indicated operation and, if possible, simplify.

a) $\dfrac{7}{10} - \dfrac{1}{5}$ **b)** $8 \cdot \dfrac{5}{12}$ **c)** $\dfrac{\frac{5}{6}}{\frac{25}{9}}$

SOLUTION

a) $\dfrac{7}{10} - \dfrac{1}{5} = \dfrac{7}{10} - \dfrac{1}{5} \cdot \dfrac{2}{2}$ Using 10 as the common denominator

$= \dfrac{7}{10} - \dfrac{2}{10}$

$= \dfrac{5}{10} = \dfrac{1 \cdot \cancel{5}}{2 \cdot \cancel{5}} = \dfrac{1}{2}$ Removing a factor equal to 1: $\dfrac{5}{5} = 1$

b) $8 \cdot \dfrac{5}{12} = \dfrac{8 \cdot 5}{12}$ Multiplying numerators and denominators. Think of 8 as $\frac{8}{1}$.

$= \dfrac{2 \cdot 2 \cdot 2 \cdot 5}{2 \cdot 2 \cdot 3}$ Factoring; $\dfrac{4 \cdot 2 \cdot 5}{4 \cdot 3}$ can also be used.

$= \dfrac{\cancel{2} \cdot \cancel{2} \cdot 2 \cdot 5}{\cancel{2} \cdot \cancel{2} \cdot 3}$ Removing a factor equal to 1: $\dfrac{2 \cdot 2}{2 \cdot 2} = 1$

$= \dfrac{10}{3}$ Simplifying

c) $\dfrac{\frac{5}{6}}{\frac{25}{9}} = \dfrac{5}{6} \div \dfrac{25}{9}$ Rewriting horizontally. Remember that a fraction bar indicates division.

$= \dfrac{5}{6} \cdot \dfrac{9}{25}$ Multiplying by the reciprocal of $\frac{25}{9}$

$= \dfrac{5 \cdot 3 \cdot 3}{2 \cdot 3 \cdot 5 \cdot 5}$ Writing as one fraction and factoring

$= \dfrac{\cancel{5} \cdot \cancel{3} \cdot 3}{2 \cdot \cancel{3} \cdot \cancel{5} \cdot 5}$ Removing a factor equal to 1: $\dfrac{5 \cdot 3}{3 \cdot 5} = 1$

$= \dfrac{3}{10}$ Simplifying

TRY EXERCISE 65

TECHNOLOGY CONNECTION

Some graphing calculators can perform operations using fraction notation. Others can convert answers given in decimal notation to fraction notation. Often this conversion is done using a command found in a **menu** of options that appears when a key is pressed. To select an item from a menu, we highlight its number and press **ENTER** or simply press the number of the item.

For example, to find fraction notation for $\frac{2}{15} + \frac{7}{12}$, we enter the expression as $2/15 + 7/12$. The answer is given in decimal notation. To convert this to fraction notation, we press **MATH** and select the Frac option. In this case, the notation Ans ▶ Frac shows that the graphing calculator will convert .7166666667 to fraction notation.

```
2/15+7/12
                    .7166666667
Ans▶Frac
                           43/60
```

We see that $\frac{2}{15} + \frac{7}{12} = \frac{43}{60}$.

1.3   **EXERCISE SET**

To the student and the instructor: Beginning in this section, selected exercises are marked with the symbol Aha!. *Students who pause to inspect an Aha! exercise should find the answer more readily than those who proceed mechanically. This is done to discourage rote memorization. Some later "Aha!" exercises in this exercise set are unmarked, to encourage students to always pause before working a problem.*

🔖 *Concept Reinforcement   In each of Exercises 1–4, match the description with a number from the list on the right.*

1. ____ A factor of 35   **a)** 2

2. ____ A number that has 3 as a factor   **b)** 7

3. ____ An odd composite number   **c)** 60

4. ____ The only even prime number   **d)** 65

Label each of the following numbers as prime, composite, or neither.

5. 9 **6.** 15 **7.** 41 **8.** 49

9. 77 **10.** 37 **11.** 2 **12.** 1

13. 0 **14.** 16

Write all two-factor factorizations of each number. Then list all the factors of the number.

15. 50 **16.** 70 **17.** 42 **18.** 60

Find the prime factorization of each number. If the number is prime, state this.

19. 39 **20.** 34 **21.** 30

22. 55 **23.** 27 **24.** 98

25. 150 **26.** 54 **27.** 40

28. 56 **29.** 31 **30.** 180

31. 210 **32.** 79 **33.** 115

34. 143

Simplify.

35. $\dfrac{21}{35}$ **36.** $\dfrac{20}{26}$ **37.** $\dfrac{16}{56}$

38. $\dfrac{72}{27}$ **39.** $\dfrac{12}{48}$ **40.** $\dfrac{18}{84}$

41. $\dfrac{52}{13}$ **42.** $\dfrac{132}{11}$ **43.** $\dfrac{19}{76}$

44. $\dfrac{17}{51}$ **45.** $\dfrac{150}{25}$ **46.** $\dfrac{180}{36}$

47. $\dfrac{42}{50}$ **48.** $\dfrac{75}{80}$ **49.** $\dfrac{120}{82}$

50. $\dfrac{75}{45}$ **51.** $\dfrac{210}{98}$ **52.** $\dfrac{140}{350}$

Perform the indicated operation and, if possible, simplify.

53. $\dfrac{1}{2} \cdot \dfrac{3}{5}$ **54.** $\dfrac{11}{10} \cdot \dfrac{8}{5}$ **55.** $\dfrac{9}{2} \cdot \dfrac{4}{3}$

Aha! **56.** $\dfrac{11}{12} \cdot \dfrac{12}{11}$ **57.** $\dfrac{1}{8} + \dfrac{3}{8}$ **58.** $\dfrac{1}{2} + \dfrac{1}{8}$

59. $\dfrac{4}{9} + \dfrac{13}{18}$ **60.** $\dfrac{4}{5} + \dfrac{8}{15}$ **61.** $\dfrac{3}{a} \cdot \dfrac{b}{7}$

62. $\dfrac{x}{5} \cdot \dfrac{y}{z}$ **63.** $\dfrac{4}{n} + \dfrac{6}{n}$ **64.** $\dfrac{9}{x} - \dfrac{5}{x}$

65. $\dfrac{3}{10} + \dfrac{8}{15}$ **66.** $\dfrac{7}{8} + \dfrac{5}{12}$ **67.** $\dfrac{11}{7} - \dfrac{4}{7}$

68. $\dfrac{12}{5} - \dfrac{2}{5}$ **69.** $\dfrac{13}{18} - \dfrac{4}{9}$ **70.** $\dfrac{13}{15} - \dfrac{11}{45}$

Aha! **71.** $\dfrac{20}{30} - \dfrac{2}{3}$ **72.** $\dfrac{5}{7} - \dfrac{5}{21}$ **73.** $\dfrac{7}{6} \div \dfrac{3}{5}$

74. $\dfrac{7}{5} \div \dfrac{10}{3}$ **75.** $\dfrac{8}{9} \div \dfrac{4}{15}$ **76.** $\dfrac{9}{4} \div 9$

77. $12 \div \dfrac{4}{9}$ **78.** $\dfrac{1}{10} \div \dfrac{1}{5}$ Aha! **79.** $\dfrac{7}{13} \div \dfrac{7}{13}$

80. $\dfrac{17}{8} \div \dfrac{5}{6}$ **81.** $\dfrac{\frac{2}{7}}{\frac{5}{3}}$ **82.** $\dfrac{\frac{3}{8}}{\frac{1}{5}}$

83. $\dfrac{9}{\frac{1}{2}}$ **84.** $\dfrac{\frac{3}{7}}{6}$

85. Under what circumstances would the sum of two fractions be easier to compute than the product of the same two fractions?

86. Under what circumstances would the product of two fractions be easier to compute than the sum of the same two fractions?

Skill Review

Use a commutative law to write an equivalent expression. There can be more than one correct answer. [1.2]

87. $5(x + 3)$ **88.** $7 + (a + b)$

Synthesis

89. Bryce insists that $(2 + x)/8$ is equivalent to $(1 + x)/4$. What mistake do you think is being made and how could you demonstrate to Bryce that the two expressions are not equivalent?

90. Why are 0 and 1 considered neither prime nor composite?

91. In the following table, the top number can be factored in such a way that the sum of the factors is the bottom number. For example, in the first column, 56 is factored as $7 \cdot 8$, since $7 + 8 = 15$, the bottom number. Find the missing numbers in each column.

Product	56	63	36	72	140	96	1(
Factor	7						
Factor	8						
Sum	15	16	20	38	24	20	2

92. *Packaging.* Tritan Candies uses two sizes of boxes, 6 in. long and 8 in. long. These are packed end to end in bigger cartons to be shipped. What is the shortest-length carton that will accommodate boxes of either size without any room left over? (Each carton must contain boxes of only one size; no mixing is allowed.)

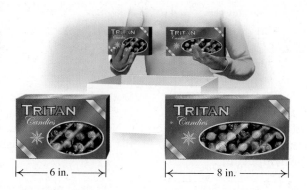

Simplify.

93. $\dfrac{16 \cdot 9 \cdot 4}{15 \cdot 8 \cdot 12}$

94. $\dfrac{9 \cdot 8xy}{2xy \cdot 36}$

95. $\dfrac{45pqrs}{9prst}$

96. $\dfrac{247}{323}$

97. $\dfrac{15 \cdot 4xy \cdot 9}{6 \cdot 25x \cdot 15y}$

98. $\dfrac{10x \cdot 12 \cdot 25y}{2z \cdot 30x \cdot 20y}$

99. $\dfrac{\frac{27ab}{15mn}}{\frac{18bc}{25np}}$

100. $\dfrac{\frac{45xyz}{24ab}}{\frac{30xz}{32ac}}$

101. $\dfrac{5\frac{3}{4}rs}{4\frac{1}{2}st}$

102. $\dfrac{3\frac{5}{7}mn}{2\frac{4}{5}np}$

Find the area of each figure.

103.

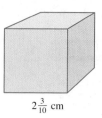

104.

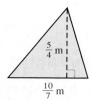

105. Find the perimeter of a square with sides of length $3\frac{5}{9}$ m.

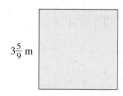

106. Find the perimeter of the rectangle in Exercise 103.

107. Find the total length of the edges of a cube with sides of length $2\frac{3}{10}$ cm.

1.4   Positive and Negative Real Numbers

The Integers ■ The Rational Numbers ■ Real Numbers and Order ■ Absolute Value

A **set** is a collection of objects. The set containing 1, 3, and 7 is usually written $\{1, 3, 7\}$. In this section, we examine some important sets of numbers. More on sets can be found in Appendix B.

The Integers

Natural numbers = $\{1, 2, 3, \ldots\}$

Whole numbers = $\{0, 1, 2, 3, \ldots\}$

Two sets of numbers were mentioned in Section 1.3. We represent these sets using dots on a number line, as shown at left.

To create the set of *integers,* we include all whole numbers, along with their *opposites.* To find the opposite of a number, we locate the number that is the same distance from 0 but on the other side of the number line. For example,

the opposite of 1 is negative 1, written −1;

and

the opposite of 3 is negative 3, written −3.

The **integers** consist of all whole numbers and their opposites.

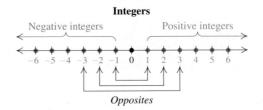

Opposites are discussed in more detail in Section 1.6. Note that, except for 0, opposites occur in pairs. Thus, 5 is the opposite of −5, just as −5 is the opposite of 5. Note that 0 acts as its own opposite.

STUDENT NOTES

It is not uncommon in mathematics for a symbol to have more than one meaning in different contexts. The symbol "−" in 5 − 3 indicates subtraction. The same symbol in −10 indicates the opposite of 10, or negative 10.

Set of Integers

The set of integers = $\{\ldots, -4, -3, -2, -1, 0, 1, 2, 3, 4, \ldots\}$.

Integers are associated with many real-world problems and situations.

EXAMPLE 1   State which integer(s) corresponds to each situation.

a) In 2006, there was $13 trillion in outstanding mortgage debt in the United States.
Source: Board of Governors of the Federal Reserve System

b) Part of Death Valley is 200 ft below sea level.

c) To lose one pound of fat, it is necessary for most people to create a 3500-calorie deficit.
Source: World Health Organization

SOLUTION

a) The integer −13,000,000,000,000 corresponds to a debt of $13 trillion.

b) The integer −200 corresponds to 200 ft below sea level.

c) The integer −3500 corresponds to a deficit of 3500 calories.

TRY EXERCISE 9

STUDY SKILLS ———————

Try to Get Ahead

Try to keep one section ahead of your instructor. If you study ahead of your lectures, you can concentrate on what is being explained in class, rather than trying to write everything down. You can then write notes on only special points or questions related to what is happening in class.

The Rational Numbers

A number like $\frac{5}{9}$, although built out of integers, is not itself an integer. Another set of numbers, the **rational numbers**, contains integers, fractions, and decimals. Some examples of rational numbers are

$$\frac{5}{9}, \quad -\frac{4}{7}, \quad 95, \quad -16, \quad 0, \quad \frac{-35}{8}, \quad 2.4, \quad -0.31.$$

In Section 1.7, we show that $-\frac{4}{7}$ can be written as $\frac{-4}{7}$ or $\frac{4}{-7}$. Indeed, every number listed above can be written as an integer over an integer. For example, 95 can be written as $\frac{95}{1}$ and 2.4 can be written as $\frac{24}{10}$. In this manner, any *rati*onal number can be expressed as the *ratio* of two integers. Rather than attempt to list all rational numbers, we use this idea of ratio to describe the set as follows.

Set of Rational Numbers

The set of rational numbers $= \left\{ \dfrac{a}{b} \,\middle|\, a \text{ and } b \text{ are integers and } b \neq 0 \right\}.$

This is read "the set of all numbers a over b, where a and b are integers and b does not equal zero."

In Section 1.7, we explain why b cannot equal 0.

To *graph* a number is to mark its location on a number line.

EXAMPLE **2**   Graph each of the following rational numbers: **(a)** $\frac{5}{2}$; **(b)** -3.2; **(c)** $\frac{11}{8}$.

SOLUTION

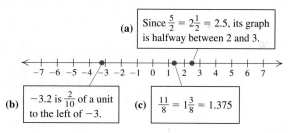

(a) Since $\frac{5}{2} = 2\frac{1}{2} = 2.5$, its graph is halfway between 2 and 3.

(b) -3.2 is $\frac{2}{10}$ of a unit to the left of -3.

(c) $\frac{11}{8} = 1\frac{3}{8} = 1.375$

> TRY EXERCISE ▸ 19

It is important to remember that every rational number can be written using fraction notation or decimal notation.

EXAMPLE **3**   Convert to decimal notation: $-\frac{5}{8}$.

SOLUTION   We first find decimal notation for $\frac{5}{8}$. Since $\frac{5}{8}$ means $5 \div 8$, we divide.

$$
\begin{array}{r}
0.6\,2\,5 \\
8\overline{)5.0\,0\,0} \\
\underline{4\,8\,0\,0} \\
2\,0\,0 \\
\underline{1\,6\,0} \\
4\,0 \\
\underline{4\,0} \\
0 \quad \leftarrow \text{The remainder is 0.}
\end{array}
$$

Thus, $\frac{5}{8} = 0.625$, so $-\frac{5}{8} = -0.625$.

> TRY EXERCISE ▸ 25

Because the division in Example 3 ends with the remainder 0, we consider -0.625 a **terminating decimal**. If we are "bringing down" zeros and a remainder reappears, we have a **repeating decimal**, as shown in the next example.

EXAMPLE 4

Convert to decimal notation: $\frac{7}{11}$.

SOLUTION   We divide:

$$
\begin{array}{r}
0.6\,3\,6\,3\ldots \\
11\overline{)7.0\,0\,0\,0} \\
\underline{6\,6} \\
4\,0 \\
\underline{3\,3} \\
7\,0 \\
\underline{6\,6} \\
4\,0
\end{array}
$$

4 reappears as a remainder, so the pattern of 6's and 3's in the quotient will continue.

We abbreviate repeating decimals by writing a bar over the repeating part—in this case, $0.\overline{63}$. Thus, $\frac{7}{11} = 0.\overline{63}$.

TRY EXERCISE 29

Although we do not prove it here, every rational number can be expressed as either a terminating or repeating decimal, and every terminating or repeating decimal can be expressed as a ratio of two integers.

Real Numbers and Order

Some numbers, when written in decimal form, neither terminate nor repeat. Such numbers are called **irrational numbers**.

What sort of numbers are irrational? One example is π (the Greek letter *pi*, read "pie"), which is used to find the area and the circumference of a circle: $A = \pi r^2$ and $C = 2\pi r$.

Another irrational number, $\sqrt{2}$ (read "the square root of 2"), is the length of the diagonal of a square with sides of length 1. It is also the number that, when multiplied by itself, gives 2. No rational number can be multiplied by itself to get 2, although some approximations come close:

1.4 is an *approximation* of $\sqrt{2}$ because $(1.4)(1.4) = 1.96$;

1.41 is a better approximation because $(1.41)(1.41) = 1.9881$;

1.4142 is an even better approximation because $(1.4142)(1.4142) = 1.99996164$.

To approximate $\sqrt{2}$ on some calculators, we simply press ② and then √. With other calculators, we press √, ②, and **ENTER**, or consult a manual.

EXAMPLE 5

Graph the real number $\sqrt{3}$ on the number line.

SOLUTION   We use a calculator and approximate: $\sqrt{3} \approx 1.732$ ("$\approx$" means "approximately equals"). Then we locate this number on the number line.

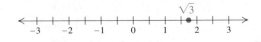

TRY EXERCISE 37

TECHNOLOGY CONNECTION

To approximate $\sqrt{3}$ on most graphing calculators, we press $\boxed{\sqrt{}}$ and then enter 3 enclosed by parentheses. Some graphing calculators will supply the left parenthesis automatically when $\boxed{\sqrt{}}$ is pressed.

Approximate each of the following to nine decimal places.

1. $\sqrt{5}$ 2. $\sqrt{7}$

3. $\sqrt{13}$ 4. $\sqrt{27}$

5. $\sqrt{38}$ 6. $\sqrt{50}$

The rational numbers and the irrational numbers together correspond to all the points on the number line and make up what is called the **real-number system**.

Set of Real Numbers

The set of real numbers = The set of all numbers corresponding to points on the number line.

The following figure shows the relationships among various kinds of numbers.

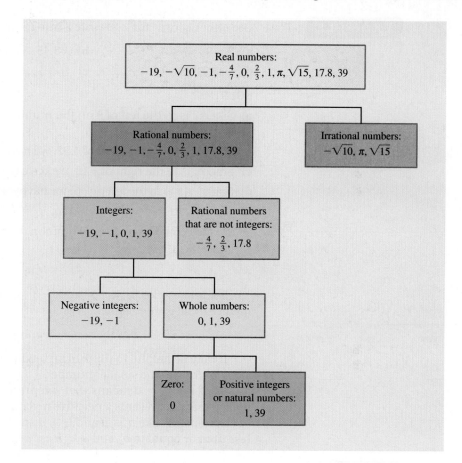

EXAMPLE 6 Which numbers in the following list are **(a)** whole numbers? **(b)** integers? **(c)** rational numbers? **(d)** irrational numbers? **(e)** real numbers?

$$-38, \quad -\frac{8}{5}, \quad 0, \quad 0.\overline{3}, \quad 4.5, \quad \sqrt{30}, \quad 52$$

SOLUTION

a) 0 and 52 are whole numbers.

b) -38, 0, and 52 are integers.

c) -38, $-\frac{8}{5}$, 0, $0.\overline{3}$, 4.5, and 52 are rational numbers.

d) $\sqrt{30}$ is an irrational number.

e) -38, $-\frac{8}{5}$, 0, $0.\overline{3}$, 4.5, $\sqrt{30}$, and 52 are real numbers.

TRY EXERCISE 75

Real numbers are named in order on the number line, with larger numbers further to the right. For any two numbers, the one to the left is less than the one to the right. We use the symbol $<$ to mean "**is less than**." The sentence $-8 < 6$ means "-8 is less than 6." The symbol $>$ means "**is greater than**." The sentence $-3 > -7$ means "-3 is greater than -7."

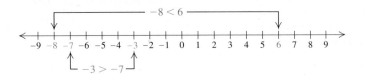

EXAMPLE   7

Use either $<$ or $>$ for ▦ to write a true sentence.

a) $2 \ \blacksquare \ 9$ **b)** $-3.45 \ \blacksquare \ 1.32$ **c)** $6 \ \blacksquare \ -12$

d) $-18 \ \blacksquare \ -5$ **e)** $\frac{7}{11} \ \blacksquare \ \frac{5}{8}$

SOLUTION

a) Since 2 is to the left of 9 on the number line, we know that 2 is less than 9, so $2 < 9$.

b) Since -3.45 is to the left of 1.32, we have $-3.45 < 1.32$.

c) Since 6 is to the right of -12, we have $6 > -12$.

d) Since -18 is to the left of -5, we have $-18 < -5$.

e) We convert to decimal notation: $\frac{7}{11} = 0.\overline{63}$ and $\frac{5}{8} = 0.625$. Thus, $\frac{7}{11} > \frac{5}{8}$.

We also could have used a common denominator: $\frac{7}{11} = \frac{56}{88} > \frac{55}{88} = \frac{5}{8}$.

> **TRY EXERCISES** ▸ 41 and 45

Sentences like "$a < -5$" and "$-3 > -8$" are **inequalities**. It is useful to remember that every inequality can be written in two ways. For example,

$$-3 > -8 \quad \text{has the same meaning as} \quad -8 < -3.$$

It may be helpful to think of an inequality sign as an "arrow" with the smaller side pointing to the smaller number.

Note that $a > 0$ means that a represents a positive real number and $a < 0$ means that a represents a negative real number.

Statements like $a \leq b$ and $b \geq a$ are also inequalities. We read $a \leq b$ as "a **is less than or equal to** b" and $a \geq b$ as "a **is greater than or equal to** b."

EXAMPLE   8

Classify each inequality as true or false.

a) $-3 \leq 5$ **b)** $-3 \leq -3$ **c)** $-5 \geq 4$

STUDENT NOTES —————

It is important to remember that just because an equation or inequality is written or printed, it is not necessarily *true*. For instance, $6 = 7$ is an equation and $2 > 5$ is an inequality. Of course, both statements are *false*.

SOLUTION

a) $-3 \leq 5$ is *true* because $-3 < 5$ is true.

b) $-3 \leq -3$ is *true* because $-3 = -3$ is true.

c) $-5 \geq 4$ is *false* since neither $-5 > 4$ nor $-5 = 4$ is true.

> **TRY EXERCISE** ▸ 57

Absolute Value

There is a convenient terminology and notation for the distance a number is from 0 on the number line. It is called the **absolute value** of the number.

> ### Absolute Value
>
> We write $|a|$, read "the absolute value of a," to represent the number of units that a is from zero.

EXAMPLE **9**   Find each absolute value: **(a)** $|-3|$; **(b)** $|7.2|$; **(c)** $|0|$.

SOLUTION

a) $|-3| = 3$ since -3 is 3 units from 0.

b) $|7.2| = 7.2$ since 7.2 is 7.2 units from 0.

c) $|0| = 0$ since 0 is 0 units from itself.

```
      3 units        7.2 units
    ←─────┼──────────────────────→
   -4 -3 -2 -1  0  1  2  3  4  5  6  7  8
```

TRY EXERCISE 63

Distance is never negative, so numbers that are opposites have the same absolute value. If a number is nonnegative, its absolute value is the number itself. If a number is negative, its absolute value is its opposite.

1.4   EXERCISE SET

↝ *Concept Reinforcement*   *In each of Exercises 1–8, fill in the blank using one of the following words:* natural number, whole number, integer, rational number, terminating, repeating, irrational number, absolute value.

1. Division can be used to show that $\frac{4}{7}$ can be written as a(n) _____ decimal.

2. Division can be used to show that $\frac{3}{20}$ can be written as a(n) _____ decimal.

3. If a number is a(n) _____, it is either a whole number or the opposite of a whole number.

4. 0 is the only _____ that is not a natural number.

5. Any number of the form a/b, where a and b are integers, with $b \neq 0$, is an example of a(n) _____.

6. A number like $\sqrt{5}$, which cannot be written precisely in fraction notation or decimal notation, is an example of a(n) _____.

7. If a number is a(n) _____, then it can be thought of as a counting number.

8. When two numbers are opposites, they have the same _____.

State which real number(s) correspond to each situation.

9. *Student loans and grants.*   The maximum amount that a student may borrow each year with a Stafford Loan is $10,500. The maximum annual award for the Nurse Educator Scholarship Program is $27,482.
   Sources: www.studentaid.ed.gov and www.collegezone.com

10. Using a NordicTrack exercise machine, LaToya burned 150 calories. She then drank an isotonic drink containing 65 calories.

11. The highest temperature ever recorded in a desert was 136 degrees Fahrenheit (°F) at Al-Aziziyah in the Sahara, Libya. The coldest temperature recorded in a desert was 4°F below zero in the McMurdo Dry Valleys, Antarctica.
   Source: *Guinness World Records* 2007

12. The Dead Sea is 1312 ft below sea level, whereas Mt. Everest is 29,035 ft above sea level.
   Source: *Guinness World Records* 2007

13. *Stock market.* The Dow Jones Industrial Average is an indicator of the stock market. On October 12, 1997, the Dow Jones fell a record 554 points. On March 16, 2002, the Dow Jones gained a record 499.19 points.
   Source: www.finfacts.ie

14. Ignition occurs 10 sec before liftoff. A spent fuel tank is detached 235 sec after liftoff.

15. Kim deposited $650 in a savings account. Two weeks later, she withdrew $180.

16. *Birth and death rates.* Recently, the world birth rate was 20.09 per thousand. The death rate was 8.37 per thousand.
   Source: Central Intelligence Agency, 2007

17. The halfback gained 8 yd on the first play. The quarterback was tackled for a 5-yd loss on the second play.

18. In the 2007 Masters Tournament, golfer Tiger Woods finished 3 over par. In the World Golf Championship, he finished 10 under par.
   Source: PGA Tour Inc.

Graph each rational number on a number line.

19. $\frac{10}{3}$

20. $-\frac{17}{5}$

21. -4.3

22. 3.87

23. -2

24. 5

Write decimal notation for each number.

25. $\frac{7}{8}$

26. $-\frac{1}{8}$

27. $-\frac{3}{4}$

28. $\frac{11}{6}$

29. $-\frac{7}{6}$

30. $-\frac{5}{12}$

31. $\frac{2}{3}$

32. $\frac{1}{4}$

33. $-\frac{1}{2}$

34. $-\frac{1}{9}$

Aha! 35. $\frac{13}{100}$

36. $-\frac{9}{20}$

Graph each irrational number on a number line.

37. $\sqrt{5}$

38. $\sqrt{92}$

39. $-\sqrt{22}$

40. $-\sqrt{54}$

Write a true sentence using either $<$ or $>$.

41. $5 \quad 0$

42. $8 \quad -8$

43. $-9 \quad 9$

44. $0 \quad -7$

45. $-8 \quad -5$

46. $-4 \quad -3$

47. $-5 \quad -11$

48. $-3 \quad -4$

49. $-12.5 \quad -10.2$

50. $-10.3 \quad -14.5$

51. $\frac{5}{12} \quad \frac{11}{25}$

52. $-\frac{14}{17} \quad -\frac{27}{35}$

For each of the following, write a second inequality with the same meaning.

53. $-2 > x$

54. $a > 9$

55. $10 \le y$

56. $-12 \ge t$

Classify each inequality as either true or false.

57. $-3 \ge -11$

58. $5 \le -5$

59. $0 \ge 8$

60. $-5 \le 7$

61. $-8 \le -8$

62. $10 \ge 10$

Find each absolute value.

63. $|-58|$

64. $|-47|$

65. $|-12.2|$

66. $|4.3|$

67. $|\sqrt{2}|$

68. $|-456|$

69. $\left|-\frac{9}{7}\right|$

70. $|-\sqrt{3}|$

71. $|0|$

72. $\left|-\frac{3}{4}\right|$

73. $|x|$, for $x = -8$

74. $|a|$, for $a = -5$

For Exercises 75–80, consider the following list:
$$-83, \quad -4.7, \quad 0, \quad \frac{5}{9}, \quad 2.\overline{16}, \quad \pi, \quad \sqrt{17}, \quad 62.$$

75. List all rational numbers.

76. List all natural numbers.

77. List all integers.

78. List all irrational numbers.

79. List all real numbers.

80. List all nonnegative integers.

81. Is every integer a rational number? Why or why not?

82. Is every integer a natural number? Why or why not?

Skill Review

83. Evaluate $3xy$ for $x = 2$ and $y = 7$. [1.1]

84. Use a commutative law to write an expression equivalent to $ab + 5$. [1.2]

Synthesis

85. Is the absolute value of a number always positive? Why or why not?

86. How many rational numbers are there between 0 and 1? Justify your answer.

87. Does "nonnegative" mean the same thing as "positive"? Why or why not?

List in order from least to greatest.

88. $13, -12, 5, -17$

89. $-23, 4, 0, -17$

90. $-\frac{2}{3}, \frac{1}{2}, -\frac{3}{4}, -\frac{5}{6}, \frac{3}{8}, \frac{1}{6}$

91. $\frac{4}{5}, \frac{4}{3}, \frac{4}{8}, \frac{4}{6}, \frac{4}{9}, \frac{4}{2}, -\frac{4}{3}$

Write a true sentence using either $<$, $>$, or $=$.

92. $|-5| \ \blacksquare \ |-2|$

93. $|4| \ \blacksquare \ |-7|$

94. $|-8| \ \blacksquare \ |8|$

95. $|23| \ \blacksquare \ |-23|$

96. $|-11| \ \blacksquare \ |5|$

Solve. Consider only integer replacements.

Aha! **97.** $|x| = 19$

98. $|x| < 3$

99. $2 < |x| < 5$

Given that $0.3\overline{3} = \frac{1}{3}$ and $0.6\overline{6} = \frac{2}{3}$, express each of the following as a ratio of two integers.

100. $0.1\overline{1}$

101. $0.9\overline{9}$

102. $5.5\overline{5}$

103. $7.7\overline{7}$

Translate to an inequality.

104. A number a is negative.

105. A number x is nonpositive.

106. The distance from x to 0 is no more than 10.

107. The distance from t to 0 is at least 20.

To the student and the instructor: *The calculator icon, ▦, is used to indicate those exercises designed to be solved with a calculator.*

108. When Helga's calculator gives a decimal value for $\sqrt{2}$ and that value is promptly squared, the result is 2. Yet when that same decimal approximation is entered by hand and then squared, the result is not exactly 2. Why do you suppose this is?

109. Is the following statement true? Why or why not?
$$\sqrt{a^2} = |a| \quad \text{for any real number } a.$$

1.5	**Addition of Real Numbers**

Adding with the Number Line ▪ Adding Without the Number Line ▪ Problem Solving ▪ Combining Like Terms

We now consider addition of real numbers. To gain understanding, we will use the number line first. After observing the principles involved, we will develop rules that allow us to work more quickly without the number line.

Adding with the Number Line

To add $a + b$ on the number line, we start at a and move according to b.

a) If b is positive, we move to the right (the positive direction).

b) If b is negative, we move to the left (the negative direction).

c) If b is 0, we stay at a.

EXAMPLE **1**   Add: $-4 + 9$.

SOLUTION   To add on the number line, we locate the first number, -4, and then move 9 units to the right. Note that it requires 4 units to reach 0. The difference between 9 and 4 is where we finish.

$$-4 + 9 = 5$$

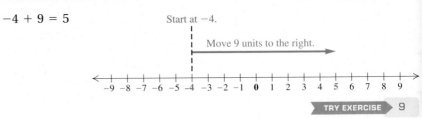

> **TRY EXERCISE** 9

EXAMPLE **2**   Add: $3 + (-5)$.

STUDENT NOTES

Parentheses are essential when a negative sign follows an operation. Just as we would never write $8 \div \times 2$, it is improper to write $3 + -5$.

SOLUTION   We locate the first number, 3, and then move 5 units to the left. Note that it requires 3 units to reach 0. The difference between 5 and 3 is 2, so we finish 2 units to the left of 0.

$$3 + (-5) = -2$$

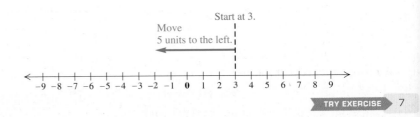

> **TRY EXERCISE** 7

EXAMPLE **3**   Add: $-4 + (-3)$.

SOLUTION   After locating -4, we move 3 units to the left. We finish a total of 7 units to the left of 0.

$$-4 + (-3) = -7$$

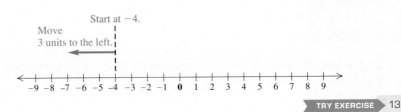

> **TRY EXERCISE** 13

EXAMPLE **4**   Add: $-5.2 + 0$.

SOLUTION   We locate -5.2 and move 0 units. Thus we finish where we started, at -5.2.

$$-5.2 + 0 = -5.2$$

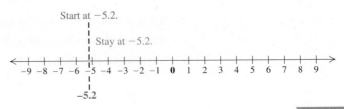

> **TRY EXERCISE** 11

From Examples 1–4, the following rules emerge.

Rules for Addition of Real Numbers

1. *Positive numbers*: Add as usual. The answer is positive.
2. *Negative numbers*: Add absolute values and make the answer negative (see Example 3).
3. *A positive number and a negative number*: Subtract the smaller absolute value from the greater absolute value. Then:

   a) If the positive number has the greater absolute value, the answer is positive (see Example 1).
   b) If the negative number has the greater absolute value, the answer is negative (see Example 2).
   c) If the numbers have the same absolute value, the answer is 0.

4. *One number is zero*: The sum is the other number (see Example 4).

Rule 4 is known as the **identity property of 0**.

Identity Property of 0

For any real number a,

$$a + 0 = 0 + a = a.$$

(Adding 0 to a number gives that same number.) The number 0 is called the *additive identity*.

Adding Without the Number Line

The rules listed above can be used without drawing the number line.

EXAMPLE 5   Add without using the number line.

a) $-12 + (-7)$ b) $-1.4 + 8.5$
c) $-36 + 21$ d) $1.5 + (-1.5)$
e) $-\frac{7}{8} + 0$ f) $\frac{2}{3} + \left(-\frac{5}{8}\right)$

SOLUTION

a) $-12 + (-7) = -19$ Two negatives. *Think:* Add the absolute values, 12 and 7, to get 19. Make the answer *negative*, -19.

b) $-1.4 + 8.5 = 7.1$ A negative and a positive. *Think:* The difference of absolute values is $8.5 - 1.4$, or 7.1. The positive number has the greater absolute value, so the answer is *positive*, 7.1.

c) $-36 + 21 = -15$ A negative and a positive. *Think:* The difference of absolute values is $36 - 21$, or 15. The negative number has the greater absolute value, so the answer is *negative*, -15.

d) $1.5 + (-1.5) = 0$ A negative and a positive. *Think:* Since the numbers are opposites, they have the same absolute value and the answer is 0.

e) $-\dfrac{7}{8} + 0 = -\dfrac{7}{8}$ **One number is zero.** The sum is the other number, $-\frac{7}{8}$.

f) $\dfrac{2}{3} + \left(-\dfrac{5}{8}\right) = \dfrac{16}{24} + \left(-\dfrac{15}{24}\right)$ This is similar to part (b) above. We find a common denominator and then add.

$$= \dfrac{1}{24}$$

TRY EXERCISES 15 and 21

If we are adding several numbers, some positive and some negative, the commutative and associative laws allow us to add all the positives, then add all the negatives, and then add the results. Of course, we can also add from left to right, if we prefer.

EXAMPLE **6**

Add: $15 + (-2) + 7 + 14 + (-5) + (-12)$.

SOLUTION

$$15 + (-2) + 7 + 14 + (-5) + (-12)$$
$$= 15 + 7 + 14 + (-2) + (-5) + (-12)$$ Using the commutative law of addition

$$= (15 + 7 + 14) + [(-2) + (-5) + (-12)]$$ Using the associative law of addition

$$= 36 + (-19)$$ Adding the positives; adding the negatives

$$= 17$$ Adding a positive and a negative

TRY EXERCISE 55

Problem Solving

EXAMPLE **7**

Interest rates.   Between 1994 and 2007, the average interest rate for a 30-yr fixed-rate mortgage dropped 2.5 percent, rose 1.75 percent, dropped 3.25 percent, and rose 1 percent. By how much did the average interest rate change?

Source: Mortgage-X.com

SOLUTION   The problem translates to a sum:

Rewording: The 1st change   plus   the 2nd change   plus   the 3rd change   plus   the 4th change   is   the total change.

Translating: -2.5 $+$ 1.75 $+$ (-3.25) $+$ 1 $=$ Total change

Adding from left to right, we have

$$-2.5 + 1.75 + (-3.25) + 1 = -0.75 + (-3.25) + 1 = -4 + 1 = -3.$$

The average interest rate dropped 3 percent between 1994 and 2007.

TRY EXERCISE 59

Combining Like Terms

When two terms have variable factors that are exactly the same, like $5a$ and $-7a$, the terms are called **like**, or **similar**, **terms**.* The distributive law enables us to **combine**, or **collect**, **like terms**. The above rules for addition will again apply.

EXAMPLE **8**   Combine like terms.

a) $-7x + 9x$

b) $2a + (-3b) + (-5a) + 9b$

c) $6 + y + (-3.5y) + 2$

SOLUTION

a) $\begin{aligned} -7x + 9x &= (-7 + 9)x &&\text{Using the distributive law} \\ &= 2x &&\text{Adding } -7 \text{ and } 9 \end{aligned}$

b) $\begin{aligned} 2a &+ (-3b) + (-5a) + 9b \\ &= 2a + (-5a) + (-3b) + 9b &&\text{Using the commutative law of addition} \\ &= (2 + (-5))a + (-3 + 9)b &&\text{Using the distributive law} \\ &= -3a + 6b &&\text{Adding} \end{aligned}$

c) $\begin{aligned} 6 + y + (-3.5y) + 2 &= y + (-3.5y) + 6 + 2 &&\text{Using the commutative law of addition} \\ &= (1 + (-3.5))y + 6 + 2 &&\text{Using the distributive law} \\ &= -2.5y + 8 &&\text{Adding} \end{aligned}$

TRY EXERCISE 69

With practice we can omit some steps, combining like terms mentally. Note that numbers like 6 and 2 in the expression $6 + y + (-3.5y) + 2$ are constants and are also considered to be like terms.

1.5   EXERCISE SET

Concept Reinforcement   *In each of Exercises 1–6, match the term with a like term from the column on the right.*

1. _____ $8n$

2. _____ $7m$

3. _____ 43

4. _____ $28z$

5. _____ $-2x$

6. _____ $-9t$

a) $-3z$

b) $5x$

c) $2t$

d) $-4m$

e) 9

f) $-3n$

Add using the number line.

7. $5 + (-8)$

8. $2 + (-5)$

9. $-6 + 10$

10. $-3 + 8$

11. $-7 + 0$

12. $-6 + 0$

13. $-3 + (-5)$

14. $-4 + (-6)$

Add. Do not use a number line except as a check.

15. $-35 + 0$

16. $-68 + 0$

17. $0 + (-8)$

18. $0 + (-2)$

19. $12 + (-12)$

20. $17 + (-17)$

---

*Like terms are discussed in greater detail in Section 1.8.

21. $-24 + (-17)$

22. $-17 + (-25)$

23. $-13 + 13$

24. $-31 + 31$

25. $20 + (-11)$

26. $8 + (-5)$

27. $10 + (-12)$

28. $9 + (-13)$

29. $-3 + 14$

30. $25 + (-6)$

31. $-24 + (-19)$

32. $11 + (-9)$

33. $19 + (-19)$

34. $-20 + (-6)$

35. $23 + (-5)$

36. $-15 + (-7)$

37. $-31 + (-14)$

38. $40 + (-8)$

39. $40 + (-40)$

40. $-25 + 25$

41. $85 + (-69)$

42. $63 + (-13)$

43. $-3.6 + 2.8$

44. $-6.5 + 4.7$

45. $-5.4 + (-3.7)$

46. $-3.8 + (-9.4)$

47. $\frac{4}{5} + \left(\frac{-1}{5}\right)$

48. $\frac{-2}{7} + \frac{3}{7}$

49. $\frac{-4}{7} + \frac{-2}{7}$

50. $\frac{-5}{9} + \frac{-2}{9}$

51. $-\frac{2}{5} + \frac{1}{3}$

52. $-\frac{4}{13} + \frac{1}{2}$

53. $\frac{-4}{9} + \frac{2}{3}$

54. $\frac{1}{9} + \left(\frac{-1}{3}\right)$

55. $35 + (-14) + (-19) + (-5)$

56. $-28 + (-44) + 17 + 31 + (-94)$

Aha! **57.** $-4.9 + 8.5 + 4.9 + (-8.5)$

58. $24 + 3.1 + (-44) + (-8.2) + 63$

Solve. Write your answer as a complete sentence.

59. *Gasoline prices.* In a recent year, the price of a gallon of 87-octane gasoline was $2.89. The price rose 15¢, then dropped 3¢, and then rose 17¢. By how much did the price change during that period?

60. *Natural gas prices.* In a recent year, the price of a gallon of natural gas was $1.88. The price dropped 2¢, then rose 25¢, and then dropped 43¢. By how much did the price change during that period?

61. *Telephone bills.* Chloe's cell-phone bill for July was $82. She sent a check for $50 and then ran up $63 in charges for August. What was her new balance?

62. *Profits and losses.* The following table lists the profits and losses of Premium Sales over a 3-yr period. Find the profit or loss after this period of time.

Year	Profit or loss
2006	−$26,500
2007	−$10,200
2008	+$32,400

63. *Yardage gained.* In an intramural football game, the quarterback attempted passes with the following results.

First try	13-yd loss
Second try	12-yd gain
Third try	21-yd gain

Find the total gain (or loss).

64. *Account balance.* Aiden has $450 in a checking account. He writes a check for $530, makes a deposit of $75, and then writes a check for $90. What is the balance in the account?

65. *Lake level.* Between October 2003 and February 2005, the south end of the Great Salt Lake dropped $\frac{2}{5}$ ft, rose $1\frac{1}{5}$ ft, and dropped $\frac{1}{2}$ ft. By how much did the level change?
Source: U.S. Geological Survey

66. *Peak elevation.* The tallest mountain in the world, as measured from base to peak, is Mauna Kea in Hawaii. From a base 19,684 ft below sea level, it rises 33,480 ft. What is the elevation of its peak?
Source: *Guinness World Records* 2007

67. *Credit-card bills.* Logan's credit-card bill indicates that he owes $470. He sends a check to the credit-card company for $45, charges another $160 in merchandise, and then pays off another $500 of his bill. What is Logan's new balance?

68. *Class size.* During the first two weeks of the semester, 5 students withdrew from Hailey's algebra class, 8 students were added to the class, and 4 students were dropped as "no-shows." By how many students did the original class size change?

Combine like terms.

69. $7a + 10a$

70. $3x + 8x$

71. $-3x + 12x$

72. $-2m + (-7m)$

73. $4t + 21t$

74. $5a + 8a$

75. $7m + (-9m)$

76. $-4x + 4x$

77. $-8y + (-2y)$

78. $10n + (-17n)$

79. $-3 + 8x + 4 + (-10x)$

80. $8a + 5 + (-a) + (-3)$

Find the perimeter of each figure.

81.

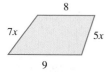

82.

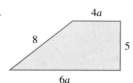

83.

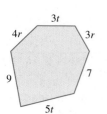

84.

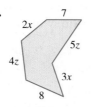

85.

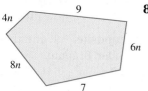

86.

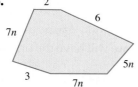

87. Explain in your own words why the sum of two negative numbers is negative.

88. Without performing the actual addition, explain why the sum of all integers from -10 to 10 is 0.

Skill Review

89. Multiply: $7(3z + 2y + 1)$. [1.2]

90. Divide and simplify: $\frac{7}{2} \div \frac{3}{8}$. [1.3]

Synthesis

91. Under what circumstances will the sum of one positive number and several negative numbers be positive?

92. Is it possible to add real numbers without knowing how to calculate $a - b$ with a and b both nonnegative and $a \geq b$? Why or why not?

93. *Banking.* Travis had $257.33 in his checking account. After depositing $152 in the account and writing a check, his account was overdrawn by $42.37. What was the amount of the check?

94. *Sports-card values.* The value of a sports card dropped $12 and then rose $17.50 before settling at $61. What was the original value of the card?

Find the missing term or terms.

95. $4x + \underline{\hspace{0.6cm}} + (-9x) + (-2y) = -5x - 7y$

96. $-3a + 9b + \underline{\hspace{0.6cm}} + 5a = 2a - 6b$

97. $3m + 2n + \underline{\hspace{0.6cm}} + (-2m) = 2n + (-6m)$

98. $\underline{\hspace{0.6cm}} + 9x + (-4y) + x = 10x - 7y$

Aha! **99.** $7t + 23 + \underline{\hspace{0.6cm}} + \underline{\hspace{0.6cm}} = 0$

100. *Geometry.* The perimeter of a rectangle is $7x + 10$. If the length of the rectangle is 5, express the width in terms of x.

101. *Golfing.* After five rounds of golf, a golf pro was 3 under par twice, 2 over par once, 2 under par once, and 1 over par once. On average, how far above or below par was the golfer?

1.6   Subtraction of Real Numbers

Opposites and Additive Inverses ▪ Subtraction ▪ Problem Solving

In arithmetic, when a number b is subtracted from another number a, the difference, $a - b$, is the number that when added to b gives a. For example, $45 - 17 = 28$ because $28 + 17 = 45$. We will use this approach to develop an efficient way of finding the value of $a - b$ for any real numbers a and b. Before doing so, however, we must develop some terminology.

Opposites and Additive Inverses

Numbers such as 6 and -6 are *opposites*, or *additive inverses*, of each other. Whenever opposites are added, the result is 0; and whenever two numbers add to 0, those numbers are opposites.

EXAMPLE **1**   Find the opposite of each number: **(a)** 34; **(b)** −8.3; **(c)** 0.

SOLUTION

a) The opposite of 34 is -34: $34 + (-34) = 0.$
b) The opposite of −8.3 is 8.3: $-8.3 + 8.3 = 0.$
c) The opposite of 0 is 0: $0 + 0 = 0.$

> TRY EXERCISE ▶ 19

To write the opposite, we use the symbol −, as follows.

> **Opposite**
>
> The *opposite*, or *additive inverse*, of a number a is written $-a$ (read "the opposite of a" or "the additive inverse of a").

Note that if we take a number, say 8, and find its opposite, −8, and then find the opposite of the result, we will have the original number, 8, again.

EXAMPLE **2**   Find $-x$ and $-(-x)$ when $x = 16.$

SOLUTION

If $x = 16$, then $-x = -16.$ The opposite of 16 is $-16.$
If $x = 16$, then $-(-x) = -(-16) = 16.$ The opposite of the opposite of 16 is 16.

> TRY EXERCISE ▶ 25

> **The Opposite of an Opposite**
>
> For any real number a,
>
> $$-(-a) = a.$$
>
> (The opposite of the opposite of a is a.)

EXAMPLE **3**   Find $-x$ and $-(-x)$ when $x = -3.$

SOLUTION

If $x = -3$, then $-x = -(-3) = 3.$ The opposite of −3 is 3
Since $-(-x) = x$, it follows that $-(-(-3)) = -3.$ Finding the opposite of an opposite

> TRY EXERCISE ▶ 31

Note in Example 3 that an extra set of parentheses is used to show that we are substituting the negative number −3 for x. The notation $- -x$ is not used.

A symbol such as −8 is usually read "negative 8." It could be read "the additive inverse of 8," because the additive inverse of 8 is negative 8. It could also be read "the opposite of 8," because the opposite of 8 is −8.

A symbol like $-x$, which has a variable, should be read "the opposite of x" or "the additive inverse of x" and *not* "negative x," since to do so suggests that $-x$ represents a negative number.

The symbol "$-$" is read differently depending on where it appears. For example, $-5 - (-x)$ should be read "negative five minus the opposite of x."

EXAMPLE 4 Write each of the following in words.

a) $2 - 8$ **b)** $5 - (-4)$ **c)** $-6 - (-x)$

SOLUTION

a) $2 - 8$ is read "two minus eight."

b) $5 - (-4)$ is read "five minus negative four."

c) $-6 - (-x)$ is read "negative six minus the opposite of x."

TRY EXERCISE 11

STUDENT NOTES

As you read mathematics, it is important to verbalize correctly the words and symbols to yourself. Consistently reading the expression $-x$ as "the opposite of x" is a good step in this direction.

As we saw in Example 3, $-x$ can represent a positive number. This notation can be used to restate a result from Section 1.5 as *the law of opposites*.

> ### The Law of Opposites
> For any two numbers a and $-a$,
> $$a + (-a) = 0.$$
> (When opposites are added, their sum is 0.)

A negative number is said to have a "negative *sign*." A positive number is said to have a "positive *sign*." If we change a number to its opposite, or additive inverse, we say that we have "changed or reversed its sign."

EXAMPLE 5 Change the sign (find the opposite) of each number: **(a)** -3; **(b)** -10; **(c)** 14.

SOLUTION

a) When we change the sign of -3, we obtain 3.

b) When we change the sign of -10, we obtain 10.

c) When we change the sign of 14, we obtain -14.

TRY EXERCISE 35

Subtraction

Opposites are helpful when subtraction involves negative numbers. To see why, look for a pattern in the following:

Subtracting		*Adding the Opposite*
$9 - 5 = 4$	since $4 + 5 = 9$	$9 + (-5) = 4$
$5 - 8 = -3$	since $-3 + 8 = 5$	$5 + (-8) = -3$
$-6 - 4 = -10$	since $-10 + 4 = -6$	$-6 + (-4) = -10$
$-7 - (-10) = 3$	since $3 + (-10) = -7$	$-7 + 10 = 3$
$-7 - (-2) = -5$	since $-5 + (-2) = -7$	$-7 + 2 = -5$

The matching results suggest that we can subtract by adding the opposite of the number being subtracted. This can always be done and often provides the easiest way to subtract real numbers.

Subtraction of Real Numbers

For any real numbers a and b,

$$a - b = a + (-b).$$

(To subtract, add the opposite, or additive inverse, of the number being subtracted.)

EXAMPLE   6

Subtract each of the following and then check with addition.

a) $2 - 6$ b) $4 - (-9)$ c) $-4.2 - (-3.6)$

d) $-1.8 - (-7.5)$ e) $\frac{1}{5} - \left(-\frac{3}{5}\right)$

SOLUTION

a) $2 - 6 = 2 + (-6) = -4$

The opposite of 6 is -6. We change the subtraction to addition and add the opposite. *Check:* $-4 + 6 = 2.$

b) $4 - (-9) = 4 + 9 = 13$

The opposite of -9 is 9. We change the subtraction to addition and add the opposite. *Check:* $13 + (-9) = 4.$

c) $-4.2 - (-3.6) = -4.2 + 3.6$
$$= -0.6$$

Adding the opposite of -3.6. *Check:* $-0.6 + (-3.6) = -4.2.$

d) $-1.8 - (-7.5) = -1.8 + 7.5$
$$= 5.7$$

Adding the opposite. *Check:* $5.7 + (-7.5) = -1.8.$

e) $\dfrac{1}{5} - \left(-\dfrac{3}{5}\right) = \dfrac{1}{5} + \dfrac{3}{5}$ Adding the opposite

$$= \frac{1 + 3}{5}$$ A common denominator exists so we add in the numerator.

$$= \frac{4}{5}$$

Check: $\dfrac{4}{5} + \left(-\dfrac{3}{5}\right) = \dfrac{4}{5} + \dfrac{-3}{5} = \dfrac{4 + (-3)}{5} = \dfrac{1}{5}.$

TRY EXERCISES 39 and 47

EXAMPLE   7

Simplify: $8 - (-4) - 2 - (-5) + 3.$

SOLUTION

$8 - (-4) - 2 - (-5) + 3 = 8 + 4 + (-2) + 5 + 3$ To subtract, we add the opposite.

$$= 18$$

TRY EXERCISE 109

Recall from Section 1.2 that the terms of an algebraic expression are separated by plus signs. This means that the terms of $5x - 7y - 9$ are $5x$, $-7y$, and -9, since $5x - 7y - 9 = 5x + (-7y) + (-9)$.

EXAMPLE **8**

Identify the terms of $4 - 2ab + 7a - 9$.

SOLUTION   We have

$$4 - 2ab + 7a - 9 = 4 + (-2ab) + 7a + (-9),$$ Rewriting as addition

so the terms are 4, $-2ab$, $7a$, and -9.

> TRY EXERCISE ▶117

EXAMPLE **9**

Combine like terms.

a) $1 + 3x - 7x$

b) $-5a - 7b - 4a + 10b$

c) $4 - 3m - 9 + 2m$

SOLUTION

a) $1 + 3x - 7x = 1 + 3x + (-7x)$ Adding the opposite

$= 1 + (3 + (-7))x$ ⎫   Using the distributive law.
$= 1 + (-4)x$ ⎭   Try to do this mentally.

$= 1 - 4x$ Rewriting as subtraction to be more concise

b) $-5a - 7b - 4a + 10b = -5a + (-7b) + (-4a) + 10b$ Adding the opposite

$= -5a + (-4a) + (-7b) + 10b$ Using the commutative law of addition

$= -9a + 3b$ Combining like terms mentally

c) $4 - 3m - 9 + 2m = 4 + (-3m) + (-9) + 2m$ Rewriting as addition

$= 4 + (-9) + (-3m) + 2m$ Using the commutative law of addition

$= -5 + (-1m)$ We can write $-1m$ as $-m$.

$= -5 - m$

> TRY EXERCISE ▶121

Problem Solving

We use subtraction to solve problems involving differences. These include problems that ask "How much more?" or "How much higher?"

EXAMPLE **10**

Record elevations.   The current world records for the highest parachute jump and the lowest manned vessel ocean dive were both set in 1960. On August 16 of that year, Captain Joseph Kittinger jumped from a height of 102,800 ft above sea level. Earlier, on January 23, Jacques Piccard and Navy Lieutenant Donald Walsh descended in a bathyscaphe 35,797 ft below sea level. What was the difference in elevation between the highest parachute jump and the lowest ocean dive?

Sources: www.firstflight.org and www.seasky.org

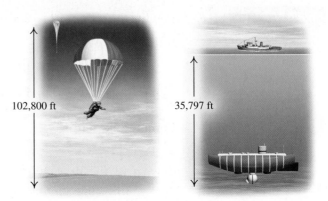

102,800 ft   35,797 ft

SOLUTION   To find the difference between two elevations, we always subtract the lower elevation from the higher elevation:

$$\underbrace{\text{Higher elevation}} \quad - \quad \underbrace{\text{Lower elevation}}$$

$$102{,}800 \quad - \quad (-35{,}797)$$
$$= 102{,}800 + 35{,}797$$
$$= 138{,}597.$$

The parachute jump began 138,597 ft higher than the ocean dive ended.

▶ **TRY EXERCISE** ▶ 135

1.6   EXERCISE SET

For Extra Help   *Math XL*   **MyMathLab**   PRACTICE   WATCH   DOWNLOAD

🔖 *Concept Reinforcement*   *In each of Exercises 1–8, match the expression with the appropriate wording from the column on the right.*

1. _____ $-x$

2. _____ $12 - x$

3. _____ $12 - (-x)$

4. _____ $x - 12$

5. _____ $x - (-12)$

6. _____ $-x - 12$

7. _____ $-x - x$

8. _____ $-x - (-12)$

a) x minus negative twelve

b) The opposite of x minus x

c) The opposite of x minus twelve

d) The opposite of x

e) The opposite of x minus negative twelve

f) Twelve minus the opposite of x

g) Twelve minus x

h) x minus twelve

Write each of the following in words.

9. $6 - 10$

10. $5 - 13$

11. $2 - (-12)$

12. $4 - (-1)$

13. $9 - (-t)$

14. $8 - (-m)$

15. $-x - y$

16. $-a - b$

17. $-3 - (-n)$

18. $-7 - (-m)$

Find the opposite, or additive inverse.

19. 51

20. -17

21. $-\frac{11}{3}$

22. $\frac{7}{2}$

23. -3.14

24. 48.2

Find $-x$ when x is each of the following.

25. -45

26. 26

27. $-\frac{14}{3}$

28. $\frac{1}{328}$

29. 0.101

30. 0

Find $-(-x)$ when x is each of the following.

31. 37

32. 29

33. $-\frac{2}{5}$

34. -9.1

Change the sign. (Find the opposite.)

35. -1

36. -7

37. 15

38. 10

Subtract.

39. $7 - 10$

40. $4 - 13$

41. $0 - 6$

42. $0 - 8$

43. $2 - 5$

44. $3 - 13$

45. $-4 - 3$

46. $-5 - 6$

47. $-9 - (-3)$

48. $-9 - (-5)$

49. $-8 - (-8)$

50. $-10 - (-10)$

51. $14 - 19$

52. $12 - 16$

53. $30 - 40$

54. $20 - 27$

55. $0 - 11$

56. $0 - 31$

57. $-9 - (-9)$

58. $-40 - (-40)$

59. $5 - 5$

60. $7 - 7$

61. $4 - (-4)$

62. $6 - (-6)$

63. $-7 - 4$

64. $-6 - 8$

65. $6 - (-10)$

66. $3 - (-12)$

67. $-4 - 15$

68. $-14 - 2$

69. $-6 - (-7)$

70. $-4 - (-7)$

71. $5 - (-12)$

72. $5 - (-6)$

73. $0 - (-3)$

74. $0 - (-5)$

75. $-5 - (-2)$

76. $-3 - (-1)$

77. $-7 - 14$

78. $-9 - 16$

79. $0 - (-10)$

80. $0 - (-1)$

81. $-8 - 0$

82. $-9 - 0$

83. $-52 - 8$

84. $-63 - 11$

85. $2 - 25$

86. $18 - 63$

87. $-4.2 - 3.1$

88. $-10.1 - 2.6$

89. $-1.3 - (-2.4)$

90. $-5.8 - (-7.3)$

91. $3.2 - 8.7$

92. $1.5 - 9.4$

93. $0.072 - 1$

94. $0.825 - 1$

95. $\frac{2}{11} - \frac{9}{11}$

96. $\frac{3}{7} - \frac{5}{7}$

97. $\frac{-1}{5} - \frac{3}{5}$

98. $\frac{-2}{9} - \frac{5}{9}$

99. $-\frac{4}{17} - \left(-\frac{9}{17}\right)$

100. $-\frac{2}{13} - \left(-\frac{5}{13}\right)$

In each of Exercises 101–104, translate the phrase to mathematical language and simplify. See the solution to Example 10.

101. The difference between 3.8 and -5.2

102. The difference between -2.1 and -5.9

103. The difference between 114 and -79

104. The difference between 23 and -17

105. Subtract 32 from -8.

106. Subtract 19 from -7.

107. Subtract -25 from 18.

108. Subtract -31 from -5.

Simplify.

109. $16 - (-12) - 1 - (-2) + 3$

110. $22 - (-18) + 7 + (-42) - 27$

111. $-31 + (-28) - (-14) - 17$

112. $-43 - (-19) - (-21) + 25$

113. $-34 - 28 + (-33) - 44$

114. $39 + (-88) - 29 - (-83)$

Aha! **115.** $-93 + (-84) - (-93) - (-84)$

116. $84 + (-99) + 44 - (-18) - 43$

Identify the terms in each expression.

117. $-3y - 8x$

118. $7a - 9b$

119. $9 - 5t - 3st$

120. $-4 - 3x + 2xy$

Combine like terms.

121. $10x - 13x$

122. $3a - 14a$

123. $7a - 12a + 4$

124. $-9x - 13x + 7$

125. $-8n - 9 + 7n$

126. $-7 + 9n - 8n$

127. $5 - 3x - 11$

128. $2 + 3a - 7$

129. $2 - 6t - 9 - 2t$

130. $-5 + 4b - 7 - 5b$

131. $5y + (-3x) - 9x + 1 - 2y + 8$

132. $14 - (-5x) + 2z - (-32) + 4z - 2x$

133. $13x - (-2x) + 45 - (-21) - 7x$

134. $8t - (-2t) - 14 - (-5t) + 53 - 9t$

Solve.

135. *Temperature extremes.* The highest temperature ever recorded in the United States is 134°F in Greenland Ranch, California, on July 10, 1913. The lowest temperature ever recorded is −80°F in Prospect Creek, Alaska, on January 23, 1971. How much higher was the temperature in Greenland Ranch than that in Prospect Creek?
Source: Information Please Database 2007, Pearson Education, Inc.

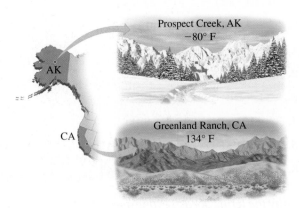

136. *Temperature change.* In just 12 hr on February 21, 1918, the temperature in Granville, North Dakota, rose from −33°F to 50°F. By how much did the temperature change?
Source: Information Please Database 2007, Pearson Education, Inc.

137. *Elevation extremes.* The lowest elevation in Asia, the Dead Sea, is 1312 ft below sea level. The highest elevation in Asia, Mount Everest, is 29,035 ft. Find the difference in elevation.
Source: Guinness World Records 2007

138. *Elevation extremes.* The elevation of Mount Whitney, the highest peak in California, is 14,776 ft more than the elevation of Death Valley, California.

If Death Valley is 282 ft below sea level, find the elevation of Mount Whitney.
Source: *The Columbia Electronic Encyclopedia*, 6th ed., 2007 (New York: Columbia University Press)

139. *Changes in elevation.* The lowest point in Africa is Lake Assal, which is 156 m below sea level. The lowest point in South America is the Valdes Peninsula, which is 40 m below sea level. How much lower is Lake Assal than the Valdes Peninsula?
Source: Information Please Database 2007, Pearson Education, Inc.

140. *Underwater elevation.* The deepest point in the Pacific Ocean is the Marianas Trench, with a depth of 10,911 m. The deepest point in the Atlantic Ocean is the Puerto Rico Trench, with a depth of 8648 m. What is the difference in elevation of the two trenches?
Source: *Guinness World Records* 2007

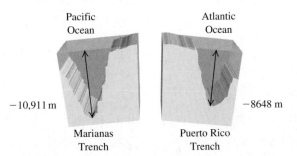

141. Jeremy insists that if you can *add* real numbers, then you can also *subtract* real numbers. Do you agree? Why or why not?

142. Are the expressions $-a + b$ and $a + (-b)$ opposites of each other? Why or why not?

Skill Review

143. Find the area of a rectangle when the length is 36 ft and the width is 12 ft. [1.1]

144. Find the prime factorization of 864. [1.3]

Synthesis

145. Explain the different uses of the symbol "−". Give examples of each and how they should be read.

146. If a and b are both negative, under what circumstances will $a - b$ be negative?

147. *Power outages.* During the Northeast's electrical blackout of August 14, 2003, residents of Bloomfield, New Jersey, lost power at 4:00 P.M. One resident returned from vacation at 3:00 P.M. the following day to find the clocks in her apartment reading 8:00 A.M. At what time, and on what day, was power restored?

Tell whether each statement is true or false for all real numbers m and n. Use various replacements for m and n to support your answer.

148. If $m > n$, then $m - n > 0$.

149. If $m > n$, then $m + n > 0$.

150. If m and n are opposites, then $m - n = 0$.

151. If $m = -n$, then $m + n = 0$.

152. A gambler loses a wager and then loses "double or nothing" (meaning the gambler owes twice as much) twice more. After the three losses, the gambler's assets are $-\$20$. Explain how much the gambler originally bet and how the $20 debt occurred.

153. List the keystrokes needed to compute $-9 - (-7)$.

154. If n is positive and m is negative, what is the sign of $n + (-m)$? Why?

1.7   Multiplication and Division of Real Numbers

Multiplication ▪ Division

We now develop rules for multiplication and division of real numbers. Because multiplication and division are closely related, the rules are quite similar.

Multiplication

We already know how to multiply two nonnegative numbers. To see how to multiply a positive number and a negative number, consider the following pattern in which multiplication is regarded as repeated addition:

This number → $4(-5) = (-5) + (-5) + (-5) + (-5) = -20$ ← This number
decreases by $3(-5) =$ $\quad (-5) + (-5) + (-5) = -15$ increases by
1 each time. $2(-5) =$ $\qquad\qquad (-5) + (-5) = -10$ 5 each time.
                 $1(-5) =$ $\qquad\qquad\qquad (-5) = \ -5$
                 $0(-5) =$ $\qquad\qquad\qquad\qquad 0 = \ \ 0$

This pattern illustrates that the product of a negative number and a positive number is negative.

> ### The Product of a Negative Number and a Positive Number
>
> To multiply a positive number and a negative number, multiply their absolute values. The answer is negative.

EXAMPLE   1   Multiply: **(a)** $8(-5)$; **(b)** $-\frac{1}{3} \cdot \frac{5}{7}$.

SOLUTION

a) $8(-5) = -40$ *Think:* $8 \cdot 5 = 40$; make the answer negative.

b) $-\frac{1}{3} \cdot \frac{5}{7} = -\frac{5}{21}$ *Think:* $\frac{1}{3} \cdot \frac{5}{7} = \frac{5}{21}$; make the answer negative.

TRY EXERCISE ▶ 11

The pattern developed above includes not just products of positive numbers and negative numbers, but a product involving zero as well.

> ## The Multiplicative Property of Zero
> For any real number a,
> $$0 \cdot a = a \cdot 0 = 0.$$
> (The product of 0 and any real number is 0.)

EXAMPLE   2   Multiply: $173(-452)0$.

SOLUTION   We have

$$173(-452)0 = 173[(-452)0]$$ Because of the associative law of multiplication, we can multiply the last two factors first.

$$= 173[0]$$ Using the multiplicative property of zero

$$= 0.$$ Using the multiplicative property of zero again

Note that whenever 0 appears as a factor, the product is 0.

TRY EXERCISE ▶ 33

We can extend the above pattern still further to examine the product of two negative numbers.

This number → decreases by 1 each time.

$$2(-5) = (-5) + (-5) = -10$$ ← This number increases by 5 each time.
$$1(-5) = (-5) = -5$$
$$0(-5) = 0 = 0$$
$$-1(-5) = -(-5) = 5$$
$$-2(-5) = -(-5) - (-5) = 10$$

According to the pattern, the product of two negative numbers is positive.

> ## The Product of Two Negative Numbers
> To multiply two negative numbers, multiply their absolute values. The answer is positive.

EXAMPLE 3

Multiply: **(a)** $(-6)(-8)$; **(b)** $(-1.2)(-3)$.

SOLUTION

a) The absolute value of -6 is 6 and the absolute value of -8 is 8. Thus,

$$(-6)(-8) = 6 \cdot 8 \qquad \text{Multiplying absolute values. The answer is positive.}$$
$$= 48.$$

b) $(-1.2)(-3) = (1.2)(3) \qquad$ Multiplying absolute values. The answer is positive.
$$= 3.6 \qquad \text{Try to go directly to this step.}$$

> **TRY EXERCISE** 17

When three or more numbers are multiplied, we can order and group the numbers as we please, because of the commutative and associative laws.

EXAMPLE 4

Multiply: **(a)** $-3(-2)(-5)$; **(b)** $-4(-6)(-1)(-2)$.

SOLUTION

a) $-3(-2)(-5) = 6(-5) \qquad$ Multiplying the first two numbers. The product of two negatives is positive.

$$= -30 \qquad \text{The product of a positive and a negative is negative.}$$

b) $-4(-6)(-1)(-2) = 24 \cdot 2 \qquad$ Multiplying the first two numbers and the last two numbers

$$= 48$$

> **TRY EXERCISE** 43

We can see the following pattern in the results of Example 4.

The product of an even number of negative numbers is positive.

The product of an odd number of negative numbers is negative.

Division

Recall that $a \div b$, or $\dfrac{a}{b}$, is the number, if one exists, that when multiplied by b gives a. For example, to show that $10 \div 2$ is 5, we need only note that $5 \cdot 2 = 10$. Thus division can always be checked with multiplication.

EXAMPLE 5

Divide, if possible, and check your answer.

a) $14 \div (-7)$ \qquad\qquad **b)** $\dfrac{-32}{-4}$

c) $\dfrac{-10}{9}$ \qquad\qquad **d)** $\dfrac{-17}{0}$

SOLUTION

a) $14 \div (-7) = -2 \qquad$ We look for a number that when multiplied by -7 gives 14. That number is -2. *Check:* $(-2)(-7) = 14$.

b) $\dfrac{-32}{-4} = 8 \qquad$ We look for a number that when multiplied by -4 gives -32. That number is 8. *Check:* $8(-4) = -32$.

c) $\dfrac{-10}{9} = -\dfrac{10}{9} \qquad$ We look for a number that when multiplied by 9 gives -10. That number is $-\frac{10}{9}$. *Check:* $-\frac{10}{9} \cdot 9 = -10$.

d) $\dfrac{-17}{0}$ is **undefined**. \qquad We look for a number that when multiplied by 0 gives -17. There is no such number because if 0 is a factor, the product is 0, not -17.

> **TRY EXERCISE** 57

STUDENT NOTES

Try to regard "undefined" as a mathematical way of saying "we do not give any meaning to this expression."

The rules for signs for division are the same as those for multiplication: The quotient of a positive number and a negative number is negative; the quotient of two negative numbers is positive.

> ## Rules for Multiplication and Division
>
> To multiply or divide two nonzero real numbers:
>
> 1. Using the absolute values, multiply or divide, as indicated.
> 2. If the signs are the same, the answer is positive.
> 3. If the signs are different, the answer is negative.

Had Example 5(a) been written as $-14 \div 7$ or $-\frac{14}{7}$, rather than $14 \div (-7)$, the result would still have been -2. Thus from Examples 5(a)–5(c), we have the following:

$$\frac{-a}{b} = \frac{a}{-b} = -\frac{a}{b} \quad \text{and} \quad \frac{-a}{-b} = \frac{a}{b}.$$

EXAMPLE 6   Rewrite each of the following in two equivalent forms: **(a)** $\frac{5}{-2}$; **(b)** $-\frac{3}{10}$.

SOLUTION   We use one of the properties just listed.

a) $\dfrac{5}{-2} = \dfrac{-5}{2}$ and $\dfrac{5}{-2} = -\dfrac{5}{2}$

b) $-\dfrac{3}{10} = \dfrac{-3}{10}$ and $-\dfrac{3}{10} = \dfrac{3}{-10}$

Since $\dfrac{-a}{b} = \dfrac{a}{-b} = -\dfrac{a}{b}$

> **TRY EXERCISE** 81

When a fraction contains a negative sign, it can be helpful to rewrite (or simply visualize) the fraction in an equivalent form.

EXAMPLE 7   Perform the indicated operation: **(a)** $\left(-\frac{4}{5}\right)\left(\frac{-7}{3}\right)$; **(b)** $-\frac{2}{7} + \frac{9}{-7}$.

SOLUTION

a) $\left(-\dfrac{4}{5}\right)\left(\dfrac{-7}{3}\right) = \left(-\dfrac{4}{5}\right)\left(-\dfrac{7}{3}\right)$ Rewriting $\dfrac{-7}{3}$ as $-\dfrac{7}{3}$

$\qquad\qquad\qquad = \dfrac{28}{15}$ Try to go directly to this step.

b) Given a choice, we generally choose a positive denominator:

$-\dfrac{2}{7} + \dfrac{9}{-7} = \dfrac{-2}{7} + \dfrac{-9}{7}$ Rewriting both fractions with a common denominator of 7

$\qquad\qquad\qquad = \dfrac{-11}{7}, \text{ or } -\dfrac{11}{7}.$

> **TRY EXERCISE** 101

To divide with fraction notation, it is usually easiest to find a reciprocal and then multiply.

EXAMPLE **8**   Find the reciprocal of each number, if it exists.

a) -27 b) $\frac{-3}{4}$

c) $-\frac{1}{5}$ d) 0

SOLUTION   Recall from Section 1.3 that we can check that two numbers are reciprocals of each other by confirming that their product is 1.

a) The reciprocal of -27 is $\frac{1}{-27}$. More often, this number is written as $-\frac{1}{27}$.
    Check: $(-27)\left(-\frac{1}{27}\right) = \frac{27}{27} = 1$.

b) The reciprocal of $\frac{-3}{4}$ is $\frac{4}{-3}$, or, equivalently, $-\frac{4}{3}$.   *Check:* $\frac{-3}{4} \cdot \frac{4}{-3} = \frac{-12}{-12} = 1$.

c) The reciprocal of $-\frac{1}{5}$ is -5.   *Check:* $-\frac{1}{5}(-5) = \frac{5}{5} = 1$.

d) The reciprocal of 0 does not exist. To see this, recall that there is no number r for which $0 \cdot r = 1$.   **TRY EXERCISE** 89

EXAMPLE **9**   Divide: **(a)** $-\frac{2}{3} \div \left(-\frac{5}{4}\right)$; **(b)** $-\frac{3}{4} \div \frac{3}{10}$.

SOLUTION   We divide by multiplying by the reciprocal of the divisor.

a) $-\dfrac{2}{3} \div \left(-\dfrac{5}{4}\right) = -\dfrac{2}{3} \cdot \left(-\dfrac{4}{5}\right) = \dfrac{8}{15}$ Multiplying by the reciprocal

> Be careful not to change the sign when taking a reciprocal!

b) $-\dfrac{3}{4} \div \dfrac{3}{10} = -\dfrac{3}{4} \cdot \left(\dfrac{10}{3}\right) = -\dfrac{30}{12} = -\dfrac{5}{2} \cdot \dfrac{6}{6} = -\dfrac{5}{2}$ Removing a factor equal to 1: $\frac{6}{6} = 1$

TRY EXERCISE 109

To divide with decimal notation, it is usually easiest to carry out the division.

EXAMPLE **10**   Divide: $27.9 \div (-3)$.

SOLUTION

$$27.9 \div (-3) = \frac{27.9}{-3} = -9.3 \qquad \text{Dividing: } 3\overline{)27.9}\,.$$
$$\text{The answer is negative.}$$

TRY EXERCISE 67

In Example 5(d), we explained why we cannot divide -17 by 0. To see why *no* nonzero number b can be divided by 0, remember that $b \div 0$ would have to be the number that when multiplied by 0 gives b. But since the product of 0 and any number is 0, not b, we say that $b \div 0$ is **undefined** for $b \neq 0$. In the special case of $0 \div 0$, we look for a number r such that $0 \div 0 = r$ and $r \cdot 0 = 0$. But, $r \cdot 0 = 0$ for *any* number r. For this reason, we say that $b \div 0$ is undefined for any choice of b.*

Finally, note that $0 \div 7 = 0$ since $0 \cdot 7 = 0$. This can be written $0/7 = 0$. It is important not to confuse division *by* 0 with division *into* 0.

---

*Sometimes $0 \div 0$ is said to be *indeterminate*.

EXAMPLE 11   Divide, if possible: **(a)** $\frac{0}{-2}$; **(b)** $\frac{5}{0}$.

SOLUTION

a) $\dfrac{0}{-2} = 0$ We can divide 0 by a nonzero number.
           Check: $0(-2) = 0$.

b) $\dfrac{5}{0}$ is undefined.   We cannot divide by 0.

TRY EXERCISE 73

Division Involving Zero

For any real number a,

$$\frac{a}{0} \text{ is undefined,}$$

and for $a \neq 0$,

$$\frac{0}{a} = 0.$$

It is important *not* to confuse *opposite* with *reciprocal*. Keep in mind that the opposite, or additive inverse, of a number is what we add to the number to get 0. The reciprocal, or multiplicative inverse, is what we multiply the number by to get 1.

Compare the following.

Number	Opposite (Change the sign.)	Reciprocal (Invert but do not change the sign.)	
$-\dfrac{3}{8}$	$\dfrac{3}{8}$	$-\dfrac{8}{3}$	$\left(-\dfrac{3}{8}\right)\left(-\dfrac{8}{3}\right) = 1$
19	-19	$\dfrac{1}{19}$	$-\dfrac{3}{8} + \dfrac{3}{8} = 0$
$\dfrac{18}{7}$	$-\dfrac{18}{7}$	$\dfrac{7}{18}$	
-7.9	7.9	$-\dfrac{1}{7.9}$, or $-\dfrac{10}{79}$	
0	0	Undefined	

| **1.7** | **EXERCISE SET** | For Extra Help
 MyMathLab | Math XL
 PRACTICE | WATCH | DOWNLOAD |

🐦 *Concept Reinforcement*   *In each of Exercises 1–10, replace the blank with either 0 or 1 to match the description given.*

1. The product of two reciprocals ＿＿

2. The sum of a pair of opposites ＿＿

3. The sum of a pair of additive inverses ＿＿

4. The product of two multiplicative inverses ＿＿

5. This number has no reciprocal. ＿＿

6. This number is its own reciprocal. ＿＿

7. This number is the multiplicative identity. ____

8. This number is the additive identity. ____

9. A nonzero number divided by itself ____

10. Division by this number is undefined. ____

___

Multiply.

11. $-4 \cdot 10$

12. $-5 \cdot 6$

13. $-8 \cdot 7$

14. $-9 \cdot 2$

15. $4 \cdot (-10)$

16. $9 \cdot (-5)$

17. $-9 \cdot (-8)$

18. $-10 \cdot (-11)$

19. $-6 \cdot 7$

20. $-2 \cdot 5$

21. $-5 \cdot (-9)$

22. $-9 \cdot (-2)$

23. $-19 \cdot (-10)$

24. $-12 \cdot (-10)$

25. $11 \cdot (-12)$

26. $-13 \cdot (-15)$

27. $-25 \cdot (-48)$

28. $15 \cdot (-43)$

29. $4.5 \cdot (-28)$

30. $-49 \cdot (-2.1)$

31. $-5 \cdot (-2.3)$

32. $-6 \cdot 4.8$

33. $(-25) \cdot 0$

34. $0 \cdot (-4.7)$

35. $\frac{2}{5} \cdot \left(-\frac{5}{7}\right)$

36. $\frac{5}{7} \cdot \left(-\frac{2}{3}\right)$

37. $-\frac{3}{8} \cdot \left(-\frac{2}{9}\right)$

38. $-\frac{5}{8} \cdot \left(-\frac{2}{5}\right)$

39. $(-5.3)(2.1)$

40. $(9.5)(-3.7)$

41. $-\frac{5}{9} \cdot \frac{3}{4}$

42. $-\frac{8}{3} \cdot \frac{9}{4}$

43. $3 \cdot (-7) \cdot (-2) \cdot 6$

44. $9 \cdot (-2) \cdot (-6) \cdot 7$

45. $27 \cdot (-34) \cdot 0$

46. $-43 \cdot (-74) \cdot 0$

47. $-\frac{1}{3} \cdot \frac{1}{4} \cdot \left(-\frac{3}{7}\right)$

48. $-\frac{1}{2} \cdot \frac{3}{5} \cdot \left(-\frac{2}{7}\right)$

49. $-2 \cdot (-5) \cdot (-3) \cdot (-5)$

50. $-3 \cdot (-5) \cdot (-2) \cdot (-1)$

51. $(-31) \cdot (-27) \cdot 0 \cdot (-13)$

52. $7 \cdot (-6) \cdot 5 \cdot (-4) \cdot 3 \cdot (-2) \cdot 1 \cdot 0$

53. $(-8)(-9)(-10)$

54. $(-7)(-8)(-9)(-10)$

55. $(-6)(-7)(-8)(-9)(-10)$

56. $(-5)(-6)(-7)(-8)(-9)(-10)$

Divide, if possible, and check. If a quotient is undefined, state this.

57. $18 \div (-2)$

58. $\frac{24}{-3}$

59. $\frac{36}{-9}$

60. $26 \div (-13)$

61. $\frac{-56}{8}$

62. $\frac{-35}{-7}$

63. $\frac{-48}{-12}$

64. $-63 \div (-9)$

65. $-72 \div 8$

66. $\frac{-50}{25}$

67. $-10.2 \div (-2)$

68. $-2 \div 0.8$

69. $-100 \div (-11)$

70. $\frac{-64}{-7}$

71. $\frac{400}{-50}$

72. $-300 \div (-13)$

73. $\frac{48}{0}$

74. $\frac{0}{-5}$

75. $-4.8 \div 1.2$

76. $-3.9 \div 1.3$

77. $\frac{0}{-9}$

78. $0 \div 18$

Aha! **79.** $\frac{9.7(-2.8)0}{4.3}$

80. $\frac{(-4.9)(7.2)}{0}$

Write each expression in two equivalent forms, as in Example 6.

81. $\frac{-8}{3}$

82. $\frac{18}{-7}$

83. $\frac{29}{-35}$

84. $\frac{-10}{3}$

85. $-\frac{7}{3}$

86. $-\frac{4}{15}$

87. $\frac{-x}{2}$

88. $\frac{9}{-a}$

Find the reciprocal of each number, if it exists.

89. $-\frac{4}{5}$

90. $-\frac{13}{11}$

91. $\frac{51}{-10}$

92. $\frac{43}{-24}$

93. -10

94. 34

95. 4.3

96. -1.7

97. $\frac{-9}{4}$

98. $\frac{-6}{11}$

99. 0

100. -1

Perform the indicated operation and, if possible, simplify. If a quotient is undefined, state this.

101. $\left(\frac{-7}{4}\right)\left(-\frac{3}{5}\right)$

102. $\left(-\frac{5}{6}\right)\left(\frac{-1}{3}\right)$

103. $\frac{-3}{8} + \frac{-5}{8}$

104. $\frac{-4}{5} + \frac{7}{5}$

Aha! **105.** $\left(\frac{-9}{5}\right)\left(\frac{5}{-9}\right)$

106. $\left(-\frac{2}{7}\right)\left(\frac{5}{-8}\right)$

107. $\left(-\frac{3}{11}\right) - \left(-\frac{6}{11}\right)$

108. $\left(-\frac{4}{7}\right) - \left(-\frac{2}{7}\right)$

109. $\frac{7}{8} \div \left(-\frac{1}{2}\right)$

110. $\frac{3}{4} \div \left(-\frac{2}{3}\right)$

Aha! **111.** $-\frac{5}{9} \div \left(-\frac{5}{9}\right)$

112. $\frac{-5}{12} \div \frac{15}{7}$

113. $\frac{-3}{10} + \frac{2}{5}$

114. $\frac{-5}{9} + \frac{2}{3}$

115. $\frac{7}{10} \div \left(\frac{-3}{5}\right)$

116. $\left(\frac{-3}{5}\right) \div \frac{6}{15}$

117. $\frac{14}{-9} \div \frac{0}{3}$

118. $\frac{0}{-10} \div \frac{-3}{8}$

119. $\frac{-4}{15} + \frac{2}{-3}$

120. $\frac{3}{-10} + \frac{-1}{5}$

121. Most calculators have a key, often appearing as **1/x**, for finding reciprocals. To use this key, we enter a number and then press **1/x** to find its reciprocal. What should happen if we enter a number and then press the reciprocal key twice? Why?

122. Multiplication can be regarded as repeated addition. Using this idea and a number line, explain why $3 \cdot (-5) = -15$.

Skill Review

123. Simplify: $\frac{264}{468}$. [1.3]

124. Combine like terms: $x + 12y + 11x - 13y - 9$. [1.5]

Synthesis

125. If two nonzero numbers are opposites of each other, are their reciprocals opposites of each other? Why or why not?

126. If two numbers are reciprocals of each other, are their opposites reciprocals of each other? Why or why not?

Translate to an algebraic expression or equation.

127. The reciprocal of a sum

128. The sum of two reciprocals

129. The opposite of a sum

130. The sum of two opposites

131. A real number is its own opposite.

132. A real number is its own reciprocal.

133. Show that the reciprocal of a sum is *not* the sum of the two reciprocals.

134. Which real numbers are their own reciprocals?

135. Jenna is a meteorologist. On December 10, she notes that the temperature is $-3°F$ at 6:00 A.M. She predicts that the temperature will rise at a rate of 2° per hour for 3 hr, and then rise at a rate of 3° per hour for 6 hr. She also predicts that the temperature will then fall at a rate of 2° per hour for 3 hr, and then fall at a rate of 5° per hour for 2 hr. What is Jenna's temperature forecast for 8:00 P.M?

Tell whether each expression represents a positive number or a negative number when m and n are negative.

136. $\frac{m}{-n}$

137. $\frac{-n}{-m}$

138. $-m \cdot \left(\frac{-n}{m}\right)$

139. $-\left(\frac{n}{-m}\right)$

140. $(m + n) \cdot \frac{m}{n}$

141. $(-n - m)\frac{n}{m}$

142. What must be true of m and n if $-mn$ is to be **(a)** positive? **(b)** zero? **(c)** negative?

143. The following is a proof that a positive number times a negative number is negative. Provide a reason for each step. Assume that $a > 0$ and $b > 0$.

$$a(-b) + ab = a[-b + b]$$
$$= a(0)$$
$$= 0$$

Therefore, $a(-b)$ is the opposite of ab.

144. Is it true that for any numbers a and b, if a is larger than b, then the reciprocal of a is smaller than the reciprocal of b? Why or why not?

CONNECTING the CONCEPTS

The rules for multiplication and division of real numbers differ significantly from the rules for addition and subtraction. When simplifying an expression, look at the operation first to determine which set of rules to follow.

Addition

If the signs are the same, add absolute values.

- *Both numbers are positive:* Add as usual. The answer is positive.
- *Both numbers are negative:* Add absolute values and make the answer negative.

If the signs are different, subtract absolute values.

- *The positive number has the greater absolute value:* The answer is positive.
- *The negative number has the greater absolute value:* The answer is negative.
- *The numbers have the same absolute value:* The answer is 0.

If one number is zero, the sum is the other number.

Subtraction

Add the opposite of the number being subtracted.

Multiplication

If the signs are the same, multiply absolute values. The answer is positive.

If the signs are different, multiply absolute values. The answer is negative.

If one number is zero, the product is 0.

Division

Multiply by the reciprocal of the divisor.

MIXED REVIEW

Perform the indicated operation and, if possible, simplify.

1. $-8 + (-2)$

2. $-8 \cdot (-2)$

3. $-8 \div (-2)$

4. $-8 - (-2)$

5. $12 \cdot (-10)$

6. $13 - 20$

7. $-5 - 18$

8. $-12 \div 4$

9. $\dfrac{3}{5} - \dfrac{8}{5}$

10. $\dfrac{-12}{5} + \left(\dfrac{-3}{5}\right)$

11. $-5.6 + 4.8$

12. $1.3 \cdot (-2.9)$

13. $-44.1 \div 6.3$

14. $6.6 + (-10.7)$

15. $\dfrac{9}{5} \cdot \left(-\dfrac{20}{3}\right)$

16. $-\dfrac{5}{4} \div \left(-\dfrac{3}{4}\right)$

17. $38 - (-62)$

18. $-17 + 94$

19. $(-15) \cdot (-12)$

20. $-26 - 26$

1.8   Exponential Notation and Order of Operations

Exponential Notation   ▪   Order of Operations   ▪   Simplifying and the Distributive Law   ▪
The Opposite of a Sum

Algebraic expressions often contain *exponential notation*. In this section, we learn how to use exponential notation as well as rules for the *order of operations* in performing certain algebraic manipulations.

STUDY SKILLS ————————

A Journey of 1000 Miles Starts with a Single Step

It is extremely important to include steps when working problems. Doing so allows you and others to follow your thought process. It also helps you to avoid careless errors and to identify specific areas in which you may have made mistakes.

Exponential Notation

A product like $3 \cdot 3 \cdot 3 \cdot 3$, in which the factors are the same, is called a **power**. Powers occur often enough that a simpler notation called **exponential notation** is used. For

$$\underbrace{3 \cdot 3 \cdot 3 \cdot 3}_{4 \text{ factors}}, \quad \text{we write} \quad 3^4.$$

Because $3^4 = 81$, we can say that 81 "is a power of 3."

This is read "three to the fourth power," or simply, "three to the fourth." The number 4 is called an **exponent** and the number 3 a **base**.

Expressions like s^2 and s^3 are usually read "s squared" and "s cubed," respectively. This comes from the fact that a square with sides of length s has an area given by $A = s^2$ and a cube with sides of length s has a volume V given by $V = s^3$.

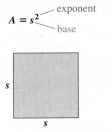
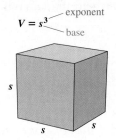

EXAMPLE **1**   Write exponential notation for $10 \cdot 10 \cdot 10 \cdot 10 \cdot 10$.

SOLUTION

Exponential notation is 10^5.   5 is the exponent.
10 is the base.

TRY EXERCISE 3

EXAMPLE **2**   Simplify: **(a)** 5^2; **(b)** $(-5)^3$; **(c)** $(2n)^3$.

SOLUTION

a) $5^2 = 5 \cdot 5 = 25$ The exponent 2 indicates two factors of 5.

b) $(-5)^3 = (-5)(-5)(-5)$ The exponent 3 indicates three factors of -5.

$ = 25(-5)$ Using the associative law of multiplication

$ = -125$

c) $(2n)^3 = (2n)(2n)(2n)$ The exponent 3 indicates three factors of $2n$.

$ = 2 \cdot 2 \cdot 2 \cdot n \cdot n \cdot n$ Using the associative and commutative laws of multiplication

$ = 8n^3$

TRY EXERCISE 13

STUDENT NOTES

Although most scientific and graphing calculators follow the rules for order of operations when evaluating expressions, some calculators do not. Try calculating $4 + 2 \times 5$ on your calculator. If the result shown is 30, your calculator does not follow the rules for order of operations. In this case, you will have to multiply 2×5 first and then add 4.

To determine what the exponent 1 will mean, look for a pattern in the following:

$$\begin{aligned} 7 \cdot 7 \cdot 7 \cdot 7 &= 7^4 \\ 7 \cdot 7 \cdot 7 &= 7^3 \\ 7 \cdot 7 &= 7^2 \\ ? &= 7^1 \end{aligned}$$

The exponent decreases by 1 each time.

The number of factors decreases by 1 each time. To extend the pattern, we say that

$$7 = 7^1.$$

Exponential Notation

For any natural number n,

$$b^n \quad \text{means} \quad \overbrace{b \cdot b \cdot b \cdot b \cdots b}^{n \text{ factors}}.$$

Order of Operations

How should $4 + 2 \times 5$ be computed? If we multiply 2 by 5 and then add 4, the result is 14. If we add 2 and 4 first and then multiply by 5, the result is 30. Since these results differ, the order in which we perform operations matters. If grouping symbols such as parentheses ( ), brackets [ ], braces { }, absolute-value symbols | |, or fraction bars appear, they tell us what to do first. For example,

$$(4 + 2) \times 5 \quad \text{indicates} \quad 6 \times 5, \quad \text{resulting in 30,}$$

and

$$4 + (2 \times 5) \quad \text{indicates} \quad 4 + 10, \quad \text{resulting in 14.}$$

Besides grouping symbols, the following conventions exist for determining the order in which operations should be performed.

Rules for Order of Operations
1. Calculate within the innermost grouping symbols, ( ), [ ], { }, | |, and above or below fraction bars.
2. Simplify all exponential expressions.
3. Perform all multiplications and divisions, working from left to right.
4. Perform all additions and subtractions, working from left to right.

Thus the correct way to compute $4 + 2 \times 5$ is to first multiply 2 by 5 and then add 4. The result is 14.

EXAMPLE 3

Simplify: $15 - 2 \cdot 5 + 3$.

SOLUTION   When no groupings or exponents appear, we *always* multiply or divide before adding or subtracting:

$$\begin{aligned} 15 - 2 \cdot 5 + 3 &= 15 - 10 + 3 \qquad &\text{Multiplying} \\ &= 5 + 3 \quad\Big\} &\text{Subtracting and adding from} \\ &= 8. \quad\;\;\Big\rfloor &\text{left to right} \end{aligned}$$

TRY EXERCISE 31

Always calculate within parentheses first. When there are exponents and no parentheses, we simplify powers before multiplying or dividing.

EXAMPLE **4**

Simplify: **(a)** $(3 \cdot 4)^2$; **(b)** $3 \cdot 4^2$.

SOLUTION

a) $(3 \cdot 4)^2 = (12)^2$ Working within parentheses first

          $= 144$

b) $3 \cdot 4^2 = 3 \cdot 16$ Simplifying the power

          $= 48$ Multiplying

Note that $(3 \cdot 4)^2 \neq 3 \cdot 4^2$.

TRY EXERCISE 37

CAUTION! Example 4 illustrates that, in general, $(ab)^2 \neq ab^2$.

EXAMPLE **5**

Evaluate when $x = 5$: **(a)** $(-x)^2$; **(b)** $-x^2$.

SOLUTION

a) $(-x)^2 = (-5)^2 = (-5)(-5) = 25$ We square the opposite of 5.

b) $-x^2 = -5^2 = -25$ We square 5 and then find the opposite.

TRY EXERCISE 15

CAUTION! Example 5 illustrates that, in general, $(-x)^2 \neq -x^2$.

To simplify $-x^2$, it may help to write

$$-x^2 = (-1)x^2.$$

EXAMPLE **6**

Evaluate $-15 \div 3(6 - a)^3$ when $a = 4$.

SOLUTION

$$-15 \div 3(6 - a)^3 = -15 \div 3(6 - 4)^3$$ Substituting 4 for a

$$= -15 \div 3(2)^3$$ Working within parentheses first

$$= -15 \div 3 \cdot 8$$ Simplifying the exponential expression

$$= -5 \cdot 8$$
$$= -40$$ Dividing and multiplying from left to right

TRY EXERCISE 67

STUDENT NOTES ───────

When simplifying an expression, it is important to copy the entire expression on each line, not just the parts that have been simplified in a given step. As shown in Examples 6 and 7, each line should be equivalent to the line above it.

───────────────

The symbols ( ), [ ], and { } are all used in the same way. Used inside or next to each other, they make it easier to locate the left and right sides of a grouping. When combinations of grouping symbols are used, we begin with the innermost grouping symbols and work to the outside.

EXAMPLE **7**   Simplify: $8 \div 4 + 3[9 + 2(3 - 5)^3]$.

SOLUTION

$8 \div 4 + 3[9 + 2(3 - 5)^3] = 8 \div 4 + 3[9 + 2(-2)^3]$ Doing the calculations in the innermost grouping symbols first

$\qquad\qquad\qquad\qquad = 8 \div 4 + 3[9 + 2(-8)]$ $(-2)^3 = (-2)(-2)(-2)$
$\qquad\qquad\qquad\qquad\qquad\qquad\qquad\qquad\qquad = -8$

$\qquad\qquad\qquad\qquad = 8 \div 4 + 3[9 + (-16)]$

$\qquad\qquad\qquad\qquad = 8 \div 4 + 3[-7]$ Completing the calculations within the brackets

$\qquad\qquad\qquad\qquad = 2 + (-21)$ Multiplying and dividing from left to right

$\qquad\qquad\qquad\qquad = -19$ **TRY EXERCISE** 47

EXAMPLE **8**   Calculate: $\dfrac{12(9 - 7) + 4 \cdot 5}{3^4 + 2^3}$.

SOLUTION   An equivalent expression with brackets is

$$[12(9 - 7) + 4 \cdot 5] \div [3^4 + 2^3].$$ Here the grouping symbols are necessary.

In effect, we need to simplify the numerator, simplify the denominator, and then divide the results:

$$\frac{12(9 - 7) + 4 \cdot 5}{3^4 + 2^3} = \frac{12(2) + 4 \cdot 5}{81 + 8}$$

$$= \frac{24 + 20}{89} = \frac{44}{89}.$$ **TRY EXERCISE** 55

Simplifying and the Distributive Law

Sometimes we cannot simplify within grouping symbols. When a sum or a difference is being grouped, the distributive law provides a method for removing the grouping symbols.

EXAMPLE **9**   Simplify: $5x - 9 + 2(4x + 5)$.

SOLUTION

$$5x - 9 + 2(4x + 5) = 5x - 9 + 8x + 10$$ Using the distributive law
$$= 13x + 1$$ Combining like terms

TRY EXERCISE 85

Now that exponents have been introduced, we can make our definition of *like* or *similar terms* more precise. **Like**, or **similar**, **terms** are either constant terms or terms containing the same variable(s) raised to the same power(s). Thus, 5 and -7, $19xy$ and $2yx$, and $4a^3b$ and a^3b are all pairs of like terms.

EXAMPLE   10   Simplify: $7x^2 + 3[x^2 + 2x] - 5x$.

SOLUTION

$$7x^2 + 3[x^2 + 2x] - 5x = 7x^2 + 3x^2 + 6x - 5x \qquad \text{Using the distributive law}$$

$$= 10x^2 + x \qquad \text{Combining like terms}$$

TRY EXERCISE   91

The Opposite of a Sum

When a number is multiplied by -1, the result is the opposite of that number. For example, $-1(7) = -7$ and $-1(-5) = 5$.

> ### The Property of -1
>
> For any real number a,
>
> $$-1 \cdot a = -a.$$
>
> (Negative one times a is the opposite of a.)

An expression such as $-(x + y)$ indicates the *opposite*, or *additive inverse*, of the sum of x and y. When a sum within grouping symbols is preceded by a "$-$" symbol, we can multiply the sum by -1 and use the distributive law. In this manner, we can find an equivalent expression for the opposite of a sum.

EXAMPLE   11   Write an expression equivalent to $-(3x + 2y + 4)$ without using parentheses.

SOLUTION

$$-(3x + 2y + 4) = -1(3x + 2y + 4) \qquad \text{Using the property of } -1$$

$$= -1(3x) + (-1)(2y) + (-1)4 \qquad \text{Using the distributive law}$$

$$= -3x - 2y - 4 \qquad \text{Using the associative law and the property of } -1$$

TRY EXERCISE   73

Example 11 illustrates an important property of real numbers.

> ### The Opposite of a Sum
>
> For any real numbers a and b,
>
> $$-(a + b) = -a + (-b) = -a - b.$$
>
> (The opposite of a sum is the sum of the opposites.)

To remove parentheses from an expression like $-(x - 7y + 5)$, we can first rewrite the subtraction as addition:

$$-(x - 7y + 5) = -(x + (-7y) + 5) \qquad \text{Rewriting as addition}$$

$$= -x + 7y - 5. \qquad \text{Taking the opposite of a sum}$$

This procedure is normally streamlined to one step in which we find the opposite by "removing parentheses and changing the sign of every term":

$$-(x - 7y + 5) = -x + 7y - 5.$$

EXAMPLE 12   Simplify: $3x - (4x + 2)$.

SOLUTION

$$
\begin{aligned}
3x - (4x + 2) &= 3x + [-(4x + 2)] && \text{Adding the opposite of } 4x + 2 \\
&= 3x + [-4x - 2] && \text{Taking the opposite of } 4x + 2 \\
&= 3x + (-4x) + (-2) && \\
&= 3x - 4x - 2 && \text{Try to go directly to this step.} \\
&= -x - 2 && \text{Combining like terms}
\end{aligned}
$$

TRY EXERCISE 81

In practice, the first three steps of Example 12 are generally skipped.

EXAMPLE 13   Simplify: $5t^2 - 2t - (-4t^2 + 9t)$.

SOLUTION

$$
\begin{aligned}
5t^2 - 2t - (-4t^2 + 9t) &= 5t^2 - 2t + 4t^2 - 9t && \text{Removing parentheses} \\
& && \text{and changing the sign} \\
& && \text{of each term inside} \\
&= 9t^2 - 11t && \text{Combining like terms}
\end{aligned}
$$

TRY EXERCISE 89

Expressions such as $7 - 3(x + 2)$ can be simplified as follows:

$$
\begin{aligned}
7 - 3(x + 2) &= 7 + [-3(x + 2)] && \text{Adding the opposite of } 3(x + 2) \\
&= 7 + [-3x - 6] && \text{Multiplying } x + 2 \text{ by } -3 \\
&= 7 - 3x - 6 && \text{Try to go directly to this step.} \\
&= 1 - 3x. && \text{Combining like terms}
\end{aligned}
$$

EXAMPLE 14   Simplify: **(a)** $3n - 2(4n - 5)$; **(b)** $7x^3 + 2 - [5(x^3 - 1) + 8]$.

SOLUTION

a)
$$
\begin{aligned}
3n - 2(4n - 5) &= 3n - 8n + 10 && \text{Multiplying each term inside the} \\
& && \text{parentheses by } -2 \\
&= -5n + 10 && \text{Combining like terms}
\end{aligned}
$$

b)
$$
\begin{aligned}
7x^3 + 2 - [5(x^3 - 1) + 8] &= 7x^3 + 2 - [5x^3 - 5 + 8] && \text{Removing} \\
& && \text{parentheses} \\
&= 7x^3 + 2 - [5x^3 + 3] && \\
&= 7x^3 + 2 - 5x^3 - 3 && \text{Removing brackets} \\
&= 2x^3 - 1 && \text{Combining like terms}
\end{aligned}
$$

TRY EXERCISE 93

As we progress through our study of algebra, it is important that we be able to distinguish between the two tasks of **simplifying an expression** and **solving an equation**. In Chapter 1, we have not solved equations, but we have simplified expressions. This enabled us to write *equivalent expressions* that were simpler than the given expression. In Chapter 2, we will continue to simplify expressions, but we will also begin to solve equations.

1.8   EXERCISE SET

↪ *Concept Reinforcement   In each part of Exercises 1 and 2, name the operation that should be performed first. Do not perform the calculations.*

1. a) $4 + 8 \div 2 \cdot 2$

   b) $7 - 9 + 15$

   c) $5 - 2(3 + 4)$

   d) $6 + 7 \cdot 3$

   e) $18 - 2[4 + (3 - 2)]$

   f) $\dfrac{5 - 6 \cdot 7}{2}$

2. a) $9 - 3 \cdot 4 \div 2$

   b) $8 + 7(6 - 5)$

   c) $5 \cdot [2 - 3(4 + 1)]$

   d) $8 - 7 + 2$

   e) $4 + 6 \div 2 \cdot 3$

   f) $\dfrac{37}{8 - 2 \cdot 2}$

Write exponential notation.

3. $x \cdot x \cdot x \cdot x \cdot x \cdot x$

4. $y \cdot y \cdot y \cdot y \cdot y \cdot y$

5. $(-5)(-5)(-5)$

6. $(-7)(-7)(-7)(-7)$

7. $3t \cdot 3t \cdot 3t \cdot 3t \cdot 3t$

8. $5m \cdot 5m \cdot 5m \cdot 5m \cdot 5m$

9. $2 \cdot n \cdot n \cdot n \cdot n$

10. $8 \cdot a \cdot a \cdot a$

Simplify.

11. 4^2

12. 5^3

13. $(-3)^2$

14. $(-7)^2$

15. -3^2

16. -7^2

17. 4^3

18. 9^1

19. $(-5)^4$

20. 5^4

21. 7^1

22. $(-1)^7$

23. $(-2)^5$

24. -2^5

25. $(3t)^4$

26. $(5t)^2$

27. $(-7x)^3$

28. $(-5x)^4$

29. $5 + 3 \cdot 7$

30. $3 - 4 \cdot 2$

31. $10 \cdot 5 + 1 \cdot 1$

32. $19 - 5 \cdot 4 + 3$

33. $6 - 70 \div 7 - 2$

34. $12 \div 3 + 18 \div 2$

Aha! 35. $14 \cdot 19 \div (19 \cdot 14)$

36. $18 - 6 \div 3 \cdot 2 + 7$

37. $3(-10)^2 - 8 \div 2^2$

38. $9 - 3^2 \div 9(-1)$

39. $8 - (2 \cdot 3 - 9)$

40. $(8 - 2 \cdot 3) - 9$

41. $(8 - 2)(3 - 9)$

42. $32 \div (-2)^2 \cdot 4$

43. $13(-10)^2 + 45 \div (-5)$

44. $2^4 + 2^3 - 10 \div (-1)^4$

45. $5 + 3(2 - 9)^2$

46. $9 - (3 - 5)^3 - 4$

47. $[2 \cdot (5 - 8)]^2$

48. $3(5 - 7)^3 \div 4$

49. $\dfrac{7 + 2}{5^2 - 4^2}$

50. $\dfrac{(5^2 - 3^2)^2}{2 \cdot 6 - 4}$

51. $8(-7) + |3(-4)|$

52. $|10(-5)| + 1(-1)$

53. $36 \div (-2)^2 + 4[5 - 3(8 - 9)^5]$

54. $-48 \div (7 - 9)^3 - 2[1 - 5(2 - 6) + 3^2]$

55. $\dfrac{7^2 - (-1)^7}{5 \cdot 7 - 4 \cdot 3^2 - 2^2}$

56. $\dfrac{(-2)^3 + 4^2}{2 \cdot 3 - 5^2 + 3 \cdot 7}$

57. $\dfrac{-3^3 - 2 \cdot 3^2}{8 \div 2^2 - (6 - |2 - 15|)}$

58. $\dfrac{(-5)^2 - 3 \cdot 5}{3^2 + 4 \cdot |6 - 7| \cdot (-1)^5}$

Evaluate.

59. $9 - 4x$, for $x = 7$

60. $1 + x^3$, for $x = -2$

61. $24 \div t^3$, for $t = -2$

62. $-100 \div a^2$, for $a = -5$

63. $45 \div a \cdot 5$, for $a = -3$

64. $50 \div 2 \cdot t$, for $t = 5$

65. $5x \div 15x^2$, for $x = 3$

66. $6a \div 12a^3$, for $a = 2$

67. $45 \div 3^2 x(x - 1)$, for $x = 3$

68. $-30 \div t(t + 4)^2$, for $t = -6$

69. $-x^2 - 5x$, for $x = -3$

70. $(-x)^2 - 5x$, for $x = -3$

71. $\dfrac{3a - 4a^2}{a^2 - 20}$, for $a = 5$

72. $\dfrac{a^3 - 4a}{a(a - 3)}$, for $a = -2$

Write an equivalent expression without using grouping symbols.

73. $-(9x + 1)$

74. $-(3x + 5)$

75. $-[-7n + 8]$

76. $-(6x - 7)$

77. $-(4a - 3b + 7c)$

78. $-[5n - m - 2p]$

79. $-(3x^2 + 5x - 1)$

80. $-(-9x^3 + 8x + 10)$

Simplify.

81. $8x - (6x + 7)$

82. $2a - (5a - 9)$

83. $2x - 7x - (4x - 6)$

84. $2a + 5a - (6a + 8)$

85. $9t - 7r + 2(3r + 6t)$

86. $4m - 9n + 3(2m - n)$

87. $15x - y - 5(3x - 2y + 5z)$

88. $4a - b - 4(5a - 7b + 8c)$

89. $3x^2 + 11 - (2x^2 + 5)$

90. $5x^4 + 3x - (5x^4 + 3x)$

91. $5t^3 + t + 3(t - 2t^3)$

92. $8n^2 - 3n + 2(n - 4n^2)$

93. $12a^2 - 3ab + 5b^2 - 5(-5a^2 + 4ab - 6b^2)$

94. $-8a^2 + 5ab - 12b^2 - 6(2a^2 - 4ab - 10b^2)$

95. $-7t^3 - t^2 - 3(5t^3 - 3t)$

96. $9t^4 + 7t - 5(9t^3 - 2t)$

97. $5(2x - 7) - [4(2x - 3) + 2]$

98. $3(6x - 5) - [3(1 - 8x) + 5]$

99. Some students use the mnemonic device PEMDAS to help remember the rules for the order of operations. Explain how this can be done and how the order of the letters in PEMDAS could lead a student to a wrong conclusion about the order of some operations.

100. Jake keys $18/2 \cdot 3$ into his calculator and expects the result to be 3. What mistake is he probably making?

Skill Review

Translate to an algebraic expression. [1.1]

101. Nine less than twice a number

102. Half of the sum of two numbers

Synthesis

103. Write the sentence $(-x)^2 \neq -x^2$ in words. Explain why $(-x)^2$ and $-x^2$ are not equivalent.

104. Write the sentence $-|x| \neq -x$ in words. Explain why $-|x|$ and $-x$ are not equivalent.

Simplify.

105. $5t - \{7t - [4r - 3(t - 7)] + 6r\} - 4r$

106. $z - \{2z - [3z - (4z - 5z) - 6z] - 7z\} - 8z$

107. $\{x - [f - (f - x)] + [x - f]\} - 3x$

108. Is it true that for all real numbers a and b,
$$ab = (-a)(-b)?$$
Why or why not?

109. Is it true that for all real numbers a, b, and c,
$$a|b - c| = ab - ac?$$
Why or why not?

If $n > 0$, $m > 0$, and $n \neq m$, classify each of the following as either true or false.

110. $-n + m = -(n + m)$

111. $m - n = -(n - m)$

112. $n(-n - m) = -n^2 + nm$

113. $-m(n - m) = -(mn + m^2)$

114. $-n(-n - m) = n(n + m)$

Evaluate.

Aha! **115.** $[x + 3(2 - 5x) \div 7 + x](x - 3)$, for $x = 3$

Aha! **116.** $[x + 2 \div 3x] \div [x + 2 \div 3x]$, for $x = -7$

117. $\dfrac{x^2 + 2^x}{x^2 - 2^x}$, for $x = 3$

118. $\dfrac{x^2 + 2^x}{x^2 - 2^x}$, for $x = 2$

119. In Mexico, between 500 B.C. and 600 A.D., the Mayans represented numbers using powers of 20 and certain symbols. For example, the symbols

represent $4 \cdot 20^3 + 17 \cdot 20^2 + 10 \cdot 20^1 + 0 \cdot 20^0$. Evaluate this number.

Source: National Council of Teachers of Mathematics, 1906 Association Drive, Reston, VA 22091

120. Examine the Mayan symbols and the numbers in Exercise 119. What numbers do

  and

each represent?

121. Calculate the volume of the tower shown below.

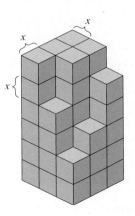

CORNER

Select the Symbols

Focus: Order of operations

Time: 15 minutes

Group size: 2

One way to master the rules for the order of operations is to insert symbols within a display of numbers in order to obtain a predetermined result. For example, the display

$$1 \quad 2 \quad 3 \quad 4 \quad 5$$

can be used to obtain the result 21 as follows:

$$(1 + 2) \div 3 + 4 \cdot 5.$$

Note that without an understanding of the rules for the order of operations, solving a problem of this sort is impossible.

ACTIVITY

1. Each group should prepare an exercise similar to the example shown above. (Exponents are not allowed.) To do so, first select five single-digit numbers for display. Then insert operations and grouping symbols and calculate the result.

2. Pair with another group. Each group should give the other its result along with its five-number display, and challenge the other group to insert symbols that will make the display equal the result given.

3. Share with the entire class the various mathematical statements developed by each group.

Study Summary

SECTION 1.1: INTRODUCTION TO ALGEBRA

An **algebraic expression** is a collection of **variables** and **constants** on which operations are performed.

$5ab^3$ is an algebraic expression; 5 is a constant; and a and b are variables.

To **evaluate** an algebraic expression, substitute a number for each variable and carry out the operations. The result is a **value** of that expression.

Evaluate $\dfrac{x + y}{8}$ *for* $x = 15$ *and* $y = 9$.

$$\frac{x + y}{8} = \frac{15 + 9}{8} = \frac{24}{8} = 3$$

To find the area of a rectangle, a triangle, or a parallelogram, evaluate the appropriate formula for the given values.

Find the area of a triangle with base 3.1 m *and height* 6 m.
$$A = \tfrac{1}{2}bh = \tfrac{1}{2}(3.1 \text{ m})(6 \text{ m}) = \tfrac{1}{2}(3.1)(6)(\text{m} \cdot \text{m}) = 9.3 \text{ m}^2$$

Many problems can be solved by **translating** phrases to algebraic expressions and then forming an equation. The table on p. 4 shows translations of many words that occur in problems.

Translate to an equation. Do not solve.

When 34 is subtracted from a number, the result is 13. What is the number?

Let n represent the number.

Rewording: 34 subtracted from a number   is   13

Translating: $n - 34$ $=$ 13

An **equation** is a number sentence with the verb $=$. A substitution for the variable in an equation that makes the equation true is a **solution** of the equation.

Determine whether 9 *is a solution of* $47 - n = 38$.

$$47 - n = 38$$
$$\frac{47 - 9 \;\big|\; 38}{38 \overset{?}{=} 38} \quad \text{TRUE}$$

Since $38 = 38$ is true, 9 is a solution.

SECTION 1.2: THE COMMUTATIVE, ASSOCIATIVE, AND DISTRIBUTIVE LAWS

Equivalent expressions represent the same value for any replacement of the variable.

$x + 10$ and $3 + 7 + x$ are equivalent expressions.

The Commutative Laws

$$a + b = b + a;$$
$$ab = ba$$

$$3 + (-5) = -5 + 3;$$
$$8(10) = 10(8)$$

The Associative Laws

$$a + (b + c) = (a + b) + c;$$
$$a \cdot (b \cdot c) = (a \cdot b) \cdot c$$

$$-5 + (5 + 6) = (-5 + 5) + 6;$$
$$2 \cdot (5 \cdot 9) = (2 \cdot 5) \cdot 9$$

The Distributive Law
$$a(b + c) = ab + ac$$

$$4(x + 2) = 4 \cdot x + 4 \cdot 2 = 4x + 8$$

The distributive law is used to multiply and to **factor** expressions.

Multiply: $3(2x + 5y)$.
$$3(2x + 5y) = 3 \cdot 2x + 3 \cdot 5y = 6x + 15y$$

Factor: $16x + 24y + 8$.
$$16x + 24y + 8 = 8(2x + 3y + 1)$$

SECTION 1.3: FRACTION NOTATION

Natural numbers: $\{1, 2, 3, \ldots\}$
Whole numbers: $\{0, 1, 2, 3, \ldots\}$

15, 39, and 1567 are some natural numbers.
0, 5, 16, and 2890 are some whole numbers.

A **prime** number has only two different factors, the number itself and 1. Natural numbers that have factors other than 1 and the number itself are **composite** numbers.

2, 3, 5, 7, 11, and 13 are the first six prime numbers.
4, 6, 8, 24, and 100 are examples of composite numbers.

The **prime factorization** of a composite number expresses that number as a product of prime numbers.

The prime factorization of 136 is $2 \cdot 2 \cdot 2 \cdot 17$.

For any nonzero number a,
$$\frac{a}{a} = 1.$$

$$\frac{15}{15} = 1 \quad \text{and} \quad \frac{2x}{2x} = 1$$

The Identity Property of 1
$$a \cdot 1 = 1 \cdot a = a$$

The number 1 is called the **multiplicative identity**.

$$\frac{2}{3} = \frac{2}{3} \cdot \frac{5}{5} \quad \text{since} \quad \frac{5}{5} = 1.$$

$$\frac{a}{d} + \frac{b}{d} = \frac{a + b}{d}$$

$$\frac{a}{d} - \frac{b}{d} = \frac{a - b}{d}$$

$$\frac{a}{b} \cdot \frac{c}{d} = \frac{a \cdot c}{b \cdot d}$$

$$\frac{a}{b} \div \frac{c}{d} = \frac{a}{b} \cdot \frac{d}{c}$$

$$\frac{1}{6} + \frac{3}{8} = \frac{4}{24} + \frac{9}{24} = \frac{13}{24}$$

$$\frac{5}{12} - \frac{1}{6} = \frac{5}{12} - \frac{2}{12} = \frac{3}{12} = \frac{1 \cdot 3}{4 \cdot 3} = \frac{1}{4} \cdot \frac{3}{3} = \frac{1}{4} \cdot 1 = \frac{1}{4}$$

$$\frac{2}{5} \cdot \frac{7}{8} = \frac{2 \cdot 7}{5 \cdot 2 \cdot 4} = \frac{7}{20} \qquad \text{Removing a factor equal to 1: } \frac{2}{2} = 1$$

$$\frac{10}{9} \div \frac{4}{15} = \frac{10}{9} \cdot \frac{15}{4} = \frac{2 \cdot 5 \cdot 3 \cdot 5}{3 \cdot 3 \cdot 2 \cdot 2} = \frac{25}{6} \qquad \text{Removing a factor equal to 1: } \frac{2 \cdot 3}{2 \cdot 3} = 1$$

SECTION 1.4: POSITIVE AND NEGATIVE REAL NUMBERS

Integers:
$\{\ldots, -3, -2, -1, 0, 1, 2, 3, \ldots\}$

$-25, -2, 0, 1,$ and 2000 are some integers.

Rational numbers:

$$\left\{\frac{a}{b} \,\middle|\, a \text{ and } b \text{ are integers and } b \neq 0\right\}$$

$\dfrac{1}{6}, \dfrac{-3}{7}, 0, 17, 0.758,$ and $9.\overline{608}$ are some rational numbers.

The rational numbers and the **irrational numbers** make up the set of **real numbers**.

$\sqrt{7}$ and π are some irrational numbers.

Every rational number can be written using fraction notation or decimal notation. When written in decimal notation, a rational number either **repeats** or **terminates**.

$-\dfrac{1}{16} = -0.0625$ This is a terminating decimal.

$\dfrac{5}{6} = 0.8333\ldots = 0.8\overline{3}$ This is a repeating decimal.

Every real number corresponds to a point on the number line. For any two numbers, the one to the left is less than the one to the right. The symbol $<$ means "**is less than**" and the symbol $>$ means "**is greater than**."

$4 > -3.1$ $-\dfrac{1}{2} < \sqrt{2}$

The **absolute value** of a number is the number of units that number is from zero on the number line.

$|3| = 3$ since 3 is 3 units from 0.
$|-3| = 3$ since -3 is 3 units from 0.

SECTION 1.5: ADDITION OF REAL NUMBERS

To **add** two real numbers, use the rules on p. 39.

$-8 + (-3) = -11;$
$-8 + 3 = -5;$
$8 + (-3) = 5;$
$-8 + 8 = 0$

The Identity Property of 0

$$a + 0 = 0 + a = a$$

The number 0 is called the **additive identity**.

$-35 + 0 = -35;$

$0 + \dfrac{2}{9} = \dfrac{2}{9}$

SECTION 1.6: SUBTRACTION OF REAL NUMBERS

The **opposite**, or **additive inverse**, of a number a is written $-a$. The opposite of the opposite of a is a.

$$-(-a) = a$$

Find $-x$ and $-(-x)$ when $x = -11$.

$-x = -(-11) = 11;$
$-(-x) = -(-(-11)) = -11$ $-(-x) = x$

To **subtract** two real numbers, add the opposite of the number being subtracted.	$-10 - 12 = -10 + (-12) = -22;$ $-10 - (-12) = -10 + 12 = 2$
The **terms** of an expression are separated by plus signs. **Like terms** either are constants or have the same variable factors raised to the same power. Like terms can be **combined** using the distributive law.	In the expression $-2x + 3y + 5x - 7y$: 　　The terms are $-2x, 3y, 5x,$ and $-7y.$ 　　The like terms are $-2x$ and $5x,$ and $3y$ and $-7y.$ Combining like terms gives $$-2x + 3y + 5x - 7y = -2x + 5x + 3y - 7y$$ $$= (-2 + 5)x + (3 - 7)y = 3x - 4y.$$

SECTION 1.7: MULTIPLICATION AND DIVISION OF REAL NUMBERS

To **multiply** or **divide** two real numbers, use the rules on p. 54. Division by 0 is undefined.	$(-5)(-2) = 10;$ $30 \div (-6) = -5;$ $0 \div (-3) = 0;$ $-3 \div 0$ is undefined.

SECTION 1.8: EXPONENTIAL NOTATION AND ORDER OF OPERATIONS

Exponential notation: Exponent 　　　　　　　n factors 　　$b^n = b \cdot b \cdot b \cdots b$ Base	$6^2 = 6 \cdot 6 = 36;$ $(-6)^2 = (-6) \cdot (-6) = 36;$ $-6^2 = -6 \cdot 6 = -36;$ $(6x)^2 = (6x) \cdot (6x) = 36x^2$
To perform multiple operations, use the rules for **order of operations** on p. 61.	$-3 + (3 - 5)^3 \div 4(-1) = -3 + (-2)^3 \div 4(-1)$ $\qquad\qquad\qquad = -3 + (-8) \div 4(-1)$ $\qquad\qquad\qquad = -3 + (-2)(-1)$ $\qquad\qquad\qquad = -3 + 2$ $\qquad\qquad\qquad = -1$
The Property of -1 For any real number $a,$ 　　$-1 \cdot a = -a.$	$-1 \cdot 5x = -5x$　and　$-5x = -1(5x)$
The Opposite of a Sum For any real numbers a and $b,$ 　　$-(a + b) = -a - b.$	$-(2x - 3y) = -(2x) - (-3y) = -2x + 3y$
Expressions containing parentheses can be simplified by removing parentheses using the distributive law.	*Simplify:* $3x^2 - 5(x^2 - 4xy + 2y^2) - 7y^2.$ $3x^2 - 5(x^2 - 4xy + 2y^2) - 7y^2 = 3x^2 - 5x^2 + 20xy - 10y^2 - 7y^2$ $\qquad\qquad\qquad\qquad\qquad = -2x^2 + 20xy - 17y^2$

Review Exercises: Chapter 1

▶ *Concept Reinforcement* In each of Exercises 1–10, classify the statement as either true or false.

1. $4x - 5y$ and $12 - 7a$ are both algebraic expressions containing two terms. [1.2]

2. $3t + 1 = 7$ and $8 - 2 = 9$ are both equations. [1.1]

3. The fact that $2 + x$ is equivalent to $x + 2$ is an illustration of the associative law for addition. [1.2]

4. The statement $4(a + 3) = 4 \cdot a + 4 \cdot 3$ illustrates the distributive law. [1.2]

5. The number 2 is neither prime nor composite. [1.3]

6. Every irrational number can be written as a repeating decimal or a terminating decimal. [1.4]

7. Every natural number is a whole number and every whole number is an integer. [1.4]

8. The expressions $9r^2s$ and $5rs^2$ are like terms. [1.8]

9. The opposite of x, written $-x$, never represents a positive number. [1.6]

10. The number 0 has no reciprocal. [1.7]

Evaluate.

11. $8t$, for $t = 3$ [1.1]

12. $\dfrac{x - y}{3}$, for $x = 17$ and $y = 5$ [1.1]

13. $9 - y^2$, for $y = -5$ [1.8]

14. $-10 + a^2 \div (b + 1)$, for $a = 5$ and $b = -6$ [1.8]

Translate to an algebraic expression. [1.1]

15. 7 less than y

16. 10 more than the product of x and z

17. 15 times the difference of Brandt's speed and the wind speed

18. Determine whether 35 is a solution of $x/5 = 8$. [1.1]

19. Translate to an equation. Do not solve. [1.1]

According to Photo Marketing Association International, in 2006, 14.1 billion prints were made from film. This number is 3.2 billion more than the number of digital prints made. How many digital prints were made in 2006?

20. Use the commutative law of multiplication to write an expression equivalent to $3t + 5$. [1.2]

21. Use the associative law of addition to write an expression equivalent to $(2x + y) + z$. [1.2]

22. Use the commutative and associative laws to write three expressions equivalent to $4(xy)$. [1.2]

Multiply. [1.2]

23. $6(3x + 5y)$

24. $8(5x + 3y + 2)$

Factor. [1.2]

25. $21x + 15y$

26. $22a + 99b + 11$

27. Find the prime factorization of 56. [1.3]

Simplify. [1.3]

28. $\dfrac{20}{48}$

29. $\dfrac{18}{8}$

Perform the indicated operation and, if possible, simplify. [1.3]

30. $\dfrac{5}{12} + \dfrac{3}{8}$

31. $\dfrac{9}{16} \div 3$

32. $\dfrac{2}{3} - \dfrac{1}{15}$

33. $\dfrac{9}{10} \cdot \dfrac{6}{5}$

34. Tell which integers correspond to this situation. [1.4]

Natalie borrowed $3600 for an entertainment center. Sean has $1350 in his savings account.

35. Graph on a number line: $\frac{-1}{3}$. [1.4]

36. Write an inequality with the same meaning as $-3 < x$. [1.4]

37. Classify as true or false: $2 \geq -8$. [1.4]

38. Classify as true or false: $0 \leq -1$. [1.4]

39. Find decimal notation: $-\dfrac{4}{9}$. [1.4]

40. Find the absolute value: $|-1|$. [1.4]

41. Find $-(-x)$ when x is -12. [1.6]

Simplify.

42. $-3 + (-7)$ [1.5]

43. $-\frac{2}{3} + \frac{1}{12}$ [1.5]

44. $10 + (-9) + (-8) + 7$ [1.5]

45. $-3.8 + 5.1 + (-12) + (-4.3) + 10$ [1.5]

46. $-2 - (-10)$ [1.6]

47. $-\frac{9}{10} - \frac{1}{2}$ [1.6]

48. $-3.8 - 4.1$ [1.6]

49. $-9 \cdot (-7)$ [1.7]

50. $-2.7(3.4)$ [1.7]

51. $\frac{2}{3} \cdot \left(-\frac{3}{7}\right)$ [1.7]

52. $2 \cdot (-7) \cdot (-2) \cdot (-5)$ [1.7]

53. $35 \div (-5)$ [1.7]

54. $-5.1 \div 1.7$ [1.7]

55. $-\frac{3}{5} \div \left(-\frac{4}{15}\right)$ [1.7]

56. $120 - 6^2 \div 4 \cdot 8$ [1.8]

57. $(120 - 6^2) \div 4 \cdot 8$ [1.8]

58. $(120 - 6^2) \div (4 \cdot 8)$ [1.8]

59. $16 \div (-2)^3 - 5[3 - 1 + 2(4 - 7)]$ [1.8]

60. $|-3 \cdot 5 - 4 \cdot 8| - 3(-2)$ [1.8]

61. $\dfrac{4(18 - 8) + 7 \cdot 9}{9^2 - 8^2}$ [1.8]

Combine like terms.

62. $11a + 2b + (-4a) + (-3b)$ [1.5]

63. $7x - 3y - 11x + 8y$ [1.6]

64. Find the opposite of -7. [1.6]

65. Find the reciprocal of -7. [1.7]

66. Write exponential notation for $2x \cdot 2x \cdot 2x \cdot 2x$. [1.8]

67. Simplify: $(-5x)^3$. [1.8]

Remove parentheses and simplify. [1.8]

68. $2a - (5a - 9)$

69. $5b + 3(2b - 9)$

70. $11x^4 + 2x + 8(x - x^4)$

71. $2n^2 - 5(-3n^2 + m^2 - 4mn) + 6m^2$

72. $8(x + 4) - 6 - [3(x - 2) + 4]$

Synthesis

73. Explain the difference between a constant and a variable. [1.1]

74. Explain the difference between a term and a factor. [1.2]

75. Describe at least three ways in which the distributive law was used in this chapter. [1.2]

76. Devise a rule for determining the sign of a negative number raised to a power. [1.8]

77. Evaluate $a^{50} - 20a^{25}b^4 + 100b^8$ for $a = 1$ and $b = 2$. [1.8]

78. If $0.090909\ldots = \frac{1}{11}$ and $0.181818\ldots = \frac{2}{11}$, what rational number is named by each of the following?

   a) $0.272727\ldots$ [1.4]   **b)** $0.909090\ldots$ [1.4]

Simplify. [1.8]

79. $-\left|\frac{7}{8} - \left(-\frac{1}{2}\right) - \frac{3}{4}\right|$

80. $(|2.7 - 3| + 3^2 - |-3|) \div (-3)$

Match each phrase in the left column with the most appropriate choice from the right column.

81. ____ A number is nonnegative. [1.4]

82. ____ The product of a number and its reciprocal is 1. [1.7]

83. ____ A number squared [1.8]

84. ____ A sum of squares [1.8]

85. ____ The opposite of an opposite is the original number. [1.6]

86. ____ The order in which numbers are added does not change the result. [1.2]

87. ____ A number is positive. [1.4]

88. ____ The absolute value of a product [1.4]

89. ____ A sum of a number and its reciprocal [1.7]

90. ____ The square of a sum [1.8]

91. ____ The absolute value of one number is less than the absolute value of another number. [1.4]

a) a^2

b) $a + b = b + a$

c) $a > 0$

d) $a + \dfrac{1}{a}$

e) $|ab|$

f) $(a + b)^2$

g) $|a| < |b|$

h) $a^2 + b^2$

i) $a \geq 0$

j) $a \cdot \dfrac{1}{a} = 1$

k) $-(-a) = a$

1. Evaluate $\dfrac{2x}{y}$ for $x = 10$ and $y = 5$.

2. Write an algebraic expression: Nine less than the product of two numbers.

3. Find the area of a triangle when the height h is 30 ft and the base b is 16 ft.

4. Use the commutative law of addition to write an expression equivalent to $3p + q$.

5. Use the associative law of multiplication to write an expression equivalent to $x \cdot (4 \cdot y)$.

6. Determine whether 7 is a solution of $65 - x = 69$.

7. Translate to an equation. Do not solve.

In the summer of 2005, member utilities of the Florida Reliability Coordinating Council had a demand of 45,950 megawatts. This is only 4250 megawatts less than its maximum production capability. What is the maximum capability of production?

Source: Energy Information Administration

Multiply.

8. $7(5 + x)$

9. $-5(y - 2)$

Factor.

10. $11 + 44x$

11. $7x + 7 + 49y$

12. Find the prime factorization of 300.

13. Simplify: $\dfrac{24}{56}$.

Write a true sentence using either $<$ or $>$.

14. $-4 \ \blacksquare \ 0$

15. $-3 \ \blacksquare \ -8$

Find the absolute value.

16. $\left|\dfrac{9}{4}\right|$

17. $|-3.8|$

18. Find the opposite of $-\dfrac{2}{3}$.

19. Find the reciprocal of $-\dfrac{4}{7}$.

20. Find $-x$ when x is -10.

21. Write an inequality with the same meaning as $x \le -5$.

Perform the indicated operations and, if possible, simplify.

22. $3.1 - (-4.7)$

23. $-8 + 4 + (-7) + 3$

24. $3.2 - 5.7$

25. $-\dfrac{1}{8} - \dfrac{3}{4}$

26. $4 \cdot (-12)$

27. $-\dfrac{1}{2} \cdot \left(-\dfrac{4}{9}\right)$

28. $-66 \div 11$

29. $-\dfrac{3}{5} \div \left(-\dfrac{4}{5}\right)$

30. $4.864 \div (-0.5)$

31. $-2(16) - |2(-8) - 5^3|$

32. $9 + 7 - 4 - (-3)$

33. $256 \div (-16) \cdot 4$

34. $2^3 - 10[4 - (-2 + 18)3]$

35. Combine like terms: $18y + 30a - 9a + 4y$.

36. Simplify: $(-2x)^4$.

Remove parentheses and simplify.

37. $4x - (3x - 7)$

38. $4(2a - 3b) + a - 7$

39. $3[5(y - 3) + 9] - 2(8y - 1)$

Synthesis

40. Evaluate $\dfrac{5y - x}{2}$ when $x = 20$ and y is 4 less than half of x.

41. Insert one pair of parentheses to make the following a true statement:

$$9 - 3 - 4 + 5 = 15.$$

Simplify.

42. $|-27 - 3(4)| - |-36| + |-12|$

43. $a - \{3a - [4a - (2a - 4a)]\}$

44. Classify the following as either true or false:

$$a|b - c| = |ab| - |ac|.$$

Equations, Inequalities, and Problem Solving

DEBORAH ELIAS
EVENT COORDINATOR
Houston, Texas

s an event planner, I am con-
ntly using math. Calculations
ge from figuring the tax and
uity percentage to add to the
bill to finding dimensions of
ns to fit a table properly. For
every client, I also determine
a budget with income
and expenses.

AN APPLICATION

Event promoters use the formula

$$p = \frac{1.2x}{s}$$

to determine a ticket price p for an event with x dollars of expenses and s anticipated ticket sales. Grand Events expects expenses for an upcoming concert to be $80,000 and anticipates selling 4000 tickets. What should the ticket price be?

Source: *The Indianapolis Star,* 2/27/03

This problem appears as Example 1 in Section 2.3.

S olving equations and inequalities is a recurring theme in much of mathematics. In this chapter, we will study some of the principles used to solve equations and inequalities. We will then use equations and inequalities to solve applied problems.

2.1 Solving Equations

Equations and Solutions ▪ The Addition Principle ▪ The Multiplication Principle ▪ Selecting the Correct Approach

Solving equations is essential for problem solving in algebra. In this section, we study two of the most important principles used for this task.

Equations and Solutions

We have already seen that an equation is a number sentence stating that the expressions on either side of the equals sign represent the same number. Some equations, like $3 + 2 = 5$ or $2x + 6 = 2(x + 3)$, are *always* true and some, like $3 + 2 = 6$ or $x + 2 = x + 3$, are *never* true. In this text, we will concentrate on equations like $x + 6 = 13$ or $7x = 141$ that are *sometimes* true, depending on the replacement value for the variable.

> **Solution of an Equation**
>
> Any replacement for the variable that makes an equation true is called a *solution* of the equation. To *solve* an equation means to find all of its solutions.

To determine whether a number is a solution, we substitute that number for the variable throughout the equation. If the values on both sides of the equals sign are the same, then the number that was substituted is a solution.

EXAMPLE **1** Determine whether 7 is a solution of $x + 6 = 13$.

SOLUTION   We have

$$
\begin{array}{c|c}
x + 6 = 13 & \text{Writing the equation} \\
\hline
7 + 6 \mid 13 & \text{Substituting 7 for } x \\
13 \stackrel{?}{=} 13 \quad \text{TRUE} & 13 = 13 \text{ is a true statement.}
\end{array}
$$

Since the left-hand side and the right-hand side are the same, 7 is a solution.

> *CAUTION!*   Note that in Example 1, the solution is 7, not 13.

EXAMPLE 2

Determine whether $\frac{2}{3}$ is a solution of $156x = 117$.

SOLUTION   We have

$$156x = 117 \qquad \text{Writing the equation}$$

$$156\left(\frac{2}{3}\right) \;\bigg|\; 117 \qquad \text{Substituting } \tfrac{2}{3} \text{ for } x$$

$$104 \overset{?}{=} 117 \quad \text{FALSE} \qquad \text{The statement } 104 = 117 \text{ is false.}$$

Since the left-hand side and the right-hand side differ, $\frac{2}{3}$ is not a solution.

The Addition Principle

Consider the equation

$$x = 7.$$

We can easily see that the solution of this equation is 7. Replacing x with 7, we get

$$7 = 7, \quad \text{which is true.}$$

Now consider the equation

$$x + 6 = 13.$$

In Example 1, we found that the solution of $x + 6 = 13$ is also 7. Although the solution of $x = 7$ may seem more obvious, because $x + 6 = 13$ and $x = 7$ have identical solutions, the equations are said to be **equivalent**.

> ### Equivalent Equations
> Equations with the same solutions are called *equivalent equations*.

There are principles that enable us to begin with one equation and end up with an equivalent equation, like $x = 7$, for which the solution is obvious. One such principle concerns addition. The equation $a = b$ says that a and b stand for the same number. Suppose this is true, and some number c is added to a. We get the same result if we add c to b, because a and b are the same number.

> ### The Addition Principle
> For any real numbers a, b, and c,
> $$a = b \quad \text{is equivalent to} \quad a + c = b + c.$$

To visualize the addition principle, consider a balance similar to one a jeweler might use. When the two sides of a balance hold equal weight, the balance is level. If weight is then added or removed, equally, on both sides, the balance will remain level.

$a = b$ $\qquad\qquad\qquad$ $a + c = b + c$

When using the addition principle, we often say that we "add the same num-ber to both sides of an equation." We can also "subtract the same number from both sides," since subtraction can be regarded as the addition of an opposite.

EXAMPLE 3

Solve: $x + 5 = -7$.

SOLUTION   We can add any number we like to both sides. Since -5 is the opposite, or additive inverse, of 5, we add -5 to each side:

$$x + 5 = -7$$
$$x + 5 - 5 = -7 - 5 \qquad \text{Using the addition principle: adding } -5 \text{ to both sides or subtracting 5 from both sides}$$
$$x + 0 = -12 \qquad \text{Simplifying; } x + 5 - 5 = x + 5 + (-5) = x + 0$$
$$x = -12. \qquad \text{Using the identity property of 0}$$

The equation $x = -12$ is equivalent to the equation $x + 5 = -7$ by the addition principle, so the solution of $x = -12$ is the solution of $x + 5 = -7$.

It is obvious that the solution of $x = -12$ is the number -12. To check the answer in the original equation, we substitute.

Check:
$$\begin{array}{c|c} x + 5 = -7 \\ \hline -12 + 5 & -7 \\ -7 \stackrel{?}{=} -7 & \text{TRUE} \qquad -7 = -7 \text{ is true.} \end{array}$$

The solution of the original equation is -12.

▶ **TRY EXERCISE** 11

In Example 3, note that because we added the *opposite*, or *additive inverse*, of 5, the left side of the equation simplified to x plus the *additive identity*, 0, or simply x. These steps effectively replaced the 5 on the left with a 0. To solve $x + a = b$ for x, we add $-a$ to (or subtract a from) both sides.

EXAMPLE 4

Solve: $-6.5 = y - 8.4$.

SOLUTION   The variable is on the right side this time. We can isolate y by adding 8.4 to each side:

$$-6.5 = y - 8.4 \qquad y - 8.4 \text{ can be regarded as } y + (-8.4).$$
$$-6.5 + 8.4 = y - 8.4 + 8.4 \qquad \text{Using the addition principle: Adding 8.4 to both sides "eliminates" } -8.4 \text{ on the right side.}$$
$$1.9 = y. \qquad y - 8.4 + 8.4 = y + (-8.4) + 8.4 = y + 0 = y$$

Check:
$$\begin{array}{c|c} -6.5 = y - 8.4 \\ \hline -6.5 & 1.9 - 8.4 \\ -6.5 \stackrel{?}{=} -6.5 & \text{TRUE} \qquad -6.5 = -6.5 \text{ is true.} \end{array}$$

The solution is 1.9.

▶ **TRY EXERCISE** 15

Note that the equations $a = b$ and $b = a$ have the same meaning. Thus $-6.5 = y - 8.4$ could have been rewritten as $y - 8.4 = -6.5$.

The Multiplication Principle

A second principle for solving equations concerns multiplying. Suppose a and b are equal. If a and b are multiplied by some number c, then ac and bc will also be equal.

> **The Multiplication Principle**
>
> For any real numbers a, b, and c, with $c \neq 0$,
> $$a = b \quad \text{is equivalent to} \quad a \cdot c = b \cdot c.$$

EXAMPLE 5

Solve: $\frac{5}{4}x = 10$.

SOLUTION   We can multiply both sides by any nonzero number we like. Since $\frac{4}{5}$ is the reciprocal of $\frac{5}{4}$, we decide to multiply both sides by $\frac{4}{5}$:

$$\frac{5}{4}x = 10$$

$$\frac{4}{5} \cdot \frac{5}{4}x = \frac{4}{5} \cdot 10 \qquad \text{Using the multiplication principle: Multiplying both sides by } \frac{4}{5} \text{ "eliminates" the } \frac{5}{4} \text{ on the left.}$$

$$1 \cdot x = 8 \qquad \text{Simplifying}$$

$$x = 8. \qquad \text{Using the identity property of 1}$$

Check:
$$\frac{5}{4}x = 10$$
$$\begin{array}{c|c} \frac{5}{4} \cdot 8 & 10 \\ \frac{40}{4} & \end{array} \qquad \text{Think of 8 as } \frac{8}{1}.$$
$$10 \stackrel{?}{=} 10 \quad \text{TRUE} \qquad 10 = 10 \text{ is true.}$$

The solution is 8.

TRY EXERCISE ▶ 49

In Example 5, to get x alone, we multiplied by the *reciprocal*, or *multiplicative inverse* of $\frac{5}{4}$. We then simplified the left-hand side to x times the *multiplicative identity*, 1, or simply x. These steps effectively replaced the $\frac{5}{4}$ on the left with 1.

Because division is the same as multiplying by a reciprocal, the multiplication principle also tells us that we can "divide both sides by the same nonzero number." That is,

$$\text{if } a = b, \text{ then } \frac{1}{c} \cdot a = \frac{1}{c} \cdot b \quad \text{and} \quad \frac{a}{c} = \frac{b}{c} \quad (\text{provided } c \neq 0).$$

In a product like $3x$, the multiplier 3 is called the **coefficient**. *When the coefficient of the variable is an integer or a decimal, it is usually easiest to solve an equation by dividing on both sides. When the coefficient is in fraction notation, it is usually easiest to multiply by the reciprocal.*

EXAMPLE 6

Solve: **(a)** $-4x = 9$; **(b)** $-x = 5$; **(c)** $\dfrac{2y}{9} = \dfrac{8}{3}$.

SOLUTION

a) In $-4x = 9$, the coefficient of x is an integer, so we *divide* on both sides:

$$\frac{-4x}{-4} = \frac{9}{-4} \qquad \text{Using the multiplication principle: Dividing both sides by } -4 \text{ is the same as multiplying by } -\frac{1}{4}.$$

$$1 \cdot x = -\frac{9}{4} \qquad \text{Simplifying}$$

$$x = -\frac{9}{4}. \qquad \text{Using the identity property of 1}$$

Check:

$$\frac{-4x = 9}{-4\left(-\frac{9}{4}\right) \,\Big|\, 9}$$

$$9 \overset{?}{=} 9 \quad \text{TRUE} \qquad 9 = 9 \text{ is true.}$$

The solution is $-\frac{9}{4}$.

b) To solve an equation like $-x = 5$, remember that when an expression is multi-plied or divided by -1, its sign is changed. Here we divide both sides by -1 to change the sign of $-x$:

$$-x = 5 \qquad \text{Note that } -x = -1 \cdot x.$$

$$\frac{-x}{-1} = \frac{5}{-1} \qquad \begin{array}{l}\text{Dividing both sides by } -1. \text{ (Multiplying by } -1 \text{ would also}\\ \text{work. Note that the reciprocal of } -1 \text{ is } -1.)\end{array}$$

$$x = -5. \qquad \text{Note that } \frac{-x}{-1} \text{ is the same as } \frac{x}{1}.$$

Check:

$$\frac{-x = 5}{-(-5) \,\Big|\, 5}$$

$$5 \overset{?}{=} 5 \quad \text{TRUE} \qquad 5 = 5 \text{ is true.}$$

The solution is -5.

c) To solve an equation like $\frac{2y}{9} = \frac{8}{3}$, we rewrite the left-hand side as $\frac{2}{9} \cdot y$ and then use the multiplication principle, multiplying by the reciprocal of $\frac{2}{9}$:

$$\frac{2y}{9} = \frac{8}{3}$$

$$\frac{2}{9} \cdot y = \frac{8}{3} \qquad \text{Rewriting } \frac{2y}{9} \text{ as } \frac{2}{9} \cdot y$$

$$\frac{9}{2} \cdot \frac{2}{9} \cdot y = \frac{9}{2} \cdot \frac{8}{3} \qquad \text{Multiplying both sides by } \frac{9}{2}$$

$$1y = \frac{3 \cdot \cancel{3} \cdot \cancel{2} \cdot 4}{\cancel{2} \cdot \cancel{3}} \qquad \text{Removing a factor equal to 1: } \frac{3 \cdot 2}{2 \cdot 3} = 1$$

$$y = 12.$$

Check:

$$\frac{2y}{9} = \frac{8}{3}$$

$$\frac{\dfrac{2 \cdot 12}{9}}{} \,\Bigg|\, \frac{8}{3}$$

$$\frac{24}{9}$$

$$\frac{8}{3} \overset{?}{=} \frac{8}{3} \quad \text{TRUE} \qquad \frac{8}{3} = \frac{8}{3} \text{ is true.}$$

The solution is 12.

 **TRY EXERCISE** 35

Selecting the Correct Approach

It is important that you be able to determine which principle should be used to solve a particular equation.

EXAMPLE 7

Solve: **(a)** $-\frac{2}{3} + x = \frac{5}{2}$; **(b)** $12.6 = 3t$.

SOLUTION

a) To undo addition of $-\frac{2}{3}$, we subtract $-\frac{2}{3}$ from both sides. Subtracting $-\frac{2}{3}$ is the same as adding $\frac{2}{3}$.

$$-\frac{2}{3} + x = \frac{5}{2}$$
$$-\frac{2}{3} + x + \frac{2}{3} = \frac{5}{2} + \frac{2}{3} \qquad \text{Using the addition principle}$$
$$x = \frac{5}{2} + \frac{2}{3}$$
$$x = \frac{5}{2} \cdot \frac{3}{3} + \frac{2}{3} \cdot \frac{2}{2} \qquad \text{Finding a common denominator}$$
$$x = \frac{15}{6} + \frac{4}{6}$$
$$x = \frac{19}{6}$$

Check:

$$\begin{array}{c|c} -\frac{2}{3} + x = \frac{5}{2} \\ \hline -\frac{2}{3} + \frac{19}{6} & \frac{5}{2} \\ -\frac{4}{6} + \frac{19}{6} & \\ \frac{15}{6} & \\ \frac{5 \cdot 3}{2 \cdot 3} & \\ \frac{5}{2} \overset{?}{=} \frac{5}{2} & \text{TRUE} \end{array}$$

$-\frac{2}{3} \cdot \frac{2}{2} = -\frac{4}{6}$

Removing a factor equal to 1: $\frac{3}{3} = 1$

$\frac{5}{2} = \frac{5}{2}$ is true.

The solution is $\frac{19}{6}$.

b) To undo multiplication by 3, we either divide both sides by 3 or multiply both sides by $\frac{1}{3}$:

$$12.6 = 3t$$
$$\frac{12.6}{3} = \frac{3t}{3} \qquad \text{Using the multiplication principle}$$
$$4.2 = t. \qquad \text{Simplifying}$$

Check:

$$\begin{array}{c|c} 12.6 = 3t \\ \hline 12.6 & 3(4.2) \\ 12.6 \overset{?}{=} 12.6 & \text{TRUE} \end{array}$$

$12.6 = 12.6$ is true.

The solution is 4.2.

TRY EXERCISES 59 and 67

STUDY SKILLS

Seeking Help?

A variety of resources are available to help make studying easier and more enjoyable.

- **Textbook supplements.** See the preface for a description of the supplements for this textbook: the *Student's Solutions Manual*, a complete set of videos on DVD, MathXL tutorial exercises on CD, and complete online courses in MathXL and MyMathLab.

- **Your college or university.** Your own college or university probably has resources to enhance your math learning: a learning lab or tutoring center, study skills workshops or group tutoring sessions tailored for the course you are taking, or a bulletin board or network where you can locate the names of experienced private tutors.

- **Your instructor.** Find out your instructor's office hours and make it a point to visit when you need additional help. Many instructors also welcome student e-mail.

2.1 EXERCISE SET

Concept Reinforcement *For each of Exercises 1–6, match the statement with the most appropriate choice from the column on the right.*

1. _____ The equations $x + 3 = 7$ and $6x = 24$

2. _____ The expressions $3(x - 2)$ and $3x - 6$

3. _____ A replacement that makes an equation true

4. _____ The role of 9 in $9ab$

5. _____ The principle used to solve $\frac{2}{3} \cdot x = -4$

6. _____ The principle used to solve $\frac{2}{3} + x = -4$

a) Coefficient

b) Equivalent expressions

c) Equivalent equations

d) The multiplication principle

e) The addition principle

f) Solution

For each of Exercises 7–10, match the equation with the step, from the column on the right, that would be used to solve the equation.

7. $6x = 30$ a) Add 6 to both sides.

8. $x + 6 = 30$ b) Subtract 6 from both sides.

9. $\frac{1}{6}x = 30$ c) Multiply both sides by 6.

10. $x - 6 = 30$ d) Divide both sides by 6.

To the student and the instructor: The ▶ TRY EXERCISES *for examples are indicated by a shaded block on the exercise number. Complete step-by-step solutions for these exercises appear online at www.pearsonhighered.com/ bittingerellenbogen.*

Solve using the addition principle. Don't forget to check!

11. $x + 10 = 21$ 12. $t + 9 = 47$

13. $y + 7 = -18$ 14. $x + 12 = -7$

15. $-6 = y + 25$ 16. $-5 = x + 8$

17. $x - 18 = 23$ 18. $x - 19 = 16$

19. $12 = -7 + y$ 20. $15 = -8 + z$

21. $-5 + t = -11$ 22. $-6 + y = -21$

23. $r + \frac{1}{3} = \frac{8}{3}$ 24. $t + \frac{3}{8} = \frac{5}{8}$

25. $x - \frac{3}{5} = -\frac{7}{10}$ 26. $x - \frac{2}{3} = -\frac{5}{6}$

27. $x - \frac{5}{6} = \frac{7}{8}$ 28. $y - \frac{3}{4} = \frac{5}{6}$

29. $-\frac{1}{5} + z = -\frac{1}{4}$ 30. $-\frac{2}{3} + y = -\frac{3}{4}$

31. $m - 2.8 = 6.3$ 32. $y - 5.3 = 8.7$

33. $-9.7 = -4.7 + y$ 34. $-7.8 = 2.8 + x$

Solve using the multiplication principle. Don't forget to check!

35. $8a = 56$ 36. $6x = 72$

37. $84 = 7x$ 38. $45 = 9t$

39. $-x = 38$ 40. $100 = -x$

Aha! 41. $-t = -8$ 42. $-68 = -r$

43. $-7x = 49$ 44. $-4x = 36$

45. $-1.3a = -10.4$ 46. $-3.4t = -20.4$

47. $\frac{y}{8} = 11$ 48. $\frac{a}{4} = 13$

49. $\frac{4}{5}x = 16$ 50. $\frac{3}{4}x = 27$

51. $\frac{-x}{6} = 9$ 52. $\frac{-t}{4} = 8$

53. $\frac{1}{9} = \frac{z}{-5}$ 54. $\frac{2}{7} = \frac{x}{-3}$

Aha! 55. $-\frac{3}{5}r = -\frac{3}{5}$ 56. $-\frac{2}{5}y = -\frac{4}{15}$

57. $\frac{-3r}{2} = -\frac{27}{4}$ 58. $\frac{5x}{7} = -\frac{10}{14}$

Solve. The icon ▤ indicates an exercise designed to give practice using a calculator.

59. $4.5 + t = -3.1$ 60. $\frac{3}{4}x = 18$

61. $-8.2x = 20.5$ 62. $t - 7.4 = -12.9$

63. $x - 4 = -19$ 64. $y - 6 = -14$

65. $t - 3 = -8$ 66. $t - 9 = -8$

67. $-12x = 14$ 68. $-15x = 20$

69. $48 = -\frac{3}{8}y$ 70. $14 = t + 27$

71. $a - \frac{1}{6} = -\frac{2}{3}$ 72. $-\frac{x}{6} = \frac{2}{9}$

73. $-24 = \frac{8x}{5}$ 74. $\frac{1}{5} + y = -\frac{3}{10}$

75. $-\frac{4}{3}t = -12$ 76. $\frac{17}{35} = -x$

▤ 77. $-483.297 = -794.053 + t$

▤ 78. $-0.2344x = 2028.732$

79. When solving an equation, how do you determine what number to add, subtract, multiply, or divide by on both sides of that equation?

80. What is the difference between equivalent expressions and equivalent equations?

Skill Review

To prepare for Section 2.2, review the rules for order of operations (Section 1.8).

Simplify. [1.8]

81. $3 \cdot 4 - 18$

82. $14 - 2(7 - 1)$

83. $16 \div (2 - 3 \cdot 2) + 5$

84. $12 - 5 \cdot 2^3 + 4 \cdot 3$

Synthesis

85. To solve $-3.5 = 14t$, Anita adds 3.5 to both sides. Will this form an equivalent equation? Will it help solve the equation? Explain.

86. Explain why it is not necessary to state a subtraction principle: For any real numbers a, b, and c, $a = b$ is equivalent to $a - c = b - c$.

Solve for x. Assume a, c, m ≠ 0.

87. $mx = 11.6m$

88. $x - 4 + a = a$

89. $cx + 5c = 7c$

90. $c \cdot \dfrac{21}{a} = \dfrac{7cx}{2a}$

91. $7 + |x| = 30$

92. $ax - 3a = 5a$

93. If $t - 3590 = 1820$, find $t + 3590$.

94. If $n + 268 = 124$, find $n - 268$.

95. Lydia makes a calculation and gets an answer of 22.5. On the last step, she multiplies by 0.3 when she should have divided by 0.3. What should the correct answer be?

96. Are the equations $x = 5$ and $x^2 = 25$ equivalent? Why or why not?

2.2 Using the Principles Together

Applying Both Principles ∎ Combining Like Terms ∎ Clearing Fractions and Decimals ∎ Contradictions and Identities

An important strategy for solving new problems is to find a way to make a new problem look like a problem that we already know how to solve. This is precisely the approach taken in this section. You will find that the last steps of the examples in this section are nearly identical to the steps used for solving the equations of Section 2.1. What is new in this section appears in the early steps of each example.

Applying Both Principles

The addition and multiplication principles, along with the laws discussed in Chapter 1, are our tools for solving equations. In this section, we will find that the sequence and manner in which these tools are used is especially important.

EXAMPLE 1   Solve: $5 + 3x = 17$.

SOLUTION   Were we to evaluate $5 + 3x$, the rules for the order of operations direct us to *first* multiply by 3 and *then* add 5. Because of this, we can isolate $3x$ and then x by reversing these operations: We first subtract 5 from both sides and then divide both sides by 3. Our goal is an equivalent equation of the form $x = a$.

$$5 + 3x = 17$$
$$5 + 3x - 5 = 17 - 5 \quad \text{Using the addition principle: subtracting 5 from both sides (adding } -5)$$
$$5 + (-5) + 3x = 12 \quad \text{Using a commutative law. Try to perform this step mentally.}$$

Isolate the x-term. $\quad 3x = 12 \quad$ Simplifying

$$\frac{3x}{3} = \frac{12}{3} \quad \text{Using the multiplication principle: dividing both sides by 3 (multiplying by } \tfrac{1}{3})$$

Isolate x. $\quad x = 4 \quad$ Simplifying

Check:
$$\begin{array}{c|c} 5 + 3x = 17 \\ \hline 5 + 3 \cdot 4 & 17 \\ 5 + 12 & \\ 17 \stackrel{?}{=} 17 & \text{TRUE} \end{array}$$

We use the rules for order of operations: Find the product, $3 \cdot 4$, and then add.

The solution is 4.

TRY EXERCISE 7

EXAMPLE **2**

Solve: $\frac{4}{3}x - 7 = 1$.

SOLUTION In $\frac{4}{3}x - 7$, we multiply first and then subtract. To reverse these steps, we first add 7 and then either divide by $\frac{4}{3}$ or multiply by $\frac{3}{4}$.

$$\frac{4}{3}x - 7 = 1$$

$$\frac{4}{3}x - 7 + 7 = 1 + 7 \qquad \text{Adding 7 to both sides}$$

$$\frac{4}{3}x = 8$$

$$\frac{3}{4} \cdot \frac{4}{3}x = \frac{3}{4} \cdot 8 \qquad \text{Multiplying both sides by } \frac{3}{4}$$

$$\left. \begin{array}{l} 1 \cdot x = \dfrac{3 \cdot 4 \cdot 2}{4} \\[2mm] x = 6 \end{array} \right\} \qquad \text{Simplifying}$$

Check:

$$\begin{array}{r|l} \frac{4}{3}x - 7 = 1 \\ \hline \frac{4}{3} \cdot 6 - 7 & 1 \\ 8 - 7 & \\ 1 \overset{?}{=} 1 & \text{TRUE} \end{array}$$

The solution is 6.

TRY EXERCISE 27

EXAMPLE **3**

Solve: $45 - t = 13$.

SOLUTION We have

$$45 - t = 13$$

$$45 - t - 45 = 13 - 45 \qquad \text{Subtracting 45 from both sides}$$

$$\left. \begin{array}{l} 45 + (-t) + (-45) = 13 - 45 \\ 45 + (-45) + (-t) = 13 - 45 \end{array} \right\} \qquad \text{Try to do these steps mentally.}$$

$$-t = -32 \qquad \text{Try to go directly to this step.}$$

$$(-1)(-t) = (-1)(-32) \qquad \begin{array}{l}\text{Multiplying both sides by } -1 \\ \text{(Dividing by } -1 \text{ would also} \\ \text{work.)}\end{array}$$

$$t = 32.$$

Check:

$$\begin{array}{r|l} 45 - t = 13 \\ \hline 45 - 32 & 13 \\ 13 \overset{?}{=} 13 & \text{TRUE} \end{array}$$

The solution is 32.

TRY EXERCISE 19

As our skills improve, certain steps can be streamlined.

EXAMPLE 4   Solve: $16.3 - 7.2y = -8.18$.

SOLUTION   We have

$$16.3 - 7.2y = -8.18$$

$$16.3 - 7.2y - 16.3 = -8.18 - 16.3 \qquad \text{Subtracting 16.3 from both sides}$$

$$-7.2y = -24.48 \qquad \text{Simplifying}$$

$$\frac{-7.2y}{-7.2} = \frac{-24.48}{-7.2} \qquad \text{Dividing both sides by } -7.2$$

$$y = 3.4. \qquad \text{Simplifying}$$

Check:

$$\begin{array}{c|c}
16.3 - 7.2y = -8.18 \\
\hline
16.3 - 7.2(3.4) & -8.18 \\
16.3 - 24.48 & \\
-8.18 \overset{?}{=} -8.18 & \text{TRUE}
\end{array}$$

The solution is 3.4.

TRY EXERCISE 23

Combining Like Terms

If like terms appear on the same side of an equation, we combine them and then solve. Should like terms appear on both sides of an equation, we can use the addition principle to rewrite all like terms on one side.

EXAMPLE 5   Solve.

a) $3x + 4x = -14$ b) $-x + 5 = -8x + 6$

c) $6x + 5 - 7x = 10 - 4x + 7$ d) $2 - 5(x + 5) = 3(x - 2) - 1$

SOLUTION

a) $3x + 4x = -14$

$$7x = -14 \qquad \text{Combining like terms}$$

$$\frac{7x}{7} = \frac{-14}{7} \qquad \text{Dividing both sides by 7}$$

$$x = -2 \qquad \text{Simplifying}$$

The check is left to the student. The solution is -2.

b) To solve $-x + 5 = -8x + 6$, we must first write only variable terms on one side and only constant terms on the other. This can be done by subtracting 5 from both sides, to get all constant terms on the right, and adding $8x$ to both sides, to get all variable terms on the left.

Isolate variable terms on one side and constant terms on the other side.

$$-x + 5 = -8x + 6$$

$$-x + 8x + 5 = -8x + 8x + 6 \qquad \text{Adding } 8x \text{ to both sides}$$

$$7x + 5 = 6 \qquad \text{Simplifying}$$

$$7x + 5 - 5 = 6 - 5 \qquad \text{Subtracting 5 from both sides}$$

$$7x = 1 \qquad \text{Combining like terms}$$

$$\frac{7x}{7} = \frac{1}{7} \qquad \text{Dividing both sides by 7}$$

$$x = \frac{1}{7}$$

The check is left to the student. The solution is $\frac{1}{7}$.

Most graphing calculators have a TABLE feature that lists the value of a variable expression for different choices of x. For example, to evaluate $6x + 5 - 7x$ for $x = 0, 1, 2, \ldots,$ we first use $\boxed{\text{Y=}}$ to enter $6x + 5 - 7x$ as y_1. We then use $\boxed{\text{2ND}}$ $\boxed{\text{TBLSET}}$ to specify TblStart $= 0$, ΔTbl $= 1$, and select AUTO twice. By pressing $\boxed{\text{2ND}}$ $\boxed{\text{TABLE}}$, we can generate a table in which the value of $6x + 5 - 7x$ is listed for values of x starting at 0 and increasing by ones.

X	Y₁	
0	5	
1	4	
2	3	
3	2	
4	1	
5	0	
6	−1	

X = 0

1. Create the above table on your graphing calculator. Scroll up and down to extend the table.
2. Enter $10 - 4x + 7$ as y_2. Your table should now have three columns.
3. For what x-value is y_1 the same as y_2? Compare this with the solution of Example 5(c). Is this a reliable way to solve equations? Why or why not?

c)

$$6x + 5 - 7x = 10 - 4x + 7$$

$-x + 5 = 17 - 4x$	Combining like terms within each side
$-x + 5 + 4x = 17 - 4x + 4x$	Adding $4x$ to both sides
$5 + 3x = 17$	Simplifying. This is identical to Example 1.
$3x = 12$	Subtracting 5 from both sides
$\dfrac{3x}{3} = \dfrac{12}{3}$	Dividing both sides by 3
$x = 4$	

Check:

$$6x + 5 - 7x = 10 - 4x + 7$$

$$\begin{array}{c|c} 6 \cdot 4 + 5 - 7 \cdot 4 & 10 - 4 \cdot 4 + 7 \\ 24 + 5 - 28 & 10 - 16 + 7 \\ 1 & \overset{?}{=} 1 \end{array}$$

TRUE

The student can confirm that 4 checks and is the solution.

d)

$$2 - 5(x + 5) = 3(x - 2) - 1$$

$2 - 5x - 25 = 3x - 6 - 1$	Using the distributive law. This is now similar to part (c) above.
$-5x - 23 = 3x - 7$	Combining like terms on each side
$\left.\begin{array}{l} -5x - 23 + 7 = 3x \\ -23 + 7 = 3x + 5x \end{array}\right\}$	Adding 7 and $5x$ to both sides. This isolates the x-terms on one side and the constant terms on the other.
$-16 = 8x$	Simplifying
$\dfrac{-16}{8} = \dfrac{8x}{8}$	Dividing both sides by 8
$-2 = x$	This is equivalent to $x = -2$.

The student can confirm that -2 checks and is the solution.

⟩ **TRY EXERCISE** 39

Clearing Fractions and Decimals

Equations are generally easier to solve when they do not contain fractions or decimals. The multiplication principle can be used to "clear" fractions or decimals, as shown here.

Clearing Fractions	Clearing Decimals
$\frac{1}{2}x + 5 = \frac{3}{4}$	$2.3x + 7 = 5.4$
$4\left(\frac{1}{2}x + 5\right) = 4 \cdot \frac{3}{4}$	$10(2.3x + 7) = 10 \cdot 5.4$
$2x + 20 = 3$	$23x + 70 = 54$

In each case, the resulting equation is equivalent to the original equation, but easier to solve.

The easiest way to clear an equation of fractions is to multiply *both sides* of the equation by the smallest, or *least*, common denominator of the fractions in the equation.

EXAMPLE 6

Solve: **(a)** $\frac{2}{3}x - \frac{1}{6} = 2x$; **(b)** $\frac{2}{5}(3x + 2) = 8$.

SOLUTION

a) We multiply both sides by 6, the least common denominator of $\frac{2}{3}$ and $\frac{1}{6}$.

$$6\left(\frac{2}{3}x - \frac{1}{6}\right) = 6 \cdot 2x \qquad \text{Multiplying both sides by 6}$$

$$6 \cdot \frac{2}{3}x - 6 \cdot \frac{1}{6} = 6 \cdot 2x \longleftarrow$$

> **CAUTION!**   Be sure the distributive law is used to multiply *all* the terms by 6.

$$4x - 1 = 12x \qquad \text{Simplifying. Note that the fractions are cleared: } 6 \cdot \frac{2}{3} = 4, 6 \cdot \frac{1}{6} = 1, \text{ and } 6 \cdot 2 = 12.$$

$$-1 = 8x \qquad \text{Subtracting } 4x \text{ from both sides}$$

$$\frac{-1}{8} = \frac{8x}{8} \qquad \text{Dividing both sides by 8}$$

$$-\frac{1}{8} = x$$

The student can confirm that $-\frac{1}{8}$ checks and is the solution.

b) To solve $\frac{2}{5}(3x + 2) = 8$, we can multiply both sides by $\frac{5}{2}$ (or divide by $\frac{2}{5}$) to "undo" the multiplication by $\frac{2}{5}$ on the left side.

$$\frac{5}{2} \cdot \frac{2}{5}(3x + 2) = \frac{5}{2} \cdot 8 \qquad \text{Multiplying both sides by } \frac{5}{2}$$

$$3x + 2 = 20 \qquad \text{Simplifying; } \frac{5}{2} \cdot \frac{2}{5} = 1 \text{ and } \frac{5}{2} \cdot \frac{8}{1} = 20$$

$$3x = 18 \qquad \text{Subtracting 2 from both sides}$$

$$x = 6 \qquad \text{Dividing both sides by 3}$$

The student can confirm that 6 checks and is the solution.

> **TRY EXERCISE** 69

   To clear an equation of decimals, we count the greatest number of decimal places in any one number. If the greatest number of decimal places is 1, we multiply both sides by 10; if it is 2, we multiply by 100; and so on. This procedure is the same as multiplying by the least common denominator after converting the decimals to fractions.

EXAMPLE 7

Solve: $16.3 - 7.2y = -8.18$.

STUDENT NOTES ———

Compare the steps of Examples 4 and 7. Note that although the two approaches differ, they yield the same solution. Whenever you can use two approaches to solve a problem, try to do so, both as a check and as a valuable learning experience.

SOLUTION   The greatest number of decimal places in any one number is *two*. Multiplying by 100 will clear all decimals.

$$100(16.3 - 7.2y) = 100(-8.18) \qquad \text{Multiplying both sides by 100}$$

$$100(16.3) - 100(7.2y) = 100(-8.18) \qquad \text{Using the distributive law}$$

$$1630 - 720y = -818 \qquad \text{Simplifying}$$

$$-720y = -818 - 1630 \qquad \text{Subtracting 1630 from both sides}$$

$$-720y = -2448 \qquad \text{Combining like terms}$$

$$y = \frac{-2448}{-720} \qquad \text{Dividing both sides by } -720$$

$$y = 3.4$$

In Example 4, the same solution was found without clearing decimals. Finding the same answer in two ways is a good check. The solution is 3.4.

> **TRY EXERCISE** 75

An Equation-Solving Procedure

1. Use the multiplication principle to clear any fractions or decimals. (This is optional, but can ease computations. See Examples 6 and 7.)
2. If necessary, use the distributive law to remove parentheses. Then combine like terms on each side. (See Example 5.)
3. Use the addition principle, as needed, to isolate all variable terms on one side. Then combine like terms. (See Examples 1–7.)
4. Multiply or divide to solve for the variable, using the multiplication principle. (See Examples 1–7.)
5. Check all possible solutions in the original equation. (See Examples 1–4.)

Contradictions and Identities

All of the equations we have examined so far had a solution. Equations that are true for some values (solutions), but not for others, are called **conditional equations**. Equations that have no solution, such as $x + 1 = x + 2$, are called **contradictions**. If, when solving an equation, we obtain an equation that is false for any value of x, the equation has no solution.

EXAMPLE **8** Solve: $3x - 5 = 3(x - 2) + 4$.

SOLUTION

$$3x - 5 = 3(x - 2) + 4$$
$$3x - 5 = 3x - 6 + 4 \qquad \text{Using the distributive law}$$
$$3x - 5 = 3x - 2 \qquad \text{Combining like terms}$$
$$-3x + 3x - 5 = -3x + 3x - 2 \qquad \text{Using the addition principle}$$
$$-5 = -2$$

Since the original equation is equivalent to $-5 = -2$, which is false regardless of the choice of x, the original equation has no solution. There is no solution of $3x - 5 = 3(x - 2) + 4$. The equation is a contradiction. It is *never* true.

> **TRY EXERCISE** 45

Some equations, like $x + 1 = x + 1$, are true for all replacements. Such an equation is called an **identity**.

EXAMPLE **9** Solve: $2x + 7 = 7(x + 1) - 5x$.

SOLUTION

$$2x + 7 = 7(x + 1) - 5x$$
$$2x + 7 = 7x + 7 - 5x \qquad \text{Using the distributive law}$$
$$2x + 7 = 2x + 7 \qquad \text{Combining like terms}$$

The equation $2x + 7 = 2x + 7$ is true regardless of the replacement for x, so all real numbers are solutions. Note that $2x + 7 = 2x + 7$ is equivalent to $2x = 2x$, $7 = 7$, or $0 = 0$. All real numbers are solutions and the equation is an identity.

> **TRY EXERCISE** 33

EXERCISE SET

↪ *Concept Reinforcement* *In each of Exercises 1–6,* match the equation with an equivalent equation from the column on the right that could be the next step in finding a solution.

1. ___ $3x - 1 = 7$

2. ___ $4x + 5x = 12$

3. ___ $6(x - 1) = 2$

4. ___ $7x = 9$

5. ___ $4x = 3 - 2x$

6. ___ $8x - 5 = 6 - 2x$

a) $6x - 6 = 2$

b) $4x + 2x = 3$

c) $3x = 7 + 1$

d) $8x + 2x = 6 + 5$

e) $9x = 12$

f) $x = \frac{9}{7}$

Solve and check. Label any contradictions or identities.

7. $2x + 9 = 25$

8. $3x - 11 = 13$

9. $6z + 5 = 47$

10. $5z + 2 = 57$

11. $7t - 8 = 27$

12. $6x - 5 = 2$

13. $3x - 9 = 1$

14. $5x - 9 = 41$

15. $8z + 2 = -54$

16. $4x + 3 = -21$

17. $-37 = 9t + 8$

18. $-39 = 1 + 5t$

19. $12 - t = 16$

20. $9 - t = 21$

21. $-6z - 18 = -132$

22. $-7x - 24 = -129$

23. $5.3 + 1.2n = 1.94$

24. $6.4 - 2.5n = 2.2$

25. $32 - 7x = 11$

26. $27 - 6x = 99$

27. $\frac{3}{5}t - 1 = 8$

28. $\frac{2}{3}t - 1 = 5$

29. $6 + \frac{7}{2}x = -15$

30. $6 + \frac{5}{4}x = -4$

31. $-\dfrac{4a}{5} - 8 = 2$

32. $-\dfrac{8a}{7} - 2 = 4$

33. $4x = x + 3x$

34. $-3z + 8z = 45$

35. $4x - 6 = 6x$

36. $5x - x = x + 3x$

37. $2 - 5y = 26 - y$

38. $6x - 5 = 7 + 2x$

39. $7(2a - 1) = 21$

40. $5(3 - 3t) = 30$

Aha! 41. $11 = 11(x + 1)$

42. $9 = 3(5x - 2)$

43. $2(3 + 4m) - 6 = 48$

44. $3(5 + 3m) - 8 = 7$

45. $3(x + 4) = 3(x - 1)$

46. $5(x - 7) = 3(x - 2) + 2x$

47. $2r + 8 = 6r + 10$

48. $3b - 2 = 7b + 4$

49. $6x + 3 = 2x + 3$

50. $5y + 3 = 2y + 15$

51. $5 - 2x = 3x - 7x + 25$

52. $10 - 3x = x - 2x + 40$

53. $7 + 3x - 6 = 3x + 5 - x$

54. $5 + 4x - 7 = 4x - 2 - x$

55. $4y - 4 + y + 24 = 6y + 20 - 4y$

56. $5y - 10 + y = 7y + 18 - 5y$

57. $4 + 7x = 7(x + 1)$

58. $3(t + 2) + t = 2(3 + 2t)$

59. $19 - 3(2x - 1) = 7$

60. $5(d + 4) = 7(d - 2)$

61. $7(5x - 2) = 6(6x - 1)$

62. $5(t + 1) + 8 = 3(t - 2) + 6$

63. $2(3t + 1) - 5 = t - (t + 2)$

64. $4x - (x + 6) = 5(3x - 1) + 8$

65. $2(7 - x) - 20 = 7x - 3(2 + 3x)$

66. $5(x - 7) = 3(x - 2) + 2x$

67. $19 - (2x + 3) = 2(x + 3) + x$

68. $13 - (2c + 2) = 2(c + 2) + 3c$

Clear fractions or decimals, solve, and check.

69. $\frac{2}{3} + \frac{1}{4}t = 2$

70. $-\frac{5}{6} + x = -\frac{1}{2} - \frac{2}{3}$

71. $\frac{2}{3} + 4t = 6t - \frac{2}{15}$

72. $\frac{1}{2} + 4m = 3m - \frac{5}{2}$

73. $\frac{1}{3}x + \frac{2}{5} = \frac{4}{5} + \frac{3}{5}x - \frac{2}{3}$

74. $1 - \frac{2}{3}y = \frac{9}{5} - \frac{1}{5}y + \frac{3}{5}$

75. $2.1x + 45.2 = 3.2 - 8.4x$

76. $0.91 - 0.2z = 1.23 - 0.6z$

77. $0.76 + 0.21t = 0.96t - 0.49$

78. $1.7t + 8 - 1.62t = 0.4t - 0.32 + 8$

79. $\frac{2}{5}x - \frac{3}{2}x = \frac{3}{4}x + 3$

80. $\frac{5}{16}y + \frac{3}{8}y = 2 + \frac{1}{4}y$

81. $\frac{1}{3}(2x - 1) = 7$

82. $\frac{1}{5}(4x - 1) = 7$

83. $\frac{3}{4}(3t - 4) = 15$

84. $\frac{3}{2}(2x + 5) = -\frac{15}{2}$

85. $\frac{1}{6}\left(\frac{3}{4}x - 2\right) = -\frac{1}{5}$

86. $\frac{2}{3}\left(\frac{7}{8} - 4x\right) - \frac{5}{8} = \frac{3}{8}$

87. $0.7(3x + 6) = 1.1 - (x - 3)$

88. $0.9(2x - 8) = 4 - (x + 5)$

89. $a + (a - 3) = (a + 2) - (a + 1)$

90. $0.8 - 4(b - 1) = 0.2 + 3(4 - b)$

91. Tyla solves $45 - t = 13$ (Example 3) by adding $t - 13$ to both sides. Is this approach preferable to the one used in Example 3? Why or why not?

92. Why must the rules for the order of operations be understood before solving the equations in this section?

Skill Review

To prepare for Section 2.3, review evaluating algebraic expressions (Section 1.8).

Evaluate. [1.8]

93. $3 - 5a$, for $a = 2$

94. $12 \div 4 \cdot t$, for $t = 5$

95. $7x - 2x$, for $x = -3$

96. $t(8 - 3t)$, for $t = -2$

Synthesis

97. What procedure would you use to solve an equation like $0.23x + \frac{17}{3} = -0.8 + \frac{3}{4}x$? Could your procedure be streamlined? If so, how?

98. Dave is determined to solve $3x + 4 = -11$ by first using the multiplication principle to "eliminate" the 3. How should he proceed and why?

Solve. Label any contradictions or identities.

99. $8.43x - 2.5(3.2 - 0.7x) = -3.455x + 9.04$

100. $0.008 + 9.62x - 42.8 = 0.944x + 0.0083 - x$

101. $-2[3(x - 2) + 4] = 4(5 - x) - 2x$

102. $0 = t - (-6) - (-7t)$

103. $2x(x + 5) - 3(x^2 + 2x - 1) = 9 - 5x - x^2$

104. $x(x - 4) = 3x(x + 1) - 2(x^2 + x - 5)$

105. $9 - 3x = 2(5 - 2x) - (1 - 5x)$

Aha! **106.** $[7 - 2(8 \div (-2))]x = 0$

107. $\dfrac{x}{14} - \dfrac{5x + 2}{49} = \dfrac{3x - 4}{7}$

108. $\dfrac{5x + 3}{4} + \dfrac{25}{12} = \dfrac{5 + 2x}{3}$

109. $2\{9 - 3[-2x - 4]\} = 12x + 42$

110. $-9t + 2 = 2 - 9t - 5(8 \div 4(1 + 3^4))$

COLLABORATIVE CORNER

Step-by-Step Solutions

Focus: Solving linear equations

Time: 20 minutes

Group size: 3

In general, there is more than one correct sequence of steps for solving an equation. This makes it important that you write your steps clearly and logically so that others can follow your approach.

ACTIVITY

1. Each group member should select a different one of the following equations and, on a fresh sheet of paper, perform the first step of the solution.

$$4 - 3(x - 3) = 7x + 6(2 - x)$$
$$5 - 7[x - 2(x - 6)] = 3x + 4(2x - 7) + 9$$
$$4x - 7[2 + 3(x - 5) + x] = 4 - 9(-3x - 19)$$

2. Pass the papers around so that the second and third steps of each solution are performed by the other two group members. Before writing, make sure that the previous step is correct. If a mistake is discovered, return the problem to the person who made the mistake for repairs. Continue passing the problems around until all equations have been solved.

3. Each group should reach a consensus on what the three solutions are and then compare their answers to those of other groups.

2.3 Formulas

Evaluating Formulas ▪ Solving for a Variable

Many applications of mathematics involve relationships among two or more quantities. An equation that represents such a relationship will use two or more letters and is known as a **formula**. Most of the letters in this book are variables, but some are constants. For example, c in $E = mc^2$ represents the speed of light.

Evaluating Formulas

EXAMPLE 1   *Event promotion.*   Event promoters use the formula

$$p = \frac{1.2x}{s}$$

to determine a ticket price p for an event with x dollars of expenses and s anticipated ticket sales. Grand Events expects expenses for an upcoming concert to be $80,000 and anticipates selling 4000 tickets. What should the ticket price be?

Source: *The Indianapolis Star, 2/27/03*

SOLUTION   We substitute 80,000 for x and 4000 for s in the formula and calculate p:

$$p = \frac{1.2x}{s} = \frac{1.2(80,000)}{4000} = 24.$$

The ticket price should be $24.

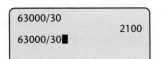 TRY EXERCISE   1

Solving for a Variable

In the Northeast, the formula $B = 30a$ is used to determine the minimum furnace output B, in British thermal units (Btu's), for a well-insulated home with a square feet of flooring. Suppose that a contractor has an extra furnace and wants to determine the size of the largest (well-insulated) house in which it can be used. The contractor can substitute the amount of the furnace's output in Btu's—say, 63,000—for B, and then solve for a:

$$63,000 = 30a \qquad \text{Replacing } B \text{ with } 63,000$$
$$2100 = a. \qquad \text{Dividing both sides by 30}$$

The home should have no more than 2100 ft^2 of flooring.

Were these calculations to be performed for a variety of furnaces, the contractor would find it easier to first solve $B = 30a$ for a, and *then* substitute values for B. Solving for a variable can be done in much the same way that we solved equations in Sections 2.1 and 2.2.

EXAMPLE   2

Solve for a: $B = 30a$.

SOLUTION   We have

$$B = 30\overset{\downarrow}{a} \qquad \text{We want this letter alone.}$$
$$\frac{B}{30} = a. \qquad \text{Dividing both sides by 30}$$

The equation $a = B/30$ gives a quick, easy way to determine the floor area of the largest (well-insulated) house that a furnace supplying B Btu's could heat.

TRY EXERCISE   9

To see how solving a formula is just like solving an equation, compare the following. In (A), we solve as usual; in (B), we show steps but do not simplify; and in (C), we *cannot* simplify because a, b, and c are unknown.

A. $5x + 2 = 12$

$5x = 12 - 2$

$5x = 10$

$x = \dfrac{10}{5} = 2$

B. $5x + 2 = 12$

$5x = 12 - 2$

$x = \dfrac{12 - 2}{5}$

C. $ax + b = c$

$ax = c - b$

$x = \dfrac{c - b}{a}$

TECHNOLOGY CONNECTION

Suppose that after calculating $63{,}000 \div 30$, we wish to find $72{,}000 \div 30$. Pressing **2ND** **(ENTRY)** gives the following.

```
63000/30
                2100
63000/30█
```

Moving the cursor left, we can change 63,000 to 72,000 and press **ENTER**.

```
63000/30
                2100
72000/30
                2400
```

1. Verify the work above and then use **2ND** **(ENTRY)** to find $72{,}000 \div 90$.

EXAMPLE 3

Circumference of a circle. The formula $C = 2\pi r$ gives the *circumference C* of a circle with radius r. Solve for r.

SOLUTION   The **circumference** is the distance around a circle.

| Given a radius r, we can use this equation to find a circle's circumference C. | $C = 2\pi r$ | We want this variable alone. |

$$\frac{C}{2\pi} = \frac{2\pi r}{2\pi}$$ Dividing both sides by 2π

| Given a circle's circumference C, we can use this equation to find the radius r. | $\frac{C}{2\pi} = r$ |

TRY EXERCISE 13

EXAMPLE 4

Solve for y: $3x - 4y = 10$.

SOLUTION   There is one term that contains y, so we begin by isolating that term on one side of the equation.

$$3x - 4y = 10$$ We want this variable alone.

$$-4y = 10 - 3x$$ Subtracting $3x$ from both sides

$$-\tfrac{1}{4}(-4y) = -\tfrac{1}{4}(10 - 3x)$$ Multiplying both sides by $-\tfrac{1}{4}$

$$y = -\tfrac{10}{4} + \tfrac{3}{4}x$$ Multiplying using the distributive law

$$y = -\tfrac{5}{2} + \tfrac{3}{4}x$$ Simplifying the fraction

TRY EXERCISE 33

EXAMPLE 5

Nutrition. The number of calories K needed each day by a moderately active woman who weighs w pounds, is h inches tall, and is a years old, can be estimated using the formula

$$K = 917 + 6(w + h - a).*$$

Solve for w.

SOLUTION   We reverse the order in which the operations occur on the right side:

We want w alone.

$$K = 917 + 6(w + h - a)$$

$$K - 917 = 6(w + h - a)$$ Subtracting 917 from both sides

$$\frac{K - 917}{6} = w + h - a$$ Dividing both sides by 6

$$\frac{K - 917}{6} + a - h = w.$$ Adding a and subtracting h on both sides

This formula can be used to estimate a woman's weight, if we know her age, height, and caloric needs.

TRY EXERCISE 43

*Based on information from M. Parker (ed.), *She Does Math!* (Washington, D.C.: Mathematical Association of America, 1995), p. 96.

The above steps are similar to those used in Section 2.2 to solve equations. We use the addition and multiplication principles just as before. An important differ-ence that we will see in the next example is that we will sometimes need to factor.

> **To Solve a Formula for a Given Variable**
> 1. If the variable for which you are solving appears in a fraction, use the multiplication principle to clear fractions.
> 2. Isolate the term(s), with the variable for which you are solving on one side of the equation.
> 3. If two or more terms contain the variable for which you are solving, factor the variable out.
> 4. Multiply or divide to solve for the variable in question.

We can also solve for a letter that represents a constant.

EXAMPLE 6   *Surface area of a right circular cylinder.*   The formula $A = 2\pi rh + 2\pi r^2$ gives the surface area A of a right circular cylinder of height h and radius r. Solve for π.

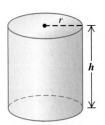

SOLUTION   We have

$$A = 2\pi rh + 2\pi r^2 \qquad \text{We want this letter alone.}$$

$$A = \pi(2rh + 2r^2) \qquad \text{Factoring}$$

$$\frac{A}{2rh + 2r^2} = \pi. \qquad \text{Dividing both sides by } 2rh + 2r^2, \text{ or multiplying both sides by } 1/(2rh + 2r^2)$$

We can also write this as

$$\pi = \frac{A}{2rh + 2r^2}.$$

TRY EXERCISE 47

> *CAUTION!*   Had we performed the following steps in Example 6, we would *not* have solved for π:
>
> $$A = 2\pi rh + 2\pi r^2 \qquad \text{We want } \pi \text{ alone.}$$
>
> $$A - 2\pi r^2 = 2\pi rh \qquad \text{Subtracting } 2\pi r^2 \text{ from both sides}$$
>
> $$\text{Two occurrences of } \pi$$
>
> $$\frac{A - 2\pi r^2}{2rh} = \pi. \qquad \text{Dividing both sides by } 2rh$$
>
> The mathematics of each step is correct, but because π occurs on both sides of the formula, *we have not solved the formula for π*. Remember that the letter being solved for should be alone on one side of the equation, with no occur-rence of that letter on the other side!

2.3 EXERCISE SET

For Extra Help
MathXL

PRACTICE

WATCH

DOWNLOAD

1. *Outdoor concerts.* The formula $d = 344t$ can be used to determine how far d, in meters, sound travels through room-temperature air in t seconds. At a large concert, fans near the back of the crowd experienced a 0.9-sec time lag between the time each word was pronounced on stage (as shown on large video monitors) and the time the sound reached their ears. How far were these fans from the stage?

2. *Furnace output.* Contractors in the Northeast use the formula $B = 30a$ to determine the minimum furnace output B, in British thermal units (Btu's), for a well-insulated house with a square feet of flooring. Determine the minimum furnace output for an 1800-ft² house that is well insulated.
   Source: U.S. Department of Energy

3. *College enrollment.* At many colleges, the number of "full-time-equivalent" students f is given by
   $$f = \frac{n}{15},$$
   where n is the total number of credits for which students have enrolled in a given semester. Determine the number of full-time-equivalent students on a campus in which students registered for a total of 21,345 credits.

4. *Distance from a storm.* The formula $M = \frac{1}{5}t$ can be used to determine how far M, in miles, you are from lightning when its thunder takes t seconds to reach your ears. If it takes 10 sec for the sound of thunder to reach you after you have seen the lightning, how far away is the storm?

5. *Federal funds rate.* The Federal Reserve Board sets a target f for the federal funds rate, that is, the interest rate that banks charge each other for overnight borrowing of Federal funds. This target rate can be estimated by
   $$f = 8.5 + 1.4(I - U),$$
   where I is the core inflation rate over the previous 12 months and U is the seasonally adjusted unemployment rate. If core inflation is 0.025 and unemployment is 0.044, what should the federal funds rate be?
   Source: Greg Mankiw, Harvard University, www.gregmankiw .blogspot.com/2006/06/what-would-alan-do.html

6. *Calorie density.* The calorie density D, in calories per ounce, of a food that contains c calories and weighs w ounces is given by
   $$D = \frac{c}{w}.^*$$
   Eight ounces of fat-free milk contains 84 calories. Find the calorie density of fat-free milk.

7. *Absorption of ibuprofen.* When 400 mg of the painkiller ibuprofen is swallowed, the number of milligrams n in the bloodstream t hours later (for $0 \le t \le 6$) is estimated by
   $$n = 0.5t^4 + 3.45t^3 - 96.65t^2 + 347.7t.$$
   How many milligrams of ibuprofen remain in the blood 1 hr after 400 mg has been swallowed?

8. *Size of a league schedule.* When all n teams in a league play every other team twice, a total of N games are played, where
   $$N = n^2 - n.$$
   If a soccer league has 7 teams and all teams play each other twice, how many games are played?

In Exercises 9–48, solve each formula for the indicated letter.

9. $A = bh$, for b
   (Area of parallelogram with base b and height h)

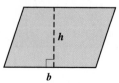

10. $A = bh$, for h

11. $d = rt$, for r
    (A distance formula, where d is distance, r is speed, and t is time)

Source: Nutrition Action Healthletter, March 2000, p. 9. Center for Science in the Public Interest, Suite 300; 1875 Connecticut Ave NW, Washington, D.C. 20008.

12. $d = rt$, for t

13. $I = Prt$, for P
(Simple-interest formula, where I is interest, P is principal, r is interest rate, and t is time)

14. $I = Prt$, for t

15. $H = 65 - m$, for m
(To determine the number of heating degree days H for a day with m degrees Fahrenheit as the average temperature)

16. $d = h - 64$, for h
(To determine how many inches d above average an h-inch-tall woman is)

17. $P = 2l + 2w$, for l
(Perimeter of a rectangle of length l and width w)

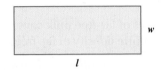

18. $P = 2l + 2w$, for w

19. $A = \pi r^2$, for π
(Area of a circle with radius r)

20. $A = \pi r^2$, for r^2

21. $A = \frac{1}{2}bh$, for h
(Area of a triangle with base b and height h)

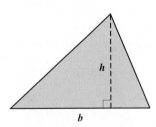

22. $A = \frac{1}{2}bh$, for b

23. $E = mc^2$, for c^2
(A relativity formula from physics)

24. $E = mc^2$, for m

25. $Q = \dfrac{c + d}{2}$, for d **26.** $Q = \dfrac{p - q}{2}$, for p

27. $A = \dfrac{a + b + c}{3}$, for b **28.** $A = \dfrac{a + b + c}{3}$, for c

29. $w = \dfrac{r}{f}$, for r
(To compute the wavelength w of a musical note with frequency f and speed of sound r)

30. $M = \dfrac{A}{s}$, for A
(To compute the Mach number M for speed A and speed of sound s)

31. $F = \dfrac{9}{5}C + 32$, for C
(To convert the Celsius temperature C to the Fahrenheit temperature F)

32. $M = \dfrac{5}{9}n + 18$, for n

33. $2x - y = 1$, for y

34. $3x - y = 7$, for y

35. $2x + 5y = 10$, for y

36. $3x + 2y = 12$, for y

37. $4x - 3y = 6$, for y

38. $5x - 4y = 8$, for y

39. $9x + 8y = 4$, for y

40. $x + 10y = 2$, for y

41. $3x - 5y = 8$, for y

42. $7x - 6y = 7$, for y

43. $z = 13 + 2(x + y)$, for x

44. $A = 115 + \dfrac{1}{2}(p + s)$, for s

45. $t = 27 - \dfrac{1}{4}(w - l)$, for l

46. $m = 19 - 5(x - n)$, for n

47. $A = at + bt$, for t

48. $S = rx + sx$, for x

49. *Area of a trapezoid.* The formula
$$A = \tfrac{1}{2}ah + \tfrac{1}{2}bh$$
can be used to find the area A of a trapezoid with bases a and b and height h. Solve for h. (*Hint*: First clear fractions.)

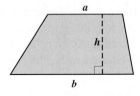

60. *Compounding interest.* The formula

$$A = P + Prt$$

is used to find the amount A in an account when simple interest is added to an investment of P dollars (see Exercise 13). Solve for P.

61. *Chess rating.* The formula

$$R = r + \frac{400(W - L)}{N}$$

is used to establish a chess player's rating R after that player has played N games, won W of them, and lost L of them. Here r is the average rating of the opponents. Solve for L.

Source: The U.S. Chess Federation

62. *Angle measure.* The angle measure S of a sector of a circle is given by

$$S = \frac{360A}{\pi r^2},$$

where r is the radius, A is the area of the sector, and S is in degrees. Solve for r^2.

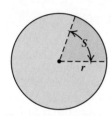

63. Naomi has a formula that allows her to convert Celsius temperatures to Fahrenheit temperatures. She needs a formula for converting Fahrenheit temperatures to Celsius temperatures. What advice can you give her?

64. Under what circumstances would it be useful to solve $d = rt$ for r? (See Exercise 11.)

Skill Review

Review simplifying expressions (Sections 1.6, 1.7, and 1.8).

Perform the indicated operations.

65. $-2 + 5 - (-4) - 17$ [1.6]

66. $-98 \div \frac{1}{2}$ [1.7]

67. $4.2(-11.75)(0)$ [1.7]

68. $(-2)^5$ [1.8]

Simplify. [1.8]

69. $20 \div (-4) \cdot 2 - 3$

70. $5|8 - (2 - 7)|$

Synthesis

61. The equations

$$P = 2l + 2w \quad \text{and} \quad w = \frac{P}{2} - l$$

are equivalent formulas involving the perimeter P, length l, and width w of a rectangle. Devise a problem for which the second of the two formulas would be more useful.

62. While solving $2A = ah + bh$ for h, Lea writes $\frac{2A - ah}{b} = h$. What is her mistake?

63. The Harris–Benedict formula gives the number of calories K needed each day by a moderately active man who weighs w kilograms, is h centimeters tall, and is a years old as

$$K = 21.235w + 7.75h - 10.54a + 102.3.$$

If Janos is moderately active, weighs 80 kg, is 190 cm tall, and needs to consume 2852 calories a day, how old is he?

64. *Altitude and temperature.* Air temperature drops about 1° Celsius (C) for each 100-m rise above ground level, up to 12 km. If the ground level temperature is t°C, find a formula for the temperature T at an elevation of h meters.

Source: *A Sourcebook of School Mathematics*, Mathematical Association of America, 1980

65. *Surface area of a cube.* The surface area A of a cube with side s is given by

$$A = 6s^2.$$

If a cube's surface area is 54 in², find the volume of the cube.

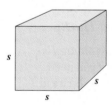

66. *Weight of a fish.* An ancient fisherman's formula for estimating the weight of a fish is

$$w = \frac{lg^2}{800},$$

where w is the weight, in pounds, l is the length, in inches, and g is the girth (distance around the midsection), in inches. Estimate the girth of a 700-lb yellow tuna that is 8 ft long.

67. *Dosage size.* Clark's rule for determining the size of a particular child's medicine dosage c is

$$c = \frac{w}{a} \cdot d,$$

where w is the child's weight, in pounds, and d is the usual adult dosage for an adult weighing a pounds. Solve for a.

Source: Olsen, June Looby, et al., *Medical Dosage Calculations.* Redwood City, CA: Addison-Wesley, 1995

Solve each formula for the given letter.

68. $\dfrac{y}{z} \div \dfrac{z}{t} = 1$, for y

69. $ac = bc + d$, for c

70. $qt = r(s + t)$, for t

71. $3a = c - a(b + d)$, for a

72. *Furnace output.* The formula

$$B = 50a$$

is used in New England to estimate the minimum furnace output B, in Btu's, for an old, poorly insulated house with a square feet of flooring. Find an equation for determining the number of Btu's saved by insulating an old house. (*Hint:* See Exercise 2.)

73. Revise the formula in Exercise 63 so that a man's weight in pounds (2.2046 lb = 1 kg) and his height in inches (0.3937 in. = 1 cm) are used.

74. Revise the formula in Example 5 so that a woman's weight in kilograms (2.2046 lb = 1 kg) and her height in centimeters (0.3937 in. = 1 cm) are used.

2.4   Applications with Percent

Converting Between Percent Notation and Decimal Notation   ●   Solving Percent Problems

Percent problems arise so frequently in everyday life that most often we are no even aware of them. In this section, we will solve some real-world percent prob lems. Before doing so, however, we need to review a few basics.

Converting Between Percent Notation and Decimal Notation

Nutritionists recommend that no more than 30% of the calories in a person's die come from fat. This means that of every 100 calories consumed, no more than 3 should come from fat. Thus, 30% is a ratio of 30 to 100.

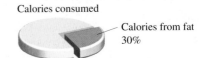

Calories consumed

Calories from fat 30%

The percent symbol % means "per hundred." We can regard the percen symbol as part of a name for a number. For example,

30% is defined to mean $\dfrac{30}{100}$,   or $30 \times \dfrac{1}{100}$,   or 30×0.01.

Percent Notation

$n\%$ means $\dfrac{n}{100}$,   or $n \times \dfrac{1}{100}$,   or $n \times 0.01$.

EXAMPLE 1 Convert to decimal notation: **(a)** 78%; **(b)** 1.3%.

SOLUTION

a) $78\% = 78 \times 0.01$ Replacing % with $\times\ 0.01$

      $= 0.78$

b) $1.3\% = 1.3 \times 0.01$ Replacing % with $\times\ 0.01$

      $= 0.013$

> TRY EXERCISE 19

As shown above, multiplication by 0.01 simply moves the decimal point two places to the left.

To convert from percent notation to decimal notation, move the decimal point two places to the left and drop the percent symbol.

EXAMPLE 2 Convert the percent notation in the following sentence to decimal notation: Only 20% of teenagers get 8 hr of sleep a night.

Source: National Sleep Foundation

SOLUTION

    $20\% = 20.0\%$ $0.20.0$ $20\% = 0.20$, or simply 0.2

        Move the decimal point two places to the left.

> TRY EXERCISE 11

The procedure used in Examples 1 and 2 can be reversed:

    $0.38 = 38 \times 0.01$

      $= 38\%$.   Replacing $\times\ 0.01$ with %

To convert from decimal notation to percent notation, move the decimal point two places to the right and write a percent symbol.

EXAMPLE 3 Convert to percent notation: **(a)** 1.27; **(b)** $\frac{1}{4}$; **(c)** 0.3.

SOLUTION

a) We first move the decimal point two places to the right: 1.27.

and then write a % symbol: 127% This is the same as multiplying 1.27 by 100 and writing %.

b) Note that $\frac{1}{4} = 0.25$. We move the decimal point two places to the right: 0.25.

and then write a % symbol: 25% Multiplying by 100 and writing %

c) We first move the decimal point two places to the right (recall that $0.3 = 0.30$): 0.30.

and then write a % symbol: 30% Multiplying by 100 and writing %

> TRY EXERCISE 33

Solving Percent Problems

In solving percent problems, we first *translate* the problem to an equation. Then we *solve* the equation using the techniques discussed in Sections 2.1–2.3. The key words in the translation are as follows.

> ### Key Words in Percent Translations
>
> **"Of"** translates to " $\cdot$ " or " $\times$ ". **"Is"** or **"Was"** translates to " $=$ ".
> **"What"** translates to a variable. **"%"** translates to " $\times \frac{1}{100}$ " or " $\times 0.01$ ".

EXAMPLE 4

What is 11% of 49?

SOLUTION

$$\text{Translate:} \quad \underset{\downarrow}{\text{What}} \quad \underset{\downarrow}{\text{is}} \quad \underset{\downarrow}{\text{11\%}} \quad \underset{\downarrow}{\text{of}} \quad \underset{\downarrow}{\text{49?}}$$

$$a \quad = \quad 0.11 \quad \cdot \quad 49 \qquad \text{"of" means multiply;}$$
$$11\% = 0.11$$

$$a = 5.39$$

Thus, 5.39 is 11% of 49. The answer is 5.39.

STUDENT NOTES

A way of checking answers is by estimating as follows:

$$11\% \times 49 \approx 10\% \times 50$$
$$= 0.10 \times 50 = 5.$$

Since 5 is close to 5.39, our answer is reasonable.

TRY EXERCISE 51

EXAMPLE 5

3 is 16 percent of what?

SOLUTION

$$\text{Translate:} \quad \underset{\downarrow}{3} \quad \underset{\downarrow}{\text{is}} \quad \underset{\downarrow}{\underbrace{\text{16 percent}}} \quad \underset{\downarrow}{\text{of}} \quad \underset{\downarrow}{\text{what?}}$$

$$3 \quad = \quad 0.16 \quad \cdot \quad y$$

$$\frac{3}{0.16} = y \qquad \text{Dividing both sides by 0.16}$$

$$18.75 = y$$

Thus, 3 is 16 percent of 18.75. The answer is 18.75.

TRY EXERCISE 47

EXAMPLE 6

What percent of $50 is $34?

SOLUTION

$$\text{Translate:} \quad \underset{\downarrow}{\underbrace{\text{What percent}}} \quad \underset{\downarrow}{\text{of}} \quad \underset{\downarrow}{\$50} \quad \underset{\downarrow}{\text{is}} \quad \underset{\downarrow}{\$34?}$$

$$n \quad \cdot \quad 50 \quad = \quad 34$$

$$n = \frac{34}{50} \qquad \text{Dividing both sides by 50}$$

$$n = 0.68 = 68\% \qquad \text{Converting to percent notation}$$

Thus, $34 is 68% of $50. The answer is 68%.

TRY EXERCISE 43

Examples 4–6 represent the three basic types of percent problems. Note tha
in all the problems, the following quantities are present:

- a percent, expressed in decimal notation in the translation,
- a base amount, indicated by "of" in the problem, and
- a percentage of the base, found by multiplying the base times the percent.

EXAMPLE 7

STUDENT NOTES

Always look for connections between examples. Here you should
look for similarities between
Examples 4 and 7 as well as between Examples 5 and 8 and
between Examples 6 and 9.

Discount stores.   In 2006, there were 300 million people in the United States, and 62.2% of them lived within 5 mi of a Wal-Mart store. How many lived within 5 mi of a Wal-Mart store?

Source: *The Wall Street Journal, 9/25/06*

SOLUTION   We first reword and then translate. We let a = the number of people in the United States, in millions, who live within 5 mi of a Wal-Mart store.

Rewording: What   is   62.2%   of   300?

Translating: a =   0.622   ×   300

The letter is by itself. To solve the equation, we need only multiply:

$$a = 0.622 \times 300 = 186.6.$$

Since 186.6 million is 62.2% of 300 million, we have found that in 2006 about 186.6 million people in the United States lived within 5 mi of a Wal-Mart store.

TRY EXERCISE 65

EXAMPLE 8

College enrollment.   About 1.6 million students who graduated from high school in 2006 were attending college in the fall of 2006. This was 66% of all 2006 high school graduates. How many students graduated from high school in 2006?

Source: U.S. Bureau of Labor Statistics

SOLUTION   Before translating the problem to mathematics, we reword and let S represent the total number of students, in millions, who graduated from high school in 2006.

Rewording: 1.6   is   66%   of S.

Translating: 1.6   =   0.66   · S

$$\frac{1.6}{0.66} = S$$ Dividing both sides by 0.66

$$2.4 \approx S$$ The symbol $\approx$ means *is approximately equal to.*

About 2.4 million students graduated from high school in 2006.

TRY EXERCISE 67

EXAMPLE 9

Automobile prices.   Recently, Harken Motors reduced the price of a Flex Fuel 2007 Chevy Impala from the manufacturer's suggested retail price (MSRP) of $20,830 to $18,955.

a) What percent of the MSRP does the sale price represent?

b) What is the percent of discount?

SOLUTION

a) We reword and translate, using n for the unknown percent.

Rewording: What percent   of   20,830   is   18,955?

Translating: n ·   20,830   =   18,955

$$n = \frac{18,955}{20,830}$$ Dividing both sides by 20,830

$$n \approx 0.91 = 91\%$$ Converting to percent notation

The sale price is about 91% of the MSRP.

b) Since the original price of $20,830 represents 100% of the MSRP, the sale price represents a discount of $(100 - 91)\%$, or 9%.

   Alternatively, we could find the amount of discount and then calculate the percent of discount:

   Amount of discount: $20,830 - $18,955 = $1875.

   Rewording: <u>What percent</u>   of   20,830   is   1875?

   Translating: n $\cdot$ 20,830 $=$ 1875

$$n = \frac{1875}{20,830}$$ Dividing both sides by 20,830

$$n \approx 0.09 = 9\%$$ Converting to percent notation

Again we find that the percent of discount is 9%.   **TRY EXERCISE** ▸ 69

2.4	**EXERCISE SET**	*For Extra Help*

☞ **Concept Reinforcement**   *In each of Exercises 1–10, match the question with the most appropriate translation from the column on the right. Some choices are used more than once.*

1. ____ What percent of 57 is 23?

2. ____ What percent of 23 is 57?

3. ____ 23 is 57% of what number?

4. ____ 57 is 23% of what number?

5. ____ 57 is what percent of 23?

6. ____ 23 is what percent of 57?

7. ____ What is 23% of 57?

8. ____ What is 57% of 23?

9. ____ 23% of what number is 57?

10. ____ 57% of what number is 23?

a) $a = (0.57)23$

b) $57 = 0.23y$

c) $n \cdot 23 = 57$

d) $n \cdot 57 = 23$

e) $23 = 0.57y$

f) $a = (0.23)57$

Convert the percent notation in each sentence to decimal notation.

11. *Energy use.* Heating accounts for 49% of all household energy use.
Source: Chevron

12. *Energy use.* Water heating accounts for 15% of all household energy use.
Source: Chevron

13. *Drinking water.* Only 1% of the water on earth is suitable for drinking.
Source: www.drinktap.org

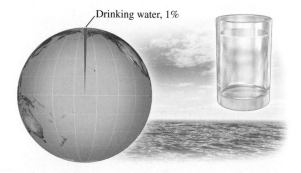
Drinking water, 1%

14. *Dehydration.* A 2% drop in water content of the body can affect one's ability to study mathematics.
Source: High Performance Nutrition

15. *College tuition.* Tuition and fees at two-year public colleges increased 4.1 percent in 2006.
Source: College Board 2006 tuition survey

16. *Plant species.* Trees make up about 3.5% of all plant species found in the United States.
Source: South Dakota Project Learning Tree

17. *Women in the workforce.* Women comprise 20% of all database administrators.
Source: U.S. Census Bureau

18. *Women in the workforce.* Women comprise 60% of all accountants and auditors.
Source: U.S. Census Bureau

Convert to decimal notation.

19. 6.25%   **20.** 8.375%

21. 0.2%   **22.** 0.8%

23. 175%   **24.** 250%

Convert the decimal notation in each sentence to percent notation.

25. *NASCAR fans.* Auto racing is the seventh most popular sport in the United States, with 0.38 of the adult population saying they are NASCAR fans.
Source: ESPN Sports poll

26. *Baseball fans.* Baseball is the second most popular sport in the United States, with 0.61 of the adult population saying they are baseball fans.
Source: ESPN Sports poll

27. *Food security.* The USDA defines food security as access to enough nutritious food for a healthy life. In 2005, 0.039 of U.S. households had very low food security.
Source: USDA

28. *Poverty rate.* In 2005, 0.199 of Americans age 65 and older were under the poverty level.
Source: www.census.gov

29. *Music downloads.* In 2006, 0.45 of Americans downloaded music.
Source: Solutions Research Group

30. *Music downloads.* In 2006, 0.23 of Americans paid to download a song.
Source: Solutions Research Group

31. *Composition of the sun.* The sun is 0.7 hydrogen.

32. *Jupiter's atmosphere.* The atmosphere of Jupiter is 0.1 helium.

Convert to percent notation.

33. 0.0009   **34.** 0.0056

35. 1.06   **36.** 1.08

37. 1.8   **38.** 2.4

39. $\frac{3}{5}$ **40.** $\frac{3}{4}$

41. $\frac{8}{25}$ **42.** $\frac{5}{8}$

Solve.

43. What percent of 76 is 19?

44. What percent of 125 is 30?

45. What percent of 150 is 39?

46. What percent of 360 is 270?

47. 14 is 30% of what number?

48. 54 is 24% of what number?

49. 0.3 is 12% of what number?

50. 7 is 175% of what number?

51. What number is 1% of one million?

52. What number is 35% of 240?

53. What percent of 60 is 75?

Aha! **54.** What percent of 70 is 70?

55. What is 2% of 40?

56. What is 40% of 2?

Aha! **57.** 25 is what percent of 50?

58. 0.8 is 2% of what number?

59. What percent of 69 is 23?

60. What percent of 40 is 9?

Riding bicycles. *There are 57 million Americans who ride a bicycle at least occasionally. The following circle graph shows the reasons people ride. In each of Exercises 61–64, determine the number of Americans who ride a bicycle for the given reason.*

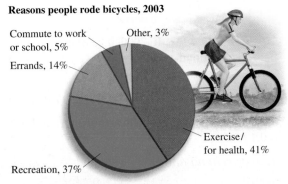

Reasons people rode bicycles, 2003

Commute to work or school, 5%
Other, 3%
Errands, 14%
Exercise/ for health, 41%
Recreation, 37%

Sources: U.S. Census Bureau; Bureau of Transportation Statistics

61. Commute to school or work

62. Run errands

63. Exercise for health

64. Recreation

65. *College graduation.* To obtain his bachelor's degree in nursing, Cody must complete 125 credit hours of instruction. If he has completed 60% of his requirement, how many credits did Cody complete?

66. *College graduation.* To obtain her bachelor's degree in journalism, Addy must complete 125 credit hours of instruction. If 20% of Addy's credit hours remain to be completed, how many credits does she still need to take?

67. *Batting average.* In the 2007 season, Magglio Ordonez of the Detroit Tigers had 216 hits. His batting average was 0.363, the highest in major league baseball for that season. This means that of the total number of at bats, 36.3% were hits. How many at bats did he have?
Source: ESPN

68. *Pass completions.* At one point in a recent season, Peyton Manning of the Indianapolis Colts had completed 357 passes. This was 62.5% of his attempts. How many attempts did he make?
Source: National Football League

69. *Tipping.* Trent left a $4 tip for a meal that cost $25.
   a) What percent of the cost of the meal was the tip?
   b) What was the total cost of the meal including the tip?

70. *Tipping.* Selena left a $12.76 tip for a meal that cost $58.
   a) What percent of the cost of the meal was the tip?
   b) What was the total cost of the meal including the tip?

71. *Crude oil imports.* In April 2007, crude oil imports to the United States averaged 10.2 million barrels per day. Of this total, 3.4 million came from Canada and Mexico. What percent of crude oil imports came from Canada and Mexico? What percent came from the rest of the world?
Source: Energy Information Administration

72. *Alternative-fuel vehicles.* Of the 550,000 alternative-fuel vehicles produced in the United States in 2004, 150,000 were E85 flexible-fuel vehicles. What percent of alternative-fuel vehicles used E85? What percent used other alternative fuels?
Source: Energy Information Administration

73. *Student loans.* Glenn takes out a subsidized federal Stafford loan for $2400. After a year, Glenn decides to pay off the interest, which is 7% of $2400. How much will he pay?

74. *Student loans.* To finance her community college education, LaTonya takes out a Stafford loan for $3500. After a year, LaTonya decides to pay off the interest, which is 8% of $3500. How much will she pay?

75. *Infant health.* In a study of 300 pregnant women with "good-to-excellent" diets, 95% had babies in good or excellent health. How many women in this group had babies in good or excellent health?

76. *Infant health.* In a study of 300 pregnant women with "poor" diets, 8% had babies in good or excellent health. How many women in this group had babies in good or excellent health?

77. *Cost of self-employment.* Because of additional taxes and fewer benefits, it has been estimated that a self-employed person must earn 20% more than a non–self-employed person performing the same task(s). If Tia earns $16 an hour working for Village

Copy, how much would she need to earn on her own for a comparable income?

78. Refer to Exercise 77. Rik earns $18 an hour working for Round Edge stairbuilders. How much would Rik need to earn on his own for a comparable income?

79. *Budget overruns.*   The Indianapolis Central Library expansion, begun in 2002, was expected to cost $103 million. By 2006, library officials estimated the cost would be $45 million over budget. By what percent did the actual cost exceed the initial estimate?
Source: *The Indianapolis Star*, 5/23/06

80. *Fastest swimmer.*   In 1990, Tom Jager of the United States set a world record by swimming 50 m at a rate of 2.29 m/s. Previously, the fastest swimming rate on record was 2.26 m/s, set in 1975 by David Holmes Edgar, also of the United States. Calculate the percentage by which the rate increased.
Source: *Guinness Book of World Records* 1975 and 1998

81. A bill at Officeland totaled $47.70. How much did the merchandise cost if the sales tax is 6%?

82. Marta's checkbook shows that she wrote a check for $987 for building materials. What was the price of the materials if the sales tax is 5%?

83. *Deducting sales tax.*   A tax-exempt school group received a bill of $157.41 for educational software. The bill incorrectly included sales tax of 6%. How much should the school group pay?

84. *Deducting sales tax.*   A tax-exempt charity received a bill of $145.90 for a sump pump. The bill incorrectly included sales tax of 5%. How much does the charity owe?

85. *Body fat.*   One author of this text exercises regularly at a local YMCA that recently offered a body-fat percentage test to its members. The device used measures the passage of a very low voltage of electricity through the body. The author's body-fat percentage was found to be 16.5% and he weighs 191 lb. What part, in pounds, of his body weight is fat?

86. *Areas of Alaska and Arizona.*   The area of Arizona is 19% of the area of Alaska. The area of Alaska is 586,400 mi². What is the area of Arizona?

87. *Direct mail.*   Only 2.15% of mailed ads lead to a sale or a response from customers. In 2006, businesses sent out 114 billion pieces of direct mail (catalogs, coupons, and so on). How many pieces of mail led to a response from customers?
Sources: Direct Marketing Association; U.S. Postal Service

88. *Kissing and colds.*   In a medical study, it was determined that if 800 people kiss someone else who has a cold, only 56 will actually catch the cold. What percent is this?

89. *Calorie content.*   Pepperidge Farm Light Style 7 Grain Bread® has 140 calories in a 3-slice serving. This is 15% less than the number of calories in a serving of regular bread. How many calories are in a serving of regular bread?

90. *Fat content.*   Peek Freans Shortbread Reduced Fat Cookies® contain 35 calories of fat in each serving. This is 40% less than the fat content in the leading imported shortbread cookie. How many calories of fat are in a serving of the leading shortbread cookie?

91. Campus Bookbuyers pays $30 for a book and sells it for $60. Is this a 100% markup or a 50% markup? Explain.

92. If Julian leaves a $12 tip for a $90 dinner, is he being generous, stingy, or neither? Explain.

Skill Review

To prepare for Section 2.5, review translating to algebraic expressions and equations (Section 1.1).

Translate to an algebraic expression or equation. [1.1]

93. Twice the length plus twice the width

94. 5% of $180

95. 5 fewer than the number of points Tino scored

96. 15 plus the product of 1.5 and x

97. The product of 10 and half of a

98. 10 more than three times a number

99. The width is 2 in. less than the length.

100. A number is four times as large as a second number.

Synthesis

101. How is the use of statistics in the following misleading?

    a) A business explaining new restrictions on sick leave cited a recent survey indicating that 40% of all sick days were taken on Monday or Friday.

    b) An advertisement urging summer installation of a security system quoted FBI statistics stating that over 26% of home burglaries occur between Memorial Day and Labor Day.

102. Erin is returning a tent that she bought during a 25%-off storewide sale that has ended. She is offered store credit for 125% of what she paid (not to be used on sale items). Is this fair to Erin? Why or why not?

103. The community of Bardville has 1332 left-handed females. If 48% of the community is female and 15% of all females are left-handed, how many people are in the community?

104. It has been determined that at the age of 10, a girl has reached 84.4% of her final adult height. Dana is 4 ft 8 in. at the age of 10. What will her final adult height be?

105. It has been determined that at the age of 15, a boy has reached 96.1% of his final adult height. Jaraan is 6 ft 4 in. at the age of 15. What will his final adult height be?

106. *Dropout rate.* Between 2002 and 2004, the high school dropout rate in the United States decreased from 105 to 103 per thousand. Calculate the percent by which the dropout rate decreased and use that percentage to estimate dropout rates for the United States in 2005 and in 2006.
Source: www.childrendsdatabank.org

107. *Photography.* A 6-in. by 8-in. photo is framed using a mat meant for a 5-in. by 7-in. photo. What percentage of the photo will be hidden by the mat?

108. Would it be better to receive a 5% raise and then, a year later, an 8% raise or the other way around? Why

109. Jorge is in the 30% tax bracket. This means that 30¢ of each dollar earned goes to taxes. Which would cost him the least: contributing $50 that is tax-deductible or contributing $40 that is not tax-deductible? Explain.

CORNER

Sales and Discounts

COLLABORATIVE

Focus: Applications and models using percent

Time: 15 minutes

Group size: 3

Materials: Calculators are optional.

Often a store will reduce the price of an item by a fixed percentage. When the sale ends, the items are returned to their original prices. Suppose a department store reduces all sporting goods 20%, all clothing 25%, and all electronics 10%.

ACTIVITY

1. Each group member should select one of the following items: a $50 basketball, an $80 jacket, or a $200 MP3 player. Fill in the first three columns of the first three rows of the chart below.

2. Apply the appropriate discount and determine the sale price of your item. Fill in the fourth column of the chart.

3. Next, find a multiplier that can be used to convert the sale price back to the original price and fill in the remaining column of the chart. Does this multiplier depend on the price of the item?

4. Working as a group, compare the results of part (3) for all three items. Then develop a formula for a multiplier that will restore a sale price to its original price, *p*, after a discount *r* has been applied. Complete the fourth row of the table and check that your formula will duplicate the results of part (3).

5. Use the formula from part (4) to find the multiplier that a store would use to return an item to its original price after a "30% off" sale expires. Fill in the last line on the chart.

6. Inspect the last column of your chart. How can these multipliers be used to determine the percentage by which a sale price is increased when a sale ends?

Original Price, *p*	Discount, *r*	1 − *r*	Sale Price	Multiplier to convert back to *p*
p	*r*	1 − *r*		
	0.30			

2.5   Problem Solving

Five Steps for Problem Solving   •   Applying the Five Steps

Probably the most important use of algebra is as a tool for problem solving. In this section, we develop a problem-solving approach that is used throughout the remainder of the text.

Five Steps for Problem Solving

In Section 2.4, we solved several real-world problems. To solve them, we first *familiarized* ourselves with percent notation. We then *translated* each problem into an equation, *solved* the equation, *checked* the solution, and *stated* the answer.

> ### Five Steps for Problem Solving in Algebra
> 1. *Familiarize* yourself with the problem.
> 2. *Translate* to mathematical language. (This often means writing an equation.)
> 3. *Carry out* some mathematical manipulation. (This often means *solving* an equation.)
> 4. *Check* your possible answer in the original problem.
> 5. *State* the answer clearly, using a complete English sentence.

Of the five steps, the most important is probably the first one: becoming familiar with the problem. Here are some hints for familiarization.

> ### To Become Familiar with a Problem
> 1. Read the problem carefully. Try to visualize the problem.
> 2. Reread the problem, perhaps aloud. Make sure you understand all important words and any symbols or abbreviations.
> 3. List the information given and the question(s) to be answered. Choose a variable (or variables) to represent the unknown and specify exactly what the variable represents. For example, let L = length in centimeters, d = distance in miles, and so on.
> 4. Look for similarities between the problem and other problems you have already solved. Ask yourself what type of problem this is.
> 5. Find more information. Look up a formula in a book, at a library, or online. Consult a reference librarian or an expert in the field.
> 6. Make a table that uses all the information you have available. Look for patterns that may help in the translation.
> 7. Make a drawing and label it with known and unknown information, using specific units if given.
> 8. Think of a possible answer and check the guess. Note the manner in which the guess is checked.

Applying the Five Steps

EXAMPLE 1

Bicycling.   After finishing college, Nico spent a week touring Tuscany, Italy, by bicycle. He biked 260 km from Pisa through Siena to Florence. At Siena, he had biked three times as far from Pisa as he would then bike to Florence. How far had he biked, and how far did he have left to go?

SOLUTION

1. **Familiarize.** It is often helpful to make a drawing. In this case, we can use a map of Nico's trip.

To gain familiarity, let's suppose that Nico has 50 km to go. Then he would have traveled three times 50 km, or 150 km, already. Since 50 km + 150 km = 200 km and 200 km < 260 km, we see that our guess is too small. Rather than guess again, we let

   d = the distance, in kilometers, from Siena to Florence

and

   $3d$ = the distance, in kilometers, from Siena to Pisa.

(We could also let x = the distance to Pisa; then the distance to Florence would be $\frac{1}{3}x$.)

2. **Translate.** The lengths of the two parts of the trip must add up to 260 km. This leads to our translation.

   Rewording: Distance to Florence   plus   distance to Pisa   is   260 km

   Translating: d + $3d$ =   260

3. **Carry out.** We solve the equation:

   $d + 3d = 260$

   $4d = 260$ Combining like terms

   $d = 65.$ Dividing both sides by 4

4. **Check.** As predicted in the *Familiarize* step, d is greater than 50 km. If d = 65 km, then $3d$ = 195 km. Since 65 km + 195 km = 260 km, we have a check.

5. **State.** At Siena, Nico had biked 195 km and had 65 km left to go to arrive in Florence.

TRY EXERCISE ▶ 9

Before we solve the next problem, we need to learn some additional terminology regarding integers.

The following are examples of **consecutive integers:** 16, 17, 18, 19, 20; and −31, −30, −29, −28. Note that consecutive integers can be represented in the form $x, x + 1, x + 2$, and so on.

The following are examples of **consecutive even integers:** 16, 18, 20, 22, 24 and −52, −50, −48, −46. Note that consecutive even integers can be represented in the form $x, x + 2, x + 4$, and so on.

The following are examples of **consecutive odd integers:** 21, 23, 25, 27, 29 and −71, −69, −67, −65. Note that consecutive odd integers can be also represented in the form $x, x + 2, x + 4$, and so on.

EXAMPLE **2**

Interstate mile markers. U.S. interstate highways post numbered markers at every mile to indicate location in case of an emergency. The sum of two consecutive mile markers on I-70 in Kansas is 559. Find the numbers on the markers.

Source: Federal Highway Administration, Ed Rotalewski

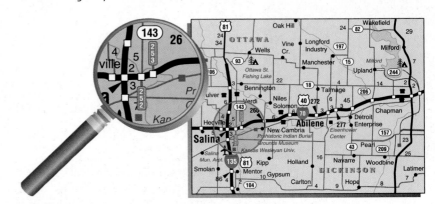

x	$x + 1$	Sum of x and $x + 1$
114	115	229
252	253	505
302	303	605

SOLUTION

1. **Familiarize.** The numbers on the mile markers are consecutive positive integers. Thus if we let $x =$ the smaller number, then $x + 1 =$ the larger number.

   To become familiar with the problem, we can make a table, as shown at left. First, we guess a value for x; then we find $x + 1$. Finally, we add the two numbers and check the sum.

   From the table, we see that the first marker will be between 252 and 302. We could continue guessing and solve the problem this way, but let's work on developing our algebra skills.

2. **Translate.** We reword the problem and translate as follows.

   Rewording: First integer plus second integer is 559.

   Translating: $x + (x + 1) = 559$

3. **Carry out.** We solve the equation:

   $$x + (x + 1) = 559$$
   $$2x + 1 = 559 \quad \text{Using an associative law and combining like terms}$$
   $$2x = 558 \quad \text{Subtracting 1 from both sides}$$
   $$x = 279. \quad \text{Dividing both sides by 2}$$

   If x is 279, then $x + 1$ is 280.

4. **Check.** Our possible answers are 279 and 280. These are consecutive positive integers and $279 + 280 = 559$, so the answers check.

5. **State.** The mile markers are 279 and 280.

TRY EXERCISE 13

EXAMPLE 3

Color printers.   Egads Computer Corporation rents a Xerox Phaser 8400 Color Laser Printer for $300 a month. A new art gallery is leasing a printer for a 2-month advertising campaign. The ink and paper for the brochures will cost an additional 21.5¢ per copy. If the gallery allots a budget of $3000, how many brochures can they print?

Source: egadscomputer.com

SOLUTION

1. **Familiarize.** Suppose that the art gallery prints 20,000 brochures. Then the cost is the monthly charges plus ink and paper cost, or

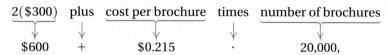

2($300)	plus	cost per brochure	times	number of brochures
$600	+	$0.215	·	20,000,

which is $4900. Our guess of 20,000 is too large, but we have familiarized ourselves with the way in which a calculation is made. Note that we convert 21.5¢ to $0.215 so that all information is in the same unit, dollars. We let c = the number of brochures that can be printed for $3000.

2. **Translate.** We reword the problem and translate as follows.

Rewording: Monthly cost   plus   ink and paper cost   is $3000.

Translating: 2($300)   +   ($0.215)c = $3000

3. **Carry out.** We solve the equation:

$$2(300) + 0.215c = 3000$$
$$600 + 0.215c = 3000$$
$$0.215c = 2400 \qquad \text{Subtracting 600 from both sides}$$
$$c = \frac{2400}{0.215} \qquad \text{Dividing both sides by 0.215}$$
$$c \approx 11{,}162. \qquad \text{We round } down \text{ to avoid going over the budget.}$$

4. **Check.** We check in the original problem. The cost for 11,162 brochures is 11,162($0.215) = $2399.83. The rental for 2 months is 2($300) = $600. The total cost is then $2399.83 + $600 = $2999.83, which is just under the amount that was allotted. Our answer is less than 20,000, as we expected from the *Familiarize* step.

5. **State.** The art gallery can make 11,162 brochures with the rental allotment of $3000.

TRY EXERCISE 37

EXAMPLE 4

Perimeter of NBA court.   The perimeter of an NBA basketball court is 288 ft. The length is 44 ft longer than the width. Find the dimensions of the court.

Source: National Basketball Association

SOLUTION

1. **Familiarize.** Recall that the perimeter of a rectangle is twice the length plus twice the width. Suppose the court were 30 ft wide. The length would then be 30 + 44, or 74 ft, and the perimeter would be 2 · 30 ft + 2 · 74 ft, or 208 ft. This shows that in order for the perimeter to be 288 ft, the width must exceed 30 ft. Instead of guessing again, we let w = the width of the court, in feet.

Since the court is "44 ft longer than it is wide," we let $w + 44 =$ the length of the court, in feet.

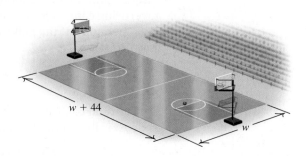

$w + 44$

w

2. **Translate.** To translate, we use $w + 44$ as the length and 288 as the perimeter. To double the length, $w + 44$, parentheses are essential.

Rewording: Twice the length plus twice the width is 288 ft.

Translating: $2(w + 44)$ $+$ $2w$ $=$ 288

3. **Carry out.** We solve the equation:

$$2(w + 44) + 2w = 288$$
$$2w + 88 + 2w = 288 \quad \text{Using the distributive law}$$
$$4w + 88 = 288 \quad \text{Combining like terms}$$
$$4w = 200$$
$$w = 50.$$

The dimensions appear to be $w = 50$ ft, and $l = w + 44 = 94$ ft.

4. **Check.** If the width is 50 ft and the length is 94 ft, then the court is 44 ft longer than it is wide. The perimeter is $2(50 \text{ ft}) + 2(94 \text{ ft}) = 100 \text{ ft} + 188 \text{ ft}$, or 288 ft as specified. We have a check.

5. **State.** An NBA court is 50 ft wide and 94 ft long.   **TRY EXERCISE** 25

STUDENT NOTES

Get in the habit of writing what each variable represents before writing an equation. In Example 4, you might write

width $= w$,

length $= w + 44$

before translating the problem to an equation. This step becomes more important as problems become more complex.

> *CAUTION!* Always be sure to answer the original problem completely. For instance, in Example 1 we needed to find *two* numbers: the distances from *each* city to Siena. Similarly, in Example 4 we needed to find two dimensions, not just the width. Be sure to label each answer with the proper unit.

EXAMPLE 5

Selling at an auction. Jared is selling his collection of Transformers at an auction. He wants to be left with $1150 after paying a seller's premium of 8% on the final bid (hammer price) for the collection. What must the hammer price be in order for him to clear $1150?

SOLUTION

1. **Familiarize.** Suppose the collection sells for $1200. The 8% seller's premium can be determined by finding 8% of $1200:

$$8\% \text{ of } \$1200 = 0.08(\$1200) = \$96.$$

Subtracting this premium from $1200 would leave Jared with

$$\$1200 - \$96 = \$1104.$$

This shows that in order for Jared to clear $1150, the collection must sell for more than $1200. We let $x =$ the hammer price, in dollars. Jared then must pay a seller's premium of $0.08x$.

2. **Translate.** We reword the problem and translate as follows.

Rewording: $\underbrace{\text{Hammer price}}$ less $\underbrace{\text{seller's premium}}$ is $\underbrace{\text{amount remaining.}}$

Translating: $\qquad x \qquad\quad - \qquad 0.08x \qquad = \qquad \$1150$

3. **Carry out.** We solve the equation:

$$x - 0.08x = 1150$$
$$1x - 0.08x = 1150$$
$$0.92x = 1150 \qquad$$ Combining like terms. Had we noted that after the premium has been paid, 92% remains, we could have begun with this equation.

$$x = \frac{1150}{0.92} \qquad$$ Dividing both sides by 0.92

$$x = 1250.$$

4. **Check.** To check, we first find 8% of $1250:

$$8\% \text{ of } \$1250 = 0.08(\$1250) = \$100. \qquad$$ This is the premium.

Next, we subtract the premium to find the remaining amount:

$$\$1250 - \$100 = \$1150.$$

Since, after Jared pays the seller's premium, he is left with $1150, our answer checks. Note that the $1250 hammer price is greater than $1200, as predicted in the *Familiarize* step.

5. **State.** Jared's collection must sell for $1250 in order for him to be left with $1150.

> **TRY EXERCISE** ▸ 7

EXAMPLE ▫ 6

Cross section of a roof.   In a triangular gable end of a roof, the angle of the peak is twice as large as the angle on the back side of the house. The measure of the angle on the front side is 20° greater than the angle on the back side. How large are the angles?

SOLUTION

1. **Familiarize.** We make a drawing. In this case, the measure of the back angle is x, the measure of the front angle is $x + 20$, and the measure of the peak angle is $2x$.

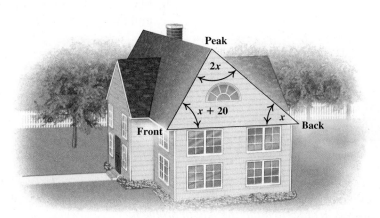

2. **Translate.** To translate, we need to recall that the sum of the measures of the angles in a triangle is 180°.

Rewording: Measure of   measure of   measure of
$\underbrace{\text{back angle}}$ + $\underbrace{\text{front angle}}$ + $\underbrace{\text{peak angle}}$ is 180°.

Translating: x + $(x + 20)$ + $2x$ =   180

3. **Carry out.** We solve:

$$x + (x + 20) + 2x = 180$$
$$4x + 20 = 180$$
$$4x = 160$$
$$x = 40.$$

The measures for the angles appear to be:

Back angle: $x = 40°$,
Front angle: $x + 20 = 40 + 20 = 60°$,
Peak angle: $2x = 2(40) = 80°$.

4. **Check.** Consider 40°, 60°, and 80°, as listed above. The measure of the front angle is 20° greater than the measure of the back angle, the measure of the peak angle is twice the measure of the back angle, and the sum is 180°. These numbers check.

5. **State.** The measures of the angles are 40°, 60°, and 80°.   **TRY EXERCISE** ▶ 31

We close this section with some tips to aid you in problem solving.

Problem-Solving Tips

1. The more problems you solve, the more your skills will improve.
2. Look for patterns when solving problems. Each time you study an example or solve an exercise, you may observe a pattern for problems found later.
3. Clearly define variables before translating to an equation.
4. Consider the dimensions of the variables and constants in the equation. The variables that represent length should all be in the same unit, those that represent money should all be in dollars or all in cents, and so on.
5. Make sure that units appear in the answer whenever appropriate and that you completely answer the original problem.

2.5   EXERCISE SET

Solve. Even though you might find the answer quickly in some other way, practice using the five-step problem-solving process in order to build the skill of problem solving.

1. Three less than twice a number is 19. What is the number?

2. Two fewer than ten times a number is 78. What is the number?

3. Five times the sum of 3 and twice some number is 70. What is the number?

4. Twice the sum of 4 and three times some number is 34. What is the number?

5. *Price of an iPod.*   Kyle paid $120 for an iPod nano during a 20%-off sale. What was the regular price?

6. *Price of sneakers.*   Amy paid $102 for a pair of New Balance 1122 running shoes during a 15%-off sale. What was the regular price?

7. *Price of a calculator.*   Kayla paid $137.80, including 6% tax, for her graphing calculator. How much did the calculator itself cost?

8. *Price of a printer.*   Laura paid $219.45, including 5% tax, for an all-in-one color printer. How much did the printer itself cost?

9. *Unicycling.*   In 2005, Ken Looi of New Zealand set a record by covering 235.3 mi in 24 hr on his unicycle. After 8 hr, he was approximately twice as far from the finish line as he was from the start. How far had he traveled?
Source: *Guinness World Records* 2007

10. *Sled-dog racing.*   The Iditarod sled-dog race extends for 1049 mi from Anchorage to Nome. If a musher is twice as far from Anchorage as from Nome, how many miles has the musher traveled?

The 1049-mile Iditarod race route

Nome   ALASKA

Anchorage

0   200
miles

11. *Indy Car racing.*   In April 2008, Danica Patrick won the Indy Japan 300 with a time of 01:51:02.6739 for the 300-mi race. At one point, Patrick was 20 mi closer to the finish than to the start. How far had Patrick traveled at that point?

12. *NASCAR racing.*   In June 2007, Carl Edwards won the Michigan 400 with a time of 2:42:5 for the 400-mi race. At one point, Edwards was 80 mi closer to the finish than to the start. How far had Edwards traveled at that point?

13. *Apartment numbers.*   The apartments in Erica's apartment house are consecutively numbered on each floor. The sum of her number and her next-door neighbor's number is 2409. What are the two numbers?

14. *Apartment numbers.*   The apartments in Brian's apartment house are numbered consecutively on each floor. The sum of his number and his next-door neighbor's number is 1419. What are the two numbers?

15. *Street addresses.*   The houses on the west side of Lincoln Avenue are consecutive odd numbers. Sam and Colleen are next-door neighbors and the sum of their house numbers is 572. Find their house numbers.

16. *Street addresses.*   The houses on the south side of Elm Street are consecutive even numbers. Wanda and Larry are next-door neighbors and the sum of their house numbers is 794. Find their house numbers.

17. The sum of three consecutive page numbers is 99. Find the numbers.

18. The sum of three consecutive page numbers is 60. Find the numbers.

19. *Longest marriage.*   As half of the world's longest-married couple, the woman was 2 yr younger than her husband. Together, their ages totaled 204 yr. How old were the man and the woman?
Source: *Guinness World Records* 2007

20. *Oldest bride.*   The world's oldest bride was 19 yr older than her groom. Together, their ages totaled 185 yr. How old were the bride and the groom?
Source: *Guinness World Records* 2007

21. *e-mail.*   In 2006, approximately 125 billion e-mail messages were sent each day. The number of spam messages was about four times the number of non-spam messages. How many of each type of message were sent each day in 2006?
Source: Ferris Research

22. *Home remodeling.*   In 2005, Americans spent a total of $26 billion to remodel bathrooms and kitchens. They spent $5 billion more on kitchens than on bathrooms. How much was spent on each?
Source: Joint Center for Housing Studies, Harvard University

23. *Page numbers.*   The sum of the page numbers on the facing pages of a book is 281. What are the page numbers?

24. *Perimeter of a triangle.*   The perimeter of a triangle is 195 mm. If the lengths of the sides are consecutive odd integers, find the length of each side.

25. *Hancock Building dimensions.* The top of the John Hancock Building in Chicago is a rectangle whose length is 60 ft more than the width. The perimeter is 520 ft. Find the width and the length of the rectangle. Find the area of the rectangle.

26. *Dimensions of a state.* The perimeter of the state of Wyoming is 1280 mi. The width is 90 mi less than the length. Find the width and the length.

27. A rectangular community garden is to be enclosed with 92 m of fencing. In order to allow for compost storage, the garden must be 4 m longer than it is wide. Determine the dimensions of the garden.

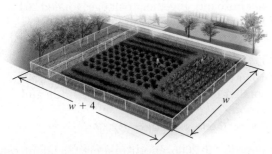

28. *Perimeter of a high school basketball court.* The perimeter of a standard high school basketball court is 268 ft. The length is 34 ft longer than the width. Find the dimensions of the court.
Source: Indiana High School Athletic Association

29. *Two-by-four.* The perimeter of a cross section of a "two-by-four" piece of lumber is $10\frac{1}{2}$ in. The length is twice the width. Find the actual dimensions of the cross section of a two-by-four.

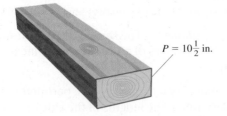

$P = 10\frac{1}{2}$ in.

30. *Standard billboard sign.* A standard rectangular highway billboard sign has a perimeter of 124 ft. The length is 6 ft more than three times the width. Find the dimensions of the sign.

31. *Angles of a triangle.* The second angle of an architect's triangle is three times as large as the first. The third angle is 30° more than the first. Find the measure of each angle.

32. *Angles of a triangle.* The second angle of a triangular garden is four times as large as the first. The third angle is 45° less than the sum of the other two angles. Find the measure of each angle.

33. *Angles of a triangle.* The second angle of a triangular kite is four times as large as the first. The third angle is 5° more than the sum of the other two angles. Find the measure of the second angle.

34. *Angles of a triangle.* The second angle of a triangular building lot is three times as large as the first. The third angle is 10° more than the sum of the other two angles. Find the measure of the third angle.

35. *Rocket sections.* A rocket is divided into three sections: the payload and navigation section in the top, the fuel section in the middle, and the rocket engine section in the bottom. The top section is one-sixth the length of the bottom section. The middle section is one-half the length of the bottom section. The total length is 240 ft. Find the length of each section.

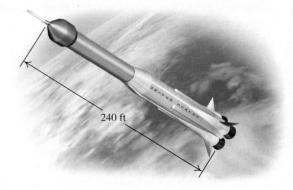

240 ft

36. *Gourmet sandwiches.* Jenny, Demi, and Drew buy an 18-in. long gourmet sandwich and take it back to their apartment. Since they have different appetites, Jenny cuts the sandwich so that Demi gets half of what Jenny gets and Drew gets three-fourths of what Jenny gets. Find the length of each person's sandwich.

37. *Taxi rates.* In Chicago, a taxi ride costs $2.25 plus $1.80 for each mile traveled. Debbie has budgeted $18 for a taxi ride (excluding tip). How far can she travel on her $18 budget?
Source: City of Chicago

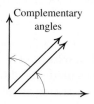

38. *Taxi fares.* In New York City, taxis charge $2.50 plus $2.00 per mile for off-peak fares. How far can Ralph travel for $17.50 (assuming an off-peak fare)?
Source: New York City Taxi and Limousine Commission

39. *Truck rentals.* Truck-Rite Rentals rents trucks at a daily rate of $49.95 plus 39¢ per mile. Concert Productions has budgeted $100 for renting a truck to haul equipment to an upcoming concert. How far can they travel in one day and stay within their budget?

40. *Truck rentals.* Fine Line Trucks rents an 18-ft truck for $42 plus 35¢ per mile. Judy needs a truck for one day to deliver a shipment of plants. How far can she drive and stay within a budget of $70?

41. *Complementary angles.* The sum of the measures of two *complementary* angles is 90°. If one angle measures 15° more than twice the measure of its complement, find the measure of each angle.

Complementary
angles

42. *Complementary angles.* Two angles are complementary. (See Exercise 41.) The measure of one angle is $1\frac{1}{2}$ times the measure of the other. Find the measure of each angle.

43. *Supplementary angles.* The sum of the measures of two *supplementary* angles is 180°. If the measure of one angle is $3\frac{1}{2}$ times the measure of the other, find the measure of each angle.

Supplementary
angles

44. *Supplementary angles.* Two angles are supplementary. (See Exercise 43.) If one angle measures 45° less than twice the measure of its supplement, find the measure of each angle.

45. *Copier paper.* The perimeter of standard-size copier paper is 99 cm. The width is 6.3 cm less than the length. Find the length and the width.

46. *Stock prices.* Sarah's investment in Jet Blue stock grew 28% to $448. How much did she originally invest?

47. *Savings interest.* Janeka invested money in a savings account at a rate of 6% simple interest. After 1 yr, she has $6996 in the account. How much did Janeka originally invest?

48. *Credit cards.* The balance in Will's Mastercard® account grew 2%, to $870, in one month. What was his balance at the beginning of the month?

49. *Scrabble®.* In a single game on October 12, 2006, Michael Cresta and Wayne Yorra set three North American Scrabble records: the most points in one game by one player, the most total points in the game, and the most points on a single turn. Cresta scored 340 points more than Yorra, and together they scored 1320 points. What was the winning score?
Source: www.slate.com

50. *Color printers.* The art gallery in Example 3 decides to raise its budget to $5000 for the 2-month period. How many brochures can they print for $5000?

51. *Selling a home.* The Brannons are planning to sell their home. If they want to be left with $117,500 after paying 6% of the selling price to a realtor as a commission, for how much must they sell the house?

52. *Budget overruns.* The massive roadworks project in Boston known as The Big Dig cost approximately $14.6 billion. This cost was 484% more than the original estimate. What was the original estimate of the cost of The Big Dig?
Sources: Taxpayers for Common Sense; www.msnbc.cmsn.com

53. *Cricket chirps and temperature.* The equation $T = \frac{1}{4}N + 40$ can be used to determine the temperature T, in degrees Fahrenheit, given the number of times N a cricket chirps per minute. Determine the number of chirps per minute for a temperature of 80°F.

54. *Race time.* The equation $R = -0.028t + 20.8$ can be used to predict the world record in the 200-m dash, where R is the record in seconds and t is the number of years since 1920. In what year will the record be 18.0 sec?

55. Sean claims he can solve most of the problems in this section by guessing. Is there anything wrong with this approach? Why or why not?

56. When solving Exercise 20, Beth used a to represent the bride's age and Ben used a to represent the groom's age. Is one of these approaches preferable to the other? Why or why not?

Skill Review

To prepare for Section 2.6, review inequalities (Section 1.4).

Write a true sentence using either $<$ or $>$. [1.4]

57. $-8 \ \blacksquare \ 1$

58. $-2 \ \blacksquare \ -5$

59. $\frac{1}{2} \ \blacksquare \ 0$

60. $-3 \ \blacksquare \ -1$

Write a second inequality with the same meaning. [1.4]

61. $x \geq -4$

62. $x < 5$

63. $5 > y$

64. $-10 \leq t$

Synthesis

65. Write a problem for a classmate to solve. Devise it so that the problem can be translated to the equation $x + (x + 2) + (x + 4) = 375$.

66. Write a problem for a classmate to solve. Devise it so that the solution is "Audrey can drive the rental truck for 50 mi without exceeding her budget."

67. *Discounted dinners.* Kate's "Dining Card" entitles her to $10 off the price of a meal after a 15% tip has been added to the cost of the meal. If, after the discount, the bill is $32.55, how much did the meal originally cost?

68. *Test scores.* Pam scored 78 on a test that had 4 fill-in questions worth 7 points each and 24 multiple-choice questions worth 3 points each. She had one fill-in question wrong. How many multiple-choice questions did Pam get right?

69. *Gettysburg Address.* Abraham Lincoln's 1863 Gettysburg Address refers to the year 1776 as "four *score* and seven years ago." Determine what a score is.

70. One number is 25% of another. The larger number is 12 more than the smaller. What are the numbers?

71. A storekeeper goes to the bank to get $10 worth of change. She requests twice as many quarters as half dollars, twice as many dimes as quarters, three times as many nickels as dimes, and no pennies or dollars. How many of each coin did the storekeeper get?

72. *Perimeter of a rectangle.* The width of a rectangle is three fourths of the length. The perimeter of the rectangle becomes 50 cm when the length and the width are each increased by 2 cm. Find the length and the width.

73. *Discounts.* In exchange for opening a new credit account, Macy's Department Stores® subtracts 10% from all purchases made the day the account is established. Julio is opening an account and has a coupon for which he receives 10% off the first day's reduced price of a camera. If Julio's final price is $77.75, what was the price of the camera before the two discounts?

74. *Sharing fruit.* Apples are collected in a basket for six people. One third, one fourth, one eighth, and one fifth of the apples are given to four people, respectively. The fifth person gets ten apples, and one apple remains for the sixth person. Find the original number of apples in the basket.

75. *eBay purchases.* An eBay seller charges $9.99 for the first DVD purchased and $6.99 for all others. For shipping and handling, he charges the full shipping fee of $3 for the first DVD, one half of the shipping charge for the second item, and one third of the shipping charge per item for all remaining items. The total cost of a shipment (excluding tax) was $45.45. How many DVDs were in the shipment?

76. *Winning percentage.* In a basketball league, the Falcons won 15 of their first 20 games. In order to win 60% of the total number of games, how many more games will they have to play, assuming they win only half of the remaining games?

77. *Taxi fares.* In New York City, a taxi ride costs $2.50 plus 40¢ per $\frac{1}{5}$ mile and 40¢ per minute stopped in traffic. Due to traffic, Glenda's taxi took 20 min to complete what is usually a 10-min drive. If she is charged $18.50 for the ride, how far did Glenda travel?
Source: New York City Taxi and Limousine Commission

78. *Test scores.* Ella has an average score of 82 on three tests. Her average score on the first two tests is 85. What was the score on the third test?

79. A school purchases a piano and must choose between paying $2000 at the time of purchase or $2150 at the end of one year. Which option should the school select and why?

80. Annette claims the following problem has no solution: "The sum of the page numbers on facing pages is 191. Find the page numbers." Is she correct? Why or why not?
Aha!

81. The perimeter of a rectangle is 101.74 cm. If the length is 4.25 cm longer than the width, find the dimensions of the rectangle.

82. The second side of a triangle is 3.25 cm longer than the first side. The third side is 4.35 cm longer than the second side. If the perimeter of the triangle is 26.87 cm, find the length of each side.

2.6 Solving Inequalities

Solutions of Inequalities ▪ Graphs of Inequalities ▪ Set-Builder and Interval Notation ▪ Solving Inequalities Using the Addition Principle ▪ Solving Inequalities Using the Multiplication Principle ▪ Using the Principles Together

Many real-world situations translate to *inequalities*. For example, a student might need to register for *at least* 12 credits; an elevator might be designed to hold *at most* 2000 pounds; a tax credit might be allowable for families with incomes of *less than* $25,000; and so on. Before solving applications of this type, we must adapt our equation-solving principles to the solving of inequalities.

Solutions of Inequalities

Recall from Section 1.4 that an inequality is a number sentence containing $>$ (is greater than), $<$ (is less than), $\geq$ (is greater than or equal to), or $\leq$ (is less than or equal to). Inequalities like

$$-7 > x, \quad t < 5, \quad 5x - 2 \geq 9, \quad \text{and} \quad -3y + 8 \leq -7$$

are true for some replacements of the variable and false for others.

Any value for the variable that makes an inequality true is called a **solution**. The set of all solutions is called the **solution set**. When all solutions of an inequality are found, we say that we have **solved** the inequality.

EXAMPLE **1**

Determine whether the given number is a solution of $x < 2$: **(a)** -3; **(b)** 2.

SOLUTION

a) Since $-3 < 2$ is true, -3 is a solution.

b) Since $2 < 2$ is false, 2 is not a solution.

> TRY EXERCISE 9

EXAMPLE **2**

Determine whether the given number is a solution of $y \geq 6$: **(a)** 6; **(b)** -4.

SOLUTION

a) Since $6 \geq 6$ is true, 6 is a solution.

b) Since $-4 \geq 6$ is false, -4 is not a solution.

> TRY EXERCISE 11

Graphs of Inequalities

Because the solutions of inequalities like $x < 2$ are too numerous to list, it is helpful to make a drawing that represents all the solutions. The **graph** of an inequality is such a drawing. Graphs of inequalities in one variable can be drawn on the number line by shading all points that are solutions. Parentheses are used to indicate endpoints that are *not* solutions and brackets to indicate endpoints that *are* solutions.*

EXAMPLE **3**

Graph each inequality: **(a)** $x < 2$; **(b)** $y \geq -3$; **(c)** $-2 < x \leq 3$.

SOLUTION

a) The solutions of $x < 2$ are those numbers less than 2. They are shown on the graph by shading all points to the left of 2. The parenthesis at 2 and the shading to its left indicate that 2 is *not* part of the graph, but numbers like 1.2 and 1.99 are.

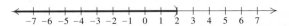

b) The solutions of $y \geq -3$ are shown on the number line by shading the points for -3 and all points to the right of -3. The bracket at -3 indicates that -3 is part of the graph.

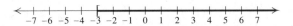

STUDENT NOTES

Note that $-2 < x < 3$ means $-2 < x$ *and* $x < 3$. Because of this, statements like $2 < x < 1$ make no sense—no number is both greater than 2 and less than 1.

c) The inequality $-2 < x \leq 3$ is read "-2 is less than x *and* x is less than or equal to 3," or "x is greater than -2 *and* less than or equal to 3." To be a solution of $-2 < x \leq 3$, a number must be a solution of both $-2 < x$ *and* $x \leq 3$. The number 1 is a solution, as are -0.5, 1.9, and 3. The parenthesis indicates that -2 is *not* a solution, whereas the bracket indicates that 3 *is* a solution. The other solutions are shaded.

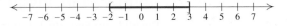

> TRY EXERCISE 17

---

*An alternative notation uses open dots to indicate endpoints that are not solutions and closed dots to indicate endpoints that are solutions. Using this notation, the solutions of $x < 2$ are graphed as ←┼┼┼┼┼┼○┼┼→ and the solutions of $y \geq -3$ are graphed as
←┼●┼┼┼┼┼┼┼→ .

Set–Builder and Interval Notation

To write the solution set of $x < 3$, we can use **set-builder notation:**

$$\{x | x < 3\}.$$

This is read "The set of all x such that x is less than 3."

Another way to write solutions of an inequality in one variable is to use **interval notation**. Interval notation uses parentheses, ( ), and brackets, [ ].

If a and b are real numbers with $a < b$, we define the **open interval (a, b)** as the set of all numbers x for which $a < x < b$. Using set-builder notation, we write

$$(a, b) = \{x | a < x < b\}.$$ Parentheses are used to exclude endpoints.

Its graph excludes the endpoints:

The **closed interval $[a, b]$** is defined as the set of all numbers x for which $a \leq x \leq b$. Thus,

$$[a, b] = \{x | a \leq x \leq b\}.$$ Brackets are used to include endpoints.

Its graph includes the endpoints:

There are two kinds of **half-open intervals**, defined as follows:

1. $(a, b] = \{x | a < x \leq b\}$. This is open on the left. Its graph is as follows:

2. $[a, b) = \{x | a \leq x < b\}$. This is open on the right. Its graph is as follows:

We use the symbols ∞ and $-\infty$ to represent positive infinity and negative infinity, respectively. Thus the notation (a, ∞) represents the set of all real numbers greater than a, and $(-\infty, a)$ represents the set of all real numbers less than a.

The notation $[a, \infty)$ or $(-\infty, a]$ is used when we want to include the endpoint a.

CAUTION! Do not confuse the *interval* (a, b) with the *ordered pair* (a, b). The context in which the notation appears should make the meaning clear.

STUDENT NOTES

You may have noticed which inequality signs in set-builder notation correspond to brackets and which correspond to parentheses. The relationship could be written informally as

$$\leq \quad \geq \quad [\ ]$$
$$< \quad > \quad (\ ).$$

EXAMPLE 4   Graph $y \geq -2$ on a number line and write the solution set using both set-builder and interval notations.

SOLUTION   Using set-builder notation, we write the solution set as $\{y | y \geq -2\}$.

Using interval notation, we write $[-2, \infty)$.

To graph the solution, we shade all numbers to the right of -2 and use a bracket to indicate that -2 is also a solution.

TRY EXERCISE 27

Being well rested, alert, and focused is very important when studying math. Often, problems that may seem confusing to a sleepy person are easily under-stood after a good night's sleep. Using your time efficiently is always important, so you should be aware that an alert, wide-awake student can often accomplish more in 10 minutes than a sleepy student can accomplish in 30 minutes.

Solving Inequalities Using the Addition Principle

Consider a balance similar to one that appears in Section 2.1. When one side of the balance holds more weight than the other, the balance tips in that direction. If equal amounts of weight are then added to or subtracted from both sides of the balance, the balance remains tipped in the same direction.

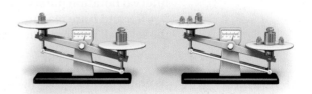

The balance illustrates the idea that when a number, such as 2, is added to (or subtracted from) both sides of a true inequality, such as $3 < 7$, we get another true inequality:

$$3 + 2 < 7 + 2, \quad \text{or} \quad 5 < 9.$$

Similarly, if we add -4 to both sides of $x + 4 < 10$, we get an *equivalent* inequality:

$$x + 4 + (-4) < 10 + (-4), \quad \text{or} \quad x < 6.$$

We say that $x + 4 < 10$ and $x < 6$ are **equivalent**, which means that both inequalities have the same solution set.

The Addition Principle for Inequalities

For any real numbers a, b, and c:

$a < b$ is equivalent to $a + c < b + c$;
$a \le b$ is equivalent to $a + c \le b + c$;
$a > b$ is equivalent to $a + c > b + c$;
$a \ge b$ is equivalent to $a + c \ge b + c$.

As with equations, our goal is to isolate the variable on one side.

EXAMPLE **5**   Solve $x + 2 > 8$ and then graph the solution.

SOLUTION   We use the addition principle, subtracting 2 from both sides:

$$x + 2 - 2 > 8 - 2 \qquad \text{Subtracting 2 from, or adding } -2 \text{ to, both sides}$$
$$x > 6.$$

From the inequality $x > 6$, we can determine the solutions easily. Any number greater than 6 makes $x > 6$ true and is a solution of that inequality as well as the inequality $x + 2 > 8$. Using set-builder notation, the solution set is $\{x \mid x > 6\}$. Using interval notation, the solution set is $(6, \infty)$. The graph is as follows:

Because most inequalities have an infinite number of solutions, we cannot possibly check them all. A partial check can be made using one of the possible solutions. For this example, we can substitute any number greater than 6—say, 6.1—into the original inequality:

$$\begin{array}{c|c} x + 2 > 8 \\ \hline 6.1 + 2 & 8 \\ 8.1 \overset{?}{>} 8 & \text{TRUE} \end{array} \quad 8.1 > 8 \text{ is a true statement.}$$

Since $8.1 > 8$ is true, 6.1 is a solution. Any number greater than 6 is a solution.

> TRY EXERCISE ▸ 43

EXAMPLE 6 Solve $3x - 1 \leq 2x - 5$ and then graph the solution.

SOLUTION   We have

$$\begin{array}{ll} 3x - 1 \leq 2x - 5 \\ 3x - 1 + 1 \leq 2x - 5 + 1 & \text{Adding 1 to both sides} \\ 3x \leq 2x - 4 & \text{Simplifying} \\ 3x - 2x \leq 2x - 4 - 2x & \text{Subtracting } 2x \text{ from both sides} \\ x \leq -4. & \text{Simplifying} \end{array}$$

The graph is as follows:

The student should check that any number less than or equal to -4 is a solution. The solution set is $\{x \mid x \leq -4\}$, or $(-\infty, -4]$.

> TRY EXERCISE ▸ 47

Solving Inequalities Using the Multiplication Principle

There is a multiplication principle for inequalities similar to that for equations, but it must be modified when multiplying both sides by a negative number. Consider the true inequality

$$3 < 7.$$

If we multiply both sides by a *positive* number—say, 2—we get another true inequality:

$$3 \cdot 2 < 7 \cdot 2, \quad \text{or} \quad 6 < 14. \qquad \text{TRUE}$$

If we multiply both sides by a negative number—say, -2—we get a *false* inequality:

$$3 \cdot (-2) < 7 \cdot (-2), \quad \text{or} \quad -6 < -14. \qquad \text{FALSE}$$

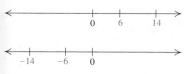

The fact that $6 < 14$ is true, but $-6 < -14$ is false, stems from the fact that the negative numbers, in a sense, *mirror* the positive numbers. Whereas 14 is to the *right* of 6, the number -14 is to the *left* of -6. Thus if we reverse the inequality symbol in $-6 < -14$, we get a true inequality:

$$-6 > -14. \qquad \text{TRUE}$$

The Multiplication Principle for Inequalities

For any real numbers a and b, and for any *positive* number c:

$$a < b \text{ is equivalent to } ac < bc, \text{ and}$$
$$a > b \text{ is equivalent to } ac > bc.$$

For any real numbers a and b, and for any *negative* number c:

$$a < b \text{ is equivalent to } ac > bc, \text{ and}$$
$$a > b \text{ is equivalent to } ac < bc.$$

Similar statements hold for $\leq$ and $\geq$.

CAUTION!   When multiplying or dividing both sides of an inequality by a negative number, don't forget to reverse the inequality symbol!

EXAMPLE **7**   Solve and graph each inequality: **(a)** $\frac{1}{4}x < 7$; **(b)** $-2y \leq 18$.

SOLUTION

a) $\frac{1}{4}x < 7$

$4 \cdot \frac{1}{4}x < 4 \cdot 7$ Multiplying both sides by 4, the reciprocal of $\frac{1}{4}$

$\uparrow$_____ The symbol stays the same, since 4 is positive.

$x < 28$ Simplifying

The solution set is $\{x \mid x < 28\}$, or $(-\infty, 28)$. The graph is shown at left.

b) $-2y \leq 18$

$\dfrac{-2y}{-2} \geq \dfrac{18}{-2}$ Multiplying both sides by $-\frac{1}{2}$, or dividing both sides by -2

$\uparrow$_____ *At this step*, we reverse the inequality, because $-\frac{1}{2}$ is negative.

$y \geq -9$ Simplifying

As a partial check, we substitute a number greater than -9, say -8, into the original inequality:

$$\frac{-2y \leq 18}{-2(-8) \mid 18}$$
$$16 \overset{?}{\leq} 18 \quad \text{TRUE} \quad 16 \leq 18 \text{ is a true statement.}$$

The solution set is $\{y \mid y \geq -9\}$, or $[-9, \infty)$. The graph is shown at left.

> TRY EXERCISE 59

Using the Principles Together

We use the addition and multiplication principles together to solve inequalities much as we did when solving equations.

EXAMPLE **8**   Solve: **(a)** $6 - 5y > 7$; **(b)** $2x - 9 < 7x + 1$.

SOLUTION

a) $6 - 5y > 7$

$-6 + 6 - 5y > -6 + 7$ Adding -6 to both sides

$-5y > 1$ Simplifying

$$-\tfrac{1}{5} \cdot (-5y) < -\tfrac{1}{5} \cdot 1$$ Multiplying both sides by $-\tfrac{1}{5}$, or dividing both sides by -5

Remember to reverse the inequality symbol!

$$y < -\tfrac{1}{5}$$ Simplifying

As a partial check, we substitute a number smaller than $-\tfrac{1}{5}$, say -1, into the original inequality:

$$\begin{array}{c|c} 6 - 5y > 7 \\ \hline 6 - 5(-1) & 7 \\ 6 - (-5) & \end{array}$$

$$11 \overset{?}{>} 7 \quad \text{TRUE} \quad 11 > 7 \text{ is a true statement.}$$

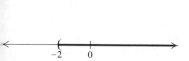

The solution set is $\left\{y \,|\, y < -\tfrac{1}{5}\right\}$, or $\left(-\infty, -\tfrac{1}{5}\right)$. We show the graph in the margin for reference.

b)

$$2x - 9 < 7x + 1$$
$$2x - 9 - 1 < 7x + 1 - 1 \quad \text{Subtracting 1 from both sides}$$
$$2x - 10 < 7x \quad \text{Simplifying}$$
$$2x - 10 - 2x < 7x - 2x \quad \text{Subtracting } 2x \text{ from both sides}$$
$$-10 < 5x \quad \text{Simplifying}$$
$$\frac{-10}{5} < \frac{5x}{5} \quad \text{Dividing both sides by 5}$$
$$-2 < x \quad \text{Simplifying}$$

The solution set is $\{x \,|\, -2 < x\}$, or $\{x \,|\, x > -2\}$, or $(-2, \infty)$.

TRY EXERCISE 69

All of the equation-solving techniques used in Sections 2.1 and 2.2 can be used with inequalities provided we remember to reverse the inequality symbol when multiplying or dividing both sides by a negative number.

EXAMPLE   9

Solve: **(a)** $16.3 - 7.2p \le -8.18$;   **(b)** $3(x - 9) - 1 \le 2 - 5(x + 6)$.

SOLUTION

a) The greatest number of decimal places in any one number is *two*. Multiplying both sides by 100 will clear decimals. Then we proceed as before.

$$16.3 - 7.2p \le -8.18$$
$$100(16.3 - 7.2p) \le 100(-8.18) \quad \text{Multiplying both sides by 100}$$
$$100(16.3) - 100(7.2p) \le 100(-8.18) \quad \text{Using the distributive law}$$
$$1630 - 720p \le -818 \quad \text{Simplifying}$$
$$-720p \le -818 - 1630 \quad \text{Subtracting 1630 from both sides}$$
$$-720p \le -2448 \quad \text{Simplifying; } -818 - 1630 = -2448$$
$$p \ge \frac{-2448}{-720} \quad \text{Dividing both sides by } -720$$

Remember to reverse the symbol!

$$p \ge 3.4$$

The solution set is $\{p \,|\, p \ge 3.4\}$, or $[3.4, \infty)$.

b) $3(x - 9) - 1 \le 2 - 5(x + 6)$

$$3x - 27 - 1 \le 2 - 5x - 30$$ Using the distributive law to remove parentheses

$$3x - 28 \le -5x - 28$$ Simplifying

$$3x - 28 + 28 \le -5x - 28 + 28$$ Adding 28 to both sides

$$3x \le -5x$$

$$3x + 5x \le -5x + 5x$$ Adding $5x$ to both sides

$$8x \le 0$$

$$x \le 0$$ Dividing both sides by 8

The solution set is $\{x \mid x \le 0\}$, or $(-\infty, 0]$.

TRY EXERCISE 83

2.6   EXERCISE SET

🌿 *Concept Reinforcement Insert the symbol $<, >, \le,$ or $\ge$ to make each pair of inequalities equivalent.*

1. $-5x \le 30$; $x \;\blacksquare\; -6$

2. $-7t \ge 56$; $t \;\blacksquare\; -8$

3. $-2t > -14$; $t \;\blacksquare\; 7$

4. $-3x < -15$; $x \;\blacksquare\; 5$

Classify each pair of inequalities as "equivalent" or "not equivalent."

5. $x < -2$; $-2 > x$

6. $t > -1$; $-1 < t$

7. $-4x - 1 \le 15$;
  $-4x \le 16$

8. $-2t + 3 \ge 11$;
  $-2t \ge 14$

Determine whether each number is a solution of the given inequality.

9. $x > -4$
  a) 4   **b)** -6 **c)** -4

10. $t < 3$
  a) -3 **b)** 3   **c)** $2\frac{19}{20}$

11. $y \le 19$
  a) 18.99   **b)** 19.01   **c)** 19

12. $n \ge -4$
  a) 0   **b)** -4.1 **c)** -3.9

13. $c \ge -7$
  a) 0   **b)** -5.4 **c)** 7.1

14. $a > 6$
  a) 6   **b)** -6.7 **c)** 0

15. $z < -3$
  a) 0   **b)** $-3\frac{1}{3}$ **c)** 1

16. $m \le -2$
  a) $-1\frac{9}{10}$ **b)** 0   **c)** $-2\frac{1}{3}$

Graph on a number line.

17. $y < 2$ **18.** $x \le 7$

19. $x \ge -1$ **20.** $t > -2$

21. $0 \le t$ **22.** $1 \le m$

23. $-5 \le x < 2$

24. $-3 < x \le 5$

25. $-4 < x < 0$

26. $0 \le x \le 5$

Graph each inequality, and write the solution set using both set-builder notation and interval notation.

27. $y < 6$ **28.** $x > 4$

29. $x \ge -4$ **30.** $t \le 6$

31. $t > -3$ **32.** $y < -3$

33. $x \le -7$ **34.** $x \ge -6$

Describe each graph using set-builder notation and interval notation.

35.

36.

37.

38.

39.

40.

41.

42.

Solve using the addition principle. Graph and write set-builder notation and interval notation for each answer.

43. $y + 6 > 9$

44. $x + 8 \leq -10$

45. $n - 6 < 11$

46. $n - 4 > -3$

47. $2x \leq x - 9$

48. $3x \leq 2x + 7$

49. $y + \frac{1}{3} \leq \frac{5}{6}$

50. $x + \frac{1}{4} \leq \frac{1}{2}$

51. $t - \frac{1}{8} > \frac{1}{2}$

52. $y - \frac{1}{3} > \frac{1}{4}$

53. $-9x + 17 > 17 - 8x$

54. $-8n + 12 > 12 - 7n$

55. $-23 < -t$

56. $19 < -x$

57. $10 - y \leq -12$

58. $3 - y \geq -6$

Solve using the multiplication principle. Graph and write set-builder notation and interval notation for each answer.

59. $4x < 28$

60. $3x \geq 24$

61. $-24 > 8t$

62. $-16x < -64$

63. $1.8 \geq -1.2n$

64. $9 \leq -2.5a$

65. $-2y \leq \frac{1}{5}$

66. $-2x \geq \frac{1}{5}$

67. $-\frac{8}{5} > 2x$

68. $-\frac{5}{8} < -10y$

Solve using the addition and multiplication principles.

69. $2 + 3x < 20$

70. $7 + 4y < 31$

71. $4t - 5 \leq 23$

72. $15x - 7 \leq -7$

73. $39 > 3 - 9x$

74. $5 > 5 - 7y$

75. $5 - 6y > 25$

76. $8 - 2y > 9$

77. $-3 < 8x + 7 - 7x$

78. $-5 < 9x + 8 - 8x$

79. $6 - 4y > 6 - 3y$

80. $7 - 8y > 5 - 7y$

81. $7 - 9y \leq 4 - 7y$

82. $6 - 13y \leq 4 - 12y$

83. $2.1x + 43.2 > 1.2 - 8.4x$

84. $0.96y - 0.79 \leq 0.21y + 0.46$

85. $1.7t + 8 - 1.62t < 0.4t - 0.32 + 8$

86. $0.7n - 15 + n \geq 2n - 8 - 0.4n$

87. $\frac{x}{3} + 4 \leq 1$

88. $\frac{2}{3} - \frac{x}{5} < \frac{4}{15}$

89. $3 < 5 - \frac{t}{7}$

90. $2 > 9 - \frac{x}{5}$

91. $4(2y - 3) \leq -44$

92. $3(2y - 3) > 21$

93. $8(2t + 1) > 4(7t + 7)$

94. $3(t - 2) \geq 9(t + 2)$

95. $3(r - 6) + 2 < 4(r + 2) - 21$

96. $5(t + 3) + 9 \geq 3(t - 2) - 10$

97. $\frac{4}{5}(3x + 4) \leq 20$

98. $\frac{2}{3}(2x - 1) \geq 10$

99. $\frac{2}{3}\left(\frac{7}{8} - 4x\right) - \frac{5}{8} < \frac{3}{8}$

100. $\frac{3}{4}\left(3x - \frac{1}{2}\right) - \frac{2}{3} < \frac{1}{3}$

101. Are the inequalities $x > -3$ and $x \geq -2$ equivalent? Why or why not?

102. Are the inequalities $t < -7$ and $t \leq -8$ equivalent? Why or why not?

Skill Review

Review simplifying expressions (Section 1.8).

Simplify. [1.8]

103. $5x - 2(3 - 6x)$

104. $8m - n - 3(2m + 5n)$

105. $x - 2[4y + 3(8 - x) - 1]$

106. $5 - 3t - 4[6 + 5(2t - 1) + t]$

107. $3[5(2a - b) + 1] - 5[4 - (a - b)]$

108. $9x - 2\{4 - 5[6 - 2(x + 1) - x]\}$

Synthesis

109. Explain how it is possible for the graph of an inequality to consist of just one number. (*Hint*: See Example 3c.)

110. The statements of the addition and multiplication principles begin with *conditions* set for the variables. Explain the conditions given for each principle.

Solve.

Aha! **111.** $x < x + 1$

112. $6[4 - 2(6 + 3t)] > 5[3(7 - t) - 4(8 + 2t)] - 20$

113. $27 - 4[2(4x - 3) + 7] \geq 2[4 - 2(3 - x)] - 3$

Solve for x.

114. $\frac{1}{2}(2x + 2b) > \frac{1}{3}(21 + 3b)$

115. $-(x + 5) \geq 4a - 5$

116. $y < ax + b$ (Assume $a < 0$.)

117. $y < ax + b$ (Assume $a > 0$.)

118. Graph the solutions of $|x| < 3$ on a number line.

Aha! **119.** Determine the solution set of $|x| > -3$.

120. Determine the solution set of $|x| < 0$.

CONNECTING the CONCEPTS

The procedure for solving inequalities is very similar to that used to solve equations. There are, however, two important differences.

- The multiplication principle for inequalities differs from the multiplication principle for equations: When we multiply or divide on both sides of an inequality by a *negative* number, we must *reverse* the direction of the inequality.

- The solution set of an equation like those we solved in this chapter typically consists of one number. The solution set of an inequality typically consists of a set of numbers and is written using set-builder notation.

Compare the following solutions.

Solve: $2 - 3x = x + 10$.

SOLUTION

$$2 - 3x = x + 10$$
$$-3x = x + 8 \qquad \text{Subtracting 2 from both sides}$$
$$-4x = 8 \qquad \text{Subtracting } x \text{ from both sides}$$
$$x = -2 \qquad \text{Dividing both sides by } -4$$

The solution is -2.

Solve: $2 - 3x > x + 10$.

SOLUTION

$$2 - 3x > x + 10$$
$$-3x > x + 8 \qquad \text{Subtracting 2 from both sides}$$
$$-4x > 8 \qquad \text{Subtracting } x \text{ from both sides}$$
$$x < -2 \qquad \text{Dividing both sides by } -4 \text{ and reversing the direction of the inequality symbol}$$

The solution is $\{x | x < -2\}$, or $(-\infty, -2)$.

MIXED REVIEW

Solve.

1. $x - 6 = 15$

2. $x - 6 \leq 15$

3. $3x = -18$

4. $3x > -18$

5. $-3x > -18$

6. $5x + 2 = 17$

7. $7 - 3x = 8$

8. $4y - 7 < 5$

9. $3 - t \geq 19$

10. $2 + 3n = 5n - 9$

11. $3 - 5a > a + 9$

12. $1.2x - 3.4 < 0.4x + 5.2$

13. $\dfrac{2}{3}(x + 5) \geq -4$

14. $\dfrac{n}{5} - 6 = 15$

15. $0.5x - 2.7 = 3x + 7.9$

16. $5(6 - t) = -45$

17. $8 - \dfrac{y}{3} \leq 7$

18. $\dfrac{1}{3}x - \dfrac{5}{6} = \dfrac{3}{2} - \dfrac{1}{6}x$

19. $-15 > 7 - 5x$

20. $10 \geq -2(a - 5)$

2.7   Solving Applications with Inequalities

Translating to Inequalities ■ Solving Problems

The five steps for problem solving can be used for problems involving inequalities.

Translating to Inequalities

Before solving problems that involve inequalities, we list some important phrases to look for. Sample translations are listed as well.

Important Words	Sample Sentence	Translation
is at least	Ming walks at least 2 mi a day.	$m \geq 2$
is at most	At most 5 students dropped the course.	$n \leq 5$
cannot exceed	The width cannot exceed 40 ft.	$w \leq 40$
must exceed	The speed must exceed 15 mph.	$s > 15$
is less than	Kamal's weight is less than 120 lb.	$w < 120$
is more than	Boston is more than 200 mi away.	$d > 200$
is between	The film was between 90 and 100 min long.	$90 < t < 100$
minimum	Ned drank a minimum of 5 glasses of water a day.	$w \geq 5$
maximum	The maximum penalty is $100.	$p \leq 100$
no more than	Alan weighs no more than 90 lb.	$w \leq 90$
no less than	Mallory scored no less than 8.3.	$s \geq 8.3$

The following phrases deserve special attention.

Translating "at least" and "at most"

The quantity x is at least some amount q: $x \geq q$.
(If x is *at least* q, it cannot be less than q.)

The quantity x is at most some amount q: $x \leq q$.
(If x is *at most* q, it cannot be more than q.)

Solving Problems

EXAMPLE **1**

Catering costs. To cater a party, Curtis' Barbeque charges a $50 setup fee plus $15 per person. The cost of Hotel Pharmacy's end-of-season softball party cannot exceed $450. How many people can attend the party?

SOLUTION

1. **Familiarize.** Suppose that 20 people were to attend the party. The cost would then be $50 + $15 · 20, or $350. This shows that more than 20 people could attend without exceeding $450. Instead of making another guess, we let n = the number of people in attendance.

2. **Translate.** The cost of the party will be $50 for the setup fee plus $15 times the number of people attending. We can reword as follows:

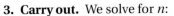

Rewording:	The setup fee	plus	the cost of the meals	cannot exceed	$450.
	↓	↓	↓	↓	↓
Translating:	50	+	15 · n	≤	450

3. **Carry out.** We solve for n:

$$50 + 15n \leq 450$$
$$15n \leq 400 \qquad \text{Subtracting 50 from both sides}$$
$$n \leq \frac{400}{15} \qquad \text{Dividing both sides by 15}$$
$$n \leq 26\frac{2}{3}. \qquad \text{Simplifying}$$

4. **Check.** Although the solution set of the inequality is all numbers less than or equal to $26\frac{2}{3}$, since n represents the number of people in attendance, we round *down* to 26. If 26 people attend, the cost will be $50 + $15 · 26, or $440, and if 27 attend, the cost will exceed $450.

5. **State.** At most 26 people can attend the party.

> TRY EXERCISE ▶ 23

CAUTION! Solutions of problems should always be checked using the original wording of the problem. In some cases, answers might need to be whole numbers or integers or rounded off in a particular direction.

Some applications with inequalities involve *averages*, or *means*. You are already familiar with the concept of averages from grades in courses that you have taken.

> **Average, or Mean**
>
> To find the **average**, or **mean**, of a set of numbers, add the numbers and then divide by the number of addends.

EXAMPLE 2

Financial aid. Full-time students in a health-care education program can receive financial aid and employee benefits from Covenant Health System by working at Covenant while attending school and also agreeing to work there after graduation. Students who work an average of at least 16 hr per week receive extra pay and part-time employee benefits. For the first three weeks of September, Dina worked 20 hr, 12 hr, and 14 hr. How many hours must she work during the fourth week in order to average at least 16 hr per week for the month?

Source: Covenant Health Systems

SOLUTION

1. **Familiarize.** Suppose Dina works 10 hr during the fourth week. Her average for the month would be

$$\frac{20 \text{ hr} + 12 \text{ hr} + 14 \text{ hr} + 10 \text{ hr}}{4} = 14 \text{ hr.}$$ There are 4 addends, so we divide by 4.

This shows that Dina must work more than 10 hr during the fourth week, if she is to average at least 16 hr of work per week. We let x represent the number of hours Dina works during the fourth week.

2. **Translate.** We reword the problem and translate as follows:

Rewording: The average number   should be   16 hr.
of hours worked   at least

Translating: $\dfrac{20 + 12 + 14 + x}{4}$ $\geq$ 16

3. **Carry out.** Because of the fraction, it is convenient to use the multiplication principle first:

$$\frac{20 + 12 + 14 + x}{4} \geq 16$$

$$4\left(\frac{20 + 12 + 14 + x}{4}\right) \geq 4 \cdot 16 \qquad \text{Multiplying both sides by 4}$$

$$20 + 12 + 14 + x \geq 64$$

$$46 + x \geq 64 \qquad \text{Simplifying}$$

$$x \geq 18. \qquad \text{Subtracting 46 from both sides}$$

4. **Check.** As a partial check, we show that if Dina works 18 hr, she will average at least 16 hr per week:

$$\frac{20 + 12 + 14 + 18}{4} = \frac{64}{4} = 16. \qquad \text{Note that 16 is at least 16.}$$

5. **State.** Dina will average at least 16 hr of work per week for September if she works at least 18 hr during the fourth week.

TRY EXERCISE 27

Translating for Success

1. Consecutive integers. The sum of two consecutive even integers is 102. Find the integers.

2. Salary increase. After Susanna earned a 5% raise, her new salary was $25,750. What was her former salary?

3. Dimensions of a rectangle. The length of a rectangle is 6 in. more than the width. The perimeter of the rectangle is 102 in. Find the length and the width.

4. Population. The population of Kelling Point is decreasing at a rate of 5% per year. The current population is 25,750. What was the population the previous year?

5. Reading assignment. Quinn has 6 days to complete a 150-page reading assignment. How many pages must he read the first day so that he has no more than 102 pages left to read on the 5 remaining days?

Translate each word problem to an equation or an inequality and select a correct translation from A–O.

A. $0.05(25,750) = x$

B. $x + 2x = 102$

C. $2x + 2(x + 6) = 102$

D. $150 - x \leq 102$

E. $x - 0.05x = 25,750$

F. $x + (x + 2) = 102$

G. $x + (x + 6) > 102$

H. $x + 5x = 150$

I. $x + 0.05x = 25,750$

J. $x + (2x + 6) = 102$

K. $x + (x + 1) = 102$

L. $102 + x > 150$

M. $0.05x = 25,750$

N. $102 + 5x > 150$

O. $x + (x + 6) = 102$

Answers on page A-5

An additional, animated version of this activity appears in MyMathLab. To use MyMathLab, you need a course ID and a student access code. Contact your instructor for more information.

6. Numerical relationship. One number is 6 more than twice another. The sum of the numbers is 102. Find the numbers.

7. DVD collections. Together Mindy and Ken have 102 DVDs. If Ken has 6 more DVDs than Mindy, how many does each have?

8. Sales commissions. Kirk earns a commission of 5% on his sales. One year he earned commission totaling $25,750. What were his total sales for the year?

9. Fencing. Jess has 102 ft of fencing that he plans to use to enclose two dog runs. The perimeter of one run is to be twice the perimeter of the other. Into what lengths should the fencing be cut?

10. Quiz scores. Lupe has a total of 102 points on the first 6 quizzes in her sociology class. How many total points must she earn on the 5 remaining quizzes in order to have more than 150 points for the semester?

2.7 EXERCISE SET

➡ *Concept Reinforcement* *In each of Exercises 1–8, match the sentence with one of the following:*

$$a < b; \quad a \le b; \quad b < a; \quad b \le a.$$

1. *a* is at least *b*

2. *a* exceeds *b*.

3. *a* is at most *b*.

4. *a* is exceeded by *b*.

5. *b* is no more than *a*.

6. *b* is no less than *a*.

7. *b* is less than *a*.

8. *b* is more than *a*.

Translate to an inequality.

9. A number is less than 10.

10. A number is greater than or equal to 4.

11. The temperature is at most −3°C.

12. The average credit-card debt is more than $8000.

13. To rent a car, a driver must have a minimum of 5 yr driving experience.

14. The Barringdean Shopping Center is no more than 20 mi away.

15. The age of the Mayan altar exceeds 1200 yr.

16. The maximum safe exposure limit of formaldehyde is 2 parts per million.

17. Tania earns between $12 and $15 an hour.

18. Leslie's test score was at least 85.

19. Wind speeds were greater than 50 mph.

20. The costs of production of that software cannot exceed $12,500.

21. A room at Pine Tree Bed and Breakfast costs no more than $120 a night.

22. The cost of gasoline was at most $4 per gallon.

Use an inequality and the five-step process to solve each problem.

23. *Furnace repairs.* RJ's Plumbing and Heating charges $55 plus $40 per hour for emergency service. Gary remembers being billed over $150 for an emergency call. How long was RJ's there?

24. *College tuition.* Karen's financial aid stipulates that her tuition not exceed $1000. If her local community college charges a $35 registration fee plus $375 per course, what is the greatest number of courses for which Karen can register?

25. *Graduate school.* An unconditional acceptance into the Master of Business Administration (MBA) program at Arkansas State University will be given to students whose GMAT score plus 200 times the undergraduate grade point average is at least 950. Robbin's GMAT score was 500. What must her grade point average be in order to be unconditionally accepted into the program?
Source: graduateschool.astate.edu

26. *Car payments.* As a rule of thumb, debt payments (other than mortgages) should be less than 8% of a consumer's monthly gross income. Oliver makes $54,000 a year and has a $100 student-loan payment every month. What size car payment can he afford?
Source: money.cnn.com

27. *Quiz average.* Rod's quiz grades are 73, 75, 89, and 91. What scores on a fifth quiz will make his average quiz grade at least 85?

28. *Nutrition.* Following the guidelines of the U.S. Department of Agriculture, Dale tries to eat at least 5 half-cup servings of vegetables each day. For the first six days of one week, she had 4, 6, 7, 4, 6, and 4 servings. How many servings of vegetables should Dale eat on Saturday, in order to average at least 5 servings per day for the week?

29. *College course load.* To remain on financial aid, Millie needs to complete an average of at least 7 credits per quarter each year. In the first three quarters of 2008, Millie completed 5, 7, and 8 credits. How many credits of course work must Millie complete in the fourth quarter if she is to remain on financial aid?

30. *Music lessons.* Band members at Colchester Middle School are expected to average at least 20 min of practice time per day. One week Monroe practiced 15 min, 28 min, 30 min, 0 min, 15 min, and 25 min. How long must he practice on the seventh day if he is to meet expectations?

31. *Baseball.* In order to qualify for a batting title, a major league baseball player must average at least 3.1 plate appearances per game. For the first nine games of the season, a player had 5, 1, 4, 2, 3, 4, 4, 3, and 2 plate appearances. How many plate appearances must the player have in the tenth game in order to average at least 3.1 per game?
Source: Major League Baseball

32. *Education.* The Mecklenberg County Public Schools stipulate that a standard school day will average at least $5\frac{1}{2}$ hr, excluding meal breaks. For the first four days of one school week, bad weather resulted in school days of 4 hr, $6\frac{1}{2}$ hr, $3\frac{1}{2}$ hr, and $6\frac{1}{2}$ hr. How long must the Friday school day be in order to average at least $5\frac{1}{2}$ hr for the week?
Source: www.meck.k12.va.us

33. *Perimeter of a triangle.* One side of a triangle is 2 cm shorter than the base. The other side is 3 cm longer than the base. What lengths of the base will allow the perimeter to be greater than 19 cm?

34. *Perimeter of a sign.* The perimeter of a rectangular sign is not to exceed 50 ft. The length is to be twice the width. What widths will meet these conditions?

35. *Well drilling.* All Seasons Well Drilling offers two plans. Under the "pay-as-you-go" plan, they charge $500 plus $8 a foot for a well of any depth. Under their "guaranteed-water" plan, they charge a flat fee of $4000 for a well that is guaranteed to provide adequate water for a household. For what depths would it save a customer money to use the pay-as-you-go plan?

36. *Cost of road service.* Rick's Automotive charges $50 plus $15 for each (15-min) unit of time when making a road call. Twin City Repair charges $70 plus $10 for each unit of time. Under what circumstances would it be more economical for a motorist to call Rick's?

37. *Insurance-covered repairs.* Most insurance companies will replace a vehicle if an estimated repair exceeds 80% of the "blue-book" value of the vehicle. Michele's insurance company paid $8500 for repairs to her Subaru after an accident. What can be concluded about the blue-book value of the car?

38. *Insurance-covered repairs.* Following an accident, Jeff's Ford pickup was replaced by his insurance company because the damage was so extensive. Before the damage, the blue-book value of the truck was $21,000. How much would it have cost to repair the truck? (See Exercise 37.)

39. *Sizes of packages.* The U.S. Postal Service defines a "package" as a parcel for which the sum of the length and the girth is less than 84 in. (Length is the longest side of a package and girth is the distance around the other two sides of the package.) A box has a fixed girth of 29 in. Determine (in terms of an inequality) those lengths for which the box is considered a "package."

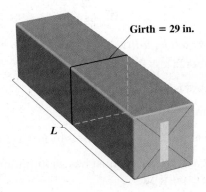

40. *Sizes of envelopes.* Rhetoric Advertising is a direct-mail company. It determines that for a particular campaign, it can use any envelope with a fixed width of $3\frac{1}{2}$ in. and an area of at least $17\frac{1}{2}$ in². Determine (in terms of an inequality) those lengths that will satisfy the company constraints.

41. *Body temperature.* A person is considered to be feverish when his or her temperature is higher than 98.6°F. The formula $F = \frac{9}{5}C + 32$ can be used to convert Celsius temperatures C to Fahrenheit temperatures F. For which Celsius temperatures is a person considered feverish?

42. *Gold temperatures.* Gold stays solid at Fahrenheit temperatures below 1945.4°. Determine (in terms of an inequality) those Celsius temperatures for which gold stays solid. Use the formula given in Exercise 41.

43. *Area of a triangular sign.* Zoning laws in Harrington prohibit displaying signs with areas exceeding 12 ft². If Flo's Marina is ordering a triangular sign with an 8-ft base, how tall can the sign be?

44. *Area of a triangular flag.* As part of an outdoor education course, Trisha needs to make a bright-colored triangular flag with an area of at least 3 ft². What heights can the triangle be if the base is $1\frac{1}{2}$ ft?

45. *Fat content in foods.* Reduced Fat Skippy® peanut butter contains 12 g of fat per serving. In order for a food to be labeled "reduced fat," it must have at least 25% less fat than the regular item. What can you conclude about the number of grams of fat in a serving of the regular Skippy peanut butter?
Source: Best Foods

46. *Fat content in foods.* Reduced Fat Chips Ahoy!® cookies contain 5 g of fat per serving. What can you conclude about the number of grams of fat in regular Chips Ahoy! cookies (see Exercise 45)?
Source: Nabisco Brands, Inc.

47. *Weight gain.* In the last weeks before the yearly Topsfield Weigh In, heavyweight pumpkins gain about 26 lb per day. Charlotte's heaviest pumpkin weighs 532 lb on September 5. For what dates will its weight exceed 818 lb?
Source: Based on a story in the *Burlington Free Press*

48. *Pond depth.* On July 1, Garrett's Pond was 25 ft deep. Since that date, the water level has dropped $\frac{2}{3}$ ft per week. For what dates will the water level not exceed 21 ft?

49. *Cell-phone budget.* Liam has budgeted $60 a month for his cell phone. For his service, he pays a monthly fee of $39.95, plus taxes of $6.65, plus 10¢ for each text message sent or received. How many text messages can he send or receive and not exceed his budget?

50. *Banquet costs.* The women's volleyball team can spend at most $700 for its awards banquet at a local restaurant. If the restaurant charges a $100 setup fee plus $24 per person, at most how many can attend?

51. *World records in the mile run.* The formula
$$R = -0.0065t + 4.3259$$
can be used to predict the world record, in minutes, for the 1-mi run t years after 1900. Determine (in terms of an inequality) those years for which the world record will be less than 3.6 min.
Source: Based on information from Information Please Database 2007, Pearson Education, Inc.

52. *Women's records in the women's 1500-m run.* The formula
$$R = -0.0026t + 4.0807$$
can be used to predict the world record, in minutes, for the 1500-m run t years after 1900. Determine (in terms of an inequality) those years for which the world record will be less than 3.8 min.
Source: Based on information from *Track and Field*

53. *Toll charges.* The equation

$$y = 0.06x + 0.50$$

can be used to determine the approximate cost y, in dollars, of driving x miles on the Pennsylvania Turnpike. For what mileages x will the cost be at most $14?

54. *Price of a movie ticket.* The average price of a movie ticket can be estimated by the equation

$$P = 0.169Y - 333.04,$$

where Y is the year and P is the average price, in dollars. For what years will the average price of a movie ticket be at least $7? (Include the year in which the $7 ticket first occurs.)
Source: National Association of Theatre Owners

55. If f represents Fran's age and t represents Todd's age, write a sentence that would translate to $t + 3 < f$.

56. Explain how the meanings of "Five more than a number" and "Five is more than a number" differ.

Skill Review

Review operations with real numbers (Sections 1.5–1.8).

Simplify.

57. $-2 + (-5) - 7$ [1.6]

58. $\dfrac{1}{2} \div \left(-\dfrac{3}{4}\right)$ [1.7]

59. $3 \cdot (-10) \cdot (-1) \cdot (-2)$ [1.7]

60. $-6.3 + (-4.8)$ [1.5]

61. $(3 - 7) - (4 - 8)$ [1.8]

62. $3 - 2 + 5 \cdot 10 \div 5^2 \cdot 2$ [1.8]

63. $\dfrac{-2 - (-6)}{8 - 10}$ [1.8]

64. $\dfrac{1 - (-7)}{-3 - 5}$ [1.8]

Synthesis

65. Write a problem for a classmate to solve. Devise the problem so the answer is "At most 18 passengers can go on the boat." Design the problem so that at least one number in the solution must be rounded down.

66. Write a problem for a classmate to solve. Devise the problem so the answer is "The Rothmans can drive 90 mi without exceeding their truck rental budget."

67. *Ski wax.* Green ski wax works best between 5° and 15° Fahrenheit. Determine those Celsius temperatures for which green ski wax works best. (See Exercise 41.)

68. *Parking fees.* Mack's Parking Garage charges $4.00 for the first hour and $2.50 for each additional hour. For how long has a car been parked when the charge exceeds $16.50?

Aha! **69.** The area of a square can be no more than 64 cm². What lengths of a side will allow this?

Aha! **70.** The sum of two consecutive odd integers is less than 100. What is the largest pair of such integers?

71. *Nutritional standards.* In order for a food to be labeled "lowfat," it must have fewer than 3 g of fat per serving. Reduced-fat tortilla chips contain 60% less fat than regular nacho cheese tortilla chips, but still cannot be labeled lowfat. What can you conclude about the fat content of a serving of nacho cheese tortilla chips?

72. *Parking fees.* When asked how much the parking charge is for a certain car (see Exercise 68), Mack replies, "between 14 and 24 dollars." For how long has the car been parked?

73. *Frequent buyer bonus.* Alice's Books allows customers to select one free book for every 10 books purchased. The price of that book cannot exceed the average cost of the 10 books. Neoma has bought 9 books whose average cost is $12 per book. How much should her tenth book cost if she wants to select a $15 book for free?

74. *Grading.* After 9 quizzes, Blythe's average is 84. Is it possible for Blythe to improve her average by two points with the next quiz? Why or why not?

75. *Discount card.* Barnes & Noble offers a member card for $25 a year. This card entitles a customer to a 40% discount off list price on hardcover bestsellers, a 20% discount on adult hardcovers, and a 10% discount on other purchases. Describe two sets of circumstances for which an individual would save money by becoming a member.
Source: Barnes & Noble

Study Summary

KEY TERMS AND CONCEPTS   EXAMPLES

SECTION 2.1: SOLVING EQUATIONS

Equivalent equations share the same solution.

$3x - 1 = 10$, $3x = 11$, and $x = \dfrac{11}{3}$ are equivalent equations.

The Addition Principle for Equations

$a = b$ is equivalent to
$a + c = b + c$.

$$x + 5 = -2 \quad \text{is equivalent to}$$
$$x + 5 + (-5) = -2 + (-5) \quad \text{and to}$$
$$x = -7.$$

The Multiplication Principle for Equations

$a = b$ is equivalent to $ac = bc$,
for $c \neq 0$.

$$-\tfrac{1}{3}x = 7 \quad \text{is equivalent to}$$
$$(-3)(-\tfrac{1}{3}x) = (-3)(7) \quad \text{and to}$$
$$x = -21.$$

SECTION 2.2: USING THE PRINCIPLES TOGETHER

We can **clear fractions** by multiplying both sides of an equation by the least common multiple of the denominators in the equation.

Solve: $\tfrac{1}{2}x - \tfrac{1}{3} = \tfrac{1}{6}x + \tfrac{2}{3}$.

$6\left(\tfrac{1}{2}x - \tfrac{1}{3}\right) = 6\left(\tfrac{1}{6}x + \tfrac{2}{3}\right)$	Multiplying by 6, the least common denominator
$6 \cdot \tfrac{1}{2}x - 6 \cdot \tfrac{1}{3} = 6 \cdot \tfrac{1}{6}x + 6 \cdot \tfrac{2}{3}$	Using the distributive law
$3x - 2 = x + 4$	Simplifying
$2x = 6$	Subtracting x from and adding 2 to both sides
$x = 3$	

We can **clear decimals** by multiplying both sides by a power of 10. If there is at most one decimal place in any one number, multiply by 10. If there are at most two decimal places, multiply by 100, and so on.

Solve: $3.6t - 1.5 = 2 - 0.8t$.

$10(3.6t - 1.5) = 10(2 - 0.8t)$	Multiplying both sides by 10 because the greatest number of decimal places is 1.
$36t - 15 = 20 - 8t$	Using the distributive law
$44t = 35$	Adding $8t$ and 15 to both sides
$t = \dfrac{35}{44}$	Dividing both sides by 44

SECTION 2.3: FORMULAS

A **formula** uses letters to show a relationship among two or more quantities. Formulas can be solved for a given letter using the addition and multiplication principles.

Solve: $x = \tfrac{2}{5}y + 7$ *for y.*

$x = \tfrac{2}{5}y + 7$	We are solving for y.
$x - 7 = \tfrac{2}{5}y$	Isolating the term containing y
$\tfrac{5}{2}(x - 7) = \tfrac{5}{2} \cdot \tfrac{2}{5}y$	Multiplying both sides by $\tfrac{5}{2}$
$\tfrac{5}{2}x - \tfrac{5}{2} \cdot 7 = 1 \cdot y$	Using the distributive law
$\tfrac{5}{2}x - \tfrac{35}{2} = y$	We have solved for y.

SECTION 2.4: APPLICATIONS WITH PERCENT

Percent Notation

$n\%$ means $\dfrac{n}{100}$, or $n \times \dfrac{1}{100}$, or $n \times 0.01$

$31\% = 0.31$; $\frac{1}{8} = 0.125 = 12.5\%$;

$2.9\% = 0.029$; $2.94 = 294\%$

Key Words in Percent Translations

"Of" translates to " $\cdot$ " or "$\times$"

"What" translates to a variable

"Is" or "Was" translates to "$=$"

"%" translates to "$\times \frac{1}{100}$" or "$\times 0.01$"

$$\underbrace{\text{What percent}}_{n} \quad \text{of} \quad \underset{60}{\text{60}} \quad \underset{=}{\text{is}} \quad \underset{7.2}{\text{7.2?}}$$

$$n \cdot 60 = 7.2$$

$$n = \frac{7.2}{60}$$

$$n = 0.12$$

Thus, 7.2 is 12% of 60.

SECTION 2.5: PROBLEM SOLVING

Five Steps for Problem Solving in Algebra

1. *Familiarize* yourself with the problem.
2. *Translate* to mathematical language. (This often means writing an equation.)
3. *Carry out* some mathematical manipulation. (This often means *solving* an equation.)
4. *Check* your possible answer in the original problem.
5. *State* the answer clearly.

The perimeter of a rectangle is 70 cm. The width is 5 cm longer than half the length. Find the length and the width.

1. **Familiarize.** Look up, if necessary, the formula for the perimeter of a rectangle:

   $$P = 2l + 2w.$$

   We are looking for two values, the length and the width. We can describe the width in terms of the length:

   $$w = \tfrac{1}{2}l + 5.$$

2. **Translate.**

   Rewording: Twice the length plus twice the width is the perimeter.

   Translating: $\quad 2l \quad + \quad 2\left(\tfrac{1}{2}l + 5\right) \quad = \quad 70$

3. **Carry out.** Solve the equation:

   $$2l + 2\left(\tfrac{1}{2}l + 5\right) = 70$$
   $$2l + l + 10 = 70 \qquad \text{Using the distributive law}$$
   $$3l + 10 = 70 \qquad \text{Combining like terms}$$
   $$3l = 60 \qquad \text{Subtracting 10 from both sides}$$
   $$l = 20. \qquad \text{Dividing both sides by 3}$$

   If $l = 20$, then $w = \tfrac{1}{2}l + 5 = \tfrac{1}{2} \cdot 20 + 5 = 10 + 5 = 15$.

4. **Check.** The width should be 5 cm longer than half the length. Since half the length is 10 cm, and 15 cm is 5 cm longer, this statement checks. The perimeter should be 70 cm. Since $2l + 2w = 2(20) + 2(15) = 40 + 30 = 70$, this statement also checks.

5. **State.** The length is 20 cm and the width is 15 cm.

SECTION 2.6: SOLVING INEQUALITIES

An **inequality** is any sentence containing $<$, $>$, $\leq$, $\geq$, or $\neq$. Solution sets of inequalities can be **graphed** and written in **set-builder notation** or **interval notation**.

Interval Notation	Set-builder Notation	Graph
(a, b)	$\{x \mid a < x < b\}$	
$[a, b]$	$\{x \mid a \leq x \leq b\}$	
$[a, b)$	$\{x \mid a \leq x < b\}$	
$(a, b]$	$\{x \mid a < x \leq b\}$	
(a, ∞)	$\{x \mid a < x\}$	
$(-\infty, a)$	$\{x \mid x < a\}$	

The Addition Principle for Inequalities

For any real numbers a, b, and c,

$a < b$ is equivalent to $a + c < b + c$;
$a > b$ is equivalent to $a + c > b + c$.

Similar statements hold for $\leq$ and $\geq$.

$x + 3 \leq 5$ is equivalent to
$x + 3 - 3 \leq 5 - 3$ and to
$\qquad x \leq 2.$

The Multiplication Principle for Inequalities

For any real numbers a and b, and for any *positive* number c,

$a < b$ is equivalent to $ac < bc$;
$a > b$ is equivalent to $ac > bc$.

For any real numbers a and b, and for any *negative* number c,

$a < b$ is equivalent to $ac > bc$;
$a > b$ is equivalent to $ac < bc$.

Similar statements hold for $\leq$ and $\geq$.

$3x > 9$ is equivalent to
$\frac{1}{3} \cdot 3x > \frac{1}{3} \cdot 9$ The inequality symbol does not change because $\frac{1}{3}$ is positive.
$\quad x > 3.$

$-3x > 9$ is equivalent to
$-\frac{1}{3} \cdot -3x < -\frac{1}{3} \cdot 9$ The inequality symbol is reversed because $-\frac{1}{3}$ is negative.
$\quad x < -3.$

SECTION 2.7: SOLVING APPLICATIONS WITH INEQUALITIES

Many real-world problems can be solved by translating the problem to an inequality and applying the five-step problem-solving strategy.

Translate to an inequality.

The test score must exceed 85.	$s > 85$
At most 15 volunteers greeted visitors.	$v \leq 15$
Ona makes no more than $100 a week.	$w \leq 100$
Herbs need at least 4 hr of sun a day.	$h \geq 4$

Review Exercises: Chapter 2

✎ **Concept Reinforcement**   *Classify each statement as either true or false.*

1. $5x - 4 = 2x$ and $3x = 4$ are equivalent equations. [2.1]

2. $5 - 2t < 9$ and $t > 6$ are equivalent inequalities. [2.6]

3. Some equations have no solution. [2.1]

4. Consecutive odd integers are 2 units apart. [2.5]

5. For any number a, $a \le a$. [2.6]

6. The addition principle is always used before the multiplication principle. [2.2]

7. A 10% discount results in a sale price that is 90% of the original price. [2.4]

8. Often it is impossible to list all solutions of an inequality number by number. [2.6]

Solve. Label any contradictions or identities.

9. $x + 9 = -16$ [2.1]

10. $-8x = -56$ [2.1]

11. $-\dfrac{x}{5} = 13$ [2.1]

12. $-8 = n - 11$ [2.1]

13. $\frac{2}{5}t = -8$ [2.1]

14. $x - 0.1 = 1.01$ [2.1]

15. $-\frac{2}{3} + x = -\frac{1}{6}$ [2.1]

16. $4y + 11 = 5$ [2.2]

17. $5 - x = 13$ [2.2]

18. $3t + 7 = t - 1$ [2.2]

19. $7x - 6 = 25x$ [2.2]

20. $\frac{1}{4}x - \frac{5}{8} = \frac{3}{8}$ [2.2]

21. $14y = 23y - 17 - 9y$ [2.2]

22. $0.22y - 0.6 = 0.12y + 3 - 0.8y$ [2.2]

23. $\frac{1}{4}x - \frac{1}{8}x = 3 - \frac{1}{16}x$ [2.2]

24. $6(4 - n) = 18$ [2.2]

25. $4(5x - 7) = -56$ [2.2]

26. $8(x - 2) = 4(x - 4)$ [2.2]

27. $3(x - 4) + 2 = x + 2(x - 5)$ [2.2]

Solve each formula for the given letter. [2.3]

28. $C = \pi d$, for d

29. $V = \dfrac{1}{3}Bh$, for B

30. $5x - 2y = 10$, for y

31. $tx = ax + b$, for x

32. Find decimal notation: 1.2%. [2.4]

33. Find percent notation: $\frac{11}{25}$. [2.4]

34. What percent of 60 is 42? [2.4]

35. 49 is 35% of what number? [2.4]

Determine whether each number is a solution of $x \le -5$. [2.6]

36. -3 37. -7 38. 4

Graph on a number line. [2.6]

39. $5x - 6 < 2x + 3$ 40. $-2 < x \le 5$

41. $t > 0$

Solve. Write the answers in set-builder notation and interval notation. [2.6]

42. $t + \frac{2}{3} \ge \frac{1}{6}$

43. $9x \ge 63$

44. $2 + 6y > 20$

45. $7 - 3y \ge 27 + 2y$

46. $3x + 5 < 2x - 6$

47. $-4y < 28$

48. $3 - 4x < 27$

49. $4 - 8x < 13 + 3x$

50. $13 \le -\frac{2}{3}t + 5$

51. $7 \le 1 - \frac{3}{4}x$

Solve.

52. In 2006, U.S. retailers lost a record $41.6 billion due to theft and fraud. Of this amount, $20 billion was due to employee theft. What percent of the total loss was employee theft? [2.4]
Source: www.wwaytv3.com

53. An 18-ft beam is cut into two pieces. One piece is 2 ft longer than the other. How long are the pieces? [2.5]

54. In 2004, a total of 103,000 students from China and Japan enrolled in U.S. colleges and universities. The number of Japanese students was 10,000 more than half the number of Chinese students. How many Chinese students and how many Japanese students enrolled in the United States? [2.5]
Source: Institute of International Education

5. The sum of two consecutive odd integers is 116. Find the integers. [2.5]

6. The perimeter of a rectangle is 56 cm. The width is 6 cm less than the length. Find the width and the length. [2.5]

7. After a 25% reduction, a picnic table is on sale for $120. What was the regular price? [2.4]

8. From 2000 to 2006, the number of U.S. wireless-phone subscribers increased by 114 percent to 233 million. How many subscribers were there in 2000? [2.4]
Source: Cellular Telecommunications and Internet Association

9. The measure of the second angle of a triangle is 50° more than that of the first. The measure of the third angle is 10° less than twice the first. Find the measures of the angles. [2.5]

0. The U.S. Centers for Disease Control recommends that for a typical 2000-calorie daily diet, no more than 65 g of fat be consumed. In the first three days of a four-day vacation, Teresa consumed 55 g, 80 g, and 70 g of fat. Determine how many grams of fat Teresa can consume on the fourth day if she is to average no more than 65 g of fat per day. [2.7]

1. *Blueprints.* To make copies of blueprints, Vantage Reprographics charges a $6 setup fee plus $4 per copy. Myra can spend no more than $65 for the copying. What number of copies will allow her to stay within budget? [2.7]

ynthesis

2. How does the multiplication principle for equations differ from the multiplication principle for inequalities? [2.1], [2.6]

3. Explain how checking the solutions of an equation differs from checking the solutions of an inequality. [2.1], [2.6]

4. A study of sixth- and seventh-graders in Boston revealed that, on average, the students spent 3 hr 20 min per day watching TV or playing video and computer games. This represents 108% more than the average time spent reading or doing homework. How much time each day was spent, on average, reading or doing homework? [2.4]
Source: Harvard School of Public Health

65. In June 2007, a team of Brazilian scientists exploring the Amazon measured its length as 65 mi longer than the Nile. If the combined length of both rivers is 8385 mi, how long is each river? [2.5]
Source: news.nationalgeographic.com

66. Kent purchased a book online at 25% off the retail price. The shipping charges were $4.95. If the amount due was $16.95, what was the retail price of the book? [2.4], [2.5]

Solve.

67. $2|n| + 4 = 50$ [1.4], [2.2]

68. $|3n| = 60$ [1.4], [2.1]

69. $y = 2a - ab + 3$, for a [2.3]

70. The Maryland Heart Center gives the following steps to calculate the number of fat grams needed daily by a moderately active woman. Write the steps as one formula relating the number of fat grams F to a woman's weight w, in pounds. [2.3]

1. Calculate the total number of calories per day.
____ pounds × 12 calories = ____ total calories per day

2. Take the total number of calories and multiply by 30 percent.
____ calories per day × 0.30 = ____ calories from fat per day.

3. Take the number of calories from fat per day and divide by 9 (there are 9 calories per gram of fat).
____ calories from fat per day divided by 9 = ____ fat grams per day

Solve. Label any contradictions or identities.

1. $t + 7 = 16$

2. $t - 3 = 12$

3. $6x = -18$

4. $-\frac{4}{7}x = -28$

5. $3t + 7 = 2t - 5$

6. $\frac{1}{2}x - \frac{3}{5} = \frac{2}{5}$

7. $8 - y = 16$

8. $4.2x + 3.5 = 1.2 - 2.5x$

9. $4(x + 2) = 36$

10. $\frac{5}{6}(3x + 1) = 20$

11. $13t - (5 - 2t) = 5(3t - 1)$

Solve. Write the answers in set-builder notation and interval notation.

12. $x + 6 > 1$

13. $14x + 9 > 13x - 4$

14. $-5y \geq 65$

15. $4y \leq -30$

16. $4n + 3 < -17$

17. $3 - 5x > 38$

18. $\frac{1}{2}t - \frac{1}{4} \leq \frac{3}{4}t$

19. $5 - 9x \geq 19 + 5x$

Solve each formula for the given letter.

20. $A = 2\pi rh$, for r

21. $w = \dfrac{P + l}{2}$, for l

22. Find decimal notation: 230%.

23. Find percent notation: 0.003.

24. What number is 18.5% of 80?

25. What percent of 75 is 33?

Graph on a number line.

26. $y < 4$

27. $-2 \leq x \leq 2$

Solve.

28. The perimeter of a rectangular calculator is 36 cm. The length is 4 cm greater than the width. Find the width and the length.

29. In 1948, Earl Shaffer became the first person to hike all 2100 mi of the Appalachian trail—from Springer Mountain, Georgia, to Mt. Katahdin, Maine. Shaffer repeated the feat 50 years later, and at age 79 became the oldest person to hike the entire trail. When Shaffer stood atop Big Walker Mountain, Virginia, he was three times as far from the northern end of the trail as from the southern end. At that point, how far was he from each end of the trail?

30. The perimeter of a triangle is 249 mm. If the sides are consecutive odd integers, find the length of eac▌ side.

31. By lowering the temperature of their electric hot-water heater from 140°F to 120°F, the Kellys' average electric bill dropped by 7% to $60.45. What was their electric bill before they lowered the temperature of their hot water?

32. *Mass transit.* Local light rail service in Denver, Colorado, costs $1.50 per trip (one way). A monthly pass costs $54. Gail is a student at Community College of Denver. Express as an inequality the number of trips per month that Gail should make if the pass is to save her money.
Source: rtd-denver.com

Synthesis

Solve.

33. $c = \dfrac{2cd}{a - d}$, for d

34. $3|w| - 8 = 37$

35. Translate to an inequality.

A plant marked "partial sun" needs at least 4 hr but no more than 6 hr of sun each day.
Source: www.yardsmarts.com

36. A concert promoter had a certain number of ticket▌ to give away. Five people got the tickets. The first go one third of the tickets, the second got one fourth o the tickets, and the third got one fifth of the tickets. The fourth person got eight tickets, and there were five tickets left for the fifth person. Find the total number of tickets given away.

Simplify.

1. $18 + (-30)$ [1.5]

2. $\frac{1}{2} - \left(-\frac{1}{4}\right)$ [1.6]

3. $-1.2(3.5)$ [1.7]

4. $-5 \div \left(-\frac{1}{2}\right)$ [1.7]

5. $150 - 10^2 \div 25 \cdot 4$ [1.8]

6. $(150 - 10^2) \div (25 \cdot 4)$ [1.8]

Remove parentheses and simplify. [1.8]

7. $5x - (3x - 1)$

8. $2(t + 6) - 12t$

9. $3[4n - 5(2n - 1)] - 3(n - 7)$

10. Graph on a number line: $-\frac{5}{2}$. [1.4]

11. Find the absolute value: $|27|$. [1.4]

12. Factor: $12x + 18y + 30z$. [1.8]

Solve.

13. $12 = -2x$ [2.1]

14. $4x - 7 = 3x + 9$ [2.1]

15. $\frac{2}{3}t + 7 = 13$ [2.2]

16. $9(2a - 1) = 4$ [2.2]

17. $12 - 3(5x - 1) = x - 1$ [2.2]

18. $3(x + 1) - 2 = 8 - 5(x + 7)$ [2.2]

Solve each formula for the given letter. [2.3]

19. $\frac{1}{2}x = 2yz$, for z

20. $4x - 9y = 1$, for y

21. $an = p - rn$, for n

22. Find decimal notation: 183%. [2.4]

23. Find percent notation: $\frac{3}{8}$. [2.4]

24. Graph on a number line: $t > -\frac{5}{2}$. [2.6]

Solve. Write the answer in set-builder notation and interval notation. [2.6]

25. $4t + 10 \le 2$

26. $8 - t > 5$

27. $4 < 10 - \dfrac{x}{5}$

28. $4(2n - 3) \le 2(5n - 8)$

Solve.

29. The total attendance at NCAA basketball games during the 2006–2007 school year was 33 million. This was 31.25% less than the total attendance at NCAA football games during that year. What was the total attendance at NCAA football games during the 2006–2007 school year? [2.4]
Source: NCAA

30. On an average weekday, a full-time college student spends a total of 7.1 hr in educational activities and in leisure activities. The average student spends 0.7 hr more in leisure activities than in educational activities. On an average weekday, how many hours does a full-time college student spend on educational activities? [2.5]
Source: U.S. Bureau of Labor Statistics

31. The wavelength w, in meters per cycle, of a musical note is given by

$$w = \frac{r}{f},$$

where r is the speed of the sound, in meters per second, and f is the frequency, in cycles per second. The speed of sound in air is 344 m/sec. What is the wavelength of a note whose frequency in air is 24 cycles per second? [2.3]

32. A 24-ft ribbon is cut into two pieces. One piece is 6 ft longer than the other. How long are the pieces? [2.5]

33. Juanita has budgeted an average of $65 a month for entertainment. For the first five months of the year, she has spent $88, $15, $125, $50, and $60. How much can Juanita spend in the sixth month without exceeding her average budget? [2.7]

34. In 2006, about 17 million Americans had diabetes. The U.S. Centers for Disease Control predicts that by 2050, 50 million Americans may have the disease. By what percent would the number of Americans with diabetes increase? [2.4]

35. The second angle of a triangle is twice as large as the first. The third angle is 5° more than four times the first. Find the measure of the largest angle. [2.5]

36. The length of a rectangular frame is 53 cm. For what widths would the perimeter be greater than 160 cm? [2.7]

Synthesis

37. Simplify: $t - \{t - [3t - (2t - t) - t] - 4t\} - t$. [1.8]

38. Solve: $3|n| + 10 = 25$. [2.2]

39. Lindy sold her Fender acoustic guitar on eBay using i-soldit.com. The i-soldit location she used charges 35% of the first $500 of the selling price and 20% of the amount over $500. After these charges were deducted from the selling price, she received $745. For how much did her guitar sell? [2.4], [2.5]

Source: Based on information in *The Wall Street Journal*, 9/11/07

Introduction to Graphing

HEATHER HUTH
DIRECTOR OF VOLUNTEERS
New Orleans, Louisiana

We average about 750 volunteers a month who come to con of Hope to help us clean Orleans' neighborhoods. We service 22 neighborhoods, so I use math to figure out how ny volunteers to send to each location, the quantity of supplies each will need, d how much time is required to complete the task.

AN APPLICATION

An increasing number of college students are donating time and energy in volunteer service. The number of college students volunteering grew from 2.7 million in 2002 to 3.3 million in 2005. Graph the given data and estimate the number of college students who volunteered in 2004, and then predict the number of college students who will volunteer in 2010.

Source: Corporation for National and Community Service

This problem appears as Example 7 in Section 3.7.

W e now begin our study of graphing. First we will examine graphs as they commonly appear in newspapers or magazines and develop some terminology. Following that, we will graph certain equations and study the connection between rate and slope. We will also learn how graphs can be used as a problem-solving tool in many applications.

Our work in this chapter centers on equations that contain two variables.

3.1   Reading Graphs, Plotting Points, and Scaling Graphs

Problem Solving with Bar, Circle, and Line Graphs   ■   Points and Ordered Pairs   ■   Numbering the Axes Appropriately

Today's print and electronic media make almost constant use of graphs. In thi section, we consider problem solving with bar graphs, line graphs, and circl graphs. Then we examine graphs that use a coordinate system.

Problem Solving with Bar, Circle, and Line Graphs

A *bar graph* is a convenient way of showing comparisons. In every bar graph, ce tain categories, such as levels of education in the example below, are paired wit certain numbers.

EXAMPLE   1

Lifetime earnings.   Getting a college degree usually means delaying the start a career. As the bar graph below shows, this loss in earnings is more than made u over a worker's lifetime.

Source: U.S. Census Bureau

a) Keagan plans to get an associate's degree. How much can he expect to make i his lifetime?

b) Isabella would like to make at least $2 million in her lifetime. What level of edu cation should she pursue?

SOLUTION

a) Since level of education is shown on the horizontal scale, we go to the top of th bar above the label "associate's degree." Then we move horizontally fron the top of the bar to the vertical scale, which shows earnings. We read there th Keagan can expect to make about $1.6 million in his lifetime.

b) By moving up the vertical scale to $2 million and then moving horizontally, we see that the first bar to reach a height of $2 million or higher corresponds to a bachelor's degree. Thus Isabella should pursue a bachelor's, master's, doctoral, or professional degree in order to make at least $2 million in her lifetime.

> TRY EXERCISE 5

Circle graphs, or *pie charts,* are often used to show what percent of the whole each particular item in a group represents.

EXAMPLE 2   *Student aid.*   The circle graph below shows the sources for student aid in 2006 and the percentage of aid students received from each source. In that year, the total amount of aid distributed was $134.8 billion. About 5,387,000 students received a federal Pell grant. What was the average amount of the aid per recipient?

Source: Trends in Student Aid 2006, www.collegeboard.com

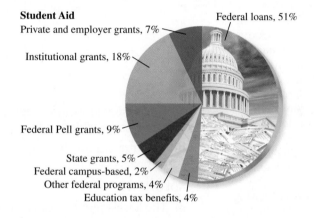

Student Aid
Private and employer grants, 7%
Federal loans, 51%
Institutional grants, 18%
Federal Pell grants, 9%
State grants, 5%
Federal campus-based, 2%
Other federal programs, 4%
Education tax benefits, 4%

SOLUTION

1. **Familiarize.** The problem involves percents, so if we were unsure of how to solve percent problems, we might review Section 2.4.

   The solution of this problem will involve two steps. We are told the total amount of student aid distributed. In order to find the average amount of a Pell grant, we must first calculate the total of all Pell grants and then divide by the number of students.

   We let g = the average amount of a Pell grant in 2006.

2. **Translate.** From the circle graph, we see that federal Pell grants were 9% of the total amount of aid. The total amount distributed was $134.8 billion, or $134,800,000,000, so we have

   Find the value of all Pell grants.

   the value of all Pell grants $= 0.09(134,800,000,000)$
   $= 12,132,000,000.$

   Then we reword the problem and translate as follows:

   Calculate the average amount of a Pell grant.

   Rewording: The average amount of a Pell grant   is   the value of all Pell grants   divided by   the number of recipients.

   Translating: g $=$ $12,132,000,000$ $\div$ $5,387,000$

3. **Carry out.** We solve the equation:

$$g = 12,132,000,000 \div 5,387,000$$
$$\approx 2252. \quad \text{Rounding to the nearest dollar}$$

4. **Check.** If each student received $2252, the total amount of aid distribute
through Pell grants would be $2252 · 5,387,000, or $12,131,524,000. Since thi
is approximately 9% of the total student aid for 2006, our answer checks.

5. **State.** In 2006, the average Pell grant was $2252.

> TRY EXERCISE ▸ 9

EXAMPLE 3

Exercise and pulse rate. The following *line graph* shows the relationship be
tween a person's resting pulse rate and months of regular exercise.* Note that th
symbol ⌇ is used to indicate that counting on the vertical scale begins at 50.

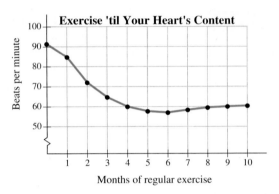

a) How many months of regular exercise are required to lower the pulse rate a
much as possible?

b) How many months of regular exercise are needed to achieve a pulse rate o
65 beats per minute?

SOLUTION

a) The lowest point on the graph occurs above the number 6. Thus, after 6 month
of regular exercise, the pulse rate is lowered as much as possible.

b) To determine how many months of exercise are needed to lower a person
resting pulse rate to 65, we locate 65 midway between 60 and 70 on the vertica
scale. From that location, we move right until the line is reached. At that poin
we move down to the horizontal scale and read the number of months re
quired, as shown.

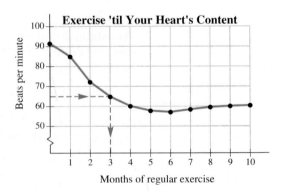

The pulse rate is 65 beats per minute after 3 months of regular exercise.

> TRY EXERCISE ▸ 17

---

*Data from *Body Clock* by Dr. Martin Hughes (New York: Facts on File, Inc.), p. 60.

moved, its coordinates appearing at the bottom of the window.

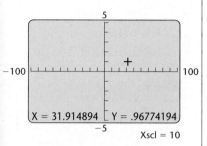

Xscl = 10

Set up the following viewing windows, choosing an appropriate scale for each axis. Then move the cursor and practice reading coordinates.

1. $[-10, 10, -10, 10]$
2. $[-5, 5, 0, 100]$
3. $[-1, 1, -0.1, 0.1]$

Points and Ordered Pairs

The line graph in Example 3 contains a collection of points. Each point pairs up a number of months of exercise with a pulse rate. To create such a graph, we **graph**, or **plot**, pairs of numbers on a plane. This is done using two perpendicular number lines called **axes** (pronounced "ak-sēz"; singular, **axis**). The point at which the axes cross is called the **origin**. Arrows on the axes indicate the positive directions.

Consider the pair $(3, 4)$. The numbers in such a pair are called **coordinates**. The **first coordinate** in this case is 3 and the **second coordinate** is 4.* To plot, or graph, $(3, 4)$, we start at the origin, move horizontally to the 3, move up vertically 4 units, and then make a "dot." Thus, $(3, 4)$ is located above 3 on the first axis and to the right of 4 on the second axis.

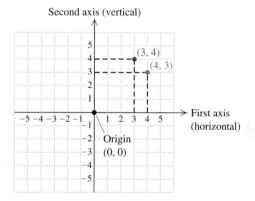

The point $(4, 3)$ is also plotted in the figure above. Note that $(3, 4)$ and $(4, 3)$ are different points. For this reason, coordinate pairs are called **ordered pairs**—the order in which the numbers appear is important.

EXAMPLE **4**

Plot the point $(-3, 4)$.

SOLUTION The first number, -3, is negative. Starting at the origin, we move 3 units in the negative horizontal direction (3 units to the left). The second number, 4, is positive, so we move 4 units in the positive vertical direction (up). The point $(-3, 4)$ is above -3 on the first axis and to the left of 4 on the second axis.

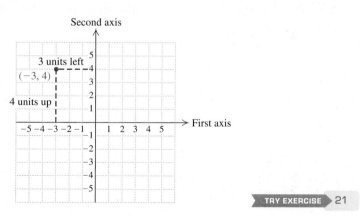

TRY EXERCISE 21

*The first coordinate is called the *abscissa* and the second coordinate is called the *ordinate*. The plane is called the *Cartesian coordinate plane* after the French mathematician René Descartes (1595–1650).

To find the coordinates of a point, we see how far to the right or left of the origin the point is and how far above or below the origin it is. Note that the coordinates of the origin itself are (0, 0).

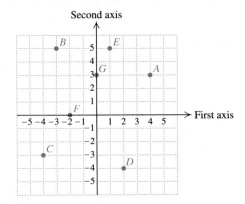

EXAMPLE 5 Find the coordinates of points *A, B, C, D, E, F,* and *G.*

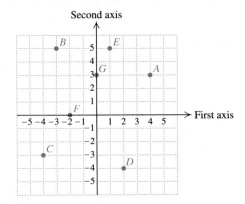

SOLUTION Point *A* is 4 units to the right of the origin and 3 units above the origin. Its coordinates are (4, 3). The coordinates of the other points are as follows:

B: $(-3, 5)$; C: $(-4, -3)$; D: $(2, -4)$;
E: $(1, 5)$; F: $(-2, 0)$; G: $(0, 3)$.

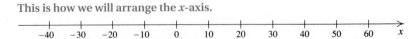 **TRY EXERCISE** 27

The variables *x* and *y* are commonly used when graphing on a plane. Coordinates of ordered pairs are often labeled

(*x*-coordinate, *y*-coordinate).

The first, or horizontal, axis is labeled the *x*-axis, and the second, or vertical, axis is labeled the *y*-axis.

Numbering the Axes Appropriately

In Examples 4 and 5, each square on the grid shown is 1 unit long and 1 unit high. The **scale** of both the *x*-axis and the *y*-axis is 1. Often it is necessary to use a different scale on one or both of the axes.

EXAMPLE 6 Use a grid 10 squares wide and 10 squares high to plot $(-34, 450)$, $(48, 95)$, and $(10, -200)$.

SOLUTION Since *x*-coordinates vary from a low of -34 to a high of 48, the 10 horizontal squares must span $48 - (-34)$, or 82 units. Because 82 is not a multiple of 10, we round *up* to the next multiple of 10, which is 90. Dividing 90 by 10, we find that if each square is 9 units wide (has a scale of 9), we could represent all the *x*-values. However, since it is more convenient to count by 10's, we will instead use a scale of 10. Starting at 0, we count backward to -40 and forward to 60.

This is how we will arrange the *x*-axis.

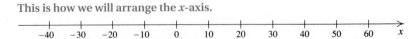

There is more than one correct way to cover the values from -34 to 48 using 10 increments. For instance, we could have counted from -60 to 90, using a scale

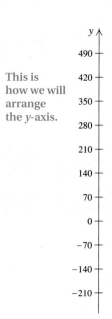

This is how we will arrange the *y*-axis.

of 15. In general, we try to use the smallest range and scale that will cover the given coordinates. Scales that are multiples of 2, 5, or 10 are especially convenient. It is essential that the numbering always begin at the origin.

Since we must be able to show *y*-values from −200 to 450, the 10 vertical squares must span 450 − (−200), or 650 units. For convenience, we round 650 *up* to 700 and then divide by 10: 700 ÷ 10 = 70. Using 70 as the scale, we count *down* from 0 until we pass −200 and *up* from 0 until we pass 450, as shown at left.

Next, we combine our work with the *x*-values and the *y*-values to draw a graph in which the *x*-axis extends from −40 to 60 with a scale of 10 and the *y*-axis extends from −210 to 490 with a scale of 70. To correctly locate the axes on the grid, the two 0's must coincide where the axes cross. Finally, once the graph has been numbered, we plot the points as shown below.

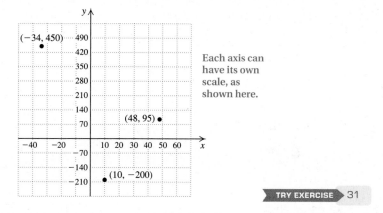

Each axis can have its own scale, as shown here.

TRY EXERCISE 31

The horizontal and vertical axes divide the plane into four regions, or **quadrants**, as indicated by Roman numerals in the following figure. Note that the point (−4, 5) is in the second quadrant and the point (5, −5) is in the fourth quadrant. The points (3, 0) and (0, 1) are on the axes and are not considered to be in any quadrant.

Second quadrant:
First coordinate negative, second coordinate positive:
(−, +)

First quadrant:
Both coordinates positive:
(+, +)

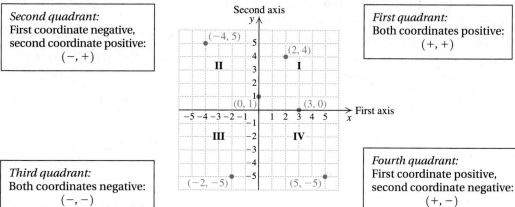

Third quadrant:
Both coordinates negative:
(−, −)

Fourth quadrant:
First coordinate positive, second coordinate negative:
(+, −)

3.1   **EXERCISE SET**

Concept Reinforcement   *In each of Exercises 1–4, match the set of coordinates with the graph on the right that would be the best for plotting the points.*

1. ____ $(-9, 3), (-2, -1), (4, 5)$

2. ____ $(-2, -1), (1, 5), (7, 3)$

3. ____ $(-2, -9), (2, 1), (4, -6)$

4. ____ $(-2, -1), (-9, 3), (-4, -6)$

a)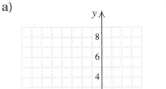

b)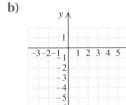

c)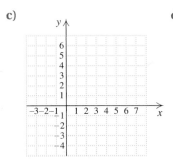

d)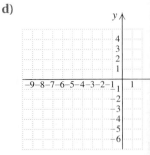

The ▶TRY EXERCISES▶ *for examples are indicated by a shaded block* ▓ *on the exercise number. Complete step-by-step solutions for these exercises appear online at www.pearsonhighered.com/bittingerellenbogen.*

Driving under the influence.   A blood-alcohol level of 0.08% or higher makes driving illegal in the United States. This bar graph shows how many drinks a person of a certain weight would need to consume in 1 hr to achieve a blood-alcohol level of 0.08%. Note that a 12-oz beer, a 5-oz glass of wine, or a cocktail containing $1\frac{1}{2}$ oz of distilled liquor all count as one drink.
Source: Adapted from soberup.com and vsa.vassar.edu/~source/drugs/alcohol.html

Friends Don't Let Friends Drive Drunk

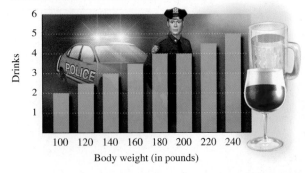

5. Approximately how many drinks would a 100-lb person have consumed in 1 hr to reach a blood-alcohol level of 0.08%?

6. Approximately how many drinks would a 160-lb person have consumed in 1 hr to reach a blood-alcohol level of 0.08%?

7. What can you conclude about the weight of some-one who has consumed 3 drinks in 1 hr without reaching a blood-alcohol level of 0.08%?

8. What can you conclude about the weight of some-one who has consumed 4 drinks in 1 hr without reaching a blood-alcohol level of 0.08%?

Student aid.   Use the information in Example 2 to answer Exercises 9–12.

9. In 2006, there were 13,334,170 full-time equivalent students in U.S. colleges and universities. What was the average federal loan per full-time equivalent student?

10. In 2006, there were 13,334,170 full-time equivalent students in U.S. colleges and universities. What was the average education tax benefit received per full-time equivalent student?

11. Approximately 8.6% of campus-based federal student aid is given to students in two-year public institutions. How much campus-based aid did students at two-year public institutions receive in 2006?

12. Approximately 17.7% of Pell grant dollars is given to students in for-profit institutions. How much did students in for-profit institutions receive in Pell grants in 2006?

Sorting solid waste.   Use the following pie chart to answer Exercises 13–16.

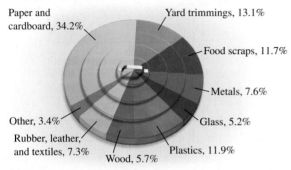

Sorting Solid Waste

Paper and cardboard, 34.2%

Yard trimmings, 13.1%

Food scraps, 11.7%

Metals, 7.6%

Other, 3.4%

Glass, 5.2%

Rubber, leather, and textiles, 7.3%

Plastics, 11.9%

Wood, 5.7%

Source: Environmental Protection Agency

13. In 2005, Americans generated 245 million tons of waste. How much of the waste was plastic?

14. In 2005, the average American generated 4.5 lb of waste per day. How much of that was paper and cardboard?

15. Americans are recycling about 25.3% of all glass that is in the waste stream. How much glass did Americans recycle in 2005? (See Exercise 13.)

16. Americans are recycling about 61.9% of all yard trimmings. What amount of yard trimmings did the average American recycle per day in 2005? (Use the information in Exercise 14.)

Home video spending.   The line graph below shows U.S. consumer spending on home-video movies.

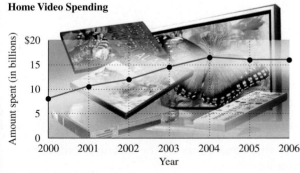

Home Video Spending

Amount spent (in billions)

Source: Adams Media Research

17. Approximately how much was spent on home videos in 2002?

18. Approximately how much was spent on home videos in 2006?

19. In what year was approximately $10.5 billion spent on home videos?

20. In what year was approximately $14.5 billion spent on home videos?

Plot each group of points.

21. $(1, 2), (-2, 3), (4, -1), (-5, -3), (4, 0), (0, -2)$

22. $(-2, -4), (4, -3), (5, 4), (-1, 0), (-4, 4), (0, 5)$

23. $(4, 4), (-2, 4), (5, -3), (-5, -5), (0, 4), (0, -4),$ $(-4, 0), (0, 0)$

24. $(2, 5), (-1, 3), (3, -2), (-2, -4), (0, 0), (0, -5),$ $(5, 0), (-5, 0)$

25. *Text messaging.*   Listed below are estimates of the number of text messages sent in the United States. Make a line graph of the data.

Year	Monthly Text Messages (in millions)
2000	12
2001	34
2002	931
2003	1221
2004	2862
2005	7253
2006	8000 (estimated)

Source: CSCA

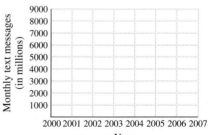

26. *Ozone layer.* Listed below are estimates of the ozone level. Make a line graph of the data, listing years on the horizontal scale.

Year	Ozone Level (in Dobson Units)
2000	287.1
2001	288.2
2002	285.8
2003	285.0
2004	281.2
2005	283.5

Source: johnstonsarchive.net

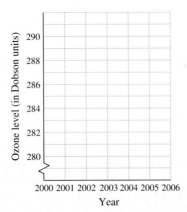

In Exercises 27–30, find the coordinates of points A, B, C, D, and E.

27.

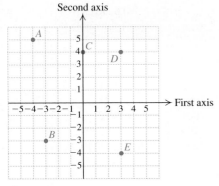

28.

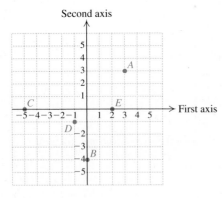

29.

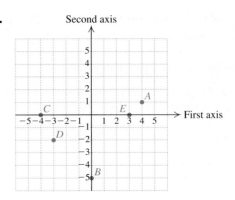

30.

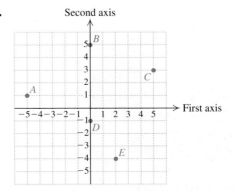

In Exercises 31–40, use a grid 10 squares wide and 10 squares high to plot the given coordinates. Choose your scale carefully. Scales may vary.

31. $(-75, 5), (-18, -2), (9, -4)$

32. $(-13, 3), (48, -1), (62, -4)$

33. $(-1, 83), (-5, -14), (5, 37)$

34. $(2, -79), (4, -25), (-4, 12)$

35. $(-10, -4), (-16, 7), (3, 15)$

36. $(5, -16), (-7, -4), (12, 3)$

37. $(-100, -5), (350, 20), (800, 37)$

38. $(750, -8), (-150, 17), (400, 32)$

39. $(-83, 491), (-124, -95), (54, -238)$

40. $(738, -89), (-49, -6), (-165, 53)$

In which quadrant is each point located?

41. $(7, -2)$ **42.** $(-1, -4)$ **43.** $(-4, -3)$

44. $(1, -5)$ **45.** $(2, 1)$ **46.** $(-4, 6)$

47. $(-4.9, 8.3)$ **48.** $(7.5, 2.9)$

49. In which quadrants are the first coordinates positive?

50. In which quadrants are the second coordinates negative?

51. In which quadrants do both coordinates have the same sign?

52. In which quadrants do the first and second coordinates have opposite signs?

53. The following graph was included in a mailing sent by Agway® to their oil customers in 2000. What information is missing from the graph and why is the graph misleading?

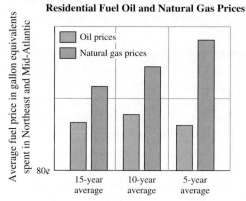

Residential Fuel Oil and Natural Gas Prices

Average fuel price in gallon equivalents spent in Northeast and Mid-Atlantic

- Oil prices
- Natural gas prices

15-year average   10-year average   5-year average

Source: Energy Research Center, Inc. *3/1/99–2/29/00

54. What do all points plotted on the vertical axis of a graph have in common?

Skill Review

To prepare for Section 3.2, review solving for a variable (Section 2.3).

Solve for y. [2.3]

55. $5y = 2x$

56. $2y = -3x$

57. $x - y = 8$

58. $2x + 5y = 10$

59. $2x + 3y = 5$

60. $5x - 8y = 1$

Synthesis

61. In an article about consumer spending on home videos (see the graph used for Exercise 17), the *Wall Street Journal* (9/2/06) stated that "the movie industry has hit a wall." To what were they referring?

62. Describe what the result would be if the first and second coordinates of every point in the following graph of an arrow were interchanged.

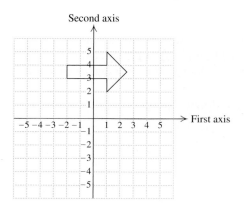

Second axis

First axis

63. In which quadrant(s) could a point be located if its coordinates are opposites of each other?

64. In which quadrant(s) could a point be located if its coordinates are reciprocals of each other?

65. The points $(-1, 1)$, $(4, 1)$, and $(4, -5)$ are three vertices of a rectangle. Find the coordinates of the fourth vertex.

66. The pairs $(-2, -3)$, $(-1, 2)$, and $(4, -3)$ can serve as three (of four) vertices for three different parallelograms. Find the fourth vertex of each parallelogram.

67. Graph eight points such that the sum of the coordinates in each pair is 7. Answers may vary.

68. Find the perimeter of a rectangle if three of its vertices are $(5, -2)$, $(-3, -2)$, and $(-3, 3)$.

69. Find the area of a triangle whose vertices have coordinates $(0, 9)$, $(0, -4)$, and $(5, -4)$.

Coordinates on the globe.   Coordinates can also be used to describe the location on a sphere: 0° latitude is the equator and 0° longitude is a line from the North Pole to the South Pole through France and Algeria. In the figure shown here, hurricane Clara is at a point about 260 mi northwest of Bermuda near latitude 36.0° North, longitude 69.0° West.

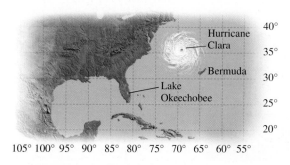

Hurricane Clara
Bermuda
Lake Okeechobee

40°
35°
30°
25°
20°

105° 100° 95° 90° 85° 80° 75° 70° 65° 60° 55°

70. Approximate the latitude and the longitude of Bermuda.

71. Approximate the latitude and the longitude of Lake Okeechobee.

72. The graph accompanying Example 3 flattens out. Why do you think this occurs?

73. In the *Star Trek* science-fiction series, a three-dimensional coordinate system is used to locate objects in space. If the center of a planet is used as the origin, how many "quadrants" will exist? Why? If possible, sketch a three-dimensional coordinate system and label each "quadrant."

COLLABORATIVE

CORNER

You Sank My Battleship!

Focus: Graphing points; logical questioning
Time: 15–25 minutes
Group size: 3–5
Materials: Graph paper

In the game Battleship®, a player places a miniature ship on a grid that only that player can see. An opponent guesses at coordinates that might "hit" the "hidden" ship. The following activity is similar to this game.

ACTIVITY

1. Using only integers from −10 to 10 (inclusive), one group member should secretly record the coordinates of a point on a slip of paper. (This point is the hidden "battleship.")

2. The other group members can then ask up to 10 "yes/no" questions in an effort to determine the coordinates of the secret point. Be sure to phrase each question mathematically (for example, "Is the *x*-coordinate negative?")

3. The group member who selected the point should answer each question. On the basis of the answer given, another group member should cross out the points no longer under consideration. All group members should check that this is done correctly.

4. If the hidden point has not been determined after 10 questions have been answered, the secret coordinates should be revealed to all group members.

5. Repeat parts (1)–(4) until each group member has had the opportunity to select the hidden point and answer questions.

3.2 Graphing Linear Equations

Solutions of Equations ▪ Graphing Linear Equations ▪ Applications

We have seen how bar, line, and circle graphs can represent information. Now w begin to learn how graphs can be used to represent solutions of equations.

Solutions of Equations

When an equation contains two variables, solutions are ordered pairs in whic each number in the pair replaces a letter in the equation. Unless stated otherwise the first number in each pair replaces the variable that occurs first alphabetically

EXAMPLE **1** Determine whether each of the following pairs is a solution of $4b - 3a = 2$
(a) $(2, 7)$; **(b)** $(1, 6)$.

SOLUTION

a) We substitute 2 for a and 7 for b (alphabetical order of variables):

$$
\begin{array}{c|c}
\multicolumn{2}{c}{4b - 3a = 22} \\
\hline
4(7) - 3(2) & 22 \\
28 - 6 & \\
22 \overset{?}{=} 22 & \text{TRUE}
\end{array}
$$

Since $22 = 22$ is *true*, the pair $(2, 7)$ *is* a solution.

b) In this case, we replace a with 1 and b with 6:

$$
\begin{array}{c|c}
\multicolumn{2}{c}{4b - 3a = 22} \\
\hline
4(6) - 3(1) & 22 \\
24 - 3 & \\
21 \overset{?}{=} 22 & \text{FALSE} \qquad 21 \neq 22
\end{array}
$$

Since $21 = 22$ is *false*, the pair $(1, 6)$ is *not* a solution.   **TRY EXERCISE** ▸ 7

EXAMPLE 2   Show that the pairs $(3, 7)$, $(0, 1)$, and $(-3, -5)$ are solutions of $y = 2x + 1$. Then graph the three points to determine another pair that is a solution.

SOLUTION   To show that a pair is a solution, we substitute, replacing x with the first coordinate and y with the second coordinate of each pair:

$$
\begin{array}{c|c}
\multicolumn{2}{c}{y = 2x + 1} \\
\hline
7 & 2 \cdot 3 + 1 \\
& 6 + 1 \\
7 \overset{?}{=} 7 & \text{TRUE}
\end{array}
\qquad
\begin{array}{c|c}
\multicolumn{2}{c}{y = 2x + 1} \\
\hline
1 & 2 \cdot 0 + 1 \\
& 0 + 1 \\
1 \overset{?}{=} 1 & \text{TRUE}
\end{array}
\qquad
\begin{array}{c|c}
\multicolumn{2}{c}{y = 2x + 1} \\
\hline
-5 & 2(-3) + 1 \\
& -6 + 1 \\
-5 \overset{?}{=} -5 & \text{TRUE}
\end{array}
$$

In each of the three cases, the substitution results in a true equation. Thus the pairs $(3, 7)$, $(0, 1)$, and $(-3, -5)$ are all solutions. We graph them as shown at left.

Note that the three points appear to "line up." Will other points that line up with these points also represent solutions of $y = 2x + 1$? To find out, we use a ruler and draw a line passing through $(-3, -5)$, $(0, 1)$, and $(3, 7)$.

The line appears to pass through $(2, 5)$. Let's check to see if this pair is a solution of $y = 2x + 1$:

$$
\begin{array}{c|c}
\multicolumn{2}{c}{y = 2x + 1} \\
\hline
5 & 2 \cdot 2 + 1 \\
& 4 + 1 \\
5 \overset{?}{=} 5 & \text{TRUE}
\end{array}
$$

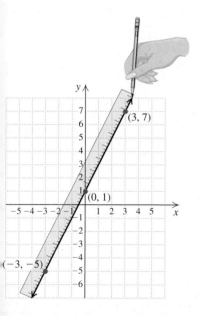

We see that $(2, 5)$ *is* a solution. You should perform a similar check for at least one other point that appears to be on the line.   **TRY EXERCISE** ▸ 13

Example 2 leads us to suspect that *any* point on the line passing through $(3, 7)$, $(0, 1)$, and $(-3, -5)$ represents a solution of $y = 2x + 1$. In fact, every solution of $y = 2x + 1$ is represented by a point on this line and every point on this line represents a solution. The line is called the **graph** of the equation.

Graphing Linear Equations

Equations like $y = 2x + 1$ or $4b - 3a = 22$ are said to be **linear** because the graph of each equation is a line. In general, any equation that can be written in the form $y = mx + b$ or $Ax + By = C$ (where $m, b, A, B,$ and C are constants and A and B are not both 0) is linear.

To *graph* an equation is to make a drawing that represents its solutions. Linear equations can be graphed as follows.

> **To Graph a Linear Equation**
> 1. Select a value for one coordinate and calculate the corresponding value of the other coordinate. Form an ordered pair. This pair is one solution of the equation.
> 2. Repeat step (1) to find a second ordered pair. A third ordered pair should be found to use as a check.
> 3. Plot the ordered pairs and draw a straight line passing through the points. The line represents all solutions of the equation.

EXAMPLE **3**

Graph: $y = -3x + 1$.

SOLUTION Since $y = -3x + 1$ is in the form $y = mx + b$, the equation is linear and the graph is a straight line. We select a convenient value for x, compute y, and form an ordered pair. Then we repeat the process for other choices of x.

If $x = 2$, then $y = -3 \cdot 2 + 1 = -5$, and $(2, -5)$ is a solution.

If $x = 0$, then $y = -3 \cdot 0 + 1 = 1$, and $(0, 1)$ is a solution.

If $x = -1$, then $y = -3(-1) + 1 = 4$, and $(-1, 4)$ is a solution.

Results are often listed in a table, as shown below. The points corresponding to each pair are then plotted.

Calculate ordered pairs.

$y = -3x + 1$

x	y	(x, y)
2	−5	$(2, -5)$
0	1	$(0, 1)$
−1	4	$(-1, 4)$

(1) Choose x.
(2) Compute y.
(3) Form the pair (x, y).

Plot the points.

(4) Plot the points.

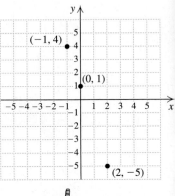

Note that all three points line up. If they didn't, we would know that we had made a mistake, because the equation is linear. When only two points are plotted, an error is more difficult to detect.

Draw the graph.

Finally, we use a ruler or other straight-edge to draw a line. We add arrowheads to the ends of the line to indicate that it extends indefinitely beyond the edge of the grid drawn. Every point on the line represents a solution of $y = -3x + 1$.

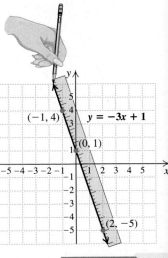

TRY EXERCISE 21

EXAMPLE 4

Graph: $y = 2x - 3$.

SOLUTION   We select some convenient x-values and compute y-values.

If $x = 0$,   then $y = 2 \cdot 0 - 3 = -3$,   and $(0, -3)$ is a solution.

If $x = 1$,   then $y = 2 \cdot 1 - 3 = -1$,   and $(1, -1)$ is a solution.

If $x = 4$,   then $y = 2 \cdot 4 - 3 = 5$,   and $(4, 5)$ is a solution.

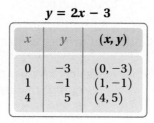

$y = 2x - 3$

x	y	(x, y)
0	−3	$(0, -3)$
1	−1	$(1, -1)$
4	5	$(4, 5)$

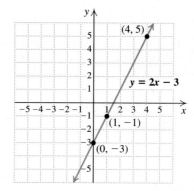

TRY EXERCISE 27

EXAMPLE 5

Graph: $4x + 2y = 12$.

SOLUTION   To form ordered pairs, we can replace either variable with a number and then calculate the other coordinate:

If $y = 0$, we have $4x + 2 \cdot 0 = 12$

$4x = 12$

$x = 3$,

so $(3, 0)$ is a solution.

If $x = 0$, we have $4 \cdot 0 + 2y = 12$

$2y = 12$

$y = 6$,

so $(0, 6)$ is a solution.

If $y = 2$, we have $4x + 2 \cdot 2 = 12$

$4x + 4 = 12$

$4x = 8$

$x = 2$,

so $(2, 2)$ is a solution.

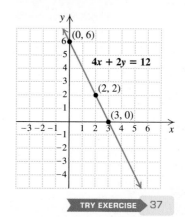

$4x + 2y = 12$

x	y	(x, y)
3	0	$(3, 0)$
0	6	$(0, 6)$
2	2	$(2, 2)$

TRY EXERCISE 37

Note that in Examples 3 and 4 the variable y is isolated on one side of the equation. This generally simplifies calculations, so it is important to be able to solve for y before graphing.

EXAMPLE **6**

Graph $3y = 2x$ by first solving for y.

SOLUTION   To isolate y, we divide both sides by 3, or multiply both sides by $\frac{1}{3}$:

$$3y = 2x$$

$$\frac{1}{3} \cdot 3y = \frac{1}{3} \cdot 2x \qquad \text{Using the multiplication principle to}$$
$$\text{multiply both sides by } \frac{1}{3}$$

$$\left. \begin{array}{l} 1y = \frac{2}{3} \cdot x \\ y = \frac{2}{3}x. \end{array} \right\} \qquad \text{Simplifying}$$

Because all the equations above are equivalent, we can use $y = \frac{2}{3}x$ to draw the graph of $3y = 2x$.

To graph $y = \frac{2}{3}x$, we can select x-values that are multiples of 3. This will allow us to avoid fractions when the corresponding y-values are computed.

$$\left. \begin{array}{l} \text{If } x = 3, \quad \text{then } y = \frac{2}{3} \cdot 3 = 2. \\ \text{If } x = -3, \quad \text{then } y = \frac{2}{3}(-3) = -2. \\ \text{If } x = 6, \quad \text{then } y = \frac{2}{3} \cdot 6 = 4. \end{array} \right\}$$
Note that when multiples of 3 are substituted for x, the y-coordinates are not fractions.

The following table lists these solutions. Next, we plot the points and see that they form a line. Finally, we draw and label the line.

$$3y = 2x, \text{ or } y = \frac{2}{3}x$$

x	y	(x, y)
3	2	$(3, 2)$
−3	−2	$(−3, −2)$
6	4	$(6, 4)$

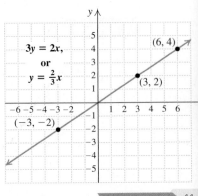

TRY EXERCISE 41

EXAMPLE **7**

Graph $x + 5y = -10$ by first solving for y.

SOLUTION   We have

$$x + 5y = -10$$

$$5y = -x - 10 \qquad \text{Adding } -x \text{ to both sides}$$

$$y = \frac{1}{5}(-x - 10) \qquad \text{Multiplying both sides by } \frac{1}{5}$$

$$y = -\frac{1}{5}x - 2. \qquad \text{Using the distributive law}$$

CAUTION!   It is very important to multiply *both* $-x$ and -10 by $\frac{1}{5}$.

Thus, $x + 5y = -10$ is equivalent to $y = -\frac{1}{5}x - 2$. It is important to note that we now choose x-values that are multiples of 5, we can avoid fractions when calculating the corresponding y-values.

$$\text{If } x = 5, \quad \text{then } y = -\frac{1}{5} \cdot 5 - 2 = -1 - 2 = -3.$$
$$\text{If } x = 0, \quad \text{then } y = -\frac{1}{5} \cdot 0 - 2 = 0 - 2 = -2.$$
$$\text{If } x = -5, \quad \text{then } y = -\frac{1}{5}(-5) - 2 = 1 - 2 = -1.$$

$$x + 5y = -10, \text{ or } y = -\frac{1}{5}x - 2$$

x	y	(x, y)
5	−3	$(5, -3)$
0	−2	$(0, -2)$
−5	−1	$(-5, -1)$

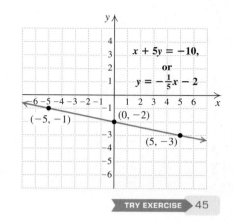

TRY EXERCISE   45

Applications

Linear equations appear in many real-life situations.

EXAMPLE 8

Fuel efficiency.   A typical tractor-trailer will move 18 tons of air per mile at 55 mph. Air resistance increases with speed, causing fuel efficiency to decrease at higher speeds. At highway speeds, a certain truck's fuel efficiency t, in miles per gallon (mpg), can be given by

$$t = -0.1s + 13.1,$$

where s is the speed of the truck, in miles per hour (mph). Graph the equation and then use the graph to estimate the fuel efficiency at 66 mph.

Source: Based on data from Kenworth Truck Co.

SOLUTION   We graph $t = -0.1s + 13.1$ by first selecting values for s and then cal-culating the associated values t. Since the equation is true for highway speeds, we use $s \geq 50$.

If $s = 50$,   then $t = -0.1(50) + 13.1 = 8.1$.
If $s = 60$,   then $t = -0.1(60) + 13.1 = 7.1$.
If $s = 70$,   then $t = -0.1(70) + 13.1 = 6.1$.

s	t
50	8.1
60	7.1
70	6.1

Because we are *selecting* values for s and *calculating* values for t, we represent s on the horizontal axis and t on the vertical axis. Counting by 5's horizontally, begin-ning at 50, and by 0.5 vertically, beginning at 4, will allow us to plot all three pairs, as shown below.

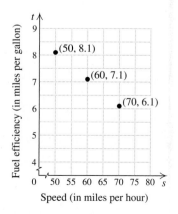

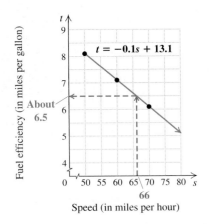

Fuel efficiency (in miles per gallon)

$t = -0.1s + 13.1$

About 6.5

66

Speed (in miles per hour)

Since the three points line up, our calculations are probably correct. We draw a line, beginning at $(50, 8.1)$. To estimate the fuel efficiency at 66 mph, we locate the point on the line that is above 66 and then find the value on the *t*-axis that corresponds to that point, as shown at left. The fuel efficiency at 66 mph is about 6.5 mpg.

TRY EXERCISE 49

> *CAUTION!* When the coordinates of a point are read from a graph, as in Example 8, values should not be considered exact.

Many equations in two variables have graphs that are not straight lines. Three such graphs are shown below. As before, each graph represents the solutions of the given equation. Graphing calculators are especially helpful when drawing these *nonlinear* graphs. Nonlinear graphs are studied later in this text and in more advanced courses.

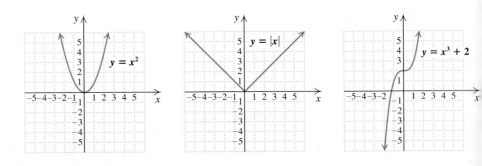

$y = x^2$

$y = |x|$

$y = x^3 + 2$

TECHNOLOGY CONNECTION

Most graphing calculators require that *y* be alone on one side before the equation is entered. For example, to graph $5y + 4x = 13$, we would first solve for *y*. The student can check that solving for *y* yields the equation $y = -\frac{4}{5}x + \frac{13}{5}$.

We press ⬤Y=, enter $-\frac{4}{5}x + \frac{13}{5}$ as Y1, and press ⬤GRAPH. The graph is shown here in the standard viewing window $[-10, 10, -10, 10]$.

Using a graphing calculator, graph each of the following. Select the "standard" $[-10, 10, -10, 10]$ window.

1. $y = -5x + 6.5$
2. $y = 3x + 4.5$
3. $7y - 4x = 22$
4. $5y + 11x = -20$
5. $2y - x^2 = 0$
6. $y + x^2 = 8$

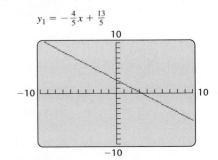

$y_1 = -\frac{4}{5}x + \frac{13}{5}$

3.2   EXERCISE SET

⮌ *Concept Reinforcement*   *Classify each statement as either true or false.*

1. A linear equation in two variables has at most one solution.

2. Every solution of $y = 3x - 7$ is an ordered pair.

3. The graph of $y = 3x - 7$ represents all solutions of the equation.

4. If a point is on the graph of $y = 3x - 7$, the corresponding ordered pair is a solution of the equation.

5. To find a solution of $y = 3x - 7$, we can choose any value for x and calculate the corresponding value for y.

6. The graph of every equation is a straight line.

Determine whether each equation has the given ordered pair as a solution.

7. $y = 4x - 7$; $(2, 1)$

8. $y = 5x + 8$; $(0, 8)$

9. $3y + 4x = 19$; $(5, 1)$

10. $5x - 3y = 15$; $(0, 5)$

11. $4m - 5n = 7$; $(3, -1)$

12. $3q - 2p = -8$; $(1, -2)$

In Exercises 13–20, an equation and two ordered pairs are given. Show that each pair is a solution of the equation. Then graph the two pairs to determine another solution. Answers may vary.

13. $y = x + 3$; $(-1, 2), (4, 7)$

14. $y = x - 2$; $(3, 1), (-2, -4)$

15. $y = \frac{1}{2}x + 3$; $(4, 5), (-2, 2)$

16. $y = \frac{1}{2}x - 1$; $(6, 2), (0, -1)$

17. $y + 3x = 7$; $(2, 1), (4, -5)$

18. $2y + x = 5$; $(-1, 3), (7, -1)$

19. $4x - 2y = 10$; $(0, -5), (4, 3)$

20. $6x - 3y = 3$; $(1, 1), (-1, -3)$

Graph each equation.

21. $y = x + 1$

22. $y = x - 1$

23. $y = -x$

24. $y = x$

25. $y = 2x$

26. $y = -3x$

27. $y = 2x + 2$

28. $y = 3x - 2$

29. $y = -\frac{1}{2}x$

30. $y = \frac{1}{4}x$

31. $y = \frac{1}{3}x - 4$

32. $y = \frac{1}{2}x + 1$

33. $x + y = 4$

34. $x + y = -5$

35. $x - y = -2$

36. $y - x = 3$

37. $x + 2y = -6$

38. $x + 2y = 8$

39. $y = -\frac{2}{3}x + 4$

40. $y = \frac{3}{2}x + 1$

41. $4x = 3y$

42. $2x = 5y$

43. $5x - y = 0$

44. $3x - 5y = 0$

45. $6x - 3y = 9$

46. $8x - 4y = 12$

47. $6y + 2x = 8$

48. $8y + 2x = -4$

49. *Student aid.*   The average award a of federal student financial assistance per student is approximated by

$$a = 0.08t + 2.5,$$

where a is in thousands of dollars and t is the number of years since 1994. Graph the equation and use the graph to estimate the average amount of federal student aid per student in 2010.
Source: Based on data from U.S. Department of Education, Office of Postsecondary Education

50. *Value of a color copier.*   The value of Dupliographic's color copier is given by

$$v = -0.68t + 3.4,$$

where v is the value, in thousands of dollars, t years from the date of purchase. Graph the equation and use the graph to estimate the value of the copier after $2\frac{1}{2}$ yr.

51. *FedEx mailing costs.*   Recently, the cost c, in dollars, of shipping a FedEx Priority Overnight package weighing 1 lb or more a distance of 1001 to 1400 mi was given by

$$c = 3.1w + 29.07,$$

where w is the package's weight, in pounds. Graph the equation and use the graph to estimate the cost of shipping a $6\frac{1}{2}$-lb package.
Source: Based on data from FedEx.com

52. *Increasing life expectancy.*   A smoker is 15 times more likely to die of lung cancer than a nonsmoker. An ex-smoker who stopped smoking t years ago is

w times more likely to die of lung cancer than a nonsmoker, where

$$w = 15 - t.$$

Graph the equation and use the graph to estimate how much more likely it is for Sandy to die of lung cancer than Polly, if Polly never smoked and Sandy quit $2\frac{1}{2}$ yr ago.

Source: Data from *Body Clock* by Dr. Martin Hughes, p. 60. New York: Facts on File, Inc.

53. *Scrapbook pricing.*   The price *p*, in dollars, of an 8-in. by 8-in. assembled scrapbook is given by

$$p = 3.5n + 9,$$

where *n* is the number of pages in the scrapbook. Graph the equation and use the graph to estimate the price of a scrapbook containing 25 pages.

Source: www.scrapbooksplease.com

54. *Value of computer software.*   The value *v* of a shopkeeper's inventory software program, in hundreds of dollars, is given by

$$v = -\tfrac{3}{4}t + 6,$$

where *t* is the number of years since the shopkeeper first bought the program. Graph the equation and use the graph to estimate what the program is worth 4 yr after it was first purchased.

55. *Bottled water.*   The number of gallons of bottled water *w* consumed by the average American in one year is given by

$$w = 1.6t + 16.7,$$

where *t* is the number of years since 2000. Graph the equation and use the graph to predict the number of gallons consumed by the average American in 2010.

Source: Based on data from Beverage Marketing Corporation

56. *Record temperature drop.*   On January 22, 1943, the temperature *T*, in degrees Fahrenheit, in Spearfish, South Dakota, could be approximated by

$$T = -2m + 54,$$

where *m* is the number of minutes since 9:00 A.M. that morning. Graph the equation and use the graph to estimate the temperature at 9:15 A.M.

Source: Based on information from the National Oceanic Atmospheric Administration

57. *Cost of college.*   The cost *T*, in hundreds of dollars, of tuition and fees at many community colleges can be approximated by

$$T = \tfrac{5}{4}c + 2,$$

where *c* is the number of credits for which a student registers. Graph the equation and use the graph to

estimate the cost of tuition and fees when a student registers for 4 three-credit courses.

Bartonville Community College

Ferndell Hall

Tuition $125 / credit
Fees
Registration $85
Transcripts $55
Computer $45
Activities $15

Activities include: Math team, fencing, drama club

58. *Cost of college.*   The cost *C*, in thousands of dollars, of a year at a private four-year college (all expenses) can be approximated by

$$C = \tfrac{13}{10}t + 21,$$

where *t* is the number of years since 1995. Graph the equation and use the graph to predict the cost of a year at a private four-year college in 2012.

Source: Based on information in *Statistical Abstract of the United States,* 2007

59. The equations $3x + 4y = 8$ and $y = -\tfrac{3}{4}x + 2$ are equivalent. Which equation would be easier to graph and why?

60. Suppose that a linear equation is graphed by plotting three points and that the three points line up with each other. Does this *guarantee* that the equation is being correctly graphed? Why or why not?

Skill Review

Review solving equations and formulas (Sections 2.2 and 2.3).

Solve and check. [2.2]

61. $5x + 3 \cdot 0 = 12$

62. $3 \cdot 0 - 8y = 6$

63. $5x + 3(2 - x) = 12$

64. $3(y - 5) - 8y = 6$

Solve. [2.3]

65. $A = \dfrac{T + Q}{2}$, for *Q*

66. $pq + p = w$, for *p*

67. $Ax + By = C$, for *y*

68. $\dfrac{y - k}{m} = x - h$, for *y*

Synthesis

69. Janice consistently makes the mistake of plotting the x-coordinate of an ordered pair using the y-axis, and the y-coordinate using the x-axis. How will Janice's incorrect graph compare with the appropriate graph?

70. Explain how the graph in Example 8 can be used to determine the speed for which the fuel efficiency is 6 mpg.

71. *Bicycling.* Long Beach Island in New Jersey is a long, narrow, flat island. For exercise, Laura routinely bikes to the northern tip of the island and back. Because of the steady wind, she uses one gear going north and another for her return. Laura's bike has 21 gears and the sum of the two gears used on her ride is always 24. Write and graph an equation that represents the different pairings of gears that Laura uses. Note that there are no fraction gears on a bicycle.

In Exercises 72–75, try to find an equation for the graph shown.

72.

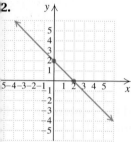

73.

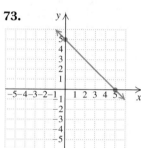

74.

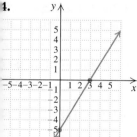

75.

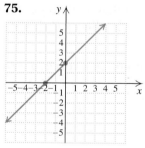

76. Translate to an equation:

 d dimes and n nickels total $1.75.

Then graph the equation and use the graph to determine three different combinations of dimes and nickels that total $1.75 (see also Exercise 90).

77. Translate to an equation:

 d $25 dinners and l $5 lunches total $225.

Then graph the equation and use the graph to determine three different combinations of lunches and dinners that total $225 (see also Exercise 90).

Use the suggested x-values $-3, -2, -1, 0, 1, 2,$ *and* 3 *to graph each equation.*

78. $y = |x|$

Aha! **79.** $y = -|x|$

Aha! **80.** $y = |x| - 2$

81. $y = x^2$

82. $y = x^2 + 1$

For Exercises 83–88, use a graphing calculator to graph the equation. Use a $[-10, 10, -10, 10]$ window.

83. $y = -2.8x + 3.5$

84. $y = 4.5x + 2.1$

85. $y = 2.8x - 3.5$

86. $y = -4.5x - 2.1$

87. $y = x^2 + 4x + 1$

88. $y = -x^2 + 4x - 7$

89. Example 8 discusses fuel efficiency. If fuel costs $3.50 a gallon, how much money will a truck driver save on a 500-mi trip by driving at 55 mph instead of 70 mph? How many gallons of fuel will be saved?

90. Study the graph of Exercises 76 and 77. Does *every* point on the graph represent a solution of the associated problem? Why or why not?

3.3 Graphing and Intercepts

Intercepts ▪ Using Intercepts to Graph ▪ Graphing Horizontal or Vertical Lines

Unless a line is horizontal or vertical, it will cross both axes. Often, findin
the points where the axes are crossed gives us a quick way of graphing linea
equations.

Intercepts

In Example 5 of Section 3.2, we graphed $4x + 2y = 12$ by plotting the point
$(3, 0)$, $(0, 6)$, and $(2, 2)$ and then drawing the line.

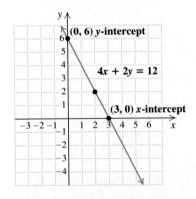

- The point at which a graph crosses the y-axis is called the **y-intercept**. In th
  figure above, the y-intercept is $(0, 6)$. The x-coordinate of a y-intercept
  always 0.
- The point at which a graph crosses the x-axis is called the **x-intercept**. In th
  figure above, the x-intercept is $(3, 0)$. The y-coordinate of an x-intercept
  always 0.

It is possible for the graph of a curve to have more than one y-intercept
more than one x-intercept.

EXAMPLE **1**   For the graph shown below, **(a)** give the coordinates of any x-intercepts and **(b)** giv
the coordinates of any y-intercepts.

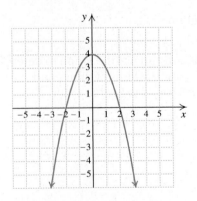

SOLUTION

a) The x-intercepts are the points at which the graph crosses the x-axis. For the graph shown, the x-intercepts are $(-2, 0)$ and $(2, 0)$.

b) The y-intercept is the point at which the graph crosses the y-axis. For the graph shown, the y-intercept is $(0, 4)$.

TRY EXERCISE 7

Using Intercepts to Graph

It is important to know how to locate a graph's intercepts from the equation being graphed.

> **To Find Intercepts**
>
> To find the y-intercept(s) of an equation's graph, replace x with 0 and solve for y.
>
> To find the x-intercept(s) of an equation's graph, replace y with 0 and solve for x.

EXAMPLE 2   Find the y-intercept and the x-intercept of the graph of $2x + 4y = 20$.

SOLUTION   To find the y-intercept, we let $x = 0$ and solve for y:

$$2 \cdot 0 + 4y = 20 \qquad \text{Replacing } x \text{ with } 0$$
$$4y = 20$$
$$y = 5.$$

Thus the y-intercept is $(0, 5)$.
 To find the x-intercept, we let $y = 0$ and solve for x:

$$2x + 4 \cdot 0 = 20 \qquad \text{Replacing } y \text{ with } 0$$
$$2x = 20$$
$$x = 10.$$

Thus the x-intercept is $(10, 0)$.

TRY EXERCISE 15

 Since two points are sufficient to graph a line, intercepts can be used to graph linear equations.

EXAMPLE 3   Graph $2x + 4y = 20$ using intercepts.

SOLUTION   In Example 2, we showed that the y-intercept is $(0, 5)$ and the x-intercept is $(10, 0)$. Before drawing a line, we plot a third point as a check. We substitute any convenient value for x and solve for y.

If we let $x = 5$, then

$$2 \cdot 5 + 4y = 20 \qquad \text{Substituting 5 for } x$$
$$10 + 4y = 20$$
$$4y = 10 \qquad \text{Subtracting 10 from both sides}$$
$$y = \tfrac{10}{4}, \text{ or } 2\tfrac{1}{2}. \qquad \text{Solving for } y$$

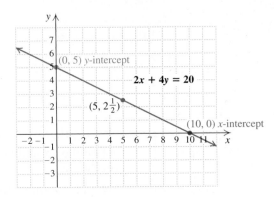

The point $\left(5, 2\tfrac{1}{2}\right)$ appears to line up with the intercepts, so our work is probably correct. To finish, we draw and label the line.

> **TRY EXERCISE** 25

Note that when we solved for the y-intercept, we replaced x with 0 and simplified $2x + 4y = 20$ to $4y = 20$. Thus, to find the y-intercept, we can momentarily ignore the x-term and solve the remaining equation.

In a similar manner, when we solved for the x-intercept, we simplified $2x + 4y = 20$ to $2x = 20$. Thus, to find the x-intercept, we can momentarily ignore the y-term and then solve this remaining equation.

EXAMPLE 4 Graph $3x - 2y = 60$ using intercepts.

SOLUTION To find the y-intercept, we let $x = 0$. This amounts to temporarily ignoring the x-term and then solving:

$$-2y = 60 \qquad \text{For } x = 0, \text{ we have } 3 \cdot 0 - 2y, \text{ or simply } -2y.$$
$$y = -30.$$

The y-intercept is $(0, -30)$.

To find the x-intercept, we let $y = 0$. This amounts to temporarily disregarding the y-term and then solving:

$$3x = 60 \qquad \text{For } y = 0, \text{ we have } 3x - 2 \cdot 0, \text{ or simply } 3x.$$
$$x = 20.$$

The x-intercept is $(20, 0)$.

To find a third point, we can replace x with 4 and solve for y:

$$3 \cdot 4 - 2y = 60 \qquad \text{Numbers other than 4 can be used for } x.$$
$$12 - 2y = 60$$
$$-2y = 48$$
$$y = -24. \qquad \text{This means that } (4, -24) \text{ is on the graph.}$$

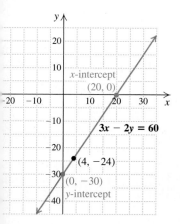

In order for us to graph all three points, the y-axis of our graph must go down to at least -30 and the x-axis must go up to at least 20. Using a scale of 5 units per square allows us to display both intercepts and $(4, -24)$, as well as the origin.

The point $(4, -24)$ appears to line up with the intercepts, so we draw and label the line, as shown at left.

TRY EXERCISE ▸ 45

TECHNOLOGY CONNECTION

When an equation has been entered into a graphing calculator, we may not be able to see both intercepts. For example, if $y = -0.8x + 17$ is graphed in the window $[-10, 10, -10, 10]$, neither intercept is visible.

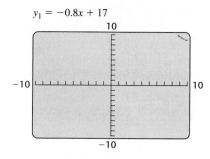

To better view the intercepts, we can change the window dimensions or we can zoom out. The ZOOM feature allows us to reduce or magnify a graph or a portion

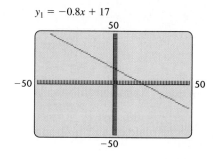

of a graph. Before zooming, the ZOOM *factors* must be set in the memory of the ZOOM key. If we zoom out with factors set at 5, both intercepts are visible but the axes are heavily drawn, as shown in the preceding figure.

This suggests that the *scales* of the axes should be changed. To do this, we use the WINDOW menu and set Xscl to 5 and Yscl to 5. The resulting graph has tick marks 5 units apart and clearly shows both intercepts. Other choices for Xscl and Yscl can also be made.

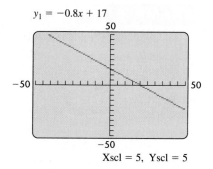

Graph each equation so that both intercepts can be easily viewed. Zoom or adjust the window settings so that tick marks can be clearly seen on both axes.

1. $y = -0.72x - 15$ 2. $y - 2.13x = 27$
3. $5x + 6y = 84$ 4. $2x - 7y = 150$
5. $19x - 17y = 200$ 6. $6x + 5y = 159$

Graphing Horizontal or Vertical Lines

The equations graphed in Examples 3 and 4 are both in the form $Ax + By = C$. We have already stated that any equation in the form $Ax + By = C$ is linear, provided A and B are not both zero. What if A or B (but not both) is zero? We will find that when A is zero, there is no x-term and the graph is a horizontal line. We will also find that when B is zero, there is no y-term and the graph is a vertical line.

EXAMPLE 5

Graph: $y = 3$.

SOLUTION   We can regard the equation $y = 3$ as $0 \cdot x + y = 3$. No matter wha number we choose for x, we find that y must be 3 if the equation is to be solve Consider the following table.

STUDENT NOTES

Many students draw horizontal lines when they should be drawing vertical lines and vice versa. To avoid this mistake, first locate the correct number on the axis whose label is given. Thus, to graph $x = 2$, we locate 2 on the x-axis and then draw a line perpendicular to that axis at that point. Note that the graph of $x = 2$ on a plane is a line, whereas the graph of $x = 2$ on a number line is a point.

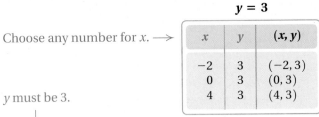

Choose any number for x. →

y must be 3.

x	y	(x, y)
-2	3	$(-2, 3)$
0	3	$(0, 3)$
4	3	$(4, 3)$

All pairs will have as the y-coordinate.

When we plot the ordered pairs $(-2, 3)$, $(0, 3)$, and $(4, 3)$ and connect the points, we obtain a horizontal line. Any ordered pair of the form $(x, 3)$ is a solution, so the line is parallel to the x-axis with y-intercept $(0, 3)$. Note that the graph of $y = 3$ has no x-intercept.

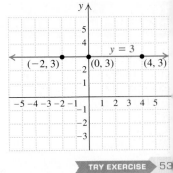

TRY EXERCISE 53

EXAMPLE 6

Graph: $x = -4$.

SOLUTION   We can regard the equation $x = -4$ as $x + 0 \cdot y = -4$. We make t a table with all -4's in the x-column.

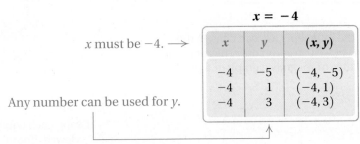

x must be -4. →

Any number can be used for y.

x	y	(x, y)
-4	-5	$(-4, -5)$
-4	1	$(-4, 1)$
-4	3	$(-4, 3)$

All pairs will have -4 as t x-coordinat

When we plot the ordered pairs $(-4, -5)$, $(-4, 1)$, and $(-4, 3)$ and connect them, we obtain a vertical line. Any ordered pair of the form $(-4, y)$ is a solution. The line is parallel to the y-axis with x-intercept $(-4, 0)$. Note that the graph of $x = -4$ has no y-intercept.

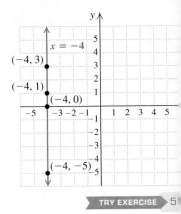

TRY EXERCISE 5

Linear Equations in One Variable

The graph of $y = b$ is a horizontal line, with y-intercept $(0, b)$.

The graph of $x = a$ is a vertical line, with x-intercept $(a, 0)$.

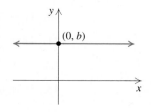

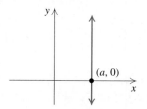

EXAMPLE **7**

Write an equation for each graph.

a)

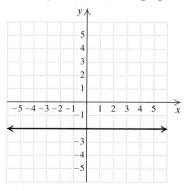

b)

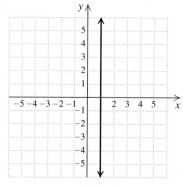

SOLUTION

a) Note that every point on the horizontal line passing through $(0, -2)$ has -2 as the y-coordinate. Thus the equation of the line is $y = -2$.

b) Note that every point on the vertical line passing through $(1, 0)$ has 1 as the x-coordinate. Thus the equation of the line is $x = 1$.

TRY EXERCISE 71

3.3 EXERCISE SET

For Extra Help **MyMathLab** | Math XL PRACTICE | WATCH | DOWNLOAD

Concept Reinforcement *In each of Exercises 1–6, match the phrase with the most appropriate choice from the column on the right.*

1. _____ A vertical line

2. _____ A horizontal line

3. _____ A y-intercept

4. _____ An x-intercept

5. _____ A third point as a check

6. _____ Use a scale of 10 units per square.

a) $2x + 5y = 100$

b) $(3, -2)$

c) $(1, 0)$

d) $(0, 2)$

e) $y = 3$

f) $x = -4$

For Exercises 7–14, list **(a)** *the coordinates of the y-intercept and* **(b)** *the coordinates of all x-intercepts.*

7.

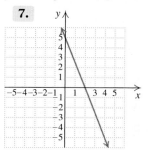

8.

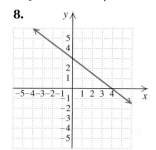

9.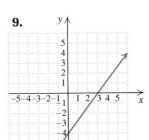

10.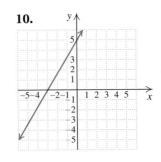

11.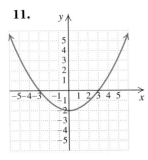

12.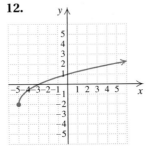

13.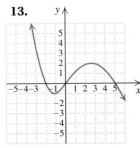

14.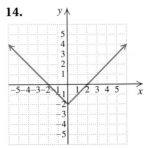

For Exercises 15–24, list **(a)** *the coordinates of any y-intercept and* **(b)** *the coordinates of any x-intercept. Do not graph.*

15. $3x + 5y = 15$

16. $2x + 7y = 14$

17. $9x - 2y = 36$

18. $10x - 3y = 60$

19. $-4x + 5y = 80$

20. $-5x + 6y = 100$

Aha! **21.** $x = 12$

22. $y = 10$

23. $y = -9$

24. $x = -5$

Find the intercepts. Then graph.

25. $3x + 5y = 15$

26. $2x + y = 6$

27. $x + 2y = 4$

28. $2x + 5y = 10$

29. $-x + 2y = 8$

30. $-x + 3y = 9$

31. $3x + y = 9$

32. $2x - y = 8$

33. $y = 2x - 6$

34. $y = -3x + 6$

35. $5x - 10 = 5y$

36. $3x - 9 = 3y$

37. $2x - 5y = 10$

38. $2x - 3y = 6$

39. $6x + 2y = 12$

40. $4x + 5y = 20$

41. $4x + 3y = 16$

42. $3x + 2y = 8$

43. $2x + 4y = 1$

44. $3x - 6y = 1$

45. $5x - 3y = 180$

46. $10x + 7y = 210$

47. $y = -30 + 3x$

48. $y = -40 + 5x$

49. $-4x = 20y + 80$

50. $60 = 20x - 3y$

51. $y - 3x = 0$

52. $x + 2y = 0$

Graph.

53. $y = 1$

54. $y = 4$

55. $x = 3$

56. $x = 6$

57. $y = -2$

58. $y = -4$

59. $x = -1$

60. $x = -6$

61. $y = -15$

62. $x = 20$

63. $y = 0$

64. $y = \frac{3}{2}$

65. $x = -\frac{5}{2}$

66. $x = 0$

67. $-4x = -100$

68. $12y = -360$

69. $35 + 7y = 0$

70. $-3x - 24 = 0$

Write an equation for each graph.

71.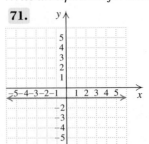

72.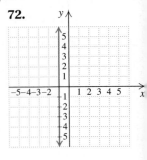

73.

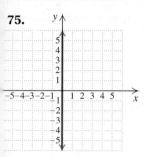

74.

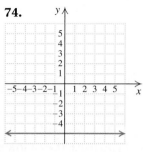

75.

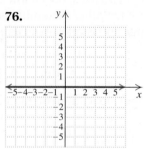

76.

77. Explain in your own words why the graph of $y = 8$ is a horizontal line.

78. Explain in your own words why the graph of $x = -4$ is a vertical line.

Skill Review

Review translating to algebraic expressions (Section 1.1).

Translate to an algebraic expression. [1.1]

79. 7 less than d

80. 5 more than w

81. The sum of 7 and four times a number

82. The product of 3 and a number

83. Twice the sum of two numbers

84. Half of the sum of two numbers

Synthesis

85. Describe what the graph of $x + y = C$ will look like for any choice of C.

86. If the graph of a linear equation has one point that is both the x- and the y-intercepts, what is that point? Why?

87. Write an equation for the x-axis.

88. Write an equation of the line parallel to the x-axis and passing through $(3, 5)$.

89. Write an equation of the line parallel to the y-axis and passing through $(-2, 7)$.

90. Find the coordinates of the point of intersection of the graphs of $y = x$ and $y = 6$.

91. Find the coordinates of the point of intersection of the graphs of the equations $x = -3$ and $y = 4$.

92. Write an equation of the line shown in Exercise 7.

93. Write an equation of the line shown in Exercise 10.

94. Find the value of C such that the graph of $3x + C = 5y$ has an x-intercept of $(-4, 0)$.

95. Find the value of C such that the graph of $4x = C - 3y$ has a y-intercept of $(0, -8)$.

96. For A and B nonzero, the graphs of $Ax + D = C$ and $By + D = C$ will be parallel to an axis. Explain why.

97. Find the x-intercept of the graph of $Ax + D = C$.

In Exercises 98–103, find the intercepts of each equation algebraically. Then adjust the window and scale so that the intercepts can be checked graphically with no further window adjustments.

98. $3x + 2y = 50$

99. $2x - 7y = 80$

100. $y = 1.3x - 15$

101. $y = 0.2x - 9$

102. $25x - 20y = 1$

103. $50x + 25y = 1$

3.4   Rates

Rates of Change   ▪   Visualizing Rates

Rates of Change

Because graphs make use of two axes, they allow us to visualize how two quantities change with respect to each other. A number accompanied by units is used to represent this type of change and is referred to as a *rate*.

> ### Rate
>
> A *rate* is a ratio that indicates how two quantities change with respect to each other.

Rates occur often in everyday life:

A business whose customer base grows by 1500 customers over a period of 2 yr has an average *growth rate* of $\frac{1500}{2}$, or 750, customers per year.

A vehicle traveling 260 mi in 4 hr is moving at a *rate* of $\frac{260}{4}$, or 65, mph (miles per hour).

A class of 25 students pays a total of $93.75 to visit a museum. The *rate* is $\frac{\$93.75}{25}$ or $3.75, per student.

> *CAUTION!*   To calculate a rate, it is important to keep track of the units being used.

EXAMPLE   **1**   On January 3, Alisha rented a Ford Focus with a full tank of gas and 9312 mi on the odometer. On January 7, she returned the car with 9630 mi on the odometer.* If the rental agency charged Alisha $108 for the rental and needed 12 gal of gas to fill up the gas tank, find the following rates.

a) The car's rate of gas consumption, in miles per gallon

b) The average cost of the rental, in dollars per day

c) The car's rate of travel, in miles per day

SOLUTION

a) The rate of gas consumption, in miles per gallon, is found by dividing the number of miles traveled by the number of gallons used for that amount of driving:

$$\text{Rate, in miles per gallon} = \frac{9630\text{ mi} - 9312\text{ mi}}{12\text{ gal}}$$

The word "per" indicates division.

$$= \frac{318\text{ mi}}{12\text{ gal}}$$

$$= 26.5\text{ mi/gal} \qquad \text{Dividing}$$

$$= 26.5\text{ miles per gallon}.$$

---

*For all problems concerning rentals, assume that the pickup time was later in the day than the return time so that no late fees were applied.

b) The average cost of the rental, in dollars per day, is found by dividing the cost of the rental by the number of days:

$$\text{Rate, in dollars per day} = \frac{108 \text{ dollars}}{4 \text{ days}}$$

From January 3 to January 7 is $7 - 3 = 4$ days.

$$= 27 \text{ dollars/day}$$
$$= \$27 \text{ per day.}$$

c) The car's rate of travel, in miles per day, is found by dividing the number of miles traveled by the number of days:

$$\text{Rate, in miles per day} = \frac{318 \text{ mi}}{4 \text{ days}}$$

$9630 \text{ mi} - 9312 \text{ mi} = 318 \text{ mi}$; From January 3 to January 7 is $7 - 3 = 4$ days.

$$= 79.5 \text{ mi/day}$$
$$= 79.5 \text{ mi per day.}$$

TRY EXERCISE ▸ 7

CAUTION!   Units are a vital part of real-world problems. They must be considered in the translation of a problem and included in the answer to a problem.

Many problems involve a rate of travel, or *speed*. The **speed** of an object is found by dividing the distance traveled by the time required to travel that distance.

EXAMPLE 2

Transportation.   An Atlantic City Express bus makes regular trips between Paramus and Atlantic City, New Jersey. At 6:00 P.M., the bus is at mileage marker 40 on the Garden State Parkway, and at 8:00 P.M. it is at marker 170. Find the average speed of the bus.

SOLUTION   Speed is the distance traveled divided by the time spent traveling:

$$\text{Bus speed} = \frac{\text{Distance traveled}}{\text{Time spent traveling}}$$
$$= \frac{\text{Change in mileage}}{\text{Change in time}}$$
$$= \frac{130 \text{ mi}}{2 \text{ hr}}$$

$170 \text{ mi} - 40 \text{ mi} = 130 \text{ mi}$; $8\text{:}00 \text{ P.M.} - 6\text{:}00 \text{ P.M.} = 2 \text{ hr}$

$$= 65 \frac{\text{mi}}{\text{hr}}$$
$$= 65 \text{ miles per hour.}$$

This *average* speed does not indicate by how much the bus speed may vary along the route.

TRY EXERCISE ▸ 13

Visualizing Rates

Graphs allow us to visualize a rate of change. As a rule, the quantity listed in the numerator appears on the vertical axis and the quantity listed in the denominator appears on the horizontal axis.

EXAMPLE **3** *Recycling.* Between 1991 and 2006, the amount of paper recycled in the United States increased at a rate of approximately 1.5 million tons per year. In 1991, approximately 31 million tons of paper was recycled. Draw a graph to represent this information.

Source: Based on information from American Forest and Paper Association

SOLUTION To label the axes, note that the rate is given as 1.5 million tons per year, or

$$1.5 \text{ million } \frac{\text{tons}}{\text{yr}}. \qquad \begin{matrix} \longleftarrow \text{Numerator: vertical axis} \\ \longleftarrow \text{Denominator: horizontal axis} \end{matrix}$$

We list *Amount of paper recycled (in millions of tons)* on the vertical axis and *Year* on the horizontal axis. (See the figure on the left below.)

Next, we select a scale for each axis that allows us to plot the given information. If we count by increments of 10 million on the vertical axis, we can show 31 million tons for 1991 and increasing amounts for later years. On the horizontal axis, we count by increments of 2 years to make certain that both 1991 and 2006 are included. (See the figure in the middle below.)

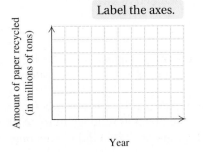

Label the axes.

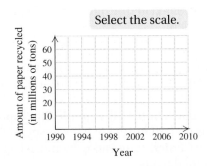

Select the scale.

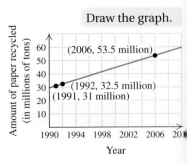

Draw the graph.

We now plot the point corresponding to (1991, 31 million). Then, to display the rate of growth, we move from that point to a second point that represents 1.5 million more tons 1 year later.

(1991,	31 million)	Beginning point
(1991 + 1,	31 million + 1.5 million)	1.5 million more tons, 1 year later
(1992,	32.5 million)	A second point on the graph

Similarly, we can find the coordinates for 2006. Since 2006 is 15 years after 1991, we add 15 to the year and 15(1.5 million) = 22.5 million to the amount.

(1991,	31 million)	Beginning point
(1991 + 15,	31 million + 22.5 million)	15(1.5) million more tons, 15 years later
(2006,	53.5 million)	A third point on the graph

After plotting the three points, we draw a line through them, as shown in the figure on the right above. This gives us the graph. **TRY EXERCISE** 19

EXAMPLE **4** *Banking.* Nadia prepared the following graph from data collected on a recent day at a branch bank.

a) What rate can be determined from the graph?

b) What is that rate?

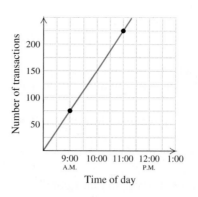

SOLUTION

a) Because the vertical axis shows the number of transactions and the horizontal axis lists the time in hour-long increments, we can find the rate *Number of transactions per hour.*

b) The points (9:00, 75) and (11:00, 225) are both on the graph. This tells us that in the 2 hours between 9:00 and 11:00, there were $225 - 75 = 150$ transactions. Thus the rate is

$$\frac{225 \text{ transactions} - 75 \text{ transactions}}{11:00 - 9:00} = \frac{150 \text{ transactions}}{2 \text{ hours}}$$

$$= 75 \text{ transactions per hour.}$$

Note that this is an *average* rate.

TRY EXERCISE ▶ 29

3.4 EXERCISE SET

For Extra Help

MyMathLab   Math XL PRACTICE   WATCH   DOWNLOAD

↪ *Concept Reinforcement* For Exercises 1–6, fill in the missing units for each rate.

1. If Eva biked 100 miles in 5 hours, her average rate was 20 _____.

2. If it took Lauren 18 hours to read 6 chapters, her average rate was 3 _____.

3. If Denny's ticket cost $300 for a 150-mile flight, his average rate was 2 _____.

4. If Geoff planted 36 petunias along a 12-ft sidewalk, his average rate was 3 _____.

5. If Christi ran 8 errands in 40 minutes, her average rate was 5 _____.

6. If Ben made 8 cakes using 20 cups of flour, his average rate was $2\frac{1}{2}$ _____.

Solve. For Exercises 7–14, round answers to the nearest cent.

7. *Car rentals.* Late on June 5, Gaya rented a Ford Focus with a full tank of gas and 13,741 mi on the odometer. On June 8, she returned the car with 14,131 mi on the odometer. The rental agency charged Gaya $118 for the rental and needed 13 gal of gas to fill up the tank.

   a) Find the car's rate of gas consumption, in miles per gallon.

   b) Find the average cost of the rental, in dollars per day.

   c) Find the average rate of travel, in miles per day.

   ▤ **d)** Find the rental rate, in cents per mile.

8. *SUV rentals.* On February 10, Oscar rented a Chevy Trailblazer with a full tank of gas and 13,091 mi on the odometer. On February 12, he returned the vehicle with 13,322 mi on the odometer. The rental agency charged $92 for the rental and needed 14 gal of gas to fill the tank.

    a) Find the SUV's rate of gas consumption, in miles per gallon.

    b) Find the average cost of the rental, in dollars per day.

    c) Find the average rate of travel, in miles per day.

    d) Find the rental rate, in cents per mile.

9. *Bicycle rentals.* At 9:00, Jodi rented a mountain bike from The Bike Rack. She returned the bicycle at 11:00, after cycling 14 mi. Jodi paid $15 for the rental.

    a) Find Jodi's average speed, in miles per hour.

    b) Find the rental rate, in dollars per hour.

    c) Find the rental rate, in dollars per mile.

10. *Bicycle rentals.* At 2:00, Braden rented a mountain bike from The Slick Rock Cyclery. He returned the bike at 5:00, after cycling 18 mi. Braden paid $12 for the rental.

    a) Find Braden's average speed, in miles per hour.

    b) Find the rental rate, in dollars per hour.

    c) Find the rental rate, in dollars per mile.

11. *Proofreading.* Sergei began proofreading at 9:00 A.M., starting at the top of page 93. He worked until 2:00 P.M. that day and finished page 195. He billed the publishers $110 for the day's work.

    a) Find the rate of pay, in dollars per hour.

    b) Find the average proofreading rate, in number of pages per hour.

    c) Find the rate of pay, in dollars per page.

12. *Temporary help.* A typist for Kelly Services reports to 3E's Properties for work at 10:00 A.M. and leaves at 6:00 P.M. after having typed from the end of page 8 to the end of page 50 of a proposal. 3E's pays $120 for the typist's services.

    a) Find the rate of pay, in dollars per hour.

    b) Find the average typing rate, in number of pages per hour.

    c) Find the rate of pay, in dollars per page.

13. *National debt.* The U.S. federal budget debt was $5770 billion in 2001 and $8612 billion in 2006. Find the rate at which the debt was increasing.
Source: U.S. Office of Management and Budget

14. *Four-year-college tuition.* The average tuition at a public four-year college was $3983 in 2001 and $5948 in 2005. Find the rate at which tuition was increasing.
Source: U.S. National Center for Education Statistics

15. *Elevators.* At 2:38, Lara entered an elevator on the 34th floor of the Regency Hotel. At 2:40, she stepped off at the 5th floor.

    a) Find the elevator's average rate of travel, in number of floors per minute.

    b) Find the elevator's average rate of travel, in seconds per floor.

16. *Snow removal.* By 1:00 P.M., Olivia had already shoveled 2 driveways, and by 6:00 P.M. that day, the number was up to 7.

    a) Find Olivia's average shoveling rate, in number of driveways per hour.

    b) Find Olivia's average shoveling rate, in hours per driveway.

17. *Mountaineering.* The fastest ascent of Mt. Everest was accomplished by the Sherpa guide Pemba Dorje of Nepal in 2004. Pemba Dorje climbed from base camp, elevation 17,552 ft, to the summit, elevation 29,028 ft, in 8 hr 10 min.
Source: *Guinness Book of World Records* 2006 Edition

    a) Find Pemba Dorje's average rate of ascent, in feet per minute.

    b) Find Pemba Dorje's average rate of ascent, in minutes per foot.

18. *Mountaineering.* As part of an ill-fated expedition to climb Mt. Everest in 1996, author Jon Krakauer departed "The Balcony," elevation 27,600 ft, at 7:00 A.M. and reached the summit, elevation 29,028 ft, at 1:25 P.M.
Source: Krakauer, Jon, *Into Thin Air, the Illustrated Edition.* New York: Random House, 1998

a) Find Krakauer's average rate of ascent, in feet per minute.
b) Find Krakauer's average rate of ascent, in minutes per foot.

In Exercises 19–28, draw a linear graph to represent the given information. Be sure to label and number the axes appropriately (see Example 3).

19. *Landfills.* In 2006, 35,700,000 tons of paper was deposited in landfills in the United States, and this figure was decreasing by 700,000 tons per year.
Source: Based on data from American Forest and Paper Association

20. *Health insurance.* In 2005, the average cost for health insurance for a family was about $11,000 and the figure was rising at a rate of about $1100 per year.
Source: Based on data from Kaiser/HRET Survey of Health Benefits

21. *Prescription drug sales.* In 2006, there were sales of approximately $11 billion of asthma drug products in the United States, and the figure was increasing at a rate of about $1.2 billion per year.
Source: *The Wall Street Journal*, 6/28/2007

22. *Violent crimes.* In 2004, there were approximately 21.1 violent crimes per 1000 population in the United States, and the figure was dropping at a rate of about 1.2 crimes per 1000 per year.
Source: U.S. Bureau of Justice Statistics

23. *Train travel.* At 3:00 P.M., the Boston–Washington Metroliner had traveled 230 mi and was cruising at a rate of 90 miles per hour.

24. *Plane travel.* At 4:00 P.M., the Seattle–Los Angeles shuttle had traveled 400 mi and was cruising at a rate of 300 miles per hour.

25. *Wages.* By 2:00 P.M., Diane had earned $50. She continued earning money at a rate of $15 per hour.

26. *Wages.* By 3:00 P.M., Arnie had earned $70. He continued earning money at a rate of $12 per hour.

27. *Telephone bills.* Roberta's phone bill was already $7.50 when she made a call for which she was charged at a rate of $0.10 per minute.

28. *Telephone bills.* At 3:00 P.M., Larry's phone bill was $6.50 and increasing at a rate of 7¢ per minute.

In Exercises 29–38, use the graph provided to calculate a rate of change in which the units of the horizontal axis are used in the denominator.

29. *Call center.* The following graph shows data from a technical assistance call center. At what rate are calls being handled?

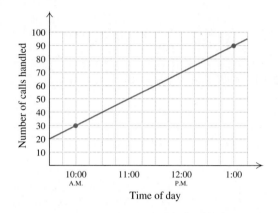

30. *Hairdresser.* Eve's Custom Cuts has a graph displaying data from a recent day of work. At what rate does Eve work?

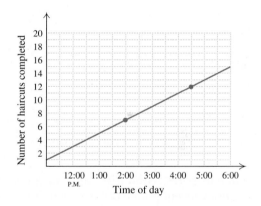

31. *Train travel.* The following graph shows data from a recent train ride from Chicago to St. Louis. At what rate did the train travel?

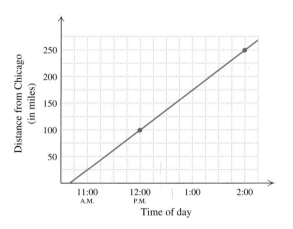

32. *Train travel.* The following graph shows data from a recent train ride from Denver to Kansas City. At what rate did the train travel?

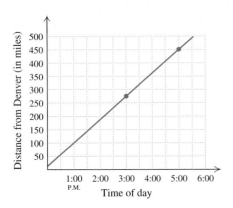

33. *Cost of a telephone call.* The following graph shows data from a recent phone call between the United States and the Netherlands. At what rate was the customer being billed?

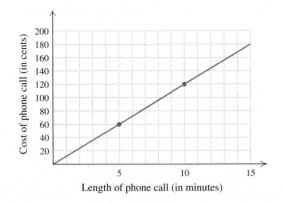

34. *Cost of a telephone call.* The following graph shows data from a recent phone call between the United States and South Korea. At what rate was the customer being billed?

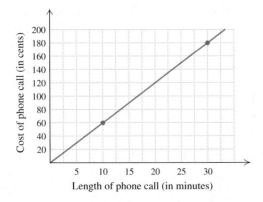

35. *Population.* The following graph shows data regarding the population of Youngstown,

Ohio. At what rate was the population changing?

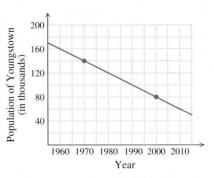

36. *Depreciation of an office machine.* Data regarding the value of a particular color copier is represented in the following graph. At what rate is the value changing?

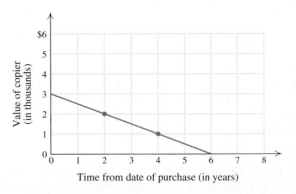

37. *Gas mileage.* The following graph shows data for a 2008 Toyota Prius driven on interstate highways. At what rate was the vehicle consuming gas?
Source: www.fueleconomy.gov

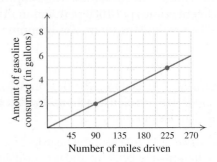

38. *Gas mileage.* The following graph shows data for a 2008 Chevy Malibu driven on city streets. At what rate was the vehicle consuming gas?
Source: Chevrolet

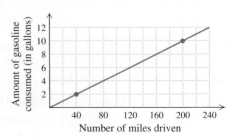

In each of Exercises 39–44, match the description with the most appropriate graph from the choices below. Scales are intentionally omitted. Assume that of the three sports listed, swimming is the slowest and biking is the fastest.

39. ____ Robin trains for triathlons by running, biking, and then swimming every Saturday.

40. ____ Gene trains for triathlons by biking, running, and then swimming every Sunday.

41. ____ Shirley trains for triathlons by swimming, biking, and then running every Sunday.

42. ____ Evan trains for triathlons by swimming, running, and then biking every Saturday.

43. ____ Angie trains for triathlons by biking, swimming, and then running every Sunday.

44. ____ Mick trains for triathlons by running, swimming, and then biking every Saturday.

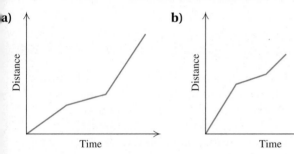

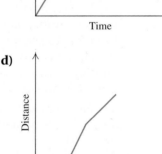

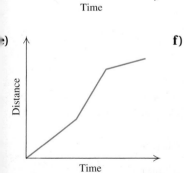

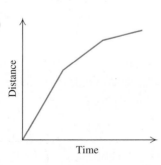

45. What does a negative rate of travel indicate? Explain.

46. Explain how to convert from kilometers per hour to meters per second.

Skill Review

To prepare for Section 3.5, review subtraction and order of operations (Sections 1.6 and 1.8).

Simplify.

47. $-2 - (-7)$ [1.6]

48. $-9 - (-3)$ [1.6]

49. $\dfrac{5 - (-4)}{-2 - 7}$ [1.8]

50. $\dfrac{8 - (-4)}{2 - 11}$ [1.8]

51. $\dfrac{-4 - 8}{11 - 2}$ [1.8]

52. $\dfrac{-5 - (-3)}{4 - 6}$ [1.8]

53. $\dfrac{-6 - (-6)}{-2 - 7}$ [1.8]

54. $\dfrac{-3 - 5}{-1 - (-1)}$ [1.8]

Synthesis

55. How would the graphs of Jon's and Jenny's total earnings compare in each of the following situations?

   a) Jon earns twice as much per hour as Jenny.
   b) Jon and Jenny earn the same hourly rate, but Jenny received a bonus for a cost-saving suggestion.
   c) Jon is paid by the hour, and Jenny is paid a weekly salary.

56. Write an exercise similar to those in Exercises 7–18 for a classmate to solve. Design the problem so that the solution is "The motorcycle's rate of gas consumption was 65 miles per gallon."

57. *Aviation.*   A Boeing 737 climbs from sea level to a cruising altitude of 31,500 ft at a rate of 6300 ft/min. After cruising for 3 min, the jet is forced to land, descending at a rate of 3500 ft/min. Represent the flight with a graph in which altitude is measured on the vertical axis and time on the horizontal axis.

58. *Wages with commissions.*   Each salesperson at Mike's Bikes is paid $140 a week plus 13% of all sales up to $2000, and then 20% on any sales in excess of $2000. Draw a graph in which sales are measured on the horizontal axis and wages on the vertical axis. Then use the graph to estimate the wages paid when a salesperson sells $2700 in merchandise in one week.

59. *Taxi fares.*   The driver of a New York City Yellow Cab recently charged $2 plus 50¢ for each fifth of a mile traveled. Draw a graph that could be used to determine the cost of a fare.

60. *Gas mileage.*   Suppose that a Kawasaki motorcycle travels three times as far as a Chevy Malibu on the same amount of gas (see Exercise 38). Draw a graph that reflects this information.

61. *Aviation.* Tim's F-16 jet is moving forward at a deck speed of 95 mph aboard an aircraft carrier that is traveling 39 mph in the same direction. How fast is the jet traveling, in minutes per mile, with respect to the sea?

62. *Navigation.* In 3 sec, Penny walks 24 ft, to the bow (front) of a tugboat. The boat is cruising at a rate of 5 ft/sec. What is Penny's rate of travel with respect to land?

63. *Running.* Anne ran from the 4-km mark to the 7-km mark of a 10-km race in 15.5 min. At this rate, how long would it take Anne to run a 5-mi race?

64. *Running.* Jerod ran from the 2-mi marker to the finish line of a 5-mi race in 25 min. At this rate, how long would it take Jerod to run a 10-km race?

65. Alex picks apples twice as fast as Ryan. By 4:30, Ryan had already picked 4 bushels of apples. Fifty minutes later, his total reached $5\frac{1}{2}$ bushels. Find Alex's picking rate. Give your answer in number of bushels per hour.

66. At 3:00 P.M., Catanya and Chad had already made 46 candles. By 5:00 P.M., the total reached 100 candles. Assuming a constant production rate, at what time did they make their 82nd candle?

COLLABORATIVE CORNER

Determining Depreciation Rates

Focus: Modeling, graphing, and rates

Time: 30 minutes

Group size: 3

Materials: Graph paper and straightedges

From the minute a new car is driven out of the dealership, it *depreciates*, or drops in value with the passing of time. The N.A.D.A. Official Used Car Guide is a periodic listing of the trade-in values of used cars. The data below are taken from two such reports from 2007.

ACTIVITY

1. Each group member should select a different one of the cars listed in the table below as his or her own. Assuming that the values are dropping linearly, each student should draw a line representing the trade-in value of his or her car. Draw all three lines on the same graph. Let the horizontal axis represent the time, in months, since January 2007, and let the vertical axis represent the trade-in value of each car. Decide as a group how many months or dollars each square should represent. Make the drawings as neat as possible.

2. At what *rate* is each car depreciating and how are the different rates illustrated in the graph of part (1)?

3. If one of the three cars had to be sold in January 2009, which one would your group sell and why? Compare answers with other groups.

Car	Trade-in Value in January 2007	Trade-in Value in June 2007
2005 Mustang V6 Coupe	$13,625	$13,125
2005 Nissan Sentra SE-R	$11,825	$11,000
2005 Volkswagen Jetta Sedan GL	$12,600	$11,425

3.5   Slope

Rate and Slope   ▪   Horizontal and Vertical Lines   ▪   Applications

In Section 3.4, we introduced *rate* as a method of measuring how two quantities change with respect to each other. In this section, we will discuss how rate can be related to the slope of a line.

Rate and Slope

Automated digitization machines use robotic arms to carefully turn pages of books so that they can take pictures of each page. Suppose that a large university library purchased a DL-1500 and an APT 1200. The DL-1500 digitizes 3 volumes of an encyclopedia every 2 hr. The APT 1200 digitizes 6 volumes of an encyclopedia every 5 hr. The following tables list the number of books digitized after various amounts of time for each machine.

Source: Based on information from Kirtas and 4DigitalBooks

DL-1500	
Hours Elapsed	**Books Digitized**
0	0
2	3
4	6
6	9
8	12

APT 1200	
Hours Elapsed	**Books Digitized**
0	0
5	6
10	12
15	18
20	24

We now graph the pairs of numbers listed in the tables, using the horizontal axis for the number of hours elapsed and the vertical axis for the number of books digitized.

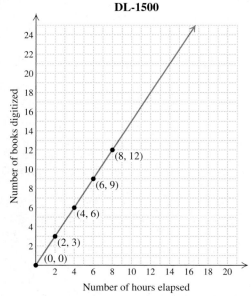

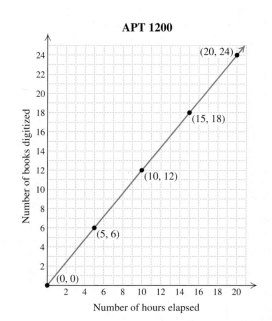

By comparing the number of books digitized by each machine over a specified period of time, we can compare the two rates. For example, the DL-1500 digitizes 3 books every 2 hr, so its *rate* is $3 \div 2 = \frac{3}{2}$ books per hour. Since the APT 1200 digitizes 6 books every 5 hr, its rate is $6 \div 5 = \frac{6}{5}$ books per hour. Note that the rate of the DL-1500 is greater so its graph is steeper.

The rates $\frac{3}{2}$ and $\frac{6}{5}$ can also be found using the coordinates of any two points that are on the line. For example, we can use the points $(6, 9)$ and $(8, 12)$ to find the digitization rate for the DL-1500. To do so, remember that these coordinates tell us that after 6 hr, 9 books have been digitized, and after 8 hr, 12 books have been digitized. In the 2 hr between the 6-hr and 8-hr points, $12 - 9$, or 3, books were digitized. Thus we have

$$\text{DL-1500 digitization rate} = \frac{\text{change in number of books digitized}}{\text{corresponding change in time}}$$

$$= \frac{12 - 9 \text{ books}}{8 - 6 \text{ hr}}$$

$$= \frac{3 \text{ books}}{2 \text{ hr}} = \frac{3}{2} \text{ books per hour.}$$

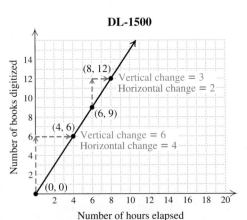

DL-1500

Number of books digitized

Number of hours elapsed

Because the line is straight, the same rate is found using *any* pair of points on the line. For example, using $(0, 0)$ and $(4, 6)$, we have

$$\text{DL-1500 digitization rate} = \frac{6 - 0 \text{ books}}{4 - 0 \text{ hr}} = \frac{6 \text{ books}}{4 \text{ hr}} = \frac{3}{2} \text{ books per hour.}$$

Note that the rate is always the vertical change divided by the corresponding horizontal change.

EXAMPLE **1** Use the graph of book digitization by the APT 1200 to find the rate at which books are digitized.

SOLUTION We can use any two points on the line, such as $(15, 18)$ and $(20, 24)$:

$$\text{APT 1200 digitization rate} = \frac{\text{change in number of books digitized}}{\text{corresponding change in time}}$$

$$= \frac{24 - 18 \text{ books}}{20 - 15 \text{ hr}}$$

$$= \frac{6 \text{ books}}{5 \text{ hr}}$$

$$= \frac{6}{5} \text{ books per hour.}$$

As a check, we can use another pair of points, like $(0, 0)$ and $(10, 12)$:

$$\text{APT 1200 digitization rate} = \frac{12 - 0 \text{ books}}{10 - 0 \text{ hr}}$$

$$= \frac{12 \text{ books}}{10 \text{ hr}}$$

$$= \frac{6}{5} \text{ books per hour.}$$

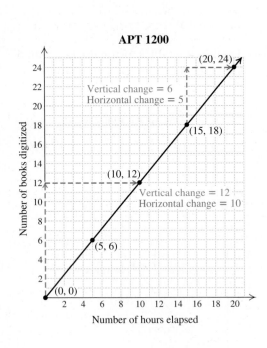

APT 1200

Number of books digitized

Number of hours elapsed

TRY EXERCISE 11

When the axes of a graph are simply labeled x and y, the ratio of vertical change to horizontal change is the rate at which y is changing with respect to x. This ratio is a measure of a line's slant, or **slope**.

Consider a line passing through $(2, 3)$ and $(6, 5)$, as shown below. We find the ratio of vertical change, or *rise*, to horizontal change, or *run*, as follows:

$$\text{Ratio of vertical change to horizontal change} = \frac{\text{change in } y}{\text{change in } x} = \frac{\text{rise}}{\text{run}}$$

$$= \frac{5 - 3}{6 - 2}$$

$$= \frac{2}{4}, \text{ or } \frac{1}{2}.$$

Note that these calculations can be performed without viewing a graph.

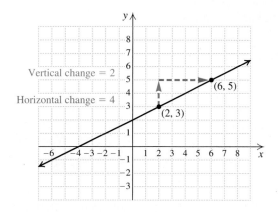

Thus the y-coordinates of points on this line increase at a rate of 2 units for every 4-unit increase in x, which is 1 unit for every 2-unit increase in x, or $\frac{1}{2}$ unit for every 1-unit increase in x. The slope of the line is $\frac{1}{2}$.

In the box below, the *subscripts* 1 and 2 are used to distinguish two arbitrary points, point 1 and point 2, from each other. The slightly lowered 1's and 2's are not exponents but are used to denote x-values (or y-values) that may differ from each other.

Slope

The *slope* of the line containing points (x_1, y_1) and (x_2, y_2) is given by

$$m = \frac{\text{change in } y}{\text{change in } x} = \frac{\text{rise}}{\text{run}} = \frac{y_2 - y_1}{x_2 - x_1}.$$

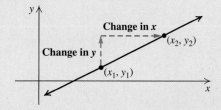

EXAMPLE **2** Graph the line containing the points $(-4, 3)$ and $(2, -6)$ and find the slope.

SOLUTION The graph is shown below. From $(-4, 3)$ to $(2, -6)$, the change in y, or rise, is $-6 - 3$, or -9. The change in x, or run, is $2 - (-4)$, or 6. Thus,

$$\text{Slope} = \frac{\text{change in } y}{\text{change in } x}$$

$$= \frac{\text{rise}}{\text{run}}$$

$$= \frac{-6 - 3}{2 - (-4)}$$

$$= \frac{-9}{6}$$

$$= -\frac{9}{6}, \text{ or } -\frac{3}{2}.$$

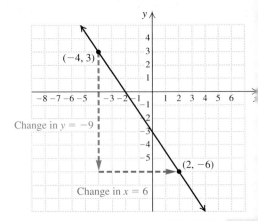

STUDENT NOTES

You may wonder which point should be regarded as (x_1, y_1) and which should be (x_2, y_2). To see that the math works out the same either way, perform both calculations on your own.

TRY EXERCISE 39

CAUTION! When we use the formula

$$m = \frac{y_2 - y_1}{x_2 - x_1},$$

it makes no difference which point is considered (x_1, y_1). What matters is that we subtract the y-coordinates in the same order that we subtract the x-coordinates.

To illustrate, we reverse *both* of the subtractions in Example 2. The slope is still $-\frac{3}{2}$:

$$\text{Slope} = \frac{\text{change in } y}{\text{change in } x} = \frac{3 - (-6)}{-4 - 2} = \frac{9}{-6} = -\frac{3}{2}.$$

As shown in the graphs below, a line with positive slope slants up from left to right, and a line with negative slope slants down from left to right. The larger the absolute value of the slope, the steeper the line.

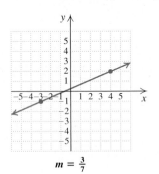

$m = \frac{3}{7}$

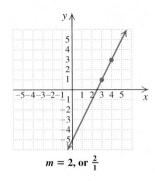

$m = 2$, or $\frac{2}{1}$

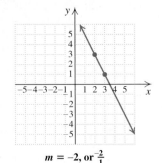

$m = -2$, or $\frac{-2}{1}$

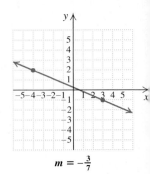

$m = -\frac{3}{7}$

Horizontal and Vertical Lines

What about the slope of a horizontal line or a vertical line?

EXAMPLE **3**

Find the slope of the line $y = 4$.

SOLUTION   Consider the points $(2, 4)$ and $(-3, 4)$, which are on the line. The change in y, or the rise, is $4 - 4$, or 0. The change in x, or the run, is $-3 - 2$, or -5. Thus,

$$m = \frac{4 - 4}{-3 - 2}$$

$$= \frac{0}{-5}$$

$$= 0.$$

Any two points on a horizontal line have the same y-coordinate. Thus the change in y is 0, so the slope is 0.

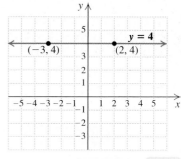

TRY EXERCISE   55

A horizontal line has slope 0.

EXAMPLE **4**

Find the slope of the line $x = -3$.

SOLUTION   Consider the points $(-3, 4)$ and $(-3, -2)$, which are on the line. The change in y, or the rise, is $-2 - 4$, or -6. The change in x, or the run, is $-3 - (-3)$, or 0. Thus,

$$m = \frac{-2 - 4}{-3 - (-3)}$$

$$= \frac{-6}{0}. \quad \text{(undefined)}$$

Since division by 0 is not defined, the slope of this line is not defined. The answer to a problem of this type is "The slope of this line is undefined."

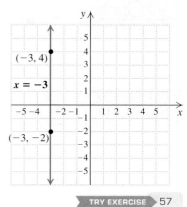

TRY EXERCISE   57

The slope of a vertical line is undefined.

Applications

We have seen that slope has many real-world applications, ranging from car speed to production rate. Some applications use slope to measure steepness. For example, numbers like 2%, 3%, and 6% are often used to represent the **grade** of a road, a measure of a road's steepness. That is, since $3\% = \frac{3}{100}$, a 3% grade means that for every horizontal distance of 100 ft, the road rises or drops 3 ft. The con cept of grade also occurs in skiing or snowboarding, where a 7% grade is consid ered very tame, but a 70% grade is considered steep.

Road grade $\frac{a}{b}$ (expressed as a percent)

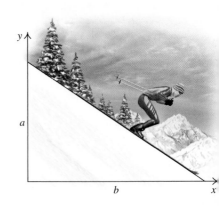

EXAMPLE 5

Skiing. Among the steepest skiable terrain in North America, the Headwall o Mount Washington, in New Hampshire, drops 720 ft over a horizontal distance o 900 ft. Find the grade of the Headwall.

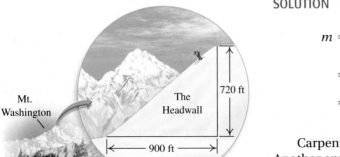

Mt. Washington

The Headwall

720 ft

900 ft

SOLUTION The grade of the Headwall is its slope, expressed as a percen

$$
\begin{aligned}
m &= \frac{720}{900} \\
&= \frac{8}{10} \\
&= 80\%.
\end{aligned}
\left.\right\} \text{Grade is slope expressed as a percent.}
$$

TRY EXERCISE 63

Carpenters use slope when designing stairs, ramps, or roof pitche Another application occurs in the engineering of a dam—the force o strength of a river depends on how much the river drops over a spec fied distance.

3.5 EXERCISE SET

 Concept Reinforcement *State whether each of the following rates is positive, negative, or zero.*

1. The rate at which a teenager's height changes

2. The rate at which an elderly person's height changes

3. The rate at which a pond's water level changes during a drought

4. The rate at which a pond's water level changes during the rainy season

5. The rate at which a runner's distance from the start- ing point changes during a race

6. The rate at which a runner's distance from the finis line changes during a race

7. The rate at which the number of U.S. senators changes

8. The rate at which the number of people in atten- dance at a basketball game changes in the moment before the opening tipoff

9. The rate at which the number of people in atten- dance at a basketball game changes in the moment after the final buzzer sounds

10. The rate at which a person's I.Q. changes during his or her sleep

1. *Blogging.*   Find the rate at which a career blogger is paid.

Source: Based on information from Wired

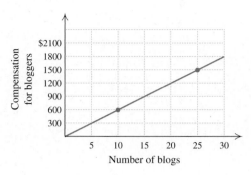

2. *Fitness.*   Find the rate at which a runner burns calories.

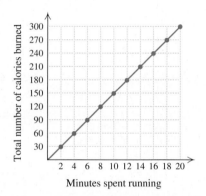

3. *Cell-phone prices.*   Find the rate of change in the average price of a new cell phone.

Source: Based on information from Market Reporter at PriceGrabber.com 2006

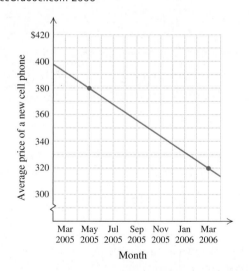

14. *Retail sales.*   Find the rate of change in the percentage of department stores' share of total retail sales.

Source: Based on information from the National Retail Federation

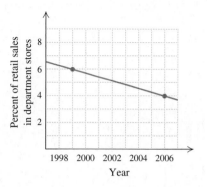

15. *College admission tests.*   Find the rate of change in SAT verbal scores with respect to family income.

Source: Based on 2004–2005 data from the National Center for Education Statistics

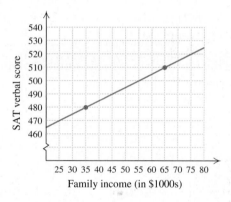

16. *Long-term care.*   Find the rate of change in Medicaid spending on long-term care.

Source: Based on data from Thomson Medstat, prepared by AARP Public Policy Institute

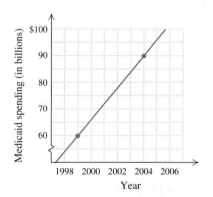

17. *Meteorology.* Find the rate of change in the temperature in Spearfish, Montana, on January 22, 1943, as shown below.

Source: National Oceanic Atmospheric Administration

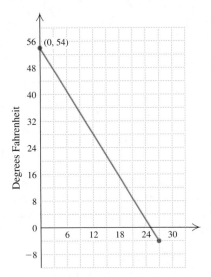

Number of minutes after 9 A.M.

18. Find the rate of change in the number of union-represented Ford employees.

Source: Ford Motor Co.

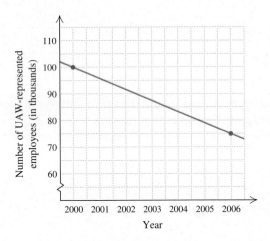

Find the slope, if it is defined, of each line. If the slope is undefined, state this.

19.

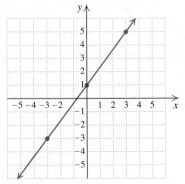

20.

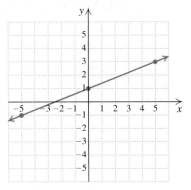

21.

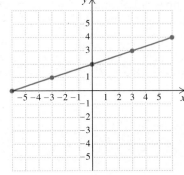

22.

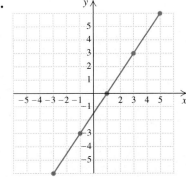

23.

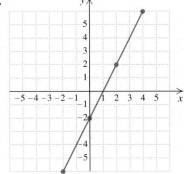

24.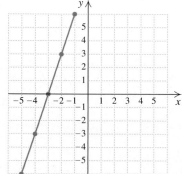

25.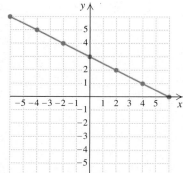

26.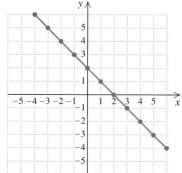

27.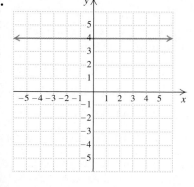

28.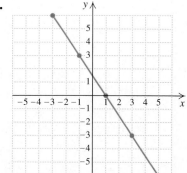

29.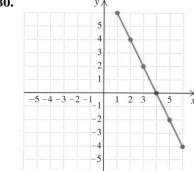

30.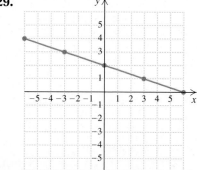

31.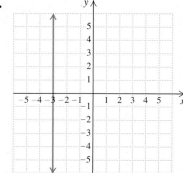

32.

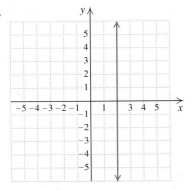

33.

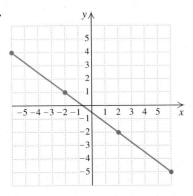

34.

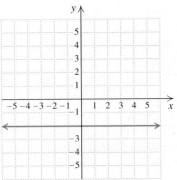

35.

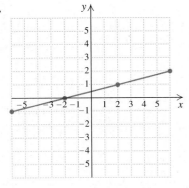

36.

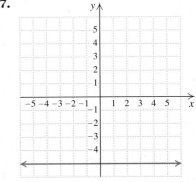

37.

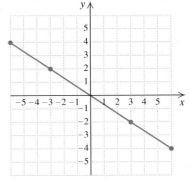

38.

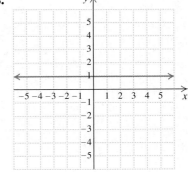

Find the slope of the line containing each given pair of points. If the slope is undefined, state this.

39. $(1, 3)$ and $(5, 8)$ **40.** $(1, 8)$ and $(6, 9)$

41. $(-2, 4)$ and $(3, 0)$ **42.** $(-4, 2)$ and $(2, -3)$

43. $(-4, 0)$ and $(5, 6)$ **44.** $(3, 0)$ and $(6, 9)$

45. $(0, 7)$ and $(-3, 10)$ **46.** $(0, 9)$ and $(-5, 0)$

47. $(-2, 3)$ and $(-6, 5)$ **48.** $(-1, 4)$ and $(5, -8)$

49. $\left(-2, \frac{1}{2}\right)$ and $\left(-5, \frac{1}{2}\right)$

50. $(-5, -1)$ and $(2, -3)$

51. $(5, -4)$ and $(2, -7)$

52. $(-10, 3)$ and $(-10, 4)$

53. $(6, -4)$ and $(6, 5)$

54. $(5, -2)$ and $(-4, -2)$

Find the slope of each line whose equation is given. If the slope is undefined, state this.

55. $y = 5$ **56.** $y = 13$

57. $x = -8$ **58.** $x = 18$

59. $x = 9$ **60.** $x = -7$

61. $y = -10$ **62.** $y = -4$

63. *Surveying.*   Lick Skillet Road, near Boulder, Colorado, climbs 792 ft over a horizontal distance of 5280 ft. What is the grade of the road?

64. *Navigation.*   Capital Rapids drops 54 ft vertically over a horizontal distance of 1080 ft. What is the slope of the rapids?

65. *Construction.*   Part of New Valley rises 28 ft over a horizontal distance of 80 ft, and is too steep to build on. What is the slope of the land?

66. *Engineering.*   At one point, Yellowstone's Beartooth Highway rises 315 ft over a horizontal distance of 4500 ft. Find the grade of the road.

67. *Carpentry.*   Find the slope (or pitch) of the roof.

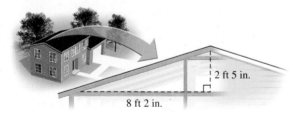

2 ft 5 in.

8 ft 2 in.

68. *Exercise.*   Find the slope (or grade) of the treadmill.

0.4 ft

5 ft

69. *Bicycling.*   To qualify as a rated climb on the Tour de France, a grade must average at least 4%. The ascent of Dooley Mountain, Oregon, part of the Elkhorn Classic, begins at 3500 ft and climbs to 5400 ft over a horizontal distance of 37,000 ft. What is the grade of the road? Would it qualify as a rated climb if it were part of the Tour de France?
Source: barkercityherald.com

70. *Construction.*   Public buildings regularly include steps with 7-in. risers and 11-in. treads. Find the grade of such a stairway.

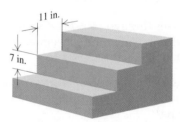

11 in.

7 in.

71. Explain why the order in which coordinates are subtracted to find slope does not matter so long as *y*-coordinates and *x*-coordinates are subtracted in the same order.

72. If one line has a slope of -3 and another has a slope of 2, which line is steeper? Why?

Skill Review

To prepare for Section 3.6, review solving a formula for a variable and graphing linear equations (Sections 2.3 and 3.2).

Solve. [2.3]

73. $ax + by = c$, for y **74.** $rx - mn = p$, for r

75. $ax - by = c$, for y **76.** $rs + nt = q$, for t

Graph. [3.2]

77. $8x + 6y = 24$ **78.** $3y = 4$

Synthesis

79. The points $(-4, -3)$, $(1, 4)$, $(4, 2)$, and $(-1, -5)$ are vertices of a quadrilateral. Use slopes to explain why the quadrilateral is a parallelogram.

80. Which is steeper and why: a ski slope that is 50° or one with a grade of 100%?

81. The plans below are for a skateboard "Fun Box". For the ramps labeled A, find the slope or grade.
Source: www.heckler.com

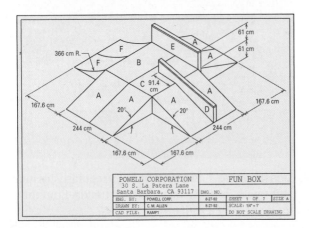

82. A line passes through $(4, -7)$ and never enters the first quadrant. What numbers could the line have for its slope?

83. A line passes through $(2, 5)$ and never enters the second quadrant. What numbers could the line have for its slope?

84. *Architecture.*   Architects often use the equation $x + y = 18$ to determine the height y, in inches, of the riser of a step when the tread is x inches wide. Express the slope of stairs designed with this equation without using the variable y.

In Exercises 85 and 86, the slope of the line is $-\frac{2}{3}$, but the numbering on one axis is missing. How many units should each tick mark on that unnumbered axis represent?

85.

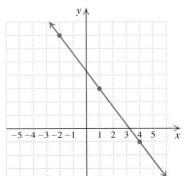

86.

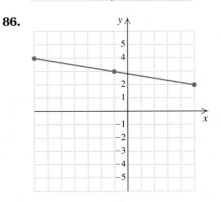

3.6   Slope–Intercept Form

Using the *y*-intercept and the Slope to Graph a Line   ■   Equations in Slope–Intercept Form   ■
Graphing and Slope–Intercept Form   ■   Parallel and Perpendicular Lines

If we know the slope and the *y*-intercept of a line, it is possible to graph the line. In this section, we will discover that a line's slope and *y*-intercept can be determined directly from the line's equation, provided the equation is written in a certain form.

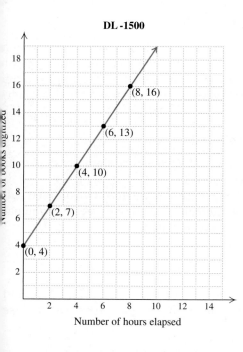

DL-1500

Using the *y*-intercept and the Slope to Graph a Line

Let's modify the book-digitization situation that first appeared in Section 3.5. Suppose that as the information technologist arrives, 4 books had already been digitized by the DL-1500. If the rate of $\frac{3}{2}$ books per hour remains in effect, the table and graph shown here can be made.

DL-1500	
Hours Elapsed	**Books Digitized**
0	4
2	7
4	10
6	13
8	16

To confirm that the digitization rate is still $\frac{3}{2}$, we calculate the slope. Recall that

$$\text{Slope} = \frac{\text{change in } y}{\text{change in } x} = \frac{\text{rise}}{\text{run}} = \frac{y_2 - y_1}{x_2 - x_1},$$

where (x_1, y_1) and (x_2, y_2) are any two points on the graphed line. Here we select $(0, 4)$ and $(2, 7)$:

$$\text{Slope} = \frac{\text{change in } y}{\text{change in } x} = \frac{7 - 4}{2 - 0} = \frac{3}{2}.$$

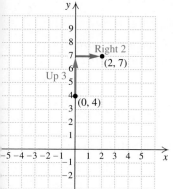

Knowing that the slope is $\frac{3}{2}$, we could have drawn the graph by plotting $(0, 4)$ and from there moving *up* 3 units and *to the right* 2 units. This would have located the point $(2, 7)$. Using $(0, 4)$ and $(2, 7)$, we can then draw the line. This is the method used in the next example.

EXAMPLE   1   Draw a line that has slope $\frac{1}{4}$ and *y*-intercept $(0, 2)$.

SOLUTION   We plot $(0, 2)$ and from there move *up* 1 unit and *to the right* 4 units. This locates the point $(4, 3)$. We plot $(4, 3)$ and draw a line passing through $(0, 2)$ and $(4, 3)$, as shown on the right below.

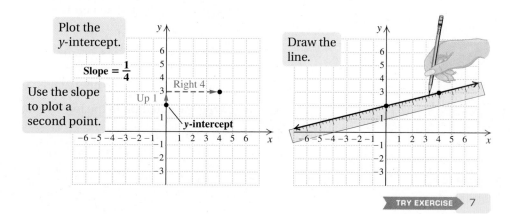

Plot the *y*-intercept.

Slope = $\frac{1}{4}$

Use the slope to plot a second point.

Draw the line.

TRY EXERCISE   7

Equations in Slope–Intercept Form

It is possible to read the slope and the *y*-intercept of a line directly from its equation. Recall from Section 3.3 that to find the *y*-intercept of an equation's graph, we replace *x* with 0 and solve the resulting equation for *y*. For example, to find the *y*-intercept of the graph of $y = 2x + 3$, we replace *x* with 0 and solve as follows:

$$y = 2x + 3$$
$$= 2 \cdot 0 + 3 = 0 + 3 = 3. \qquad \text{The } y\text{-intercept is } (0, 3).$$

The *y*-intercept of the graph of $y = 2x + 3$ is $(0, 3)$. It can be similarly shown that the graph of $y = mx + b$ has the *y*-intercept $(0, b)$.

To calculate the slope of the graph of $y = 2x + 3$, we need two ordered pairs that are solutions of the equation. The *y*-intercept $(0, 3)$ is one pair; a second pair, $(1, 5)$, can be found by substituting 1 for *x*. We then have

$$\text{Slope} = \frac{\text{change in } y}{\text{change in } x} = \frac{5 - 3}{1 - 0} = \frac{2}{1} = 2.$$

Note that the slope, 2, is also the *x*-coefficient in $y = 2x + 3$. It can be similarly shown that the graph of any equation of the form $y = mx + b$ has slope *m* (see Exercise 79).

STUDENT NOTES

An equation for a given line can be written in many different forms. Note that in the slope–intercept form, the equation is solved for *y*.

The Slope–Intercept Equation

The equation $y = mx + b$ is called the *slope–intercept equation*. The equation represents a line of slope *m* with *y*-intercept $(0, b)$.

The equation of any nonvertical line can be written in this form.

EXAMPLE 2   Find the slope and the *y*-intercept of each line whose equation is given.

a) $y = \frac{4}{5}x - 8$ **b)** $2x + y = 5$ **c)** $3x - 4y = 7$

SOLUTION

a) We rewrite $y = \frac{4}{5}x - 8$ as $y = \frac{4}{5}x + (-8)$. Now we simply read the slope and the *y*-intercept from the equation:

$$y = \tfrac{4}{5}x + (-8).$$

The slope is $\frac{4}{5}$. The *y*-intercept is $(0, -8)$.

b) We first solve for *y* to find an equivalent equation in the form $y = mx + b$:

$$2x + y = 5$$
$$y = -2x + 5. \qquad \text{Adding } -2x \text{ to both sides}$$

The slope is -2. The *y*-intercept is $(0, 5)$.

c) We rewrite the equation in the form $y = mx + b$:

$$3x - 4y = 7$$
$$-4y = -3x + 7 \qquad \text{Adding } -3x \text{ to both sides}$$
$$y = -\tfrac{1}{4}(-3x + 7) \qquad \text{Multiplying both sides by } -\tfrac{1}{4}$$
$$y = \tfrac{3}{4}x - \tfrac{7}{4}. \qquad \text{Using the distributive law}$$

The slope is $\frac{3}{4}$. The *y*-intercept is $\left(0, -\frac{7}{4}\right)$.

TRY EXERCISE ▶ 19

EXAMPLE 3

A line has slope $-\frac{12}{5}$ and y-intercept $(0, 11)$. Find an equation of the line.

SOLUTION   We use the slope–intercept equation, substituting $-\frac{12}{5}$ for m and 11 for b:

$$y = mx + b = -\frac{12}{5}x + 11.$$

The desired equation is $y = -\frac{12}{5}x + 11$.

▶ TRY EXERCISE 35

EXAMPLE 4

Threatened species.   A threatened species is a species that is likely to become endangered in the future. Determine an equation for the graph of threatened species in the Blue Mountains.

Source: Based on information from Sustainable Blue Mountains

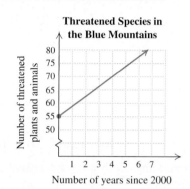

Threatened Species in the Blue Mountains

Number of years since 2000

SOLUTION   To write an equation for a line, we can use slope–intercept form, provided the slope and the y-intercept are known. From the graph, we see that $(0, 55)$ is the y-intercept. Looking closely, we see that the line passes through $(4, 70)$. We can either count squares on the graph or use the formula to calculate the slope:

$$m = \frac{\text{change in } y}{\text{change in } x} = \frac{70 - 55}{4 - 0} = \frac{15}{4}.$$

The desired equation is

$$y = \frac{15}{4}x + 55, \qquad \text{Using } \tfrac{15}{4} \text{ for } m \text{ and 55 for } b$$

where y is the number of threatened species in the Blue Mountains x years after 2000.

▶ TRY EXERCISE 43

Graphing and Slope–Intercept Form

In Example 1, we drew a graph, knowing only the slope and the y-intercept. In Example 2, we determined the slope and the y-intercept of a line by examining its equation. We now combine the two procedures to develop a quick way to graph a linear equation.

EXAMPLE 5

Graph: **(a)** $y = \frac{3}{4}x + 5$; **(b)** $2x + 3y = 3$.

SOLUTION

a) From the equation $y = \frac{3}{4}x + 5$, we see that the slope of the graph is $\frac{3}{4}$ and the y-intercept is $(0, 5)$. We plot $(0, 5)$ and then consider the slope, $\frac{3}{4}$. Starting at $(0, 5)$, we plot a second point by moving *up* 3 units (since the numerator is *positive* and corresponds to the change in y) and *to the right* 4 units (since the denominator is *positive* and corresponds to the change in x). We reach a new point, $(4, 8)$.

Remember that

$$\frac{3}{4} = \frac{-3}{-4}.$$

Similarly,

$$-\frac{3}{4} = \frac{-3}{4} = \frac{3}{-4}.$$

Also note that

$$2 = \frac{2}{1} \quad \text{and} \quad -2 = \frac{-2}{1}.$$

Since $\frac{3}{4} = \frac{-3}{-4}$, we can again start at the y-intercept, $(0, 5)$, but move *down* 3 units (since the numerator is *negative* and corresponds to the change in y) and *to the left* 4 units (since the denominator is *negative* and corresponds to the change in x). We reach another point, $(-4, 2)$. Once two or three points have been plotted, the line representing all solutions of $y = \frac{3}{4}x + 5$ can be drawn.

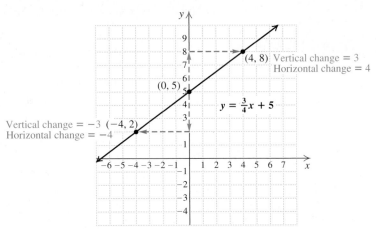

The signs of the numerator and the denominator of the slope indicate whether to move up, down, left, or right. Compare the following slopes.

$$\frac{1}{2} \quad \leftarrow 1 \text{ unit up} \\ \quad \leftarrow 2 \text{ units right}$$

$$\frac{-1}{-2} \quad \leftarrow 1 \text{ unit down} \\ \quad \leftarrow 2 \text{ units left}$$

$$\frac{-1}{2} \quad \leftarrow 1 \text{ unit down} \\ \quad \leftarrow 2 \text{ units right}$$

$$\frac{1}{-2} \quad \leftarrow 1 \text{ unit up} \\ \quad \leftarrow 2 \text{ units left}$$

b) To graph $2x + 3y = 3$, we first rewrite it in slope–intercept form:

$$2x + 3y = 3$$
$$3y = -2x + 3 \qquad \text{Adding } -2x \text{ to both sides}$$
$$y = \tfrac{1}{3}(-2x + 3) \qquad \text{Multiplying both sides by } \tfrac{1}{3}$$
$$y = -\tfrac{2}{3}x + 1. \qquad \text{Using the distributive law}$$

To graph $y = -\frac{2}{3}x + 1$, we first plot the y-intercept, $(0, 1)$. We can think of the slope as $\frac{-2}{3}$. Starting at $(0, 1)$ and using the slope, we find a second point by moving *down* 2 units (since the numerator is *negative*) and *to the right* 3 units (since the denominator is *positive*). We plot the new point, $(3, -1)$. In a similar manner, we can move from the point $(3, -1)$ to locate a third point, $(6, -3)$. The line can then be drawn.

Since $-\frac{2}{3} = \frac{2}{-3}$, an alternative approach is to again plot $(0, 1)$, but this time move *up* 2 units (since the numerator is *positive*) and *to the left* 3 units (since the denominator is *negative*). This leads to another point on the graph, $(-3, 3)$.

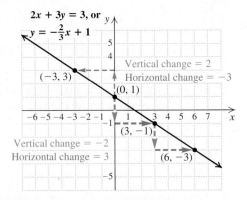

It is important to be able to use both $\frac{2}{-3}$ and $\frac{-2}{3}$ to draw the graph.

TRY EXERCISE 47

Slope–intercept form allows us to quickly determine the slope of a line by simply inspecting its equation. This can be especially helpful when attempting to decide whether two lines are parallel or perpendicular.

Using a standard $[-10, 10, -10, 10]$ window, graph the equations $y_1 = \frac{2}{3}x + 1$, $y_2 = \frac{3}{8}x + 1$, $y_3 = \frac{2}{3}x + 5$, and $y_4 = \frac{3}{8}x + 5$. If you can, use your graphing calculator in the MODE that graphs equations *simultaneously*. Once all lines have been drawn, try to decide which equation corresponds to each line. After matching equations with lines, you can check your matches by using TRACE and the up and down arrow keys to move from one line to the next. The number of the equation will appear in a corner of the screen.

1. Graph $y_1 = -\frac{3}{4}x - 2$, $y_2 = -\frac{1}{5}x - 2$, $y_3 = -\frac{3}{4}x - 5$, and $y_4 = -\frac{1}{5}x - 5$ using the SIMULTANEOUS mode. Then match each line with the corresponding equation. Check using TRACE.

Parallel and Perpendicular Lines

Two lines are parallel if they lie in the same plane and do not intersect no matter how far they are extended. If two lines are vertical, they are parallel. How can we tell if nonvertical lines are parallel? The answer is simple: We look at their slopes.

> **Slope and Parallel Lines**
>
> Two lines are parallel if they have the same slope or if both lines are vertical.

EXAMPLE 6 Determine whether the graphs of $y = -3x + 4$ and $6x + 2y = -10$ are parallel.

SOLUTION   We compare the slopes of the two lines to determine whether the graphs are parallel.

One of the two equations given is in slope–intercept form:

$$y = -3x + 4. \qquad \text{The slope is } -3 \text{ and the } y\text{-intercept is } (0, 4).$$

To find the slope of the other line, we need to rewrite the other equation in slope–intercept form:

$$6x + 2y = -10$$
$$2y = -6x - 10 \qquad \text{Adding } -6x \text{ to both sides}$$
$$y = -3x - 5. \qquad \text{The slope is } -3 \text{ and the } y\text{-intercept is } (0, -5).$$

Since both lines have slope -3 but different y-intercepts, the graphs are parallel. There is no need for us to actually graph either equation.

TRY EXERCISE 63

Two lines are perpendicular if they intersect at a right angle. If one line is vertical and another is horizontal, they are perpendicular. There are other instances in which two lines are perpendicular.

Consider a line $\overleftrightarrow{RS}$ as shown at left, with slope a/b. Then think of rotating the figure 90° to get a line $\overleftrightarrow{R'S'}$ perpendicular to $\overleftrightarrow{RS}$. For the new line, the rise and the run are interchanged, but the run is now negative. Thus the slope of the new line is $-b/a$. Let's multiply the slopes:

$$\frac{a}{b}\left(-\frac{b}{a}\right) = -1.$$

This can help us determine which lines are perpendicular.

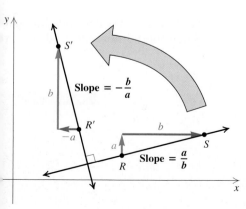

> ### Slope and Perpendicular Lines
> Two lines are perpendicular if the product of their slopes is -1 or if one line is vertical and the other line is horizontal.

Thus, if one line has slope m ($m \neq 0$), the slope of a line perpendicular to it $-1/m$. That is, we take the reciprocal of m ($m \neq 0$) and change the sign.

EXAMPLE 7   Determine whether the graphs of $2x + y = 8$ and $y = \frac{1}{2}x + 7$ are perpendicular.

SOLUTION   One of the two equations given is in slope–intercept form:

$$y = \tfrac{1}{2}x + 7.   \quad \text{The slope is } \tfrac{1}{2}.$$

To find the slope of the other line, we rewrite the other equation in slope intercept form:

$$2x + y = 8$$
$$y = -2x + 8.   \quad \text{Adding } -2x \text{ to both sides}$$

The slope of the line is -2.

The lines are perpendicular if the product of their slopes is -1. Since

$$\frac{1}{2}(-2) = -1,$$

the graphs are perpendicular.

> **TRY EXERCISE** 69

EXAMPLE 8   Write a slope–intercept equation for the line whose graph is described.

a) Parallel to the graph of $2x - 3y = 7$, with y-intercept $(0, -1)$

b) Perpendicular to the graph of $2x - 3y = 7$, with y-intercept $(0, -1)$

SOLUTION   We begin by determining the slope of the line represented $2x - 3y = 7$:

$$2x - 3y = 7$$
$$-3y = -2x + 7   \quad \text{Adding } -2x \text{ to both sides}$$
$$y = \tfrac{2}{3}x - \tfrac{7}{3}.   \quad \text{Dividing both sides by } -3$$

The slope is $\frac{2}{3}$.

a) A line parallel to the graph of $2x - 3y = 7$ has a slope of $\frac{2}{3}$. Since th y-intercept is $(0, -1)$, the slope–intercept equation is

$$y = \tfrac{2}{3}x - 1.   \quad \text{Substituting in } y = mx + b$$

b) A line perpendicular to the graph of $2x - 3y = 7$ has a slope that is th opposite of the reciprocal of $\frac{2}{3}$, or $-\frac{3}{2}$. Since the y-intercept is $(0, -1)$, th slope–intercept equation is

$$y = -\tfrac{3}{2}x - 1.   \quad \text{Substituting in } y = mx + b$$

> **TRY EXERCISE** 75

3.6   EXERCISE SET

➦ *Concept Reinforcement*   *In each of Exercises 1–6, match the phrase with the most appropriate choice from the column on the right.*

1. _____ The slope of the graph of $y = 3x - 2$

2. _____ The slope of the graph of $y = 2x - 3$

3. _____ The slope of the graph of $y = \frac{2}{3}x + 3$

4. _____ The y-intercept of the graph of $y = 2x - 3$

5. _____ The y-intercept of the graph of $y = 3x - 2$

6. _____ The y-intercept of the graph of $y = \frac{2}{3}x + \frac{3}{4}$

a) $\left(0, \frac{3}{4}\right)$

b) 2

c) $(0, -3)$

d) $\frac{2}{3}$

e) $(0, -2)$

f) 3

Draw a line that has the given slope and y-intercept.

7. Slope $\frac{2}{3}$; y-intercept $(0, 1)$

8. Slope $\frac{3}{5}$; y-intercept $(0, -1)$

9. Slope $\frac{5}{3}$; y-intercept $(0, -2)$

10. Slope $\frac{1}{2}$; y-intercept $(0, 0)$

11. Slope $-\frac{1}{3}$; y-intercept $(0, 5)$

12. Slope $-\frac{4}{5}$; y-intercept $(0, 6)$

13. Slope 2; y-intercept $(0, 0)$

14. Slope -2; y-intercept $(0, -3)$

15. Slope -3; y-intercept $(0, 2)$

16. Slope 3; y-intercept $(0, 4)$

17. Slope 0; y-intercept $(0, -5)$

18. Slope 0; y-intercept $(0, 1)$

Find the slope and the y-intercept of each line whose equation is given.

19. $y = -\frac{2}{7}x + 5$

20. $y = -\frac{3}{8}x + 4$

21. $y = \frac{1}{3}x + 7$

22. $y = \frac{4}{5}x + 1$

23. $y = \frac{9}{5}x - 4$

24. $y = -\frac{9}{10}x - 5$

25. $-3x + y = 7$

26. $-4x + y = 7$

27. $4x + 2y = 8$

28. $3x + 4y = 12$

Aha! 29. $y = 3$

30. $y - 3 = 5$

31. $2x - 5y = -8$

32. $12x - 6y = 9$

33. $9x - 8y = 0$

34. $7x = 5y$

Find the slope–intercept equation for the line with the indicated slope and y-intercept.

35. Slope 5; y-intercept $(0, 7)$

36. Slope -4; y-intercept $\left(0, -\frac{3}{5}\right)$

37. Slope $\frac{7}{8}$; y-intercept $(0, -1)$

38. Slope $\frac{5}{7}$; y-intercept $(0, 4)$

39. Slope $-\frac{5}{3}$; y-intercept $(0, -8)$

40. Slope $\frac{3}{4}$; y-intercept $(0, -35)$

Aha! 41. Slope 0; y-intercept $\left(0, \frac{1}{3}\right)$

42. Slope 7; y-intercept $(0, 0)$

Determine an equation for each graph shown.

43.

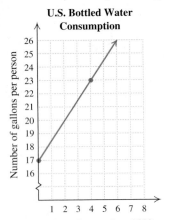

U.S. Bottled Water Consumption

Number of gallons per person

Number of years since 2000

Based on information from the International Bottled Water Association

44.

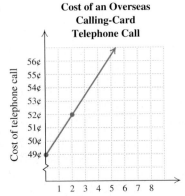

Cost of an Overseas Calling-Card Telephone Call

Cost of telephone call

Number of minutes

Source: www.pennytalk.com

45.

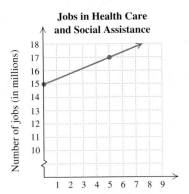

Jobs in Health Care and Social Assistance

Number of jobs (in millions)

Number of years since 2000

Source: U.S. Bureau of Labor Statistics

46.

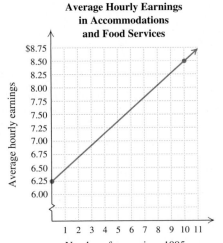

Average Hourly Earnings in Accommodations and Food Services

Average hourly earnings

Number of years since 1995

Source: U.S. Bureau of Labor Statistics

Graph.

47. $y = \frac{2}{3}x + 2$ **48.** $y = -\frac{2}{3}x - 3$

49. $y = -\frac{2}{3}x + 3$ **50.** $y = \frac{2}{3}x - 2$

51. $y = \frac{3}{2}x + 3$ **52.** $y = \frac{3}{2}x - 2$

53. $y = -\frac{4}{3}x + 3$ **54.** $y = -\frac{3}{2}x - 2$

55. $2x + y = 1$ **56.** $3x + y = 2$

57. $3x + y = 0$ **58.** $2x + y = 0$

59. $4x + 5y = 15$ **60.** $2x + 3y = 9$

61. $x - 4y = 12$ **62.** $x + 5y = 20$

Determine whether each pair of equations represents parallel lines.

63. $y = \frac{3}{4}x + 6,$
$y = \frac{3}{4}x - 2$

64. $y = \frac{1}{3}x - 2,$
$y = -\frac{1}{3}x + 1$

65. $y = 2x - 5,$
$4x + 2y = 9$

66. $y = -3x + 1,$
$6x + 2y = 8$

67. $3x + 4y = 8,$
$7 - 12y = 9x$

68. $3x = 5y - 2,$
$10y = 4 - 6x$

Determine whether each pair of equations represents perpendicular lines.

69. $y = 4x - 5,$
$4y = 8 - x$

70. $2x - 5y = -3,$
$2x + 5y = 4$

71. $x - 2y = 5,$
$2x + 4y = 8$

72. $y = -x + 7,$
$y - x = 3$

73. $2x + 3y = 1$,
$\quad\;\; 3x - 2y = 1$

74. $y = 5 - 3x$,
$\quad\;\; 3x - y = 8$

89. $-4 - 5$

90. $-6 - 5$

Write a slope–intercept equation of the line whose graph is described.

75. Parallel to the graph of $y = 5x - 7$; y-intercept $(0, 11)$

76. Parallel to the graph of $2x - y = 1$; y-intercept $(0, -3)$

77. Perpendicular to the graph of $2x + y = 0$; y-intercept $(0, 0)$

78. Perpendicular to the graph of $y = \frac{1}{3}x + 7$; y-intercept $(0, 5)$

79. Parallel to the graph of $y = x$; y-intercept $(0, 3)$

80. Perpendicular to the graph of $y = x$; y-intercept $(0, 0)$

81. Perpendicular to the graph of $x + y = 3$; y-intercept $(0, -4)$

82. Parallel to the graph of $3x + 2y = 5$; y-intercept $(0, -1)$

83. Can a horizontal line be graphed using the method of Example 5? Why or why not?

84. If two lines are perpendicular, does it follow that the lines have slopes that are negative reciprocals of each other? Why or why not?

Skill Review

To prepare for Section 3.7, review solving a formula for a variable and subtracting real numbers (Sections 1.6 and 2.3).

Solve. [2.3]

85. $y - k = m(x - h)$, for y

86. $y - 9 = -2(x + 4)$, for y

Simplify. [1.6]

87. $-10 - (-3)$

88. $8 - (-5)$

Synthesis

91. Explain how it is possible for an incorrect graph to be drawn, even after plotting three points that line up.

92. Which would you prefer, and why: graphing an equation of the form $y = mx + b$ or graphing an equation of the form $Ax + By = C$?

93. Show that the slope of the line given by $y = mx + b$ is m. (*Hint*: Substitute both 0 and 1 for x to find two pairs of coordinates. Then use the formula, Slope = change in y/change in x.)

94. Write an equation of the line with the same slope as the line given by $5x + 2y = 8$ and the same y-intercept as the line given by $3x - 7y = 10$.

95. Write an equation of the line parallel to the line given by $2x - 6y = 10$ and having the same y-intercept as the line given by $9x + 6y = 18$.

96. Write an equation of the line parallel to the line given by $3x - 2y = 8$ and having the same y-intercept as the line given by $2y + 3x = -4$.

97. Write an equation of the line perpendicular to the line given by $3x - 5y = 8$ and having the same y-intercept as the line given by $2x + 4y = 12$.

98. Write an equation of the line perpendicular to the line given by $2x + 3y = 7$ and having the same y-intercept as the line given by $5x + 2y = 10$.

99. Write an equation of the line perpendicular to the line given by $3x - 2y = 9$ and having the same y-intercept as the line given by $2x + 5y = 0$.

100. Write an equation of the line perpendicular to the line given by $2x + 5y = 6$ that passes through $(2, 6)$. (*Hint*: Draw a graph.)

CONNECTING ⬆ the CONCEPTS

If any two points are plotted on a plane, there is only one line that will go through both points. Thus, if we know that the graph of an equation is a straight line, we need only find two points that are on that line. Then we can plot those points and draw the line that goes through them.

The different graphing methods discussed in this chapter present efficient ways of finding two points that are on the graph of the equation. Following is a general strategy for graphing linear equations.

1. Make sure that the equation is linear. Linear equations can always be written in the form $Ax + By = C$. (A or B may be 0.)
2. Graph the line. Use substitution to find two points on the line, or use a more efficient method based on the form of the equation.
3. Check the graph by finding another point that should be on the line and determining whether it does actually fall on the line.

Form of Equation	Graph
$x = a$	Draw a vertical line through $(a, 0)$.
$y = b$	Draw a horizontal line through $(0, b)$.
$y = mx + b$	Plot the y-intercept $(0, b)$. Start at the y-intercept and count off the rise and run using the slope m to find another point. Draw a line through the two points.
$Ax + By = C$	Determine the x- and y-intercepts $(a, 0)$ and $(0, b)$. Draw a line through the two points.

MIXED REVIEW

For each equation, (a) determine whether it is linear and (b) if it is linear, graph the line.

1. $x = 3$
2. $y = -2$
3. $y = \frac{1}{2}x + 3$
4. $4x + 3y = 12$
5. $y - 5 = x$
6. $x + y = -2$
7. $3xy = 6$
8. $2x = 3y$
9. $3 - y = 4$
10. $y = x^2 - 4$
11. $2y = 9x - 10$
12. $x + 8 = 7$
13. $2x - 6 = 3y$
14. $y - 2x = 4$
15. $2y - x = 4$
16. $y = \frac{1}{x}$
17. $x - 2y = 0$
18. $y = 4 - x$
19. $y = 4 + x$
20. $4x - 5y = 20$

3.7 Point–Slope Form

Writing Equations in Point–Slope Form ■ Graphing and Point–Slope Form ■ Estimations and Predictions Using Two Points

There are many applications in which a slope—or a rate of change—and an ordered pair are known. When the ordered pair is the y-intercept, an equation in slope–intercept form can be easily produced. When the ordered pair represents a point other than the y-intercept, a different form, known as *point–slope form*, is more convenient.

Writing Equations in Point–Slope Form

Consider a line with slope 2 passing through the point $(4, 1)$, as shown in the figure. In order for a point (x, y) to be on the line, the coordinates x and y must be solutions of the slope equation

$$\frac{y - 1}{x - 4} = 2. \qquad \text{If } (x, y) \text{ is not on the line, this equation will not be true.}$$

Take a moment to examine this equation. Pairs like $(5, 3)$ and $(3, -1)$ are on the line and are solutions, since

$$\frac{3 - 1}{5 - 4} = 2 \quad \text{and} \quad \frac{-1 - 1}{3 - 4} = 2.$$

When $x \neq 4$, then $x - 4 \neq 0$, and we can multiply on both sides of the slope equation by $x - 4$:

$$(x - 4) \cdot \frac{y - 1}{x - 4} = 2(x - 4)$$
$$y - 1 = 2(x - 4). \qquad \text{Removing a factor equal to 1: } \frac{x - 4}{x - 4} = 1$$

Every point on the line is a solution of this equation.

This is considered **point–slope form** for the line shown in the figure at left. A point–slope equation can be written any time a line's slope and a point on the line are known.

> ### The Point–Slope Equation
> The equation $y - y_1 = m(x - x_1)$ is called the *point–slope equation* for the line with slope m that contains the point (x_1, y_1).

Point–slope form is especially useful in more advanced mathematics courses, where problems similar to the following often arise.

EXAMPLE 1 Write a point–slope equation for the line with slope $\frac{1}{5}$ that contains the point $(7, 2)$.

SOLUTION We substitute $\frac{1}{5}$ for m, 7 for x_1, and 2 for y_1:

$$y - y_1 = m(x - x_1) \qquad \text{Using the point–slope equation}$$
$$y - 2 = \frac{1}{5}(x - 7). \qquad \text{Substituting}$$

TRY EXERCISE 13

EXAMPLE 2

Write a point–slope equation for the line with slope $-\frac{4}{3}$ that contains the poin
$(1, -6)$.

SOLUTION   We substitute $-\frac{4}{3}$ for m, 1 for x_1, and -6 for y_1:

$$y - y_1 = m(x - x_1) \qquad \text{Using the point–slope equation}$$
$$y - (-6) = -\frac{4}{3}(x - 1). \qquad \text{Substituting}$$

▶ TRY EXERCISE   19

EXAMPLE 3

Write the slope–intercept equation for the line with slope 2 that contains the
point $(3, 1)$.

STUDENT NOTES ————

There are several forms in which a
line's equation can be written. For
instance, as shown in Example 3,
$y - 1 = 2(x - 3), y - 1 = 2x - 6$,
and $y = 2x - 5$ all are equations
for the same line.

SOLUTION   There are two parts to this solution. First, we write an equation in
point–slope form:

$$y - y_1 = m(x - x_1)$$
$$y - 1 = 2(x - 3). \qquad \text{Substituting} \qquad \boxed{\text{Write in point–slope form.}}$$

Next, we find an equivalent equation of the form $y = mx + b$:

$$y - 1 = 2(x - 3)$$
$$y - 1 = 2x - 6 \qquad \text{Using the distributive law} \qquad \boxed{\text{Write in slope–intercept form.}}$$
$$y = 2x - 5. \qquad \text{Adding 1 to both sides to get slope–intercept form}$$

▶ TRY EXERCISE   27

EXAMPLE 4

Consider the line given by the equation $8y = 7x - 24$.

a) Write the slope–intercept equation for a parallel line passing through $(-1, 2)$.

b) Write the slope–intercept equation for a perpendicular line passing throug
$(-1, 2)$.

SOLUTION   Both parts (a) and (b) require us to find the slope of the line given by
$8y = 7x - 24$. To do so, we solve for y to find slope–intercept form:

$$8y = 7x - 24$$
$$y = \frac{7}{8}x - 3. \qquad \text{Multiplying both sides by } \frac{1}{8}$$
The slope is $\frac{7}{8}$.

a) The slope of any parallel line will be $\frac{7}{8}$. The point–slope equation yields

$$y - 2 = \frac{7}{8}[x - (-1)] \qquad \text{Substituting } \frac{7}{8} \text{ for the slope and } (-1, 2) \text{ for the point}$$
$$y - 2 = \frac{7}{8}[x + 1]$$
$$y = \frac{7}{8}x + \frac{7}{8} + 2 \qquad \text{Using the distributive law and adding 2 to both sides}$$
$$y = \frac{7}{8}x + \frac{23}{8}.$$

b) The slope of a perpendicular line is given by the opposite of the reciprocal o
$\frac{7}{8}$, or $-\frac{8}{7}$. The point–slope equation yields

$$y - 2 = -\frac{8}{7}[x - (-1)] \qquad \text{Substituting } -\frac{8}{7} \text{ for the slope and } (-1, 2) \text{ for the point}$$
$$y - 2 = -\frac{8}{7}[x + 1]$$
$$y = -\frac{8}{7}x - \frac{8}{7} + 2 \qquad \text{Using the distributive law and adding 2 to both sides}$$
$$y = -\frac{8}{7}x + \frac{6}{7}.$$

▶ TRY EXERCISE   39

TECHNOLOGY CONNECTION

To check that the graphs of
$y = \frac{7}{8}x - 3$ and $y = -\frac{8}{7}x + \frac{6}{7}$
are perpendicular, we use the
ZSQUARE option of the ZOOM
menu to create a "squared"
window. This corrects for dis-
tortion that would result from
the units on the axes being of
different lengths.

1. Show that the graphs of
$y = \frac{3}{4}x + 2$ and $y = -\frac{4}{3}x - 1$
appear to be perpen-
dicular.

2. Show that the graphs of
$y = -\frac{2}{5}x - 4$ and $y = \frac{5}{2}x + 3$
appear to be perpen-
dicular.

3. To see that this type of
check is not foolproof,
graph

$$y = \frac{31}{40}x + 2$$

and $y = -\frac{40}{30}x - 1$.

Are the lines perpendic-
ular? Why or why not?

Graphing and Point–Slope Form

When we know a line's slope and a point that is on the line, we can draw the graph, much as we did in Section 3.6. For example, the information given in the statement of Example 3 is sufficient for drawing a graph.

EXAMPLE 5

Graph the line with slope 2 that passes through $(3, 1)$.

SOLUTION We plot $(3, 1)$, move *up* 2 and *to the right* 1 $\left(\text{since } 2 = \frac{2}{1}\right)$, and draw the line.

Plot the point.

Use the slope to plot a second point.

Draw the line.

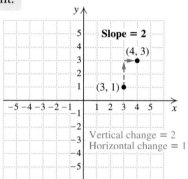

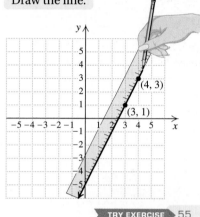

TRY EXERCISE 55

EXAMPLE 6

Graph: $y - 2 = 3(x - 4)$.

SOLUTION Since $y - 2 = 3(x - 4)$ is in point–slope form, we know that the line has slope 3, or $\frac{3}{1}$, and passes through the point $(4, 2)$. We plot $(4, 2)$ and then find a second point by moving *up* 3 units and *to the right* 1 unit. The line can then be drawn, as shown below.

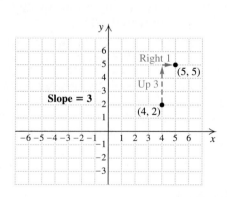

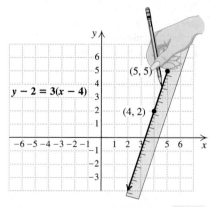

TRY EXERCISE 65

EXAMPLE 7

Graph: $y + 4 = -\frac{5}{2}(x + 3)$.

SOLUTION Once we have written the equation in point–slope form, $y - y_1 = m(x - x_1)$, we can proceed much as we did in Example 6. To find an equivalent equation in point–slope form, we subtract opposites instead of adding:

$$y + 4 = -\tfrac{5}{2}(x + 3)$$
$$y - (-4) = -\tfrac{5}{2}(x - (-3)).$$ Subtracting a negative instead of adding a positive. This is now in point–slope form.

From this last equation, $y - (-4) = -\frac{5}{2}(x - (-3))$, we see that the line passes through $(-3, -4)$ and has slope $-\frac{5}{2}$, or $\frac{5}{-2}$.

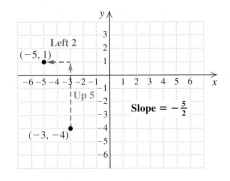

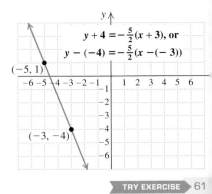

TRY EXERCISE 61

Estimations and Predictions Using Two Points

We can estimate real-life quantities that are not already known by using two points with known coordinates. When the unknown point is located *between* the two points, this process is called **interpolation**. If a graph passing through the known points is *extended* to predict future values, the process is called **extrapolation**. In statistics, methods exist for using a set of several points to interpolate or extrapolate values using curves other than lines.

EXAMPLE 8   *Student volunteers.* An increasing number of college students are donating time and energy in volunteer service. The number of college-student volunteers grew from 2.7 million in 2002 to 3.3 million in 2005.

Source: Corporation for National and Community Service

a) Graph the line passing through the given data points, letting $x =$ the number of years since 2000.

b) Determine an equation for the line and estimate the number of college students who volunteered in 2004.

c) Predict the number of college students who will volunteer in 2010.

SOLUTION

a) We first draw and label a horizontal axis to display the year and a vertical axis to display the number of college-student volunteers, in millions. Next, we number the axes, choosing scales that will include both the given values and the values to be estimated.

Since $x =$ the number of years since 2000, we plot the points $(2, 2.7)$ and $(5, 3.3)$ and draw a line passing through both points.

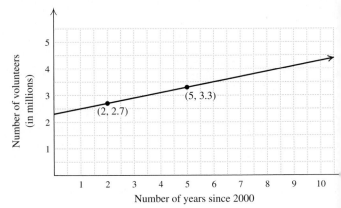

b) To find an equation for the line, we first calculate its slope:

$$m = \frac{\text{change in } y}{\text{change in } x} = \frac{3.3 - 2.7}{5 - 2} = \frac{0.6}{3} = 0.2.$$

The number of college-student volunteers increased at a rate of 0.2 million students per year. We can use either of the given points to write a point–slope equation for the line. Let's use (2, 2.7) and then write an equivalent equation in slope–intercept form:

$y - 2.7 = 0.2(x - 2)$	This is a point–slope equation.
$y - 2.7 = 0.2x - 0.4$	Using the distributive law
$y = 0.2x + 2.3.$	Adding 2.7 to both sides. This is slope–intercept form.

To estimate the number of college-student volunteers in 2004, we substitute 4 for x in the slope–intercept equation:

$$y = 0.2 \cdot 4 + 2.3 = 3.1.$$

As the graph confirms, in 2004 there were about 3.1 million college-student volunteers.

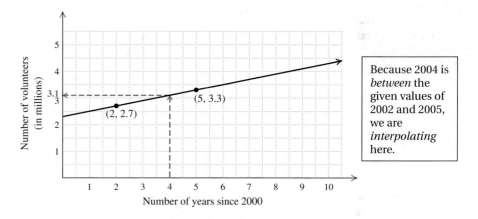

Because 2004 is *between* the given values of 2002 and 2005, we are *interpolating* here.

c) To predict the number of college-student volunteers in 2010, we again substitute for x in the slope–intercept equation:

$$y = 0.2 \cdot 10 + 2.3 = 4.3.\qquad \text{2010 is 10 yr after 2000.}$$

As we can see from the graph, if the trend continues, there will be about 4.3 million college-student volunteers in 2010.

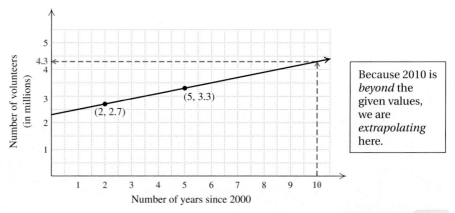

Because 2010 is *beyond* the given values, we are *extrapolating* here.

TRY EXERCISE 71

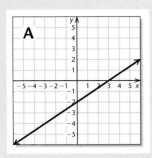

A

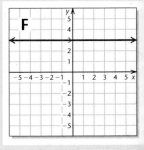

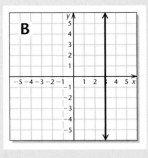

B

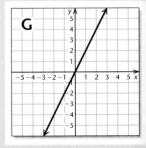

G

Match each equation with its graph.

1. $y = x + 4$

2. $y = 2x$

3. $y = 3$

4. $x = 3$

5. $y = -\frac{1}{2}x$

6. $2x - 3y = 6$

7. $y = -3x - 2$

8. $3x + 2y = 6$

9. $y - 3 = 2(x - 1)$

10. $y + 2 = \frac{1}{2}(x + 1)$

Answers on page A-13

An additional, animated version of this activity appears in MyMathLab. To use MyMathLab, you need a course ID and a student access code. Contact your instructor for more information.

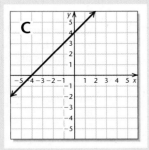

C

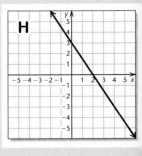

H

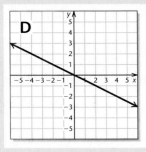

D

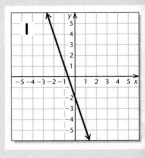

I

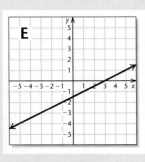

E

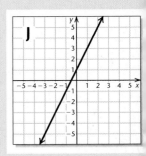

J

3.7 EXERCISE SET

Concept Reinforcement In each of Exercises 1–8, match the given information about a line with the appropriate equation from the column on the right.

1. ____ Slope 5; includes (2, 3)

2. ____ Slope 5; includes (3, 2)

3. ____ Slope −5; includes (2, 3)

4. ____ Slope −5; includes (3, 2)

5. ____ Slope −5; includes (−2, −3)

6. ____ Slope 5; includes (−2, −3)

7. ____ Slope −5; includes (−3, −2)

8. ____ Slope 5; includes (−3, −2)

a) $y + 3 = 5(x + 2)$

b) $y - 2 = 5(x - 3)$

c) $y + 2 = 5(x + 3)$

d) $y - 3 = -5(x - 2)$

e) $y + 3 = -5(x + 2)$

f) $y + 2 = -5(x + 3)$

g) $y - 3 = 5(x - 2)$

h) $y - 2 = -5(x - 3)$

In each of Exercises 9–12, match the graph with the appropriate equation from the column on the right.

9.

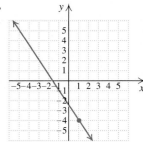

a) $y - 4 = -\frac{3}{2}(x + 1)$

b) $y - 4 = \frac{3}{2}(x + 1)$

c) $y + 4 = -\frac{3}{2}(x - 1)$

d) $y + 4 = \frac{3}{2}(x - 1)$

10.

11.

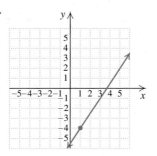

12.

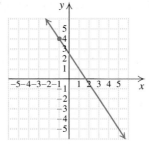

Write a point–slope equation for the line with the given slope that contains the given point.

13. $m = 3;\ (1, 6)$ **14.** $m = 2;\ (3, 7)$

15. $m = \frac{3}{5};\ (2, 8)$ **16.** $m = \frac{2}{3};\ (4, 1)$

17. $m = -4;\ (3, 1)$ **18.** $m = -5;\ (6, 2)$

19. $m = \frac{3}{2};\ (5, -4)$ **20.** $m = -\frac{4}{3};\ (7, -1)$

21. $m = -\frac{5}{4};\ (-2, 6)$ **22.** $m = \frac{7}{2};\ (-3, 4)$

23. $m = -2;\ (-4, -1)$ **24.** $m = -3;\ (-2, -5)$

25. $m = 1;\ (-2, 8)$ **26.** $m = -1;\ (-3, 6)$

Write the slope–intercept equation for the line with the given slope that contains the given point.

27. $m = 4;\ (3, 5)$ **28.** $m = 3;\ (6, 2)$

29. $m = \frac{7}{4};\ (4, -2)$ **30.** $m = \frac{8}{3};\ (3, -4)$

31. $m = -2;\ (-3, 7)$ **32.** $m = -3;\ (-2, 1)$

33. $m = -4;\ (-2, -1)$ **34.** $m = -5;\ (-1, -4)$

35. $m = \frac{2}{3};\ (5, 6)$ **36.** $m = \frac{3}{2};\ (7, 4)$

Aha! **37.** $m = -\frac{5}{6};\ (0, 4)$ **38.** $m = -\frac{3}{4};\ (0, 5)$

Write an equation of the line containing the specified point and parallel to the indicated line.

39. $(2, 5)$, $x - 2y = 3$

40. $(1, 4)$, $3x + y = 5$

Aha! **41.** $(0, -5)$, $y = 4x + 3$

42. $(0, 2)$, $y = x - 11$

43. $(-2, -3)$, $2x + 3y = -7$

44. $(-7, 0)$, $5x + 2y = 6$

45. $(5, -4)$, $x = 2$

46. $(-3, 6)$, $y = 7$

Write an equation of the line containing the specified point and perpendicular to the indicated line.

47. $(3, 1)$, $2x - 3y = 4$

48. $(6, 0)$, $5x + 4y = 1$

49. $(-4, 2)$, $x + y = 6$

50. $(-2, -5)$, $x - 2y = 3$

Aha! **51.** $(0, 6)$, $2x - 5 = y$

52. $(0, -7)$, $4x + 3 = y$

53. $(-3, 7)$, $y = 5$

54. $(4, -2)$, $x = 1$

55. Graph the line with slope $\frac{4}{3}$ that passes through the point $(1, 2)$.

56. Graph the line with slope $\frac{2}{5}$ that passes through the point $(3, 4)$.

57. Graph the line with slope $-\frac{3}{4}$ that passes through the point $(2, 5)$.

58. Graph the line with slope $-\frac{3}{2}$ that passes through the point $(1, 4)$.

Graph.

59. $y - 5 = \frac{1}{3}(x - 2)$

60. $y - 2 = \frac{1}{2}(x - 1)$

61. $y - 1 = -\frac{1}{4}(x - 3)$

62. $y - 1 = -\frac{1}{2}(x - 3)$

63. $y + 2 = \frac{2}{3}(x - 1)$

64. $y - 1 = \frac{3}{4}(x + 5)$

65. $y + 4 = 3(x + 1)$

66. $y + 3 = 2(x + 1)$

67. $y - 4 = -2(x + 1)$

68. $y + 3 = -1(x - 4)$

69. $y + 1 = -\frac{3}{5}(x - 2)$

70. $y - 2 = -\frac{2}{3}(x + 1)$

In Exercises 71–78, graph the given data and determine an equation for the related line (as in Example 8). Then use the equation to answer parts (a) and (b).

71. *Birth rate among teenagers.* The birth rate among teenagers, measured in births per 1000 females age 15–19, fell steadily from 62.1 in 1991 to 41.1 in 2007

Source: National Center for Health Statistics

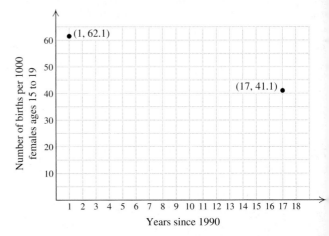

a) Calculate the birth rate among teenagers in 1999

b) Predict the birth rate among teenagers in 2008.

72. *Food-stamp program participation.* Participation in the U.S. food-stamp program grew from approximately 17.1 million people in 2000 to approximately 23 million in 2004.

Source: U.S. Department of Agriculture

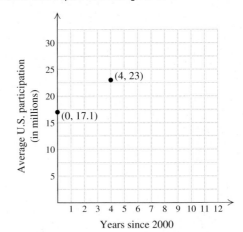

a) Calculate the number of participants in 2001.

b) Predict the number of participants in 2010.

73. *Cigarette smoking.* The percentage of people age 25–44 who smoke has changed from 14.2% in 2001 to 10.8% in 2004.

Source: Office on Smoking and Health, National Center for Chronic Disease Prevention and Health Promotion

a) Calculate the percentage of people age 25–44 who smoked in 2002.

b) Predict the percentage of people age 25–44 who will smoke in 2010.

74. *Cigarette smoking.*   The percentage of people age 18–24 who smoke has dropped from 5.2% in 2001 to 3.4% in 2004.
Source: Office on Smoking and Health, National Center for Chronic Disease Prevention and Health Promotion

a) Calculate the percentage of people age 18–24 who smoked in 2003.
b) Estimate the percentage of people age 18–24 who smoked in 2008.

75. *College enrollment.*   U.S. college enrollment has grown from approximately 14.3 million in 1995 to 17.4 million in 2005.
Source: National Center for Education Statistics

a) Calculate the U.S. college enrollment for 2002.
b) Predict the U.S. college enrollment for 2010.

76. *High school enrollment.*   U.S. high school enrollment has changed from approximately 13.7 million in 1995 to 16.3 million in 2005.
Source: National Center for Education Statistics

a) Calculate the U.S. high school enrollment for 2002.
b) Predict the U.S. high school enrollment for 2010.

77. *Aging population.*   The number of U.S. residents over the age of 65 was approximately 31 million in 1990 and 36.3 million in 2004.
Source: U.S. Census Bureau

a) Calculate the number of U.S. residents over the age of 65 in 1997.
b) Predict the number of U.S. residents over the age of 65 in 2010.

78. *Urban population.*   The percentage of the U.S. population that resides in metropolitan areas increased from about 78% in 1980 to about 83% in 2006.

a) Calculate the percentage of the U.S. population residing in metropolitan areas in 1992.

b) Predict the percentage of the U.S. population residing in metropolitan areas in 2012.

Write the slope–intercept equation for the line containing the given pair of points.

79. $(2, 3)$ and $(4, 1)$

80. $(6, 8)$ and $(3, 5)$

81. $(-3, 1)$ and $(3, 5)$

82. $(-3, 4)$ and $(3, 1)$

83. $(5, 0)$ and $(0, -2)$

84. $(-2, 0)$ and $(0, 3)$

85. $(-4, -1)$ and $(1, 9)$

86. $(-3, 5)$ and $(-1, -3)$

 87. Can equations for horizontal or vertical lines be written in point–slope form? Why or why not?

 88. Describe a situation in which it is easier to graph the equation of a line in point–slope form than in slope–intercept form.

Skill Review

To prepare for Chapter 4, review exponential notation and order of operations (Section 1.8).

Simplify. [1.8]

89. $(-5)^3$

90. $(-2)^6$

91. -2^6

92. $3 \cdot 2^4 - 5 \cdot 2^3$

93. $2 - (3 - 2^2) + 10 \div 2 \cdot 5$

94. $(5 - 7)^2(3 - 2 \cdot 2)$

Synthesis

 95. Describe a procedure that can be used to write the slope–intercept equation for any nonvertical line passing through two given points.

 96. Any nonvertical line has many equations in point–slope form, but only one in slope–intercept form. Why is this?

Graph.

Aha! **97.** $y - 3 = 0(x - 52)$

98. $y + 4 = 0(x + 93)$

Write the slope–intercept equation for each line shown.

99.

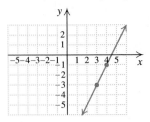

100.

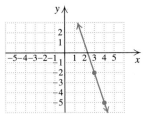

101.

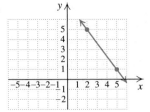

102.

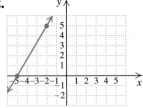

Aha! **103.** Write an equation of the line parallel to the line given by $y = 3 - 4x$ that passes through $(0, 7)$.

104. Write the slope–intercept equation of the line that has the same y-intercept as the line $x - 3y = 6$ and contains the point $(5, -1)$.

105. Write the slope–intercept equation of the line that contains the point $(-1, 5)$ and is parallel to the line passing through $(2, 7)$ and $(-1, -3)$.

106. Write the slope–intercept equation of the line that has x-intercept $(-2, 0)$ and is parallel to $4x - 8y = 12$.

Another form of a linear equation is the double-intercept *form:* $\dfrac{x}{a} + \dfrac{y}{b} = 1$. *From this form, we can read the* x-intercept $(a, 0)$ *and the* y-intercept $(0, b)$ *directly.*

107. Find the x-intercept and the y-intercept of the graph of the line given by $\dfrac{x}{2} + \dfrac{y}{5} = 1$.

108. Find the x-intercept and the y-intercept of the graph of the line given by $\dfrac{x}{10} - \dfrac{y}{3} = 1$.

109. Write the equation $4y - 3x = 12$ in double-intercept form and find the intercepts.

110. Write the equation $6x + 5y = 30$ in double-intercept form and find the intercepts.

111. Why is slope–intercept form more useful than point–slope form when using a graphing calculator? How can point–slope form be modified so that it is more easily used with graphing calculators?

CONNECTING the CONCEPTS

Any line can be described by a number of equivalent equations. We write the equation in the form that is most useful for us. For example, all four of the equations below describe the given line.

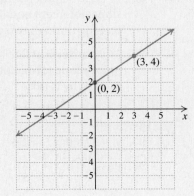

$2x - 3y = -6;$

$y = \frac{2}{3}x + 2;$

$y - 4 = \frac{2}{3}(x - 3);$

$2x + 6 = 3y$

Form of a Linear Equation	Example	Uses
Standard form: $Ax + By = C$	$2x - 3y = -6$	Finding x- and y-intercepts; Graphing using intercepts
Slope–intercept form: $y = mx + b$	$y = \dfrac{2}{3}x + 2$	Finding slope and y-intercept; Graphing using slope and y-intercept; Writing an equation given slope and y-intercept
Point–slope form: $y - y_1 = m(x - x_1)$	$y - 4 = \dfrac{2}{3}(x - 3)$	Finding slope and a point on the line; Graphing using slope and a point on the line; Writing an equation given slope and a point on the line

MIXED REVIEW

Tell whether each equation is in standard form, slope–intercept form, point–slope form, or none of these.

1. $y = -\frac{1}{2}x - 7$

2. $5x - 8y = 10$

3. $x = y + 2$

4. $\frac{1}{2}x + \frac{1}{3}y = 5$

5. $y - 2 = 5(x + 1)$

6. $3y + 7 = x$

Write each equation in standard form.

7. $2x = 5y + 10$

8. $x = y + 2$

9. $y = 2x + 7$

10. $y = -\frac{1}{2}x + 3$

11. $y - 2 = 3(x + 7)$

12. $x - 7 = 11$

Write each equation in slope–intercept form.

13. $2x - 7y = 8$

14. $y + 5 = -(x + 3)$

15. $8x = y + 3$

16. $6x + 10y = 30$

17. $9y = 5 - 8x$

18. $x - y = 3x + y$

19. $2 - 3y = 5y + 6$

20. $3(x - 4) = 6(y - 2)$

Study Summary

KEY TERMS AND CONCEPTS	EXAMPLES

SECTION 3.1: READING GRAPHS, PLOTTING POINTS, AND SCALING GRAPHS

Ordered pairs, like $(-3, 2)$ or $(4, 3)$, can be **plotted** or **graphed** using a **coordinate system** that uses two **axes**, which are most often labeled x and y. The axes intersect at the **origin**, $(0, 0)$, and divide a plane into four **quadrants**.

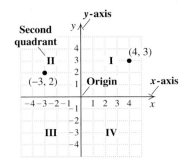

SECTION 3.2: GRAPHING LINEAR EQUATIONS

To **graph** an equation means to make a drawing that represents all of its solutions.

A **linear equation**, such as $y = 2x - 7$ or $2x + 3y = 12$, has a graph that is a straight line.

Any linear equation can be graphed by finding two ordered pairs that are solutions of the equation, plotting the corresponding points, and drawing a line through those points. Plotting a third point serves as a check.

x	y	(x, y)
1	2	$(1, 2)$
0	-1	$(0, -1)$
-1	-4	$(-1, -4)$

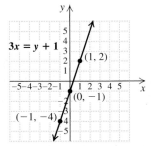

SECTION 3.3: GRAPHING AND INTERCEPTS

Intercepts
To find a y-intercept $(0, b)$, let $x = 0$ and solve for y.

To find an x-intercept $(a, 0)$, let $y = 0$ and solve for x.

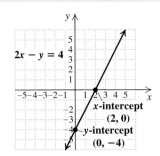

Horizontal Lines
The slope of a horizontal line is 0.
The graph of $y = b$ is a horizontal line, with y-intercept $(0, b)$.

Vertical Lines
The slope of a vertical line is undefined.
The graph of $x = a$ is a vertical line, with x-intercept $(a, 0)$.

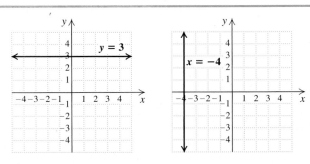

SECTION 3.4: RATES

A **rate** is a ratio that indicates how two quantities change with respect to each other.

Lara had $1500 in her savings account at the beginning of February, and $2400 at the beginning of May. Find the rate at which Lara is saving.

$$\text{Savings rate} = \frac{\text{Amount saved}}{\text{Number of months}}$$

$$= \frac{\$2400 - \$1500}{3 \text{ months}}$$

$$= \frac{\$900}{3 \text{ months}} = \$300 \text{ per month}$$

SECTION 3.5: SLOPE

Slope

$$\text{Slope} = m = \frac{\text{change in } y}{\text{change in } x}$$

$$= \frac{\text{rise}}{\text{run}} = \frac{y_2 - y_1}{x_2 - x_1}$$

The slope of the line containing the points $(-1, -4)$ and $(2, -6)$ is

$$m = \frac{-6 - (-4)}{2 - (-1)} = \frac{-2}{3} = -\frac{2}{3}.$$

A line with positive slope slants up from left to right.

A line with negative slope slants down from left to right.

The slope of a horizontal line is 0.

The slope of a vertical line is undefined.

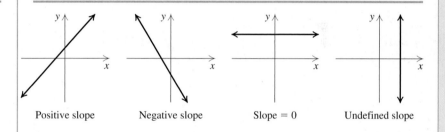

Positive slope   Negative slope   Slope $= 0$ Undefined slope

SECTION 3.6: SLOPE–INTERCEPT FORM

Slope–Intercept Form

$$y = mx + b$$

The slope of the line is m.
The y-intercept of the line is $(0, b)$.

For the line given by $y = \frac{2}{3}x - 8$:

The slope is $\frac{2}{3}$ and the y-intercept is $(0, -8)$.

To graph a line written in slope–intercept form, plot the y-intercept and count off the slope.

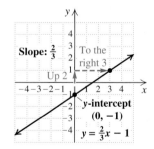

Slope: $\frac{2}{3}$ To the right 3
Up 2
y-intercept $(0, -1)$
$y = \frac{2}{3}x - 1$

Parallel and Perpendicular Lines

Two lines are parallel if they have the same slope or if both are vertical.

Determine whether the graphs of $y = \frac{2}{3}x - 5$ *and* $3y - 2x = 7$ *are parallel.*

$$y = \frac{2}{3}x - 5 \qquad 3y - 2x = 7$$

The slope is $\frac{2}{3}$.

$$3y = 2x + 7$$

$$y = \frac{2}{3}x + \frac{7}{3}$$

The slope is $\frac{2}{3}$.

Since the slopes are the same, the graphs are parallel.

Two lines are perpendicular if the product of their slopes is -1 or if one line is vertical and the other line is horizontal.

Determine whether the graphs of $y = \frac{2}{3}x - 5$ and $2y + 3x = 1$ are perpendicular.

$$y = \frac{2}{3}x - 5 \qquad\qquad 2y + 3x = 1$$
$$\text{The slope is } \tfrac{2}{3}. \qquad\qquad 2y = -3x + 1$$
$$y = -\tfrac{3}{2}x + \tfrac{1}{2}$$
$$\text{The slope is } -\tfrac{3}{2}.$$

Since $\frac{2}{3}\left(-\frac{3}{2}\right) = -1$, the graphs are perpendicular.

SECTION 3.7: POINT–SLOPE FORM

Point–Slope Form

$$y - y_1 = m(x - x_1)$$

The slope of the line is m.
The line passes through (x_1, y_1).

Write a point–slope equation for the line with slope -2 that contains the point $(3, -5)$.

$$y - y_1 = m(x - x_1)$$
$$y - (-5) = -2(x - 3)$$

Review Exercises: Chapter 3

👈 *Concept Reinforcement* *Classify each statement as either true or false.*

1. Not every ordered pair lies in one of the four quadrants. [3.1]

2. The equation of a vertical line cannot be written in slope–intercept form. [3.6]

3. Equations for lines written in slope–intercept form appear in the form $Ax + By = C$. [3.6]

4. Every horizontal line has an x-intercept. [3.3]

5. A line's slope is a measure of rate. [3.5]

6. A positive rate of ascent means that an airplane is flying increasingly higher above the earth. [3.4]

7. Any two points on a line can be used to determine the line's slope. [3.5]

8. Knowing a line's slope is enough to write the equation of the line. [3.6]

9. Knowing two points on a line is enough to write the equation of the line. [3.7]

10. Parallel lines that are not vertical have the same slope. [3.6]

The following circle graph shows the percentage of online searches done in July 2006 that were performed by a particular search engine. [3.1]
Source: NetRatings for SearchEngineWatch.com

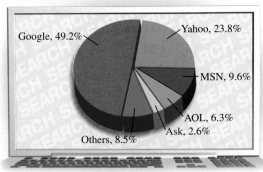

Online Searches

Google, 49.2%
Yahoo, 23.8%
MSN, 9.6%
AOL, 6.3%
Ask, 2.6%
Others, 8.5%

11. There were 5.6 billion searches done by home and business Internet users in July 2006. How many searches were done using Yahoo?

12. About 55% of the online searches done by Waterworks Graphics are image searches. In July 2006, Waterworks employees did 4200 online searches. If their search engine use is typical, how many image searches did they do using Google?

Plot each point. [3.1]

13. $(5, -1)$ **14.** $(2, 3)$ **15.** $(-4, 0)$

In which quadrant is each point located? [3.1]

16. $(-8, -7)$ **17.** $(15.3, -13.8)$ **18.** $\left(-\frac{1}{2}, \frac{1}{10}\right)$

Find the coordinates of each point in the figure. [3.1]

19. A **20.** B **21.** C

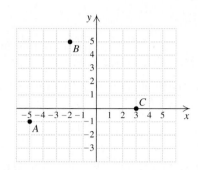

22. Use a grid 10 squares wide and 10 squares high to plot $(-65, -2), (-10, 6)$, and $(25, 7)$. Choose the scale carefully. [3.1]

23. Determine whether the equation $y = 2x + 7$ has *each* ordered pair as a solution: **(a)** $(3, 1)$; **(b)** $(-3, 1)$. [3.2]

24. Show that the ordered pairs $(0, -3)$ and $(2, 1)$ are solutions of the equation $2x - y = 3$. Then use the graph of the two points to determine another solution. Answers may vary. [3.2]

Graph.

25. $y = x - 5$ [3.2]   **26.** $y = -\frac{1}{4}x$ [3.2]

27. $y = -x + 4$ [3.2]   **28.** $4x + y = 3$ [3.2]

29. $4x + 5 = 3$ [3.3]   **30.** $5x - 2y = 10$ [3.3]

31. *TV viewing.* The average number of daily viewers v, in millions, of ABC's soap opera "General Hospital" is given by $v = -\frac{1}{4}t + 9$, where t is the number of years since 2000. Graph the equation and use the graph to predict the average number of daily viewers of "General Hospital" in 2008. [3.2]
Source: Nielsen Media Research

32. At 4:00 P.M., Jesse's Honda Civic was at mile marker 17 of Interstate 290 in Chicago. At 4:45 P.M., Jesse was at mile marker 23. [3.4]

a) Find Jesse's driving rate, in number of miles per minute.
b) Find Jesse's driving rate, in number of minutes per mile.

33. *Gas mileage.* The following graph shows data for a Ford Explorer driven on city streets. At what rate was the vehicle consuming gas? [3.4]

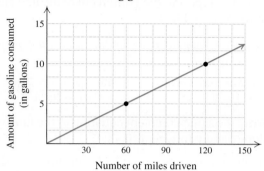

Find the slope of each line. [3.5]

34.

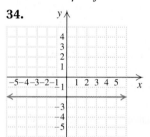

35.

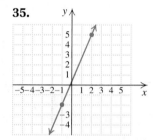

36.

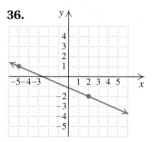

Find the slope of the line containing the given pair of points. If it is undefined, state this. [3.5]

37. $(-2, 5)$ and $(3, -1)$

38. $(6, 5)$ and $(-2, 5)$

39. $(-3, 0)$ and $(-3, 5)$

40. $(-8.3, 4.6)$ and $(-9.9, 1.4)$

41. *Architecture.* To meet federal standards, a wheelchair ramp cannot rise more than 1 ft over a horizontal distance of 12 ft. Express this slope as a grade. [3.5]

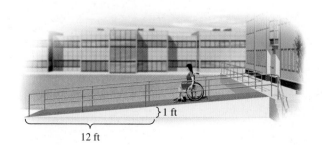

42. Find the *x*-intercept and the *y*-intercept of the line given by $5x - 8y = 80$. [3.3]

43. Find the slope and the *y*-intercept of the line given by $3x + 5y = 45$. [3.6]

Determine whether each pair of lines is parallel, perpendicular, or neither. [3.6]

44. $y + 5 = -x,$
$x - y = 2$

45. $3x - 5 = 7y,$
$7y - 3x = 7$

46. Write the slope–intercept equation of the line with slope $\frac{3}{8}$ and *y*-intercept $(0, 7)$. [3.6]

47. Write a point–slope equation for the line with slope $-\frac{1}{3}$ that contains the point $(-2, 9)$. [3.7]

48. The average tuition at a public two-year college was $1359 in 2001 and $1847 in 2005. Graph the data and determine an equation for the related line. Then **(a)** calculate the average tuition at a public two-year college in 2004 and **(b)** predict the average tuition at a public two-year college in 2012. [3.7]
Source: U.S. National Center for Education Statistics

49. Write the slope–intercept equation for the line with slope 5 that contains the point $(3, -10)$. [3.7]

50. Write the slope–intercept equation for the line that is perpendicular to the line $3x - 5y = 9$ and that contains the point $(2, -5)$ [3.7]

Graph.

51. $y = \frac{2}{3}x - 5$ [3.6]

52. $2x + y = 4$ [3.3]

53. $y = 6$ [3.3]

54. $x = -2$ [3.3]

55. $y + 2 = -\frac{1}{2}(x - 3)$ [3.7]

Synthesis

56. Can two perpendicular lines share the same *y*-intercept? Why or why not? [3.3]

57. Is it possible for a graph to have only one intercept? Why or why not? [3.3]

58. Find the value of *m* in $y = mx + 3$ such that $(-2, 5)$ is on the graph. [3.2]

59. Find the value of *b* in $y = -5x + b$ such that $(3, 4)$ i on the graph. [3.2]

60. Find the area and the perimeter of a rectangle for which $(-2, 2)$, $(7, 2)$, and $(7, -3)$ are three of the vertices. [3.1]

61. Find three solutions of $y = 4 - |x|$. [3.2]

Test: Chapter 3

Step-by-step test solutions are found c the video CD in the front of this book.

Volunteering.   The following pie chart shows the types of organizations in which college students volunteer.
Source: Corporation for National and Community Service

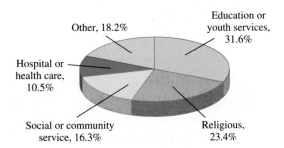

Volunteering by College Students, 2005

Other, 18.2%

Education or youth services, 31.6%

Hospital or health care, 10.5%

Social or community service, 16.3%

Religious, 23.4%

1. At Rolling Hills College, 25% of the 1200 students volunteer. If their choice of organizations is typical, how many students will volunteer in education or youth services?

2. At Valley University, $\frac{1}{3}$ of the 3900 students voluntee If their choice of organizations is typical, how man students will volunteer in hospital or health-care services?

In which quadrant is each point located?

3. $(-2, -10)$

4. $(-1.6, 2.3)$

Find the coordinates of each point in the figure.

5. *A*

6. *B*

7. *C*

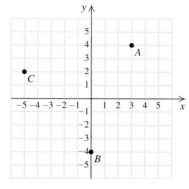

Graph.

8. $y = 2x - 1$

9. $2x - 4y = -8$

10. $y + 1 = 6$

11. $y = \frac{3}{4}x$

12. $2x - y = 3$

13. $x = -1$

Find the slope of the line containing each pair of points. If it is undefined, state this.

14. $(3, -2)$ and $(4, 3)$

15. $(-5, 6)$ and $(-1, -3)$

16. $(4, 7)$ and $(4, -8)$

17. *Running.* Jon reached the 3-km mark of a race at 2:15 P.M. and the 6-km mark at 2:24 P.M. What is his running rate?

18. At one point Filbert Street, the steepest street in San Francisco, drops 63 ft over a horizontal distance of 200 ft. Find the road grade.

19. Find the *x*-intercept and the *y*-intercept of the line given by $5x - y = 30$.

20. Find the slope and the *y*-intercept of the line given by $y - 8x = 10$.

21. Write the slope–intercept equation of the line with slope $-\frac{1}{3}$ and *y*-intercept $(0, -11)$.

Determine without graphing whether each pair of lines is parallel, perpendicular, or neither.

22. $4y + 2 = 3x,$
$-3x + 4y = -12$

23. $y = -2x + 5,$
$2y - x = 6$

24. Write the slope–intercept equation of the line that is perpendicular to the line $2x - 5y = 8$ and that contains the point $(-3, 2)$.

25. *Aerobic exercise.* A person's target heart rate is the number of beats per minute that brings the most aerobic benefit to his or her heart. The target heart rate for a 20-year-old is 150 beats per minute; for a 60-year-old, it is 120 beats per minute.

   a) Graph the data and determine an equation for the related line. Let a = age and r = target heart rate, in number of beats per minute.

   b) Calculate the target heart rate for a 36-year-old.

Graph.

26. $y = \frac{1}{4}x - 2$

27. $y + 4 = -\frac{1}{2}(x - 3)$

Synthesis

28. Write an equation of the line that is parallel to the graph of $2x - 5y = 6$ and has the same *y*-intercept as the graph of $3x + y = 9$.

29. A diagonal of a square connects the points $(-3, -1)$ and $(2, 4)$. Find the area and the perimeter of the square.

30. List the coordinates of three other points that are on the same line as $(-2, 14)$ and $(17, -5)$. Answers may vary.

Cumulative Review: Chapters 1–3

1. Evaluate $\dfrac{x}{5y}$ for $x = 70$ and $y = 2$. [1.1]

2. Multiply: $6(2a - b + 3)$. [1.2]

3. Factor: $8x - 4y + 4$. [1.2]

4. Find the prime factorization of 54. [1.3]

5. Find decimal notation: $-\frac{3}{20}$. [1.4]

6. Find the absolute value: $|-37|$. [1.4]

7. Find the opposite of $-\frac{1}{10}$. [1.6]

8. Find the reciprocal of $-\frac{1}{10}$. [1.7]

9. Find decimal notation: 36.7%. [2.4]

Simplify.

10. $\frac{3}{5} - \frac{5}{12}$ [1.3]

11. $3.4 + (-0.8)$ [1.5]

12. $(-2)(-1.4)(2.6)$ [1.7]

13. $\frac{3}{8} \div \left(-\frac{9}{10}\right)$ [1.7]

14. $1 - [32 \div (4 + 2^2)]$ [1.8]

15. $-5 + 16 \div 2 \cdot 4$ [1.8]

16. $y - (3y + 7)$ [1.8]

17. $3(x - 1) - 2[x - (2x + 7)]$ [1.8]

Solve.

18. $2.7 = 5.3 + x$ [2.1]

19. $\frac{5}{3}x = -45$ [2.1]

20. $3x - 7 = 41$ [2.2]

21. $\dfrac{3}{4} = \dfrac{-n}{8}$ [2.1]

22. $14 - 5x = 2x$ [2.2]

23. $3(5 - x) = 2(3x + 4)$ [2.2]

24. $\frac{1}{4}x - \frac{2}{3} = \frac{3}{4} + \frac{1}{3}x$ [2.2]

25. $y + 5 - 3y = 5y - 9$ [2.2]

26. $x - 28 < 20 - 2x$ [2.6]

27. $2(x + 2) \geq 5(2x + 3)$ [2.6]

28. Solve $A = 2\pi rh + \pi r^2$ for h. [2.3]

29. In which quadrant is the point $(3, -1)$ located? [3.1]

30. Graph on a number line: $-1 < x \leq 2$. [2.6]

31. Use a grid 10 squares wide and 10 squares high to plot $(-150, -40)$, $(40, -7)$, and $(0, 6)$. Choose the scale carefully. [3.1]

Graph.

32. $x = 3$ [3.3]

33. $2x - 5y = 10$ [3.3]

34. $y = -2x + 1$ [3.2]

35. $y = \frac{2}{3}x$ [3.2]

36. $y = -\frac{3}{4}x + 2$ [3.6]

37. $2y - 5 = 3$ [3.3]

Find the coordinates of the x- and y-intercepts. Do not graph.

38. $2x - 7y = 21$ [3.3]

39. $y = 4x + 5$ [3.3]

40. Find the slope and the y-intercept of the line given by $3x - y = 2$. [3.6]

41. Find the slope of the line containing the points $(-4, 1)$ and $(2, -1)$. [3.5]

42. Write an equation of the line with slope $\frac{2}{7}$ and y-intercept $(0, -4)$. [3.6]

43. Write a point–slope equation of the line with slope $-\frac{3}{8}$ that contains the point $(-6, 4)$. [3.7]

44. Write the slope–intercept form of the equation in Exercise 43. [3.6]

45. Determine an equation for the following graph. [3.6], [3.7]

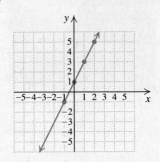

Solve.

46. U.S. bicycle sales rose from 15 million in 1995 to 20 million in 2005. Find the rate of change of bicycle sales. [3.4]
Sources: National Bicycle Dealers Association; U.S. Department of Transportation

47. A 150-lb person will burn 240 calories per hour when riding a bicycle at 6 mph. The same person will burn 410 calories per hour when cycling at 12 mph. [3.7]
Source: American Heart Association

a) Graph the data and determine an equation for the related line. Let $r =$ the rate at which the person is cycling and $c =$ the number of calories burned per hour.

b) Use the equation of part (a) to estimate the number of calories burned per hour by a 150-lb person cycling at 10 mph.

48. Americans spent an estimated $238 billion on home remodeling in 2006. This was $\frac{17}{15}$ of the amount spent on remodeling in 2005. How much was spent on remodeling in 2005? [2.5]
Source: National Association of Home Builders' Remodelers Council

49. In 2005, the mean earnings of individuals with a high school diploma was $29,448. This was about 54% of the mean earnings of those with a bachelor's degree. What were the mean earnings of individuals with a bachelor's degree in 2005? [2.4]
Source: U.S. Census Bureau

50. Recently there were 132 million Americans with either O-positive or O-negative blood. Those with O-positive blood outnumbered those with O-negative blood by 90 million. How many Americans had O-negative blood? [2.5]
Source: American Red Cross

51. Tina paid $126 for a cordless drill, including a 5% sales tax. How much did the drill itself cost? [2.4]

52. A 143-m wire is cut into three pieces. The second is 3 m longer than the first. The third is four fifths as long as the first. How long is each piece? [2.5]

53. In order to qualify for availability pay, a criminal investigator must average at least 2 hr of unscheduled duty per workday. For the first four days of one week, Alayna worked 1, 0, 3, and 2 extra hours. How many extra hours must she work on Friday in order to qualify for availability pay? [2.7]
Source: U.S. Department of Justice

Synthesis

54. Anya's salary at the end of a year is $26,780. This reflects a 4% salary increase in February and then a 3% cost-of-living adjustment in June. What was her salary at the beginning of the year? [2.4]

Solve. If no solution exists, state this.

55. $4|x| - 13 = 3$ [1.4], [2.2]

56. $4(x + 2) = 9(x - 2) + 16$ [2.2]

57. $2(x + 3) + 4 = 0$ [2.2]

58. $\dfrac{2 + 5x}{4} = \dfrac{11}{28} + \dfrac{8x + 3}{7}$ [2.2]

59. $5(7 + x) = (x + 6)5$ [2.2]

60. Solve $p = \dfrac{2}{m + Q}$ for Q. [2.3]

61. The points $(-3, 0)$, $(0, 7)$, $(3, 0)$, and $(0, -7)$ are vertices of a parallelogram. Find four equations of lines that intersect to form the parallelogram. [3.6]

Polynomials

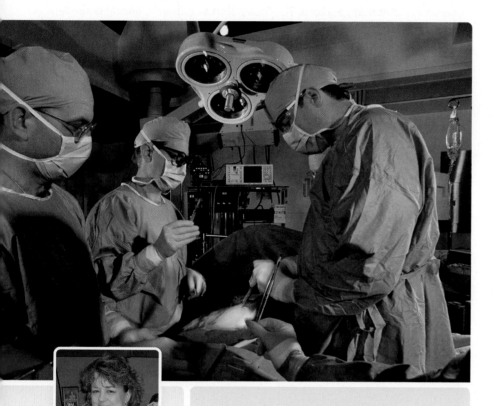

SHELLEY ZOMAK
RANSPLANT COORDINATOR
(NURSE)
Pittsburgh, Pennsylvania

s very important that a trans-
nt recipient take the medica-
ions prescribed to maintain a
ermined blood concentration
e drug. As a transplant coor-
linator, I use math to educate
ents on the correct dosing of
edications, since the doctor's
ders do not always match the
available from the pharmacy.
Some medications need to be
usted more frequently on the
basis of the patient's weight.

AN APPLICATION

Often a patient needing a kidney transplant has a willing kidney donor who does not match the patient medically. A kidney-paired donation matches donor–recipient pairs. Two kidney transplants are performed simultaneously, with each patient receiving the kidney of a stranger. The number k of such "kidney swaps" t years after 2003 can be approximated by

$$k = 14.3t^3 - 56t^2 + 57.7t + 19.$$

Estimate the number of kidney-paired donations in 2006.

Source: Based on data from United Network for Organ Sharing

This problem appears as Exercise 69 in Section 4.3.

227

Algebraic expressions such as $16t^2$, $5a^2 - 3ab$, and $3x^2 - 7x + 5$ are called polynomials. Polynomials occur frequently in applications and appear in most branches of mathematics. Thus learning to add, subtract, multiply, and divide polynomials is an important part of nearly every course in elementary algebra. The focus of this chapter is finding equivalent expressions, not solving equations.

4.1   Exponents and Their Properties

Multiplying Powers with Like Bases ▪ Dividing Powers with Like Bases ▪ Zero as an Exponent ▪
Raising a Power to a Power ▪ Raising a Product or a Quotient to a Power

In Section 4.3, we begin our study of polynomials. Before doing so, however, we must develop some rules for working with exponents.

Multiplying Powers with Like Bases

Recall from Section 1.8 that an expression like a^3 means $a \cdot a \cdot a$. We can use this fact to find the product of two expressions that have the same base:

$$a^3 \cdot a^2 = (a \cdot a \cdot a)(a \cdot a) \qquad \text{There are three factors in } a^3 \text{ and two factors in } a^2.$$

$$a^3 \cdot a^2 = a \cdot a \cdot a \cdot a \cdot a \qquad \text{Using an associative law}$$

$$a^3 \cdot a^2 = a^5.$$

Note that the exponent in a^5 is the sum of the exponents in $a^3 \cdot a^2$. That is, $3 + 2 = 5$. Similarly,

$$b^4 \cdot b^3 = (b \cdot b \cdot b \cdot b)(b \cdot b \cdot b)$$

$$b^4 \cdot b^3 = b^7, \quad \text{where } 4 + 3 = 7.$$

Adding the exponents gives the correct result.

STUDENT NOTES

There are several rules for manipulating exponents in this section. One way to remember them all is to replace variables with numbers (other than 1) and see what the results suggest. For example, multiplying $2^2 \cdot 2^3$ and examining the result is a fine way of reminding yourself that $a^m \cdot a^n = a^{m+n}$.

The Product Rule

For any number a and any positive integers m and n,

$$a^m \cdot a^n = a^{m+n}.$$

(To multiply powers with the same base, keep the base and add the exponents.)

EXAMPLE   **1**   Multiply and simplify each of the following. (Here "simplify" means express the product as one base to a power whenever possible.)

a) $2^3 \cdot 2^8$

b) $5^3 \cdot 5^8 \cdot 5^1$

c) $(r + s)^7(r + s)^6$

d) $(a^3b^2)(a^3b^5)$

SOLUTION

a) $2^3 \cdot 2^8 = 2^{3+8}$ Adding exponents: $a^m \cdot a^n = a^{m+n}$

$= 2^{11}$

> **CAUTION!** The base is unchanged: $2^3 \cdot 2^8 \neq 4^{11}$.

b) $5^3 \cdot 5^8 \cdot 5^1 = 5^{3+8+1}$ Adding exponents

$= 5^{12}$

> **CAUTION!** $5^{12} \neq 5 \cdot 12$.

c) $(r+s)^7(r+s)^6 = (r+s)^{7+6}$ The base here is $r+s$.

$= (r+s)^{13}$

> **CAUTION!** $(r+s)^{13} \neq r^{13} + s^{13}$.

d) $(a^3b^2)(a^3b^5) = a^3b^2a^3b^5$ Using an associative law

$= a^3a^3b^2b^5$ Using a commutative law

$= a^6b^7$ Adding exponents

> TRY EXERCISE 15

Dividing Powers with Like Bases

Recall that any expression that is divided or multiplied by 1 is unchanged. This, together with the fact that anything (besides 0) divided by itself is 1, can lead to a rule for division:

$$\frac{a^5}{a^2} = \frac{a \cdot a \cdot a \cdot a \cdot a}{a \cdot a}$$

$$\frac{a^5}{a^2} = \frac{a \cdot a \cdot a}{1} \cdot \frac{a \cdot a}{a \cdot a}$$

$$\frac{a^5}{a^2} = \frac{a \cdot a \cdot a}{1} \cdot 1$$

$$\frac{a^5}{a^2} = a \cdot a \cdot a = a^3.$$

Note that the exponent in a^3 is the difference of the exponents in a^5/a^2. Similarly,

$$\frac{x^4}{x^3} = \frac{x \cdot x \cdot x \cdot x}{x \cdot x \cdot x} = \frac{x}{1} \cdot \frac{x \cdot x \cdot x}{x \cdot x \cdot x} = \frac{x}{1} \cdot 1 = x = x^1.$$

Subtracting the exponents gives the correct result.

> ### The Quotient Rule
>
> For any nonzero number a and any positive integers m and n for which $m > n$,
>
> $$\frac{a^m}{a^n} = a^{m-n}.$$
>
> (To divide powers with the same base, subtract the exponent of the denominator from the exponent of the numerator.)

EXAMPLE 2   Divide and simplify. (Here "simplify" means express the quotient as one base to a power whenever possible.)

a) $\dfrac{x^8}{x^2}$ **b)** $\dfrac{7^9}{7^4}$ **c)** $\dfrac{(5a)^{12}}{(5a)^4}$ **d)** $\dfrac{4p^5q^7}{6p^2q}$

SOLUTION

a) $\dfrac{x^8}{x^2} = x^{8-2}$ Subtracting exponents: $\dfrac{a^m}{a^n} = a^{m-n}$

$= x^6$

> **CAUTION!** The base is unchanged:
>
> $\dfrac{7^9}{7^4} \neq 1^5.$

b) $\dfrac{7^9}{7^4} = 7^{9-4}$

$= 7^5$

c) $\dfrac{(5a)^{12}}{(5a)^4} = (5a)^{12-4} = (5a)^8$ The base here is $5a$.

d) $\dfrac{4p^5q^7}{6p^2q} = \dfrac{4}{6} \cdot \dfrac{p^5}{p^2} \cdot \dfrac{q^7}{q^1}$ Note that the 4 and 6 are factors, not exponents!

$= \dfrac{2}{3} \cdot p^{5-2} \cdot q^{7-1} = \dfrac{2}{3}p^3q^6$ Using the quotient rule twice; simplifying   **TRY EXERCISE** 33

Zero as an Exponent

The quotient rule can be used to help determine what 0 should mean when it appears as an exponent. Consider a^4/a^4, where a is nonzero. Since the numerator and the denominator are the same,

$$\frac{a^4}{a^4} = 1.$$

On the other hand, using the quotient rule would give us

$$\frac{a^4}{a^4} = a^{4-4} = a^0.$$ Subtracting exponents

Since $a^0 = a^4/a^4 = 1$, this suggests that $a^0 = 1$ for any nonzero value of a.

> ### The Exponent Zero
>
> For any real number a, with $a \neq 0$,
>
> $$a^0 = 1.$$
>
> (Any nonzero number raised to the 0 power is 1.)

Note that in the above box, 0^0 is not defined. For this text, we will assume that expressions like a^m do not represent 0^0.

EXAMPLE 3   Simplify: **(a)** 1948^0; **(b)** $(-9)^0$; **(c)** $(3x)^0$; **(d)** $3x^0$; **(e)** $(-1)9^0$; **(f)** -9^0.

SOLUTION

a) $1948^0 = 1$ Any nonzero number raised to the 0 power is 1.

b) $(-9)^0 = 1$ Any nonzero number raised to the 0 power is 1. The base here is -9.

c) $(3x)^0 = 1$, for any $x \neq 0$.   The parentheses indicate that the base is $3x$.

d) Since $3x^0$ means $3 \cdot x^0$, the base is x. Recall that simplifying exponential expressions is done before multiplication in the rules for order of operations:

$$3x^0 = 3 \cdot 1 = 3, \quad \text{for any } x \neq 0.$$

e) $(-1)9^0 = (-1)1 = -1$ The base here is 9.

f) -9^0 is read "the opposite of 9^0" and is equivalent to $(-1)9^0$:

$$-9^0 = (-1)9^0 = (-1)1 = -1.$$

Note from parts (b), (e), and (f) that $-9^0 = (-1)9^0$ and $-9^0 \neq (-9)^0$.

TRY EXERCISE 49

CAUTION! $-9^0 \neq (-9)^0$, and, in general, $-a^n \neq (-a)^n$.

Raising a Power to a Power

Consider an expression like $(7^2)^4$:

$$(7^2)^4 = (7^2)(7^2)(7^2)(7^2)$$ There are four factors of 7^2.

$$(7^2)^4 = (7 \cdot 7)(7 \cdot 7)(7 \cdot 7)(7 \cdot 7)$$ We could also use the product rule.

$$(7^2)^4 = 7 \cdot 7 \cdot 7 \cdot 7 \cdot 7 \cdot 7 \cdot 7 \cdot 7$$ Using an associative law

$$(7^2)^4 = 7^8.$$

Note that the exponent in 7^8 is the product of the exponents in $(7^2)^4$. Similarly,

$$(y^5)^3 = y^5 \cdot y^5 \cdot y^5$$ There are three factors of y^5.

$$(y^5)^3 = (y \cdot y \cdot y \cdot y \cdot y)(y \cdot y \cdot y \cdot y \cdot y)(y \cdot y \cdot y \cdot y \cdot y)$$

$$(y^5)^3 = y^{15}.$$

Once again, we get the same result if we multiply exponents:

$$(y^5)^3 = y^{5 \cdot 3} = y^{15}.$$

The Power Rule

For any number a and any whole numbers m and n,

$$(a^m)^n = a^{mn}.$$

(To raise a power to a power, multiply the exponents and leave the base unchanged.)

Remember that for this text we assume that 0^0 is not considered.

EXAMPLE **4**   Simplify: **(a)** $(3^5)^4$; **(b)** $(m^2)^5$.

SOLUTION

a) $(3^5)^4 = 3^{5 \cdot 4}$ Multiplying exponents: $(a^m)^n = a^{mn}$

$\qquad = 3^{20}$

b) $(m^2)^5 = m^{2 \cdot 5}$

$\qquad = m^{10}$

TRY EXERCISE 57

Raising a Product or a Quotient to a Power

When an expression inside parentheses is raised to a power, the inside expression is the base. Let's compare $2a^3$ and $(2a)^3$:

$2a^3 = 2 \cdot a \cdot a;$ The base is a.

$(2a)^3 = (2a)(2a)(2a)$ The base is $2a$.
$(2a)^3 = (2 \cdot 2 \cdot 2)(a \cdot a \cdot a)$
$(2a)^3 = 2^3 a^3$
$(2a)^3 = 8a^3.$

We see that $2a^3$ and $(2a)^3$ are *not* equivalent. Note too that $(2a)^3$ can be simplified by cubing each factor in $2a$. This leads to the following rule for raising a product to a power.

> ### Raising a Product to a Power
>
> For any numbers a and b and any whole number n,
>
> $$(ab)^n = a^n b^n.$$
>
> (To raise a product to a power, raise each factor to that power.)

EXAMPLE 5   Simplify: (a) $(4a)^3$; (b) $(-5x^4)^2$; (c) $(a^7 b)^2 (a^3 b^4)$.

SOLUTION

a) $(4a)^3 = 4^3 a^3 = 64a^3$ Raising each factor to the third power and simplifying

b) $(-5x^4)^2 = (-5)^2 (x^4)^2$ Raising each factor to the second power. Parentheses are important here.

$= 25x^8$ Simplifying $(-5)^2$ and using the power rule

c) $(a^7 b)^2 (a^3 b^4) = (a^7)^2 b^2 a^3 b^4$ Raising a product to a power

$= a^{14} b^2 a^3 b^4$ Multiplying exponents

$= a^{17} b^6$ Adding exponents   TRY EXERCISE 63

> *CAUTION!*   The rule $(ab)^n = a^n b^n$ applies only to *products* raised to a power, not to sums or differences. For example, $(3 + 4)^2 \neq 3^2 + 4^2$ since $49 \neq 9 + 16$. Similarly, $(5x)^2 = 5^2 \cdot x^2$, but $(5 + x)^2 \neq 5^2 + x^2$.

There is a similar rule for raising a quotient to a power.

> ## Raising a Quotient to a Power
>
> For any numbers a and b, $b \neq 0$, and any whole number n,
>
> $$\left(\frac{a}{b}\right)^n = \frac{a^n}{b^n}.$$
>
> (To raise a quotient to a power, raise the numerator to the power and divide by the denominator to the power.)

EXAMPLE 6   Simplify: **(a)** $\left(\dfrac{x}{5}\right)^2$; **(b)** $\left(\dfrac{5}{a^4}\right)^3$; **(c)** $\left(\dfrac{3a^4}{b^3}\right)^2$.

SOLUTION

a) $\left(\dfrac{x}{5}\right)^2 = \dfrac{x^2}{5^2} = \dfrac{x^2}{25}$ Squaring the numerator and the denominator

b) $\left(\dfrac{5}{a^4}\right)^3 = \dfrac{5^3}{(a^4)^3}$ Raising a quotient to a power

$\qquad = \dfrac{125}{a^{4\cdot3}} = \dfrac{125}{a^{12}}$ Using the power rule and simplifying

c) $\left(\dfrac{3a^4}{b^3}\right)^2 = \dfrac{(3a^4)^2}{(b^3)^2}$ Raising a quotient to a power

$\qquad = \dfrac{3^2(a^4)^2}{b^{3\cdot2}} = \dfrac{9a^8}{b^6}$ Raising a product to a power and using the power rule

> TRY EXERCISE 75

In the following summary of definitions and rules, we assume that no denominators are 0 and that 0^0 is not considered.

> ### Definitions and Properties of Exponents
>
> For any whole numbers m and n,
>
> | | |
> |---|---|
> | 1 as an exponent: | $a^1 = a$ |
> | 0 as an exponent: | $a^0 = 1$ |
> | The Product Rule: | $a^m \cdot a^n = a^{m+n}$ |
> | The Quotient Rule: | $\dfrac{a^m}{a^n} = a^{m-n}$ |
> | The Power Rule: | $(a^m)^n = a^{mn}$ |
> | Raising a product to a power: | $(ab)^n = a^n b^n$ |
> | Raising a quotient to a power: | $\left(\dfrac{a}{b}\right)^n = \dfrac{a^n}{b^n}$ |

4.1	**EXERCISE SET**

↜ **Concept Reinforcement**   *In each of Exercises 1–8, complete the sentence using the most appropriate phrase from the column on the right.*

1. To raise a product to a power, ____

2. To raise a quotient to a power, ____

3. To raise a power to a power, ____

4. To divide powers with the same base, ____

5. Any nonzero number raised to the 0 power ____

6. To multiply powers with the same base, ____

7. To square a fraction, ____

8. To square a product, ____

a) keep the base and add the exponents.

b) multiply the exponents and leave the base unchanged

c) square the numerator and square the denominator.

d) square each factor.

e) raise each factor to that power.

f) raise the numerator to the power and divide by the denominator to the power.

g) is one.

h) subtract the exponent of the denominator from the exponent of the numerator.

Identify the base and the exponent in each expression.

9. $(2x)^5$

10. $(x + 1)^0$

11. $2x^3$

12. $-y^6$

13. $\left(\dfrac{4}{y}\right)^7$

14. $(-5x)^4$

Simplify. Assume that no denominator is 0 and that 0^0 is not considered.

15. $d^3 \cdot d^{10}$

16. $8^4 \cdot 8^3$

17. $a^6 \cdot a$

18. $y^7 \cdot y^9$

19. $6^5 \cdot 6^{10}$

20. $t^0 \cdot t^{16}$

21. $(3y)^4(3y)^8$

22. $(2t)^8(2t)^{17}$

23. $(8n)(8n)^9$

24. $(5p)^0(5p)^1$

25. $(a^2b^7)(a^3b^2)$

26. $(m - 3)^4(m - 3)^5$

27. $(x + 3)^5(x + 3)^8$

28. $(a^8b^3)(a^4b)$

29. $r^3 \cdot r^7 \cdot r^0$

30. $s^4 \cdot s^5 \cdot s^2$

31. $(mn^5)(m^3n^4)$

32. $(a^3b)(ab)^4$

33. $\dfrac{7^5}{7^2}$

34. $\dfrac{4^7}{4^3}$

35. $\dfrac{t^8}{t}$

36. $\dfrac{x^7}{x}$

37. $\dfrac{(5a)^7}{(5a)^6}$

38. $\dfrac{(3m)^9}{(3m)^8}$

Aha! 39. $\dfrac{(x + y)^8}{(x + y)^8}$

40. $\dfrac{(9x)^{10}}{(9x)^2}$

41. $\dfrac{(r + s)^{12}}{(r + s)^4}$

42. $\dfrac{(a - b)^4}{(a - b)^3}$

43. $\dfrac{12d^9}{15d^2}$

44. $\dfrac{10n^7}{15n^3}$

45. $\dfrac{8a^9b^7}{2a^2b}$

46. $\dfrac{12r^{10}s^7}{4r^2s}$

47. $\dfrac{x^{12}y^9}{x^0y^2}$

48. $\dfrac{a^{10}b^{12}}{a^2b^0}$

Simplify.

49. t^0 when $t = 15$

50. y^0 when $y = 38$

51. $5x^0$ when $x = -22$

52. $7m^0$ when $m = 1.7$

53. $7^0 + 4^0$

54. $(8 + 5)^0$

55. $(-3)^1 - (-3)^0$

56. $(-4)^0 - (-4)^1$

Simplify. Assume that no denominator is 0 and that 0^0 is not considered.

57. $(x^3)^{11}$

58. $(a^5)^8$

59. $(5^8)^4$

60. $(2^5)^2$

61. $(t^{20})^4$

62. $(x^{25})^6$

63. $(10x)^2$

64. $(5a)^2$

65. $(-2a)^3$

66. $(-3x)^3$

67. $(-5n^7)^2$

68. $(-4m^4)^2$

69. $(a^2b)^7$

70. $(xy^4)^9$

71. $(r^5t)^3(r^2t^8)$

72. $(a^4b^6)(a^2b)^5$

73. $(2x^5)^3(3x^4)$

74. $(5x^3)^2(2x^7)$

75. $\left(\dfrac{x}{5}\right)^3$

76. $\left(\dfrac{2}{a}\right)^4$

77. $\left(\dfrac{7}{6n}\right)^2$

78. $\left(\dfrac{4x}{3}\right)^3$

79. $\left(\dfrac{a^3}{b^8}\right)^6$

80. $\left(\dfrac{x^5}{y^2}\right)^7$

81. $\left(\dfrac{x^2y}{z^3}\right)^4$

82. $\left(\dfrac{a^4}{b^2c}\right)^5$

83. $\left(\dfrac{a^3}{-2b^5}\right)^4$

84. $\left(\dfrac{x^5}{-3y^3}\right)^4$

85. $\left(\dfrac{5x^7y}{-2z^4}\right)^3$

86. $\left(\dfrac{-4p^5}{3m^2n^3}\right)^3$

87. $\left(\dfrac{4x^3y^5}{3z^7}\right)^0$

88. $\left(\dfrac{5a^7}{2b^5c}\right)^0$

89. Explain in your own words why $-5^2 \neq (-5)^2$.

90. Under what circumstances should exponents be added?

Skill Review

To prepare for Section 4.2, review operations with integers (Sections 1.5–1.7).

Perform the indicated operations.

91. $-10 - 14$ [1.6]

92. $-3(5)$ [1.7]

93. $-16 + 5$ [1.5]

94. $12 - (-4)$ [1.6]

95. $-3 + (-11)$ [1.5]

96. $-8 - (-12)$ [1.6]

Synthesis

97. Under what conditions does a^n represent a negative number? Why?

98. Using the quotient rule, explain why 9^0 is 1.

99. Suppose that the width of a square is three times the width of a second square. How do the areas of the squares compare? Why?

100. Suppose that the width of a cube is twice the width of a second cube. How do the volumes of the cubes compare? Why?

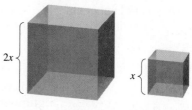

Find a value of the variable that shows that the two expressions are not equivalent. Answers may vary.

101. $3x^2$; $(3x)^2$

102. $(a + 5)^2$; $a^2 + 5^2$

103. $\dfrac{t^6}{t^2}$; t^3

104. $\dfrac{a + 7}{7}$; a

Simplify.

105. $y^{4x} \cdot y^{2x}$

106. $a^{10k} \div a^{2k}$

107. $\dfrac{x^{5t}(x^t)^2}{(x^{3t})^2}$

108. $\dfrac{\left(\frac{1}{2}\right)^3\left(\frac{2}{3}\right)^4}{\left(\frac{5}{6}\right)^3}$

109. Solve for x:

$$\dfrac{t^{26}}{t^x} = t^x.$$

Replace ▨ with $>$, $<$, or $=$ to write a true sentence.

110. 3^5 ▨ 3^4

111. 4^2 ▨ 4^3

112. 4^3 ▨ 5^3

113. 4^3 ▨ 3^4

114. 9^7 ▨ 3^{13}

115. 25^8 ▨ 125^5

Use the fact that $10^3 \approx 2^{10}$ to estimate each of the following powers of 2. Then compute the power of 2 with a calculator and find the difference between the exact value and the approximation.

116. 2^{14}

117. 2^{22}

118. 2^{26}

119. 2^{31}

In computer science, 1 KB of memory refers to 1 kilobyte, or 1×10^3 bytes, of memory. This is really an approximation of 1×2^{10} bytes (since computer memory actually uses powers of 2).

120. The TI-84 Plus graphing calculator has 480 KB of "FLASH ROM." How many bytes is this?

121. The TI-84 Plus Silver Edition graphing calculator has 1.5 MB (megabytes) of FLASH ROM, where 1 MB is 1000 KB (see Exercise 120). How many bytes of FLASH ROM does this calculator have?

4.2   Negative Exponents and Scientific Notation

Negative Integers as Exponents ▪ Scientific Notation ▪
Multiplying and Dividing Using Scientific Notation

We now attach a meaning to negative exponents. Once we understand bot[h]
positive exponents and negative exponents, we can study a method for writin[g]
numbers known as *scientific notation.*

Negative Integers as Exponents

Let's define negative exponents so that the rules that apply to whole-number ex[-]
ponents will hold for all integer exponents. To do so, consider a^{-5} and the rule f[or]
adding exponents:

$$a^{-5} = a^{-5} \cdot 1 \qquad \text{Using the identity property of 1}$$

$$= \frac{a^{-5}}{1} \cdot \frac{a^5}{a^5} \qquad \text{Writing 1 as } \frac{a^5}{a^5} \text{ and } a^{-5} \text{ as } \frac{a^{-5}}{1}$$

$$= \frac{a^{-5+5}}{a^5} \qquad \text{Adding exponents}$$

$$= \frac{1}{a^5}. \qquad -5 + 5 = 0 \text{ and } a^0 = 1$$

This leads to our definition of negative exponents.

Negative Exponents

For any real number a that is nonzero and any integer n,

$$a^{-n} = \frac{1}{a^n}.$$

(The numbers a^{-n} and a^n are reciprocals of each other.)

EXAMPLE 1

Express using positive exponents and, if possible, simplify.

a) m^{-3} **b)** 4^{-2} **c)** $(-3)^{-2}$ **d)** ab^{-1}

SOLUTION

a) $m^{-3} = \dfrac{1}{m^3}$ m^{-3} is the reciprocal of m^3.

b) $4^{-2} = \dfrac{1}{4^2} = \dfrac{1}{16}$ 4^{-2} is the reciprocal of 4^2. Note that $4^{-2} \neq 4(-2)$.

c) $(-3)^{-2} = \dfrac{1}{(-3)^2} = \dfrac{1}{(-3)(-3)} = \dfrac{1}{9}$ $(-3)^{-2}$ is the reciprocal of $(-3)^2$. Note that $(-3)^{-2} \neq -\dfrac{1}{3^2}$.

d) $ab^{-1} = a\left(\dfrac{1}{b^1}\right) = a\left(\dfrac{1}{b}\right) = \dfrac{a}{b}$ b^{-1} is the reciprocal of b^1. Note that the base is b, not ab.

▶ TRY EXERCISE 5

STUDY SKILLS

Indicate the Highlights

Most students find it helpful to draw a star or use a color, felt-tipped highlighter to indicate important concepts or trouble spots that require further study. Most campus bookstores carry a variety of highlighters that permit you to brightly color written material while keeping it easy to read.

> **CAUTION!**   A negative exponent does not, in itself, indicate that an expression is negative. As shown in Example 1,
>
> $$4^{-2} \neq 4(-2) \quad \text{and} \quad (-3)^{-2} \neq -\frac{1}{3^2}.$$

The following is another way to illustrate why negative exponents are defined as they are.

On this side, we divide by 5 at each step.		On this side, the exponents decrease by 1.
	$125 = 5^3$	
	$25 = 5^2$	
	$5 = 5^1$	
	$1 = 5^0$	
	$\dfrac{1}{5} = 5^?$	
	$\dfrac{1}{25} = 5^?$	

To continue the pattern, it follows that

$$\frac{1}{5} = \frac{1}{5^1} = 5^{-1}, \qquad \frac{1}{25} = \frac{1}{5^2} = 5^{-2}, \quad \text{and, in general,} \quad \frac{1}{a^n} = a^{-n}.$$

EXAMPLE 2

Express $\dfrac{1}{x^7}$ using negative exponents.

SOLUTION   We know that $\dfrac{1}{a^n} = a^{-n}$. Thus,

$$\frac{1}{x^7} = x^{-7}.$$

> **TRY EXERCISE** 25

The rules for powers still hold when exponents are negative.

EXAMPLE 3

Simplify. Do not use negative exponents in the answer.

a) $t^5 \cdot t^{-2}$

b) $(5x^2y^{-3})^4$

c) $\dfrac{x^{-4}}{x^{-5}}$

d) $\dfrac{1}{t^{-5}}$

e) $\dfrac{s^{-3}}{t^{-5}}$

f) $\dfrac{-10x^{-3}y}{5x^2y^5}$

SOLUTION

a) $t^5 \cdot t^{-2} = t^{5+(-2)} = t^3$ Adding exponents

b) $(5x^2y^{-3})^4 = 5^4(x^2)^4(y^{-3})^4$ Raising each factor to the fourth power

$$= 625x^8y^{-12} = \frac{625x^8}{y^{12}}$$

c) $\dfrac{x^{-4}}{x^{-5}} = x^{-4-(-5)} = x^1 = x$ We subtract exponents even if the exponent in the denominator is negative.

d) Since $\dfrac{1}{a^n} = a^{-n}$, we have $\dfrac{1}{t^{-5}} = t^{-(-5)} = t^5$.

e) $\dfrac{s^{-3}}{t^{-5}} = s^{-3} \cdot \dfrac{1}{t^{-5}}$

$$= \frac{1}{s^3} \cdot t^5 = \frac{t^5}{s^3}$$ Using the result from part (d) above

f) $\dfrac{-10x^{-3}y}{5x^2y^5} = \dfrac{-10}{5} \cdot \dfrac{x^{-3}}{x^2} \cdot \dfrac{y^1}{y^5}$ Note that the -10 and 5 are factors.

$\qquad\qquad = -2 \cdot x^{-3-2} \cdot y^{1-5}$ Using the quotient rule twice; simplifying

$\qquad\qquad = -2x^{-5}y^{-4} = \dfrac{-2}{x^5y^4}$ **TRY EXERCISE** **33**

The result from Example 3(e) can be generalized.

Factors and Negative Exponents

For any nonzero real numbers a and b and any integers m and n,

$$\frac{a^{-n}}{b^{-m}} = \frac{b^m}{a^n}.$$

(A factor can be moved to the other side of the fraction bar if the sign of the exponent is changed.)

EXAMPLE   **4**   Simplify: $\dfrac{-15x^{-7}}{5y^2z^{-4}}.$

SOLUTION   We can move the factors x^{-7} and z^{-4} to the other side of the fraction bar if we change the sign of each exponent:

$\dfrac{-15x^{-7}}{5y^2z^{-4}} = \dfrac{-15}{5} \cdot \dfrac{x^{-7}}{y^2z^{-4}}$ We can simply divide the constant factors.

$\qquad\qquad = -3 \cdot \dfrac{z^4}{y^2x^7}$

$\qquad\qquad = \dfrac{-3z^4}{x^7y^2}.$ **TRY EXERCISE** **55**

Another way to change the sign of the exponent is to take the reciprocal of the base. To understand why this is true, note that

$$\left(\frac{s}{t}\right)^{-5} = \frac{s^{-5}}{t^{-5}} = \frac{t^5}{s^5} = \left(\frac{t}{s}\right)^5.$$

This often provides the easiest way to simplify an expression containing a negative exponent.

Reciprocals and Negative Exponents

For any nonzero real numbers a and b and any integer n,

$$\left(\frac{a}{b}\right)^{-n} = \left(\frac{b}{a}\right)^n.$$

(Any base to a power is equal to the reciprocal of the base raised to the opposite power.)

EXAMPLE 5 Simplify: $\left(\dfrac{x^4}{2y}\right)^{-3}$.

SOLUTION

$$\left(\frac{x^4}{2y}\right)^{-3} = \left(\frac{2y}{x^4}\right)^3 \qquad \text{Taking the reciprocal of the base and changing the sign of the exponent}$$

$$= \frac{(2y)^3}{(x^4)^3} \qquad \text{Raising a quotient to a power by raising both the numerator and the denominator to the power}$$

$$= \frac{2^3 y^3}{x^{12}} \qquad \text{Raising a product to a power; using the power rule in the denominator}$$

$$= \frac{8y^3}{x^{12}} \qquad \text{Cubing 2}$$

▶ **TRY EXERCISE** 73

Scientific Notation

When we are working with the very large numbers or very small numbers that frequently occur in science, **scientific notation** provides a useful way of writing them. The following are examples of scientific notation.

The mass of the earth:

$$6.0 \times 10^{24} \text{ kilograms (kg)} = 6{,}000{,}000{,}000{,}000{,}000{,}000{,}000{,}000 \text{ kg}$$

The mass of a hydrogen atom:

$$1.7 \times 10^{-24} \text{ g} = 0.0000000000000000000000017 \text{ g}$$

> ### Scientific Notation
>
> *Scientific notation* for a number is an expression of the type
>
> $$N \times 10^m,$$
>
> where N is at least 1 but less than 10 (that is, $1 \le N < 10$), N is expressed in decimal notation, and m is an integer.

STUDENT NOTES

Definitions are usually written as concisely as possible, so that every phrase included is important. The definition for scientific notation states that $1 \le N < 10$. Thus, 2.68×10^5 is written in scientific notation, but 26.8×10^5 and 0.268×10^5 are *not* written in scientific notation.

Converting from scientific notation to decimal notation involves multiplying by a power of 10. Consider the following.

Scientific Notation	Multiplication	Decimal Notation
4.52×10^2	4.52×100	452.
4.52×10^1	4.52×10	45.2
4.52×10^0	4.52×1	4.52
4.52×10^{-1}	4.52×0.1	0.452
4.52×10^{-2}	4.52×0.01	0.0452

Note that when m, the power of 10, is positive, the decimal point moves right m places in decimal notation. When m is negative, the decimal point moves left $|m|$ places. We generally try to perform this multiplication mentally.

EXAMPLE 6   Convert to decimal notation: **(a)** 7.893×10^5; **(b)** 4.7×10^{-8}.

SOLUTION

a) Since the exponent is positive, the decimal point moves to the right:

> 7.89300. $7.893 \times 10^5 = 789{,}300$ The decimal point moves to the
> ⌣⌣↗   right 5 places.
> 5 places

b) Since the exponent is negative, the decimal point moves to the left:

> 0.00000004.7 $4.7 \times 10^{-8} = 0.000000047$ The decimal point
> ↖⌣⌣   moves to the left 8 places.
> 8 places

> TRY EXERCISE ▸ 85

   To convert from decimal notation to scientific notation, this procedure i
reversed.

EXAMPLE 7   Write in scientific notation: **(a)** 83,000; **(b)** 0.0327.

SOLUTION

a) We need to find m such that $83{,}000 = 8.3 \times 10^m$. To change 8.3 to 83,00
   requires moving the decimal point 4 places to the right. This can be accom
   plished by multiplying by 10^4. Thus,

> $83{,}000 = 8.3 \times 10^4.$ This is scientific notation.

b) We need to find m such that $0.0327 = 3.27 \times 10^m$. To change 3.27 to 0.032
   requires moving the decimal point 2 places to the left. This can be accom
   plished by multiplying by 10^{-2}. Thus,

> $0.0327 = 3.27 \times 10^{-2}.$ This is scientific notation.

> TRY EXERCISE ▸ 93

   Conversions to and from scientific notation are often made mentally
Remember that positive exponents are used to represent large numbers and neg
ative exponents are used to represent small numbers between 0 and 1.

Multiplying and Dividing Using Scientific Notation

Products and quotients of numbers written in scientific notation are found usin
the rules for exponents.

EXAMPLE 8   Simplify.

a) $(1.8 \times 10^9) \cdot (2.3 \times 10^{-4})$

b) $(3.41 \times 10^5) \div (1.1 \times 10^{-3})$

SOLUTION

a) $(1.8 \times 10^9) \cdot (2.3 \times 10^{-4})$

> $= 1.8 \times 2.3 \times 10^9 \times 10^{-4}$ Using the associative and commutative law
>
> $= 4.14 \times 10^{9+(-4)}$ Adding exponents
>
> $= 4.14 \times 10^5$

b) $(3.41 \times 10^5) \div (1.1 \times 10^{-3})$

$$= \frac{3.41 \times 10^5}{1.1 \times 10^{-3}}$$

$$= \frac{3.41}{1.1} \times \frac{10^5}{10^{-3}}$$

$$= 3.1 \times 10^{5-(-3)} \qquad \text{Subtracting exponents}$$

$$= 3.1 \times 10^8$$

TRY EXERCISE 103

When a problem is stated using scientific notation, we generally use scientific notation for the answer. This often requires an additional conversion.

EXAMPLE 9   Simplify.

a) $(3.1 \times 10^5) \cdot (4.5 \times 10^{-3})$ **b)** $(7.2 \times 10^{-7}) \div (8.0 \times 10^6)$

SOLUTION

a) We have

$$(3.1 \times 10^5) \cdot (4.5 \times 10^{-3}) = 3.1 \times 4.5 \times 10^5 \times 10^{-3}$$
$$= 13.95 \times 10^2.$$

Our answer is not yet in scientific notation because 13.95 is not between 1 and 10. We convert to scientific notation as follows:

$$13.95 \times 10^2 = 1.395 \times 10^1 \times 10^2 \qquad \text{Substituting } 1.395 \times 10^1 \text{ for } 13.95$$
$$= 1.395 \times 10^3. \qquad \text{Adding exponents}$$

b) $(7.2 \times 10^{-7}) \div (8.0 \times 10^6) = \dfrac{7.2 \times 10^{-7}}{8.0 \times 10^6} = \dfrac{7.2}{8.0} \times \dfrac{10^{-7}}{10^6}$

$$= 0.9 \times 10^{-13}$$

$$= 9.0 \times 10^{-1} \times 10^{-13} \qquad \text{Substituting } 9.0 \times 10^{-1} \text{ for } 0.9$$

$$= 9.0 \times 10^{-14} \qquad \text{Adding exponents}$$

TRY EXERCISE 111

TECHNOLOGY CONNECTION

A key labeled $\boxed{10^x}$, $\boxed{\frown}$, or $\boxed{\text{EE}}$ is used to enter scientific notation into a calculator. Sometimes this is a secondary function, meaning that another key—often labeled SHIFT or $\boxed{\text{2ND}}$ —must be pressed first.

To check Example 8(a), we press

     1.8 $\boxed{\text{EE}}$ 9 $\boxed{\times}$ 2.3 $\boxed{\text{EE}}$ $\boxed{(-)}$ 4.

When we then press $\boxed{=}$ or $\boxed{\text{ENTER}}$, the result 4.14E5 appears. This represents 4.14×10^5. On many calculators, the MODE Sci must be selected in order to display scientific notation.

```
1.8E9*2.3E−4
                    4.14E5
```

On some calculators, this appears as

```
4.14 05
```

or

```
4.14e+05
```

Calculate each of the following.

1. $(3.8 \times 10^9) \cdot (4.5 \times 10^7)$
2. $(2.9 \times 10^{-8}) \div (5.4 \times 10^6)$
3. $(9.2 \times 10^7) \div (2.5 \times 10^{-9})$

4.2   EXERCISE SET

Concept Reinforcement *Match each expression with an equivalent expression from the column on the right.*

1. ___ $\left(\dfrac{x^3}{y^2}\right)^{-2}$ a) $\dfrac{y^6}{x^9}$

2. ___ $\left(\dfrac{y^2}{x^3}\right)^{-2}$ b) $\dfrac{x^9}{y^6}$

3. ___ $\left(\dfrac{y^{-2}}{x^{-3}}\right)^{-3}$ c) $\dfrac{y^4}{x^6}$

4. ___ $\left(\dfrac{x^{-3}}{y^{-2}}\right)^{-3}$ d) $\dfrac{x^6}{y^4}$

Express using positive exponents. Then, if possible, simplify.

5. 2^{-3} **6.** 10^{-5} **7.** $(-2)^{-6}$

8. $(-3)^{-4}$ **9.** t^{-9} **10.** x^{-7}

11. xy^{-2} **12.** $a^{-3}b$ **13.** $r^{-5}t$

14. xy^{-9} **15.** $\dfrac{1}{a^{-8}}$ **16.** $\dfrac{1}{z^{-6}}$

17. 7^{-1} **18.** 3^{-1} **19.** $\left(\dfrac{3}{5}\right)^{-2}$

20. $\left(\dfrac{3}{4}\right)^{-2}$ **21.** $\left(\dfrac{x}{2}\right)^{-5}$ **22.** $\left(\dfrac{a}{2}\right)^{-4}$

23. $\left(\dfrac{s}{t}\right)^{-7}$ **24.** $\left(\dfrac{r}{v}\right)^{-5}$

Express using negative exponents.

25. $\dfrac{1}{9^2}$ **26.** $\dfrac{1}{5^2}$ **27.** $\dfrac{1}{y^3}$

28. $\dfrac{1}{t^4}$ **29.** $\dfrac{1}{5}$ **30.** $\dfrac{1}{8}$

31. $\dfrac{1}{t}$ **32.** $\dfrac{1}{m}$

Simplify. Do not use negative exponents in the answer.

33. $2^{-5} \cdot 2^8$ **34.** $5^{-8} \cdot 5^{10}$

35. $x^{-3} \cdot x^{-9}$ **36.** $x^{-4} \cdot x^{-7}$

37. $t^{-3} \cdot t$ **38.** $y^{-5} \cdot y$

39. $(n^{-5})^3$ **40.** $(m^{-5})^{10}$

41. $(t^{-3})^{-6}$ **42.** $(a^{-4})^{-7}$

43. $(t^4)^{-3}$ **44.** $(x^4)^{-5}$

45. $(mn)^{-7}$ **46.** $(ab)^{-9}$

47. $(3x^{-4})^2$ **48.** $(2a^{-5})^3$

49. $(5r^{-4}t^3)^2$ **50.** $(4x^5y^{-6})^3$

51. $\dfrac{t^{12}}{t^{-2}}$ **52.** $\dfrac{x^7}{x^{-2}}$

53. $\dfrac{y^{-7}}{y^{-3}}$ **54.** $\dfrac{z^{-6}}{z^{-2}}$

55. $\dfrac{15y^{-7}}{3y^{-10}}$ **56.** $\dfrac{-12a^{-5}}{2a^{-8}}$

57. $\dfrac{2x^6}{x}$ **58.** $\dfrac{3x}{x^{-1}}$

59. $\dfrac{-15a^{-7}}{10b^{-9}}$ **60.** $\dfrac{12x^{-6}}{8y^{-10}}$

Aha! **61.** $\dfrac{t^{-7}}{t^{-7}}$ **62.** $\dfrac{a^{-5}}{b^{-7}}$

63. $\dfrac{8x^{-3}}{y^{-7}z^{-1}}$ **64.** $\dfrac{10a^{-1}}{b^{-7}c^{-3}}$

65. $\dfrac{3t^4}{s^{-2}u^{-4}}$ **66.** $\dfrac{5x^{-8}}{y^{-3}z^2}$

67. $(x^4y^5)^{-3}$ **68.** $(t^5x^3)^{-4}$

69. $(3m^{-5}n^{-3})^{-2}$ **70.** $(2y^{-4}z^{-2})^{-3}$

71. $(a^{-5}b^7c^{-2})(a^{-3}b^{-2}c^6)$

72. $(x^3y^{-4}z^{-5})(x^{-4}y^{-2}z^9)$

73. $\left(\dfrac{a^4}{3}\right)^{-2}$ **74.** $\left(\dfrac{y^2}{2}\right)^{-2}$

75. $\left(\dfrac{m^{-1}}{n^{-4}}\right)^3$ **76.** $\left(\dfrac{x^2y}{z^{-5}}\right)^3$

77. $\left(\dfrac{2a^2}{3b^4}\right)^{-3}$ **78.** $\left(\dfrac{a^2b}{2d^3}\right)^{-5}$

Aha! **79.** $\left(\dfrac{5x^{-2}}{3y^{-2}z}\right)^0$ **80.** $\left(\dfrac{4a^3b^{-2}}{5c^{-3}}\right)^1$

81. $\dfrac{-6a^3b^{-5}}{-3a^7b^{-8}}$ **82.** $\dfrac{12x^{-2}y^4}{-3xy^{-7}}$

83. $\dfrac{10x^{-4}yz^7}{8x^7y^{-3}z^{-3}}$ **84.** $\dfrac{9a^6b^{-4}c^7}{27a^{-4}b^5c^9}$

Convert to decimal notation.

85. 4.92×10^3

86. 8.13×10^4

87. 8.92×10^{-3}

88. 7.26×10^{-4}

89. 9.04×10^8

90. 1.35×10^7

91. 3.497×10^{-6}

92. 9.043×10^{-3}

Convert to scientific notation.

93. 36,000,000

94. 27,400

95. 0.00583

96. 0.0814

97. 78,000,000,000

98. 3,700,000,000,000

99. 0.000000527

100. 0.0000506

101. 0.000001032

102. 0.00000008

Multiply or divide, and write scientific notation for the result.

103. $(3 \times 10^5)(2 \times 10^8)$

104. $(3.1 \times 10^7)(2.1 \times 10^{-4})$

105. $(3.8 \times 10^9)(6.5 \times 10^{-2})$

106. $(7.1 \times 10^{-7})(8.6 \times 10^{-5})$

107. $(8.7 \times 10^{-12})(4.5 \times 10^{-5})$

108. $(4.7 \times 10^5)(6.2 \times 10^{-12})$

109. $\dfrac{8.5 \times 10^8}{3.4 \times 10^{-5}}$

110. $\dfrac{5.6 \times 10^{-2}}{2.5 \times 10^5}$

111. $(4.0 \times 10^3) \div (8.0 \times 10^8)$

112. $(1.5 \times 10^{-3}) \div (1.6 \times 10^{-6})$

113. $\dfrac{7.5 \times 10^{-9}}{2.5 \times 10^{12}}$

114. $\dfrac{3.0 \times 10^{-2}}{6.0 \times 10^{10}}$

115. Without performing actual computations, explain why 3^{-29} is smaller than 2^{-29}.

116. Explain why each of the following is not scientific notation:

$$12.6 \times 10^8;$$
$$4.8 \times 10^{1.7};$$
$$0.207 \times 10^{-5}.$$

Skill Review

To prepare for Section 4.3, review combining like terms and evaluating expressions (Sections 1.6 and 1.8).

Combine like terms. [1.6]

117. $9x + 2y - x - 2y$

118. $5a - 7b - 8a + b$

119. $-3x + (-2) - 5 - (-x)$

120. $2 - t - 3t - r - 7$

Evaluate. [1.8]

121. $4 + x^3$, for $x = 10$

122. $-x^2 - 5x + 3$, for $x = -2$

Synthesis

123. Explain what requirements must be met in order for x^{-n} to represent a negative integer.

124. Explain why scientific notation cannot be used without an understanding of the rules for exponents.

125. Write the reciprocal of 1.25×10^{-6} in scientific notation.

126. Write the reciprocal of 2.5×10^9 in scientific notation.

127. Write $8^{-3} \cdot 32 \div 16^2$ as a power of 2.

128. Write $81^3 \div 27 \cdot 9^2$ as a power of 3.

Simplify each of the following. Use a calculator only where indicated.

Aha! **129.** $\dfrac{125^{-4}(25^2)^4}{125}$

130. $(13^{-12})^2 \cdot 13^{25}$

131. $[(5^{-3})^2]^{-1}$

132. $5^0 - 5^{-1}$

133. $3^{-1} + 4^{-1}$

134. $\dfrac{4.2 \times 10^8[(2.5 \times 10^{-5}) \div (5.0 \times 10^{-9})]}{3.0 \times 10^{-12}}$

135. $\dfrac{27^{-2}(81^2)^3}{9^8}$

136. $\dfrac{7.4 \times 10^{29}}{(5.4 \times 10^{-6})(2.8 \times 10^8)}$

137. $\dfrac{5.8 \times 10^{17}}{(4.0 \times 10^{-13})(2.3 \times 10^4)}$

138. $\dfrac{(7.8 \times 10^7)(8.4 \times 10^{23})}{2.1 \times 10^{-12}}$

139. $\dfrac{(2.5 \times 10^{-8})(6.1 \times 10^{-11})}{1.28 \times 10^{-3}}$

140. Determine whether each of the following is true for all pairs of integers m and n and all positive numbers x and y.

a) $x^m \cdot y^n = (xy)^{mn}$
b) $x^m \cdot y^m = (xy)^{2m}$
c) $(x - y)^m = x^m - y^m$

Solve. Write scientific notation for each answer.

141. *Ecology.*   In one year, a large tree can remove from the air the same amount of carbon dioxide produced by a car traveling 500 mi. If New York City contains approximately 600,000 trees, how many miles of car traffic can those trees clean in a year?
Sources: Colorado Tree Coalition; New York City Department of Parks and Recreations

142. *Computer technology.*   One gigabit is about 1 billion bits of information. In 2007, Intel Corp. began making silicon modulators that can encode data onto a beam of light at a rate of 40 gigabits per second. If 25 of these communication lasers are packed on a single chip, how many bits per second could that chip encode?
Source: The Wall Street Journal, 7/25/2007

143. *Hotel management.*   The new Four Seasons Hotel in Seattle contains 110,000 ft² of condominium space. If these condos sold for about $2100 per ft², how much money did the hotel make selling the condominiums?
Source: seattletimes.nwsource.com

144. *Coral reefs.*   There are 10 million bacteria per square centimeter of coral in a coral reef. The coral reefs near the Hawaiian Islands cover 14,000 km². How many bacteria are there in Hawaii's coral reefs?
Sources: livescience.com; U.S. Geological Survey

145. *Hospital care.*   In 2005, 115 million patients visited emergency rooms in the United States. If the average visit lasted 3.3 hr, how many minutes in all did people spend in emergency rooms in 2005?
Source: The Indianapolis Star, 7/25/07

CONNECTING the CONCEPTS

The following properties of exponents hold for all integers m and n, assuming that no denominator is 0 and that 0^0 is not considered.

Definitions and Properties of Exponents

The following summary assumes that no denominators are 0 and that 0^0 is not considered. For any integers m and n,

1 as an exponent:	$a^1 = a$
0 as an exponent:	$a^0 = 1$
Negative exponents:	$a^{-n} = \dfrac{1}{a^n},$
	$\dfrac{a^{-n}}{b^{-m}} = \dfrac{b^m}{a^n},$
	$\left(\dfrac{a}{b}\right)^{-n} = \left(\dfrac{b}{a}\right)^n$
The Product Rule:	$a^m \cdot a^n = a^{m+n}$
The Quotient Rule:	$\dfrac{a^m}{a^n} = a^{m-n}$
The Power Rule:	$(a^m)^n = a^{mn}$
Raising a product to a power:	$(ab)^n = a^n b^n$
Raising a quotient to a power:	$\left(\dfrac{a}{b}\right)^n = \dfrac{a^n}{b^n}$

MIXED REVIEW

Simplify. Do not use negative exponents in the answer.

1. $x^4 x^{10}$

2. $x^{-4} x^{-10}$

3. $\dfrac{x^{-4}}{x^{10}}$

4. $\dfrac{x^4}{x^{-10}}$

5. $(x^{-4})^{-10}$

6. $(x^4)^{10}$

7. $\dfrac{1}{c^{-8}}$

8. c^{-8}

9. $(2x^3 y)^4$

10. $(2x^3 y)^{-4}$

11. $(3xy^{-1}z^5)^0$

12. $(a^2 b)(a^3 b^{-1})$

13. $\left(\dfrac{a^3}{b^4}\right)^5$

14. $\left(\dfrac{a^3}{b^4}\right)^{-5}$

15. $\dfrac{30x^4 y^3}{12xy^7}$

16. $\dfrac{12ab^{-8}}{14a^{-1}b^{-3}}$

17. $\dfrac{7p^{-5}}{xt^{-6}}$

18. $\left(\dfrac{3a^{-1}}{4b^{-3}}\right)^{-2}$

19. $(2p^2 q^4)(3pq^5)^2$

20. $(2xy^{-1})^{-1}(3x^2 y^{-3})^2$

4.3   Polynomials

Terms   ▪   Types of Polynomials   ▪   Degree and Coefficients   ▪   Combining Like Terms   ▪
Evaluating Polynomials and Applications

We now examine an important algebraic expression known as a *polynomial*
Certain polynomials have appeared earlier in this text so you already have some
experience working with them.

Terms

At this point, we have seen a variety of algebraic expressions like

$$3a^2b^4, \quad 2l + 2w, \quad \text{and} \quad 5x^2 + x - 2.$$

Within these expressions, $3a^2b^4$, $2l$, $2w$, $5x^2$, x, and -2 are examples of *terms*
A **term** (see p. 17) can be a number (like -2), a variable (like x), a product of numbers and/or variables (like $3a^2b^4$, $2l$, $2w$, or $5x^2$), or a quotient of numbers and/o
variables (like $7/t$ or $(a^2b^3)/(4c)$).*

Types of Polynomials

If a term is a product of constants and/or variables, it is called a **monomial**. Note
that a term, but not a monomial, can include division by a variable. A **polynomial**
is a monomial or a sum of monomials.

Examples of monomials: $7, \quad t, \quad 2l, \quad 2w, \quad 5x^3y, \quad \frac{3}{7}a^5$

Examples of polynomials: $4x + 7, \quad \frac{2}{3}t^2, \quad 6a + 7, \quad -5n^2 + m - 1, \quad 42r^5,$
$x, \quad 0$

When a polynomial is written as a sum of monomials, each monomial is called a
term of the polynomial.

EXAMPLE   1

Identify the terms of the polynomial $3t^4 - 5t^6 - 4t + 2$.

SOLUTION   The terms are $3t^4$, $-5t^6$, $-4t$, and 2. We can see this by rewriting al
subtractions as additions of opposites:

$$3t^4 - 5t^6 - 4t + 2 = 3t^4 + (-5t^6) + (-4t) + 2.$$
$$\uparrow \qquad \uparrow \qquad \uparrow \qquad \uparrow$$

These are the terms of the polynomial.

> **TRY EXERCISE** ▶ 9

A polynomial that is composed of two terms is called a **binomial**, whereas
those composed of three terms are called **trinomials**. Polynomials with four o
more terms have no special name.

───────────────────

*Later in this text, expressions like $5x^{3/2}$ and $2a^{-7}b$ will be discussed. Such expressions are
also considered terms.

Monomials	Binomials	Trinomials	No Special Name
$4x^2$	$2x + 4$	$3t^3 + 4t + 7$	$4x^3 - 5x^2 + xy - 8$
9	$3a^5 + 6bc$	$6x^7 - 8z^2 + 4$	$z^5 + 2z^4 - z^3 + 7z + 3$
$-7a^{19}b^5$	$-9x^7 - 6$	$4x^2 - 6x - \frac{1}{2}$	$4x^6 - 3x^5 + x^4 - x^3 + 2x - 1$

The following algebraic expressions are *not* polynomials:

$$\textbf{(1)} \ \frac{x + 3}{x - 4}, \qquad \textbf{(2)} \ 5x^3 - 2x^2 + \frac{1}{x}, \qquad \textbf{(3)} \ \frac{1}{x^3 - 2}.$$

Expressions (1) and (3) are not polynomials because they represent quotients, not sums. Expression (2) is not a polynomial because $1/x$ is not a monomial.

Degree and Coefficients

The **degree of a term of a polynomial** is the number of variable factors in that term. Thus the degree of $7t^2$ is 2 because $7t^2$ has two variable factors: $7t^2 = 7 \cdot t \cdot t$. We will revisit the meaning of degree in Section 4.7 when polynomials in several variables are examined.

EXAMPLE 2 Determine the degree of each term: **(a)** $8x^4$; **(b)** $3x$; **(c)** 7.

SOLUTION

a) The degree of $8x^4$ is 4. x^4 represents 4 variable factors: $x \cdot x \cdot x \cdot x$.

b) The degree of $3x$ is 1.   There is 1 variable factor.

c) The degree of 7 is 0.   There is no variable factor.

The degree of a constant polynomial, as in Example 2(c), is 0 since there are no variable factors. There is an exception to this statement, however. Since $0 = 0x = 0x^2 = 0x^3$ and so on, we say that the polynomial 0 has *no* degree.

The part of a term that is a constant factor is the **coefficient** of that term. Thus the coefficient of $3x$ is 3, and the coefficient for the term 7 is simply 7.

EXAMPLE 3 Identify the coefficient of each term in the polynomial

$$4x^3 - 7x^2y + x - 8.$$

SOLUTION

The coefficient of $4x^3$ is 4.

The coefficient of $-7x^2y$ is -7.

The coefficient of the third term is 1, since $x = 1x$.

The coefficient of -8 is simply -8.

TRY EXERCISE 13

The **leading term** of a polynomial is the term of highest degree. Its coefficient is called the **leading coefficient** and its degree is referred to as the **degree of the polynomial**. To see how this terminology is used, consider the polynomial

$$3x^2 - 8x^3 + 5x^4 + 7x - 6.$$

The *terms* are $3x^2$, $-8x^3$, $5x^4$, $7x$, and -6.

The *coefficients* are   3, -8, 5, 7, and -6.

The *degree of each term* is   2, 3, 4, 1, and 0.

The *leading term* is $5x^4$ and the *leading coefficient* is 5.

The *degree of the polynomial* is 4.

Combining Like Terms

Recall from Section 1.8 that *like*, or *similar*, *terms* are either constant terms o[r] terms containing the same variable(s) raised to the same power(s). To simplif[y] certain polynomials, we can often *combine*, or *collect*, like terms.

EXAMPLE 4

Identify the like terms in $4x^3 + 5x - 7x^2 + 2x^3 + x^2$.

SOLUTION

Like terms:	$4x^3$ and	$2x^3$	Same variable and exponent
Like terms:	$-7x^2$ and	x^2	Same variable and exponent

EXAMPLE 5

Write an equivalent expression by combining like terms.

a) $2x^3 + 6x^3$

b) $5x^2 + 7 + 2x^4 - 6x^2 - 11 - 2x^4$

c) $7a^3 - 5a^2 + 9a^3 + a^2$

d) $\frac{2}{3}x^4 - x^3 - \frac{1}{6}x^4 + \frac{2}{5}x^3 - \frac{3}{10}x^3$

STUDENT NOTES

Remember that when we combine like terms, we are not solving equations, but are forming equivalent expressions.

SOLUTION

a) $2x^3 + 6x^3 = (2 + 6)x^3$ Using the distributive law

$\qquad = 8x^3$

b) $5x^2 + 7 + 2x^4 - 6x^2 - 11 - 2x^4$

$\qquad = 5x^2 - 6x^2 + 2x^4 - 2x^4 + 7 - 11$

$\qquad = (5 - 6)x^2 + (2 - 2)x^4 + (7 - 11)$ ⎫

$\qquad = -1x^2 + 0x^4 + (-4)$ ⎬ These steps are often done mentally.

$\qquad = -x^2 - 4$ ⎭

c) $7a^3 - 5a^2 + 9a^3 + a^2 = 7a^3 - 5a^2 + 9a^3 + 1a^2$ $a^2 = 1 \cdot a^2 = 1a^2$

$\qquad\qquad = 16a^3 - 4a^2$

d) $\frac{2}{3}x^4 - x^3 - \frac{1}{6}x^4 + \frac{2}{5}x^3 - \frac{3}{10}x^3 = \left(\frac{2}{3} - \frac{1}{6}\right)x^4 + \left(-1 + \frac{2}{5} - \frac{3}{10}\right)x^3$

$\qquad\qquad = \left(\frac{4}{6} - \frac{1}{6}\right)x^4 + \left(-\frac{10}{10} + \frac{4}{10} - \frac{3}{10}\right)x^3$

$\qquad\qquad = \frac{3}{6}x^4 - \frac{9}{10}x^3$

$\qquad\qquad = \frac{1}{2}x^4 - \frac{9}{10}x^3$ There are no similar terms, so we are done.

TRY EXERCISE 41

Note in Example 5 that the solutions are written so that the term of highes[t] degree appears first, followed by the term of next highest degree, and so on. This i[s] known as **descending order** and is the form in which answers will normally appea[r.]

Evaluating Polynomials and Applications

When each variable in a polynomial is replaced with a number, the polynomi[al] then represents a number, or *value*, that can be calculated using the rules f[or] order of operations.

EXAMPLE 6

Evaluate $-x^2 + 3x + 9$ for $x = -2$.

SOLUTION   For $x = -2$, we have

Substitute. $-x^2 + 3x + 9 = -(-2)^2 + 3(-2) + 9$ The negative sign in front of x^2 remains.

$\qquad\qquad = -(4) + 3(-2) + 9$

Simplify. $\qquad\qquad = -4 + (-6) + 9$

$\qquad\qquad = -10 + 9 = -1.$

TRY EXERCISE 51

EXAMPLE 7

Games in a sports league.   In a sports league of n teams in which each team plays every other team twice, the total number of games to be played is given by the polynomial

$$n^2 - n.$$

A girls' soccer league has 10 teams. How many games are played if each team plays every other team twice?

SOLUTION   We evaluate the polynomial for $n = 10$:

$$n^2 - n = 10^2 - 10$$
$$= 100 - 10 = 90.$$

The league plays 90 games.

TRY EXERCISE 61

EXAMPLE 8

Vehicle miles traveled.   The average annual number of vehicle miles traveled per vehicle (VMT), in thousands, for a driver of age a can be approximated by the polynomial

$$-0.003a^2 + 0.2a + 8.6.$$

Find the VMT per vehicle for a 20-year-old driver.

Source: Based on information from the Energy Information Administration

SOLUTION   To find the VMT per vehicle for a 20-year-old driver, we evaluate the polynomial for $a = 20$:

$$-0.003a^2 + 0.2a + 8.6 = -0.003(20)^2 + 0.2(20) + 8.6$$
$$= -0.003 \cdot 400 + 4 + 8.6$$
$$= -1.2 + 4 + 8.6$$
$$= 11.4.$$

The average annual number of VMT per vehicle by a 20-year-old driver is 11.4 thousand, or 11,400.

TRY EXERCISE 65

Sometimes, a graph can be used to estimate the value of a polynomial visually.

EXAMPLE 9

Vehicle miles traveled.   In the following graph, the polynomial from Example 8 has been graphed by evaluating it for several choices of a. Use the graph to estimate the number of vehicle miles traveled each year, per vehicle, by a 30-year-old driver.

TECHNOLOGY CONNECTION

One way to evaluate a polynomial is to use the TRACE key. For example, to evaluate $-0.003a^2 + 0.2a + 8.6$ in Example 9 for $a = 30$, we can enter the polynomial as $y = -0.003x^2 + 0.2x + 8.6$. We then use TRACE and enter an x-value of 30.

(continued)

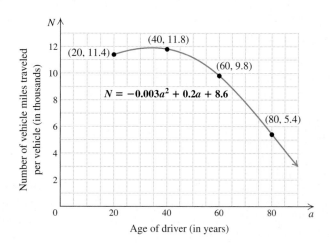

The value of the polynomial appears as y, and the cursor automatically appears at (30, 11.9). The Value option of the CALC menu works in a similar way.

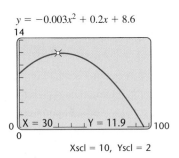

$y = -0.003x^2 + 0.2x + 8.6$

Xscl = 10, Yscl = 2

1. Use TRACE or CALC Value to find the value of $-0.003a^2 + 0.2a + 8.6$ for $a = 60$.

SOLUTION To estimate the number of vehicle miles traveled by a 30-year-old driver, we locate 30 on the horizontal axis. From there, we move vertically until we meet the curve at some point. From that point, we move horizontally to the N-axis.

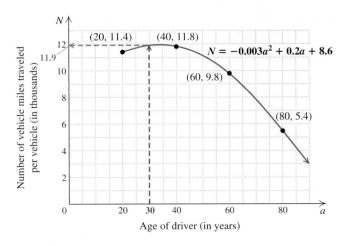

The average number of vehicle miles traveled each year, per vehicle, by a 30-year-old driver is 11.9 thousand, or 11,900. (For $a = 30$, the value of $-0.003a^2 + 0.2a + 8.6$ is approximately 11.9.)

TRY EXERCISE 71

4.3   EXERCISE SET

🐦 *Concept Reinforcement*   *In each of Exercises 1–8, match the description with the most appropriate algebraic expression from the column on the right.*

1. ____ A polynomial with four terms

2. ____ A polynomial with 7 as its leading coefficient

3. ____ A trinomial written in descending order

4. ____ A polynomial with degree 5

5. ____ A binomial with degree 7

6. ____ A monomial of degree 0

7. ____ An expression with two terms that is not a binomial

8. ____ An expression with three terms that is not a trinomial

a) $8x^3 + \dfrac{2}{x^2}$

b) $5x^4 + 3x^3 - 4x + 7$

c) $\dfrac{3}{x} - 6x^2 + 9$

d) $8t - 4t^5$

e) 5

f) $6x^2 + 7x^4 - 2x^3$

g) $4t - 2t^7$

h) $3t^2 + 4t + 7$

Identify the terms of each polynomial.

9. $8x^3 - 11x^2 + 6x + 1$

10. $5a^3 + 4a^2 - a - 7$

11. $-t^6 - 3t^3 + 9t - 4$

12. $n^5 - 4n^3 + 2n - 8$

Determine the coefficient and the degree of each term in each polynomial.

13. $8x^4 + 2x$

14. $9a^3 - 4a^2$

15. $9t^2 - 3t + 4$

16. $7x^4 + 5x - 3$

17. $6a^5 + 9a + a^3$

18. $4t^8 - t + 6t^5$

19. $x^4 - x^3 + 4x - 3$

20. $2a^5 + a^2 + 8a + 10$

For each of the following polynomials, (a) list the degree of each term; (b) determine the leading term and the leading coefficient; and (c) determine the degree of the polynomial.

21. $5t + t^3 + 8t^4$

22. $1 + 6n + 4n^2$

3. $3a^2 - 7 + 2a^4$

4. $9x^4 + x^2 + x^7 - 12$

5. $8 + 6x^2 - 3x - x^5$

6. $9a - a^4 + 3 + 2a^3$

7. Complete the following table for the polynomial
$7x^2 + 8x^5 - 4x^3 + 6 - \frac{1}{2}x^4$.

Term	Coefficient	Degree of the Term	Degree of the Polynomial
		5	
$-\frac{1}{2}x^4$			
	-4		
		2	
	6		

8. Complete the following table for the polynomial
$-3x^4 + 6x^3 - 2x^2 + 8x + 7$.

Term	Coefficient	Degree of the Term	Degree of the Polynomial
	-3		
$6x^3$			
		2	
		1	
	7		

Classify each polynomial as a monomial, a binomial, a trinomial, or a polynomial with no special name.

29. $x^2 - 23x + 17$ **30.** $-9x^2$

31. $x^3 - 7x + 2x^2 - 4$ **32.** $t^3 + 4$

33. $y + 8$ **34.** $3x^8 + 12x^3 - 9$

35. 17

36. $2x^4 - 7x^3 + x^2 + x - 6$

Combine like terms. Write all answers in descending order.

37. $5n^2 + n + 6n^2$

38. $5a + 7a^2 + 3a$

39. $3a^4 - 2a + 2a + a^4$

40. $9b^5 + 3b^2 - 2b^5 - 3b^2$

41. $7x^3 - 11x + 5x + x^2$

42. $3x^4 - 7x + x^4 - 2x$

43. $4b^3 + 5b + 7b^3 + b^2 - 6b$

44. $6x^2 + 2x^4 - 2x^2 - x^4 - 4x^2 + x$

45. $10x^2 + 2x^3 - 3x^3 - 4x^2 - 6x^2 - x^4$

46. $12t^6 - t^3 + 8t^6 + 4t^3 - t^7 - 3t^3$

47. $\frac{1}{5}x^4 + 7 - 2x^2 + 3 - \frac{2}{15}x^4 + 2x^2$

48. $\frac{1}{6}x^3 + 3x^2 - \frac{1}{3}x^3 + 7 + x^2 - 10$

49. $8.3a^2 + 3.7a - 8 - 9.4a^2 + 1.6a + 0.5$

50. $1.4y^3 + 2.9 - 7.7y - 1.3y - 4.1 + 9.6y^3$

Evaluate each polynomial for $x = 3$ and for $x = -3$.

51. $-4x + 9$ **52.** $-6x + 5$

53. $2x^2 - 3x + 7$ **54.** $4x^2 - 6x + 9$

55. $-3x^3 + 7x^2 - 4x - 8$

56. $-2x^3 - 3x^2 + 4x + 2$

57. $2x^4 - \frac{1}{9}x^3$ **58.** $\frac{1}{3}x^4 - 2x^3$

59. $-x - x^2 - x^3$ **60.** $-x^2 - 3x^3 - x^4$

Back-to-college expenses. The amount of money, in billions of dollars, spent on shoes for college can be estimated by the polynomial

$$0.4t + 1.13,$$

where t is the number of years since 2004.

Source: Based on data from the National Retail Federation

61. Estimate the amount spent on shoes for college in 2006.

62. Estimate the amount spent on shoes for college in 2010.

63. *Skydiving.* During the first 13 sec of a jump, the number of feet that a skydiver falls in t seconds is approximated by the polynomial

$$11.12t^2.$$

Approximately how far has a skydiver fallen 10 sec after having jumped from a plane?

64. *Skydiving.* For jumps that exceed 13 sec, the polynomial $173t - 369$ can be used to approximate the distance, in feet, that a skydiver has fallen in t seconds. Approximately how far has a skydiver fallen 20 sec after having jumped from a plane?

Circumference. *The circumference of a circle of radius r is given by the polynomial $2\pi r$, where π is an irrational number. For an approximation of π, use 3.14.*

65. Find the circumference of a circle with radius 10 cm.

66. Find the circumference of a circle with radius 5 ft.

Area of a circle. *The area of a circle of radius r is given by the polynomial πr^2. Use 3.14 as an approximation for π.*

67. Find the area of a circle with radius 7 m.

68. Find the area of a circle with radius 6 ft.

Kidney transplants. *Often a patient needing a kidney transplant has a willing kidney donor who does not match the patient medically. A kidney-paired donation matches donor–recipient pairs. Two kidney transplants are performed simultaneously, with each patient receiving the kidney of a stranger. The number k of such "kidney swaps" t years after 2003 can be approximated by*

$$k = 14.3t^3 - 56t^2 + 57.7t + 19.$$

Use the following graph for Exercises 69 and 70.
Source: Based on data from United Network for Organ Sharing

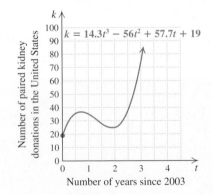

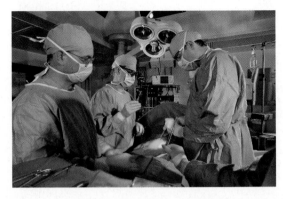

69. Estimate the number of kidney-paired donations in 2006.

70. Estimate the number of kidney-paired donations in 2004.

Memorizing words. *Participants in a psychology experiment were able to memorize an average of M words in t minutes, where $M = -0.001t^3 + 0.1t^2$. Use the following graph for Exercises 71–74.*

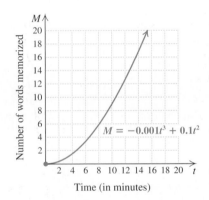

71. Estimate the number of words memorized after 10 min.

72. Estimate the number of words memorized after 14 min.

73. Find the approximate value of M for $t = 8$.

74. Find the approximate value of M for $t = 12$.

Body mass index. *The body mass index, or BMI, is one measure of a person's health. The average BMI B for males of age x, where x is between 2 and 20, is approximated by*

$$B = -0.003x^3 + 0.13x^2 - 1.2x + 18.6.$$

Use the following graph for Exercises 75 and 76.
Source: Based on information from the National Center for Health Statistics

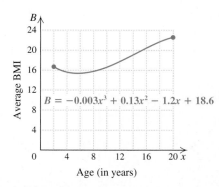

Age (in years)

75. Approximate the average BMI for 4-year-old males; for 14-year-old males.

76. Approximate the average BMI for 10-year-old males; for 16-year-old males.

77. Explain how it is possible for a term to not be a monomial.

78. Is it possible to evaluate polynomials without understanding the rules for order of operations? Why or why not?

Skill Review

To prepare for Section 4.4, review simplifying expressions containing parentheses (Section 1.8).

Simplify. [1.8]

79. $2x + 5 - (x + 8)$ **80.** $3x - 7 - (5x - 1)$

81. $4a + 3 - (-2a + 6)$ **82.** $\frac{1}{2}t - \frac{1}{4} - \left(\frac{3}{2}t + \frac{3}{4}\right)$

83. $4t^4 + 8t - (5t^4 - 9t)$

84. $0.1a^2 + 5 - (-0.3a^2 + a - 6)$

Synthesis

85. Suppose that the coefficients of a polynomial are all integers and the polynomial is evaluated for some integer. Must the value of the polynomial then also be an integer? Why or why not?

86. Is it easier to evaluate a polynomial before or after like terms have been combined? Why?

87. Construct a polynomial in x (meaning that x is the variable) of degree 5 with four terms, with coefficients that are consecutive even integers. Write in descending order.

Revenue, cost, and profit.   Gigabytes Electronics is selling a new type of computer monitor. Total revenue is the total amount of money taken in and total cost is the total amount paid for producing the items. The firm estimates that for the monitor's first year, revenue from the sale of x monitors is

$$250x - 0.5x^2 \text{ dollars,}$$

and the total cost is given by

$$4000 + 0.6x^2 \text{ dollars.}$$

Profit *is the difference between revenue and cost.*

88. Find the profit when 20 monitors are produced and sold.

89. Find the profit when 30 monitors are produced and sold.

Simplify.

90. $\frac{9}{2}x^8 + \frac{1}{9}x^2 + \frac{1}{2}x^9 + \frac{9}{2}x + \frac{9}{2}x^9 + \frac{8}{9}x^2 + \frac{1}{2}x - \frac{1}{2}x^8$

91. $(3x^2)^3 + 4x^2 \cdot 4x^4 - x^4(2x)^2 + ((2x)^2)^3 - 100x^2(x^2)^2$

92. A polynomial in x has degree 3. The coefficient of x^2 is 3 less than the coefficient of x^3. The coefficient of x is three times the coefficient of x^2. The remaining constant is 2 more than the coefficient of x^3. The sum of the coefficients is -4. Find the polynomial.

93. Use the graph for Exercises 75 and 76 to determine the ages for which the average BMI is 16.

94. *Path of the Olympic arrow.*   The Olympic flame at the 1992 Summer Olympics was lit by a flaming arrow. As the arrow moved d meters horizontally from the archer, its height h, in meters, was approximated by the polynomial

$$-0.0064d^2 + 0.8d + 2.$$

Complete the table for the choices of d given. Then plot the points and draw a graph representing the path of the arrow.

d	$-0.0064d^2 + 0.8d + 2$
0	
30	
60	
90	
120	

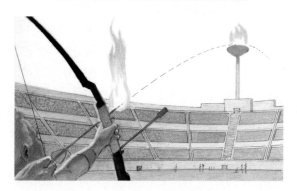

▦ *Semester averages.* *Professor Sakima calculates a student's average for her course using*

$$A = 0.3q + 0.4t + 0.2f + 0.1h,$$

with q, t, f, and h representing a student's quiz average, test average, final exam score, and homework average, respectively. In Exercises 95 and 96, find the given student's course average rounded to the nearest tenth.

95. Galina: quizzes: 60, 85, 72, 91; final exam: 84; tests: 89, 93, 90; homework: 88

96. Nigel: quizzes: 95, 99, 72, 79; final exam: 91; tests: 68, 76, 92; homework: 86

In Exercises 97 and 98, complete the table for the given choices of t. Then plot the points and connect them with a smooth curve representing the graph of the polynomial.

97.

t	$-t^2 + 10t - 18$
3	
4	
5	
6	
7	

98.

t	$-t^2 + 6t - 4$
1	
2	
3	
4	
5	

4.4   Addition and Subtraction of Polynomials

Addition of Polynomials ▪ Opposites of Polynomials ▪ Subtraction of Polynomials ▪ Problem Solving

Addition of Polynomials

To add two polynomials, we write a plus sign between them and combine like terms.

EXAMPLE **1**   Write an equivalent expression by adding.

a) $(-5x^3 + 6x - 1) + (4x^3 + 3x^2 + 2)$

b) $\left(\frac{2}{3}x^4 + 3x^2 - 7x + \frac{1}{2}\right) + \left(-\frac{1}{3}x^4 + 5x^3 - 3x^2 + 3x - \frac{1}{2}\right)$

SOLUTION

a) $(-5x^3 + 6x - 1) + (4x^3 + 3x^2 + 2)$

$$= -5x^3 + 6x - 1 + 4x^3 + 3x^2 + 2 \qquad \text{Writing without parentheses}$$

$$= -5x^3 + 4x^3 + 3x^2 + 6x - 1 + 2 \qquad \text{Using the commutative and associative laws to write like terms together}$$

$$= (-5 + 4)x^3 + 3x^2 + 6x + (-1 + 2) \qquad \text{Combining like terms; using the distributive law}$$

$$= -x^3 + 3x^2 + 6x + 1 \qquad \text{Note that } -1x^3 = -x^3.$$

b) $\left(\frac{2}{3}x^4 + 3x^2 - 7x + \frac{1}{2}\right) + \left(-\frac{1}{3}x^4 + 5x^3 - 3x^2 + 3x - \frac{1}{2}\right)$

$= \left(\frac{2}{3} - \frac{1}{3}\right)x^4 + 5x^3 + (3 - 3)x^2 + (-7 + 3)x + \left(\frac{1}{2} - \frac{1}{2}\right)$ Combining like terms

$= \frac{1}{3}x^4 + 5x^3 - 4x$ **TRY EXERCISE** ▸ 9

After some practice, polynomial addition is often performed mentally.

EXAMPLE **2**	Add: $(2 - 3x + x^2) + (-5 + 7x - 3x^2 + x^3)$.

SOLUTION   We have

$(2 - 3x + x^2) + (-5 + 7x - 3x^2 + x^3)$

$= (2 - 5) + (-3 + 7)x + (1 - 3)x^2 + x^3$ You might do this step mentally.

$= -3 + 4x - 2x^2 + x^3$.   Then you would write only this.

TRY EXERCISE ▸ 17

In the polynomials of the last example, the terms are arranged according to degree, from least to greatest. Such an arrangement is called *ascending order*. As a rule, answers are written in ascending order when the polynomials in the original problem are given in ascending order. If the polynomials in the original problem are given in descending order, the answer is usually written in descending order.

We can also add polynomials by writing like terms in columns. Sometimes this makes like terms easier to see.

EXAMPLE **3**

Add: $9x^5 - 2x^3 + 6x^2 + 3$ and $5x^4 - 7x^2 + 6$ and $3x^6 - 5x^5 + x^2 + 5$.

SOLUTION   We arrange the polynomials with like terms in columns.

$$
\begin{array}{l}
9x^5 \qquad\quad\ - 2x^3 + 6x^2 + \ 3 \\
\qquad\quad 5x^4 \qquad\quad\ - 7x^2 + \ 6 \qquad \text{We leave spaces for missing terms.} \\
\underline{3x^6 - 5x^5 \qquad\qquad\qquad + 1x^2 + \ 5} \qquad \text{Writing } x^2 \text{ as } 1x^2 \\
3x^6 + 4x^5 + 5x^4 - 2x^3 \qquad\quad + 14 \qquad \text{Adding}
\end{array}
$$

The answer is $3x^6 + 4x^5 + 5x^4 - 2x^3 + 14$.   **TRY EXERCISE** ▸ 23

Opposites of Polynomials

In Section 1.8, we used the property of -1 to show that the opposite of a sum is the sum of the opposites. This idea can be extended.

> ### The Opposite of a Polynomial
> To find an equivalent polynomial for the *opposite*, or *additive inverse*, of a polynomial, change the sign of every term. This is the same as multiplying the polynomial by -1.

EXAMPLE **4**

Write two equivalent expressions for the opposite of $4x^5 - 7x^3 - 8x + \frac{5}{6}$.

SOLUTION

i) $-\left(4x^5 - 7x^3 - 8x + \frac{5}{6}\right)$ This is one representation of the opposite of $4x^5 - 7x^3 - 8x + \frac{5}{6}$.

ii) $-4x^5 + 7x^3 + 8x - \frac{5}{6}$ Changing the sign of every term

Thus, $-\left(4x^5 - 7x^3 - 8x + \frac{5}{6}\right)$ and $-4x^5 + 7x^3 + 8x - \frac{5}{6}$ are equivalent. Both expressions represent the opposite of $4x^5 - 7x^3 - 8x + \frac{5}{6}$.   **TRY EXERCISE** ▶ 27

EXAMPLE 5   Simplify: $-\left(-7x^4 - \frac{5}{9}x^3 + 8x^2 - x + 67\right)$.

SOLUTION   We have

$$-\left(-7x^4 - \frac{5}{9}x^3 + 8x^2 - x + 67\right) = 7x^4 + \frac{5}{9}x^3 - 8x^2 + x - 67.$$

The same result can be found by multiplying by -1:

$$-\left(-7x^4 - \frac{5}{9}x^3 + 8x^2 - x + 67\right)$$
$$= -1(-7x^4) + (-1)\left(-\frac{5}{9}x^3\right) + (-1)(8x^2) + (-1)(-x) + (-1)67$$
$$= 7x^4 + \frac{5}{9}x^3 - 8x^2 + x - 67.$$ **TRY EXERCISE** ▶ 31

Subtraction of Polynomials

We can now subtract one polynomial from another by adding the opposite of the polynomial being subtracted.

EXAMPLE 6   Write an equivalent expression by subtracting.

a) $(9x^5 + x^3 - 2x^2 + 4) - (-2x^5 + x^4 - 4x^3 - 3x^2)$
b) $(7x^5 + x^3 - 9x) - (3x^5 - 4x^3 + 5)$

SOLUTION

a) $(9x^5 + x^3 - 2x^2 + 4) - (-2x^5 + x^4 - 4x^3 - 3x^2)$
$= 9x^5 + x^3 - 2x^2 + 4 + 2x^5 - x^4 + 4x^3 + 3x^2$ Adding the opposite
$= 11x^5 - x^4 + 5x^3 + x^2 + 4$ Combining like terms

b) $(7x^5 + x^3 - 9x) - (3x^5 - 4x^3 + 5)$
$= 7x^5 + x^3 - 9x + (-3x^5) + 4x^3 - 5$ Adding the opposite
$= 7x^5 + x^3 - 9x - 3x^5 + 4x^3 - 5$ Try to go directly to this step.
$= 4x^5 + 5x^3 - 9x - 5$ Combining like terms   **TRY EXERCISE** ▶ 39

To subtract using columns, we first replace the coefficients in the polynomial being subtracted with their opposites. We then add as before.

EXAMPLE 7   Write in columns and subtract: $(5x^2 - 3x + 6) - (9x^2 - 5x - 3)$.

SOLUTION

i) $\begin{array}{r} 5x^2 - 3x + 6 \\ -(9x^2 - 5x - 3) \end{array}$ Writing similar terms in columns

ii) $\begin{array}{r} 5x^2 - 3x + 6 \\ -9x^2 + 5x + 3 \end{array}$ Changing signs and removing parentheses

iii) $\begin{array}{r} 5x^2 - 3x + 6 \\ -9x^2 + 5x + 3 \\ \hline -4x^2 + 2x + 9 \end{array}$ Adding   **TRY EXERCISE** ▶ 53

If you can do so without error, you can arrange the polynomials in columns, mentally find the opposite of each term being subtracted, and write the answer. Lining up like terms is important and may require leaving some blank space.

EXAMPLE **8**   Write in columns and subtract: $(x^3 + x^2 - 12) - (-2x^3 + x^2 - 3x + 6)$.

SOLUTION   We have

$$
\begin{array}{r}
x^3 + x^2 \qquad - 12 \quad \text{Leaving a blank space for the missing term} \\
-(-2x^3 + x^2 - 3x + 6) \\
\hline
3x^3 \qquad\quad + 3x - 18
\end{array}
$$

TRY EXERCISE ▸ 55

> *CAUTION!*   Be sure to subtract every term of the polynomial being subtracted when using columns.

Problem Solving

EXAMPLE **9**   Find a polynomial for the sum of the areas of rectangles A, B, C, and D.

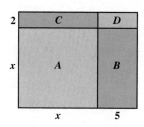

SOLUTION

1. **Familiarize.** Recall that the area of a rectangle is the product of its length and width.

2. **Translate.** We translate the problem to mathematical language. The sum of the areas is a sum of products. We find each product and then add:

   Area of A plus   area of B plus   area of C plus   area of D

   $x \cdot x$ $+$ $5x$ $+$ $2x$ $+$ $2 \cdot 5.$

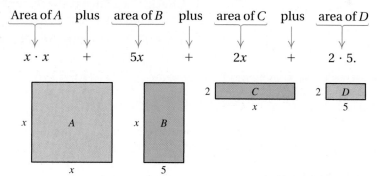

3. **Carry out.** We simplify $x \cdot x$ and $2 \cdot 5$ and combine like terms:

   $$x^2 + 5x + 2x + 10 = x^2 + 7x + 10.$$

4. **Check.** A partial check is to replace x with a number, say 3. Then we evaluate $x^2 + 7x + 10$ and compare that result with an alternative calculation:

   $$3^2 + 7 \cdot 3 + 10 = 9 + 21 + 10 = 40.$$

   When we substitute 3 for x and calculate the total area by regarding the figure as one large rectangle, we should also get 40:

   $$\text{Total area} = (x + 5)(x + 2) = (3 + 5)(3 + 2) = 8 \cdot 5 = 40.$$

Our check is only partial, since it is possible for an incorrect answer to equal 4(
when evaluated for $x = 3$. This would be unlikely, especially if a second choice
of x, say $x = 5$, also checks. We leave that check to the student.

5. **State.** A polynomial for the sum of the areas is $x^2 + 7x + 10$.

TRY EXERCISE 61

EXAMPLE **10**   A 16-ft wide round fountain is built in a square city park that measures x ft by x ft
Find a polynomial for the remaining area of the park.

SOLUTION

1. **Familiarize.** We make a drawing of the square park and the circular fountain
   and let x represent the length of a side of the park.

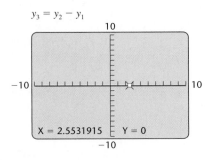

The area of a square is given by $A = s^2$, and the area of a circle is given by
$A = \pi r^2$. Note that a circle with a diameter of 16 ft has a radius of 8 ft.

2. **Translate.** We reword the problem and translate as follows.

Rewording: Area of park   minus   area of fountain   is   area left over

Translating: x ft $\cdot$ x ft $-$ $\pi \cdot 8$ ft $\cdot 8$ ft $=$ Area left over

3. **Carry out.** We carry out the multiplication:

$$x^2 \text{ ft}^2 - 64\pi \text{ ft}^2 = \text{Area left over.}$$

4. **Check.** As a partial check, note that the units in the answer are square fee
   (ft^2), a measure of area, as expected.

5. **State.** The remaining area of the park is $(x^2 - 64\pi) \text{ ft}^2$.   **TRY EXERCISE** 69

TECHNOLOGY CONNECTION

To check polynomial addition or subtraction, we can let
$y_1 = $ the expression before the addition or subtraction
has been performed and $y_2 = $ the simplified sum or difference. If the addition or subtraction is correct, y_1 will
equal y_2 and $y_2 - y_1$ will be 0. We enter $y_2 - y_1$ as y_3,
using **VARS**. Below is a check of Example 6(b) in which

$$y_1 = (7x^5 + x^3 - 9x) - (3x^5 - 4x^3 + 5),$$
$$y_2 = 4x^5 + 5x^3 - 9x - 5,$$

and

$$y_3 = y_2 - y_1.$$

We graph only y_3. If indeed y_1 and y_2 are equivalent, then
y_3 should equal 0. This means its graph should coincide
with the x-axis. The TRACE or TABLE features can confirm

that y_3 is always 0, or we can select y_3 to be drawn bold at
the   **Y=**   window.

$y_3 = y_2 - y_1$

```
                    10



  -10 |_____|_____| 10




        X = 2.5531915    Y = 0
                    -10
```

1. Use a graphing calculator to check Examples 1, 2,
   and 6.

4.4	EXERCISE SET

For Extra Help MyMathLab Math XL PRACTICE WATCH DOWNLOAD

➡ *Concept Reinforcement* *For Exercises 1–4, replace* ▦ *with the correct expression or operation sign.*

1. $(3x^2 + 2) + (6x^2 + 7) = (3 + 6)\ \blacksquare + (2 + 7)$

2. $(5t - 6) + (4t + 3) = (5 + 4)t + (\blacksquare + 3)$

3. $(9x^3 - x^2) - (3x^3 + x^2) = 9x^3 - x^2 - 3x^3\ \blacksquare\ x^2$

4. $(-2n^3 + 5) - (n^2 - 2) = -2n^3 + 5 - n^2\ \blacksquare\ 2$

Add.

5. $(3x + 2) + (x + 7)$

6. $(x + 1) + (12x + 10)$

7. $(2t + 7) + (-8t + 1)$

8. $(4t - 3) + (-11t + 2)$

9. $(x^2 + 6x + 3) + (-4x^2 - 5)$

10. $(x^2 - 5x + 4) + (8x - 9)$

11. $(7t^2 - 3t - 6) + (2t^2 + 4t + 9)$

12. $(8a^2 + 4a - 7) + (6a^2 - 3a - 1)$

13. $(4m^3 - 7m^2 + m - 5) + (4m^3 + 7m^2 - 4m - 2)$

14. $(5n^3 - n^2 + 4n + 11) + (2n^3 - 4n^2 + n - 11)$

15. $(3 + 6a + 7a^2 + a^3) + (4 + 7a - 8a^2 + 6a^3)$

16. $(7 + 4t - 5t^2 + 6t^3) + (2 + t + 6t^2 - 4t^3)$

17. $(3x^6 + 2x^4 - x^3 + 5x) + (-x^6 + 3x^3 - 4x^2 + 7x^4)$

18. $(4x^5 - 6x^3 - 9x + 1) + (3x^4 + 6x^3 + 9x^2 + x)$

19. $\left(\frac{3}{5}x^4 + \frac{1}{2}x^3 - \frac{2}{3}x + 3\right) + \left(\frac{2}{5}x^4 - \frac{1}{4}x^3 - \frac{3}{4}x^2 - \frac{1}{6}x\right)$

20. $\left(\frac{1}{3}x^9 + \frac{1}{5}x^5 - \frac{1}{2}x^2 + 7\right) + \left(-\frac{1}{5}x^9 + \frac{1}{4}x^4 - \frac{3}{5}x^5\right)$

21. $(5.3t^2 - 6.4t - 9.1) + (4.2t^3 - 1.8t^2 + 7.3)$

22. $(4.9a^3 + 3.2a^2 - 5.1a) + (2.1a^2 - 3.7a + 4.6)$

23. $\begin{array}{r} -4x^3 + 8x^2 + 3x - 2 \\ -4x^2 + 3x + 2 \\ \hline \end{array}$

24. $\begin{array}{r} -3x^4 + 6x^2 + 2x - 4 \\ -3x^2 + 2x + 4 \\ \hline \end{array}$

25. $\begin{array}{r} 0.05x^4 + 0.12x^3 - 0.5x^2 \\ - 0.02x^3 + 0.02x^2 + 2x \\ 1.5x^4 \qquad\quad + 0.01x^2 \qquad\quad + 0.15 \\ 0.25x^3 \qquad\qquad\qquad + 0.85 \\ -0.25x^4 \qquad\qquad\quad + 10x^2 \qquad\quad - 0.04 \\ \hline \end{array}$

26. $\begin{array}{r} 0.15x^4 + 0.10x^3 - 0.9x^2 \\ - 0.01x^3 + 0.01x^2 + x \\ 1.25x^4 \qquad\quad + 0.11x^2 \qquad\quad + 0.01 \\ 0.27x^3 \qquad\qquad\qquad + 0.99 \\ -0.35x^4 \qquad\qquad\quad + 15x^2 \qquad\quad - 0.03 \\ \hline \end{array}$

Write two equivalent expressions for the opposite of each polynomial, as in Example 4.

27. $-3t^3 + 4t^2 - 7$

28. $-x^3 - 5x^2 + 2x$

29. $x^4 - 8x^3 + 6x$

30. $5a^3 + 2a - 17$

Simplify.

31. $-(9x - 10)$

32. $-(-5x + 8)$

33. $-(3a^4 - 5a^2 + 1.2)$

34. $-(-6a^3 + 0.2a^2 - 7)$

35. $-\left(-4x^4 + 6x^2 + \frac{3}{4}x - 8\right)$

36. $-\left(3x^5 - 2x^3 - \frac{3}{5}x^2 + 16\right)$

Subtract.

37. $(3x + 1) - (5x + 8)$

38. $(7x + 3) - (3x + 2)$

39. $(-9t + 12) - (t^2 + 3t - 1)$

40. $(a^2 - 3a - 2) - (2a^2 - 6a - 2)$

41. $(4a^2 + a - 7) - (3 - 8a^3 - 4a^2)$

42. $(-4x^2 + 2x) - (-5x^2 + 2x^3 + 3)$

43. $(1.2x^3 + 4.5x^2 - 3.8x) - (-3.4x^3 - 4.7x^2 + 23)$

44. $(0.5x^4 - 0.6x^2 + 0.7) - (2.3x^4 + 1.8x - 3.9)$

Aha! **45.** $(7x^3 - 2x^2 + 6) - (6 - 2x^2 + 7x^3)$

46. $(8x^5 + 3x^4 + x - 1) - (8x^5 + 3x^4 - 1)$

47. $(3 + 5a + 3a^2 - a^3) - (2 + 4a - 9a^2 + 2a^3)$

48. $(7 + t - 5t^2 + 2t^3) - (1 + 2t - 4t^2 + 5t^3)$

49. $\left(\frac{5}{8}x^3 - \frac{1}{4}x - \frac{1}{3}\right) - \left(-\frac{1}{2}x^3 + \frac{1}{4}x - \frac{1}{3}\right)$

50. $\left(\frac{1}{5}x^3 + 2x^2 - \frac{3}{10}\right) - \left(-\frac{2}{5}x^3 + 2x^2 + \frac{7}{1000}\right)$

51. $(0.07t^3 - 0.03t^2 + 0.01t) - (0.02t^3 + 0.04t^2 - 1)$

52. $(0.9a^3 + 0.2a - 5) - (0.7a^4 - 0.3a - 0.1)$

53. $\quad x^3 + 3x^2 + 1$
$\underline{\;-(x^3 + \;\;x^2 - 5)\;}$

54. $\quad x^2 + 5x + 6$
$\underline{\;-(x^2 + 2x + 1)\;}$

55. $\quad 4x^4 - 2x^3$
$\underline{\;-(7x^4 + 6x^3 + 7x^2)\;}$

56. $\quad 5x^4 + 6x^3 - 9x^2$
$\underline{\;-(-6x^4 \qquad + \;\;x^2)\;}$

57. Solve.
   a) Find a polynomial for the sum of the areas of the rectangles shown in the figure.
   b) Find the sum of the areas when $x = 5$ and $x = 7$.

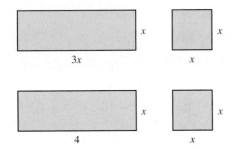

58. Solve. Leave the answers in terms of π.
   a) Find a polynomial for the sum of the areas of the circles shown in the figure.
   b) Find the sum of the areas when $r = 5$ and $r = 11.3$.

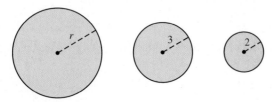

Find a polynomial for the perimeter of each figure in Exercises 59 and 60.

59.

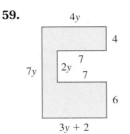

60.

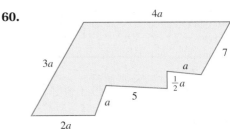

Find two algebraic expressions for the area of each figure. First, regard the figure as one large rectangle, and then regard the figure as a sum of four smaller rectangles.

61.

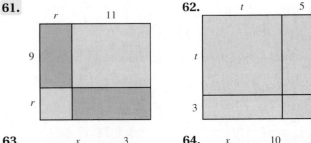

62.

63.

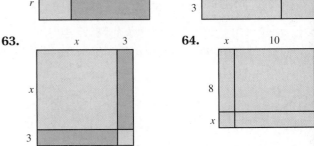

64.

Find a polynomial for the shaded area of each figure.

65.

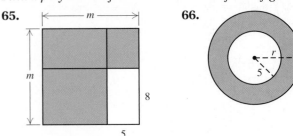

66.

7.

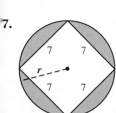

68.

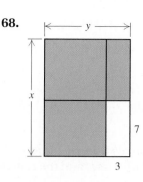

9. A 2-ft by 6-ft bath enclosure is installed in a new bathroom measuring x ft by x ft. Find a polynomial for the remaining floor area.

0. A 5-ft by 7-ft Jacuzzi™ is installed on an outdoor deck measuring y ft by y ft. Find a polynomial for the remaining area of the deck.

1. A 12-ft wide round patio is laid in a garden measuring z ft by z ft. Find a polynomial for the remaining area of the garden.

2. A 10-ft wide round water trampoline is floating in a pool measuring x ft by x ft. Find a polynomial for the remaining surface area of the pool.

3. A 12-m by 12-m mat includes a circle of diameter d meters for wrestling. Find a polynomial for the area of the mat outside the wrestling circle.

4. A 2-m by 3-m rug is spread inside a tepee that has a diameter of x meters. Find a polynomial for the area of the tepee's floor that is not covered.

5. Explain why parentheses are used in the statement of the solution of Example 10: $(x^2 - 64\pi)$ ft².

6. Is the sum of two trinomials always a trinomial? Why or why not?

kill Review

prepare for Section 4.5, review multiplying using the 'stributive law and multiplying with exponential nota-on (Sections 1.8 and 4.1).

mplify.

7. $2(x^2 - x + 3)$ [1.8]

78. $-5(3x^2 - 2x - 7)$ [1.8]

. $x^2 \cdot x^6$ [4.1]

80. $y^6 \cdot y$ [4.1]

1. $2n \cdot n^2$ [4.1]

82. $-6n^4 \cdot n^8$ [4.1]

ynthesis

. What can be concluded about two polynomials whose sum is zero?

4. Which, if any, of the commutative, associative, and distributive laws are needed for adding polynomials? Why?

Simplify.

85. $(6t^2 - 7t) + (3t^2 - 4t + 5) - (9t - 6)$

86. $(3x^2 - 4x + 6) - (-2x^2 + 4) + (-5x - 3)$

87. $4(x^2 - x + 3) - 2(2x^2 + x - 1)$

88. $3(2y^2 - y - 1) - (6y^2 - 3y - 3)$

89. $(345.099x^3 - 6.178x) - (94.508x^3 - 8.99x)$

Find a polynomial for the surface area of the right rectangular solid.

90.

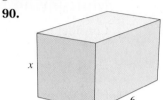

91.

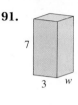

92.

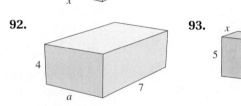

93.

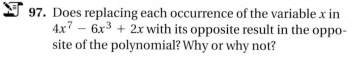

94. Find a polynomial for the total length of all edges in the figure appearing in Exercise 93.

95. Find a polynomial for the total length of all edges in the figure appearing in Exercise 90.

96. *Total profit.* Hadley Electronics is marketing a new digital camera. Total revenue is the total amount of money taken in. The firm determines that when it sells x cameras, its total revenue is given by

$$R = 175x - 0.4x^2.$$

Total cost is the total cost of producing x cameras. Hadley Electronics determines that the total cost of producing x cameras is given by

$$C = 5000 + 0.6x^2.$$

The total profit P is

$$(\text{Total Revenue}) - (\text{Total Cost}) = R - C.$$

a) Find a polynomial for total profit.
b) What is the total profit on the production and sale of 75 cameras?
c) What is the total profit on the production and sale of 120 cameras?

97. Does replacing each occurrence of the variable x in $4x^7 - 6x^3 + 2x$ with its opposite result in the opposite of the polynomial? Why or why not?

4.5 Multiplication of Polynomials

Multiplying Monomials ▪ Multiplying a Monomial and a Polynomial ▪ Multiplying Any Two Polynomials ▪ Checking by Evaluating

We now multiply polynomials using techniques based largely on the distributive, associative, and commutative laws and the rules for exponents.

Multiplying Monomials

Consider $(3x)(4x)$. We multiply as follows:

$$(3x)(4x) = 3 \cdot x \cdot 4 \cdot x \qquad \text{Using an associative law}$$
$$= 3 \cdot 4 \cdot x \cdot x \qquad \text{Using a commutative law}$$
$$= (3 \cdot 4) \cdot x \cdot x \qquad \text{Using an associative law}$$
$$= 12x^2.$$

> **To Multiply Monomials**
>
> To find an equivalent expression for the product of two monomials, multiply the coefficients and then multiply the variables using the product rule for exponents.

EXAMPLE **1**

Multiply to form an equivalent expression.

a) $(5x)(6x)$

b) $(-a)(3a)$

c) $(7x^5)(-4x^3)$

SOLUTION

a) $(5x)(6x) = (5 \cdot 6)(x \cdot x)$ Multiplying the coefficients; multiplying the variables

$= 30x^2$ Simplifying

b) $(-a)(3a) = (-1a)(3a)$ Writing $-a$ as $-1a$ can ease calculations.

$= (-1 \cdot 3)(a \cdot a)$ Using an associative law and a commutative law

$= -3a^2$

c) $(7x^5)(-4x^3) = 7(-4)(x^5 \cdot x^3)$

$= -28x^{5+3}$ $\left.\right\}$ Using the product rule for exponents

$= -28x^8$

TRY EXERCISE ▶ 13

After some practice, you can try writing only the answer.

Multiplying a Monomial and a Polynomial

To find an equivalent expression for the product of a monomial, such as $5x$, and a polynomial, such as $2x^2 - 3x + 4$, we use the distributive law.

EXAMPLE 2

Multiply: **(a)** $x(x + 3)$; **(b)** $5x(2x^2 - 3x + 4)$.

SOLUTION

a) $x(x + 3) = x \cdot x + x \cdot 3$ Using the distributive law
$\qquad\qquad = x^2 + 3x$

b) $5x(2x^2 - 3x + 4) = (5x)(2x^2) - (5x)(3x) + (5x)(4)$ Using the distributive law

$\qquad\qquad\qquad = 10x^3 - 15x^2 + 20x$ Performing the three multiplications

TRY EXERCISE 29

The product in Example 2(a) can be visualized as the area of a rectangle with width x and length $x + 3$.

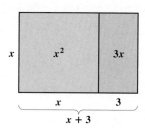

Note that the total area can be expressed as $x(x + 3)$ or, by adding the two smaller areas, $x^2 + 3x$.

> ### The Product of a Monomial and a Polynomial
>
> To multiply a monomial and a polynomial, multiply each term of the polynomial by the monomial.

Try to do this mentally, when possible. Remember that we multiply coefficients and, when the bases match, add exponents.

EXAMPLE 3

Multiply: $2x^2(x^3 - 7x^2 + 10x - 4)$.

SOLUTION

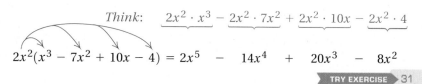

Think: $\underline{2x^2 \cdot x^3} - \underline{2x^2 \cdot 7x^2} + \underline{2x^2 \cdot 10x} - \underline{2x^2 \cdot 4}$

$2x^2(x^3 - 7x^2 + 10x - 4) = 2x^5 - 14x^4 + 20x^3 - 8x^2$

TRY EXERCISE 31

Multiplying Any Two Polynomials

Before considering the product of *any* two polynomials, let's look at product
when both polynomials are binomials.

To find an equivalent expression for the product of two binomials, we again
begin by using the distributive law. This time, however, it is a *binomial* rather than
a monomial that is being distributed.

EXAMPLE 4   Multiply each pair of binomials.

a) $x + 5$ and $x + 4$ **b)** $4x - 3$ and $x - 2$

SOLUTION

a) $(x + 5)(x + 4) = (x + 5)\,x + (x + 5)\,4$ Using the distributive law

$= x(x + 5) + 4(x + 5)$ Using the commutative law for multiplication

$= x \cdot x + x \cdot 5 + 4 \cdot x + 4 \cdot 5$ Using the distributive law (twice)

$= x^2 + 5x + 4x + 20$ Multiplying the monomials

$= x^2 + 9x + 20$ Combining like terms

STUDY SKILLS

Take a Peek Ahead

Try to at least glance at the next
section of material that will be
covered in class. This will make it
easier to concentrate on your
instructor's lecture instead of
trying to write everything down.

b) $(4x - 3)(x - 2) = (4x - 3)\,x - (4x - 3)\,2$ Using the distributive law

$= x(4x - 3) - 2(4x - 3)$ Using the commutative law for multiplication. This step is often omitted.

$= x \cdot 4x - x \cdot 3 - 2 \cdot 4x - 2(-3)$ Using the distributive law (twice)

$= 4x^2 - 3x - 8x + 6$ Multiplying the monomials

$= 4x^2 - 11x + 6$ Combining like terms

TRY EXERCISE 37

To visualize the product in Example 4(a), consider a rectangle of length $x +$
and width $x + 4$, as shown here.

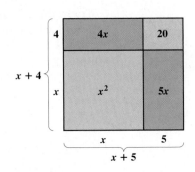

The total area can be expressed as $(x + 5)(x + 4)$ or, by adding the fou
smaller areas, $x^2 + 5x + 4x + 20$.

Let's consider the product of a binomial and a trinomial. Again we make re
peated use of the distributive law.

EXAMPLE **5**   Multiply: $(x^2 + 2x - 3)(x + 4)$.

SOLUTION

$$(x^2 + 2x - 3) \ (x + 4)$$

$$= (x^2 + 2x - 3) \ x + \ (x^2 + 2x - 3) \ 4 \qquad \text{Using the distributive law}$$

$$= x(x^2 + 2x - 3) + 4(x^2 + 2x - 3) \qquad \text{Using the commutative law}$$

$$= x \cdot x^2 + x \cdot 2x - x \cdot 3 + 4 \cdot x^2 + 4 \cdot 2x - 4 \cdot 3 \qquad \text{Using the distributive law (twice)}$$

$$= x^3 + 2x^2 - 3x + 4x^2 + 8x - 12 \qquad \text{Multiplying the monomials}$$

$$= x^3 + 6x^2 + 5x - 12 \qquad \text{Combining like terms}$$

TRY EXERCISE 57

Perhaps you have discovered the following in the preceding examples.

> ### The Product of Two Polynomials
>
> To multiply two polynomials P and Q, select one of the polynomials, say P. Then multiply each term of P by every term of Q and combine like terms.

To use columns for long multiplication, multiply each term in the top row by every term in the bottom row. We write like terms in columns, and then add the results. Such multiplication is like multiplying with whole numbers.

$$
\begin{array}{r}
321 \\
\times 12 \\
\hline
642 \\
321 \\
\hline
3852
\end{array}
\qquad
\begin{array}{r}
300 + 20 + 1 \\
\times \qquad\qquad 10 + 2 \\
\hline
600 + 40 + 2 \\
3000 + 200 + 10 \\
\hline
3000 + 800 + 50 + 2
\end{array}
\qquad
\begin{array}{l}
\text{Multiplying the top row by 2} \\
\text{Multiplying the top row by 10} \\
\text{Adding}
\end{array}
$$

EXAMPLE **6**   Multiply: $(5x^4 - 2x^2 + 3x)(x^2 + 2x)$.

SOLUTION

$$
\begin{array}{r}
5x^4 \qquad\quad - 2x^2 + 3x \\
x^2 + 2x \\
\hline
10x^5 \qquad\quad - 4x^3 + 6x^2 \\
5x^6 \qquad\quad - 2x^4 + 3x^3 \\
\hline
5x^6 + 10x^5 - 2x^4 - \ x^3 + 6x^2
\end{array}
$$

Note that each polynomial is written in descending order, and space is left for missing terms.

Multiplying the top row by $2x$

Multiplying the top row by x^2

Combining like terms

Line up like terms in columns.

TRY EXERCISE 61

With practice, you will be able to skip some steps. Sometimes we multiply horizontally, while still aligning like terms as we write the product.

EXAMPLE **7**   Multiply: $(2x^3 + 3x^2 - 4x + 6)(3x + 5)$.

SOLUTION

$$\overbrace{}^{\text{Multiplying by } 3x}$$

$$(2x^3 + 3x^2 - 4x + 6)(3x + 5) = 6x^4 + 9x^3 - 12x^2 + 18x$$
$$+ \underbrace{10x^3 + 15x^2 - 20x + 30}_{\text{Multiplying by } 5}$$
$$= 6x^4 + 19x^3 + 3x^2 - 2x + 30$$

> **TRY EXERCISE** 65

Checking by Evaluating

How can we be certain that our multiplication (or addition or subtraction) o[f]
polynomials is correct? One check is to simply review our calculations. A differ[ent]
type of check, used in Example 9 of Section 4.4, makes use of the fact tha[t]
equivalent expressions have the same value when evaluated for the sam[e]
replacement. Thus a quick, partial, check of Example 7 can be made by selectin[g]
a convenient replacement for x (say, 1) and comparing the values of the expres[-]
sions $(2x^3 + 3x^2 - 4x + 6)(3x + 5)$ and $6x^4 + 19x^3 + 3x^2 - 2x + 30$:

$$(2x^3 + 3x^2 - 4x + 6)(3x + 5) = (2 \cdot 1^3 + 3 \cdot 1^2 - 4 \cdot 1 + 6)(3 \cdot 1 + 5)$$
$$= (2 + 3 - 4 + 6)(3 + 5)$$
$$= 7 \cdot 8 = 56;$$

$$6x^4 + 19x^3 + 3x^2 - 2x + 30 = 6 \cdot 1^4 + 19 \cdot 1^3 + 3 \cdot 1^2 - 2 \cdot 1 + 30$$
$$= 6 + 19 + 3 - 2 + 30$$
$$= 28 - 2 + 30 = 56.$$

Since the value of both expressions is 56, the multiplication in Example 7 is ver[y]
likely correct.

It is possible, by chance, for two expressions that are not equivalent to share th[e]
same value when evaluated. For this reason, checking by evaluating is only a parti[al]
check. Consult your instructor for the checking approach that he or she prefers.

TECHNOLOGY CONNECTION

Tables can also be used to check polynomial multiplication. To illustrate, we can check Example 7 by entering
$y_1 = (2x^3 + 3x^2 - 4x + 6)(3x + 5)$ and
$y_2 = 6x^4 + 19x^3 + 3x^2 - 2x + 30$.

When (TABLE) is then pressed, we are shown two
columns of values—one for y_1 and one for y_2. If our multiplication was correct, the columns of values will match.

X	Y₁	Y₂
−3	36	36
−2	−10	−10
−1	22	22
0	30	30
1	56	56
2	286	286
3	1050	1050

X = −3

1. Form a table and scroll up and down to check
   Example 6.
2. Check Example 7 using the method discussed in
   Section 4.4: Let

   $$y_1 = (2x^3 + 3x^2 - 4x + 6)(3x + 5),$$
   $$y_2 = 6x^4 + 19x^3 + 3x^2 - 2x + 30,$$

   and

   $$y_3 = y_2 - y_1.$$

   Then check that y_3 is always 0.

4.5 EXERCISE SET

Concept Reinforcement *In each of Exercises 1–6, match the expression with the correct result from the column on the right. Choices may be used more than once.*

1. ___ $3x^2 \cdot 2x^4$

2. ___ $3x^8 + 5x^8$

3. ___ $4x^3 \cdot 2x^5$

4. ___ $3x^5 \cdot 2x^3$

5. ___ $4x^6 + 2x^6$

6. ___ $4x^4 \cdot 2x^2$

a) $6x^8$

b) $8x^6$

c) $6x^6$

d) $8x^8$

Multiply.

7. $(3x^5)7$

8. $2x^3 \cdot 11$

9. $(-x^3)(x^4)$

10. $(-x^2)(-x)$

11. $(-x^6)(-x^2)$

12. $(-x^5)(x^3)$

13. $4t^2(9t^2)$

14. $(6a^8)(3a^2)$

15. $(0.3x^3)(-0.4x^6)$

16. $(-0.1x^6)(0.2x^4)$

17. $\left(-\frac{1}{4}x^4\right)\left(\frac{1}{5}x^8\right)$

18. $\left(-\frac{1}{5}x^3\right)\left(-\frac{1}{3}x\right)$

19. $(-5n^3)(-1)$

20. $19t^2 \cdot 0$

21. $11x^5(-4x^5)$

22. $12x^3(-5x^3)$

23. $(-4y^5)(6y^2)(-3y^3)$

24. $7x^2(-2x^3)(2x^6)$

25. $5x(4x + 1)$

26. $3x(2x - 7)$

27. $(a - 9)3a$

28. $(a - 7)4a$

29. $x^2(x^3 + 1)$

30. $-2x^3(x^2 - 1)$

31. $-3n(2n^2 - 8n + 1)$

32. $4n(3n^3 - 4n^2 - 5n + 10)$

33. $-5t^2(3t + 6)$

34. $7t^2(2t + 1)$

35. $\frac{2}{3}a^4\left(6a^5 - 12a^3 - \frac{5}{8}\right)$

36. $\frac{3}{4}t^5\left(8t^6 - 12t^4 + \frac{12}{7}\right)$

37. $(x + 3)(x + 4)$

38. $(x + 7)(x + 3)$

39. $(t + 7)(t - 3)$

40. $(t - 4)(t + 3)$

41. $(a - 0.6)(a - 0.7)$

42. $(a - 0.4)(a - 0.8)$

43. $(x + 3)(x - 3)$

44. $(x + 6)(x - 6)$

45. $(4 - x)(7 - 2x)$

46. $(5 + x)(5 + 2x)$

47. $\left(t + \frac{3}{2}\right)\left(t + \frac{4}{3}\right)$

48. $\left(a - \frac{2}{5}\right)\left(a + \frac{5}{2}\right)$

49. $\left(\frac{1}{4}a + 2\right)\left(\frac{3}{4}a - 1\right)$

50. $\left(\frac{2}{5}t - 1\right)\left(\frac{3}{5}t + 1\right)$

Draw and label rectangles similar to those following Examples 2 and 4 to illustrate each product.

51. $x(x + 5)$

52. $x(x + 2)$

53. $(x + 1)(x + 2)$

54. $(x + 3)(x + 1)$

55. $(x + 5)(x + 3)$

56. $(x + 4)(x + 6)$

Multiply and check.

57. $(x^2 - x + 3)(x + 1)$

58. $(x^2 + x - 7)(x + 2)$

59. $(2a + 5)(a^2 - 3a + 2)$

60. $(3t - 4)(t^2 - 5t + 1)$

61. $(y^2 - 7)(3y^4 + y + 2)$

62. $(a^2 + 4)(5a^3 - 3a - 1)$

Aha! 63. $(3x + 2)(7x + 4x + 1)$

64. $(4x - 5x - 3)(1 + 2x^2)$

65. $(x^2 + 5x - 1)(x^2 - x + 3)$

66. $(x^2 - 3x + 2)(x^2 + x + 1)$

67. $\left(5t^2 - t + \frac{1}{2}\right)(2t^2 + t - 4)$

68. $(2t^2 - 5t - 4)\left(3t^2 - t + \frac{1}{2}\right)$

69. $(x + 1)(x^3 + 7x^2 + 5x + 4)$

70. $(x + 2)(x^3 + 5x^2 + 9x + 3)$

71. Is it possible to understand polynomial multiplication without understanding the distributive law? Why or why not?

72. The polynomials

$$(a + b + c + d) \quad \text{and} \quad (r + s + m + p)$$

are multiplied. Without performing the multiplication, determine how many terms the product will contain. Provide a justification for your answer.

Skill Review

Review simplifying expressions using the rules for order of operations (Section 1.8).

Simplify. [1.8]

73. $(9 - 3)(9 + 3) + 3^2 - 9^2$

74. $(7 + 2)(7 - 2) + 2^2 - 7^2$

75. $5 + \dfrac{7 + 4 + 2 \cdot 5}{7}$

76. $11 - \dfrac{2 + 6 \cdot 3 + 4}{6}$

77. $(4 + 3 \cdot 5 + 5) \div 3 \cdot 4$

78. $(2 + 2 \cdot 7 + 4) \div 2 \cdot 5$

Synthesis

79. Under what conditions will the product of two binomials be a trinomial?

80. How can the following figure be used to show that $(x + 3)^2 \neq x^2 + 9$?

Find a polynomial for the shaded area of each figure.

81.

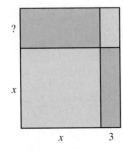

82.

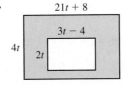

For each figure, determine what the missing number must be in order for the figure to have the given area.

83. Area is $x^2 + 8x + 15$

84. Area is $x^2 + 7x + 10$

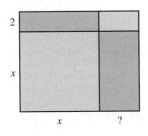

85. A box with a square bottom and no top is to be made from a 12-in.–square piece of cardboard. Squares with side x are cut out of the corners and the sides are folded up. Find the polynomials for the volume and the outside surface area of the box.

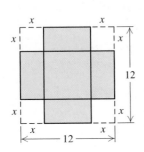

86. Find a polynomial for the volume of the solid shown below.

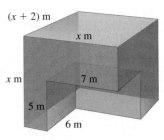

87. An open wooden box is a cube with side x cm. The box, including its bottom, is made of wood that is 1 cm thick. Find a polynomial for the interior volume of the cube.

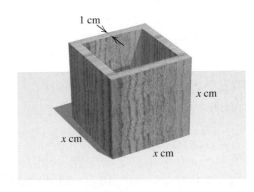

88. A side of a cube is $(x + 2)$ cm long. Find a polynomial for the volume of the cube.

89. A rectangular garden is twice as long as it is wide and is surrounded by a sidewalk that is 4 ft wide (see the figure below). The area of the sidewalk is 256 ft^2. Find the dimensions of the garden.

Compute and simplify.

90. $(x + 3)(x + 6) + (x + 3)(x + 6)$

Aha! **91.** $(x - 2)(x - 7) - (x - 7)(x - 2)$

92. $(x + 5)^2 - (x - 3)^2$

93. $(x + 2)(x + 4)(x - 5)$

94. $(x - 3)^3$

95. Extend the pattern and simplify
$$(x - a)(x - b)(x - c)(x - d) \cdots (x - z).$$

96. Use a graphing calculator to check your answers to Exercises 25, 45, and 57. Use graphs, tables, or both, as directed by your instructor.

CORNER

Slick Tricks with Algebra

Focus: Polynomial multiplication

Time: 15 minutes

Group size: 2

Consider the following dialogue.

Jinny: Cal, let me do a number trick with you. Think of a number between 1 and 7. I'll have you perform some manipulations to this number, you'll tell me the result, and I'll tell me your number.

Cal: OK. I've thought of a number.

Jinny: Good. Write it down so I can't see it. Now double it, and then subtract x from the result.

Cal: Hey, this is algebra!

Jinny: I know. Now square your binomial. After you're through squaring, subtract x^2.

Cal: How did you know I had an x^2? I *thought* this was rigged!

Jinny: It is. Now divide each of the remaining terms by 4 and tell me either your constant term

or your x-term. I'll tell you the other term and the number you chose.

Cal: OK. The constant term is 16.

Jinny: Then the other term is $-4x$ and the number you chose was 4.

Cal: You're right! How did you do it?

ACTIVITY

1. Each group member should follow Jinny's instructions. Then determine how Jinny determined Cal's number and the other term.

2. Suppose that, at the end, Cal told Jinny the x-term. How would Jinny have determined Cal's number and the other term?

3. Would Jinny's "trick" work with *any* real number? Why do you think she specified numbers between 1 and 7?

4.6   Special Products

Products of Two Binomials ▪ Multiplying Sums and Differences of Two Terms ▪
Squaring Binomials ▪ Multiplications of Various Types

We can observe patterns in the products of two binomials. These patterns allow us to compute such products quickly.

Products of Two Binomials

In Section 4.5, we found the product $(x + 5)(x + 4)$ by using the distributive law a total of three times (see p. 264). Note that each term in $x + 5$ is multiplied by each term in $x + 4$. To shorten our work, we can go right to this step:

$$\begin{aligned} (x + 5)(x + 4) &= x \cdot x + x \cdot 4 + 5 \cdot x + 5 \cdot 4 \\ &= x^2 + 4x + 5x + 20 \\ &= x^2 + 9x + 20. \end{aligned}$$

Note that $x \cdot x$ is found by multiplying the *First* terms of each binomial, $x \cdot 4$ i found by multiplying the *Outer* terms of the two binomials, $5 \cdot x$ is the product o the *Inner* terms of the two binomials, and $5 \cdot 4$ is the product of the *Last* terms o each binomial:

$$\overbrace{\text{First}}^{\text{terms}} \quad \overbrace{\text{Outer}}^{\text{terms}} \quad \overbrace{\text{Inner}}^{\text{terms}} \quad \overbrace{\text{Last}}^{\text{terms}}$$

$$(x + 5)(x + 4) = x \cdot x + 4 \cdot x + 5 \cdot x + 5 \cdot 4.$$

To remember this shortcut for multiplying, we use the initials **FOIL**.

The FOIL Method

To multiply two binomials, $A + B$ and $C + D$, multiply the First terms AC, the Outer terms AD, the Inner terms BC, and then the Last terms BD. Then combine like terms, if possible.

$$(A + B)(C + D) = AC + AD + BC + BD$$

1. Multiply First terms: AC.
2. Multiply Outer terms: AD.
3. Multiply Inner terms: BC.
4. Multiply Last terms: BD.

$$\downarrow$$
$$\text{FOIL}$$

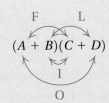

Because addition is commutative, the individual multiplications can b performed in any order. Both FLOI and FIOL yield the same result as FOIL, bu FOIL is most easily remembered and most widely used.

EXAMPLE **1**   Form an equivalent expression by multiplying: $(x + 8)(x^2 + 5)$.

SOLUTION

$$(x + 8)(x^2 + 5) = x^3 + 5x + 8x^2 + 40 \qquad \text{There are no like terms.}$$
$$= x^3 + 8x^2 + 5x + 40 \qquad \text{Writing in descending orde}$$

> **TRY EXERCISE** ▸ 5

After multiplying, remember to combine any like terms.

EXAMPLE **2**   Multiply to form an equivalent expression.

a) $(x + 7)(x + 4)$ **b)** $(y + 3)(y - 2)$

c) $(4t^3 + 5t)(3t^2 - 2)$ **d)** $(3 - 4x)(7 - 5x^3)$

SOLUTION

a) $(x + 7)(x + 4) = x^2 + 4x + 7x + 28 \qquad \text{Using FOIL}$
$$= x^2 + 11x + 28 \qquad \text{Combining like terms}$$

b) $(y + 3)(y - 2) = y^2 - 2y + 3y - 6$
$$= y^2 + y - 6$$

c) $(4t^3 + 5t)(3t^2 - 2) = 12t^5 - 8t^3 + 15t^3 - 10t$

Remember to add exponents when multiplying terms with the same base.

$$= 12t^5 + 7t^3 - 10t$$

d) $(3 - 4x)(7 - 5x^3) = 21 - 15x^3 - 28x + 20x^4$

$$= 21 - 28x - 15x^3 + 20x^4$$

In general, if the original binomials are written in *ascending* order, the answer is also written that way.

TRY EXERCISE   9

Multiplying Sums and Differences of Two Terms

Consider the product of the sum and the difference of the same two terms, such as

$$(x + 5)(x - 5).$$

Since this is the product of two binomials, we can use FOIL. In doing so, we find that the "outer" and "inner" products are opposites:

a) $(x + 5)(x - 5) = x^2 - 5x + 5x - 25$

$$= x^2 - 25;$$

b) $(3a - 2)(3a + 2) = 9a^2 + 6a - 6a - 4$

$$= 9a^2 - 4;$$

The "outer" and "inner" terms "drop out." Their sum is zero.

c) $\left(x^3 + \frac{2}{7}\right)\left(x^3 - \frac{2}{7}\right) = x^6 - \frac{2}{7}x^3 + \frac{2}{7}x^3 - \frac{4}{49}$

$$= x^6 - \frac{4}{49}.$$

Because opposites always add to zero, for products like $(x + 5)(x - 5)$ we can use a shortcut that is faster than FOIL.

The Product of a Sum and a Difference

The product of the sum and the difference of the same two terms is the square of the first term minus the square of the second term:

$$(A + B)(A - B) = A^2 - B^2.$$

This is called a *difference of squares*.

EXAMPLE   3   Multiply.

a) $(x + 4)(x - 4)$

b) $(5 + 2w)(5 - 2w)$

c) $(3a^4 - 5)(3a^4 + 5)$

SOLUTION

$$(A + B)(A - B) = A^2 - B^2$$

a) $(x + 4)(x - 4) = x^2 - 4^2$

Saying the words can help: "The square of the first term, x^2, minus the square of the second, 4^2"

$$= x^2 - 16$$ Simplifying

b) $(5 + 2w)(5 - 2w) = 5^2 - (2w)^2$

$\qquad\qquad\qquad = 25 - 4w^2$ Squaring both 5 and $2w$

c) $(3a^4 - 5)(3a^4 + 5) = (3a^4)^2 - 5^2$

$\qquad\qquad\qquad\qquad = 9a^8 - 25$ Remember to multiply exponents when raising a power to a power.

TRY EXERCISE   41

Squaring Binomials

Consider the square of a binomial, such as $(x + 3)^2$. This can be expressed a $(x + 3)(x + 3)$. Since this is the product of two binomials, we can use FOIL. Bu again, this product occurs so often that a faster method has been developed. Loo for a pattern in the following:

a) $(x + 3)^2 = (x + 3)(x + 3)$

$\qquad\qquad = x^2 + 3x + 3x + 9$

$\qquad\qquad = x^2 + 6x + 9;$

b) $(5 - 3p)^2 = (5 - 3p)(5 - 3p)$

$\qquad\qquad = 25 - 15p - 15p + 9p^2$

$\qquad\qquad = 25 - 30p + 9p^2;$

c) $(a^3 - 7)^2 = (a^3 - 7)(a^3 - 7)$

$\qquad\qquad = a^6 - 7a^3 - 7a^3 + 49$

$\qquad\qquad = a^6 - 14a^3 + 49.$

Perhaps you noticed that in each product the "outer" product and the "inne product are identical. The other two terms, the "first" product and the "last" prod uct, are squares.

The Square of a Binomial

The square of a binomial is the square of the first term, plus twice the product of the two terms, plus the square of the last term:

$$(A + B)^2 = A^2 + 2AB + B^2;$$
$$(A - B)^2 = A^2 - 2AB + B^2.$$

These are called *perfect-square trinomials.**

EXAMPLE   4   Write an equivalent expression for each square of a binomial.

a) $(x + 7)^2$ **b)** $(t - 5)^2$

c) $(3a + 0.4)^2$ **d)** $(5x - 3x^4)^2$

SOLUTION

$$(A + B)^2 = A^2 + 2 \cdot A \cdot B + B^2$$

a) $(x + 7)^2 = x^2 + 2 \cdot x \cdot 7 + 7^2$ Saying the words can help: "The square the first term, x^2, plus twice the product of the terms, $2 \cdot 7x$, plus the square of th second term, 7^2"

$\qquad\qquad = x^2 + 14x + 49$

---

*Another name for these is *trinomial squares.*

b) $(t - 5)^2 = t^2 - 2 \cdot t \cdot 5 + 5^2$
$$= t^2 - 10t + 25$$

c) $(3a + 0.4)^2 = (3a)^2 + 2 \cdot 3a \cdot 0.4 + 0.4^2$
$$= 9a^2 + 2.4a + 0.16$$

d) $(5x - 3x^4)^2 = (5x)^2 - 2 \cdot 5x \cdot 3x^4 + (3x^4)^2$
$$= 25x^2 - 30x^5 + 9x^8 \qquad \text{Using the rules for exponents}$$

TRY EXERCISE 57

CAUTION! Although the square of a product is the product of the squares, the square of a sum is *not* the sum of the squares. That is, $(AB)^2 = A^2B^2$, but

The term $2AB$ is missing.

$$(A + B)^2 \neq A^2 + B^2.$$

To confirm this inequality, note that

$$(7 + 5)^2 = 12^2 = 144,$$

whereas

$$7^2 + 5^2 = 49 + 25 = 74, \quad \text{and} \quad 74 \neq 144.$$

Geometrically, $(A + B)^2$ can be viewed as the area of a square with sides of length $A + B$:

$$(A + B)(A + B) = (A + B)^2.$$

This is equal to the sum of the areas of the four smaller regions:

$$A^2 + AB + AB + B^2 = A^2 + 2AB + B^2.$$

Thus,

$$(A + B)^2 = A^2 + 2AB + B^2.$$

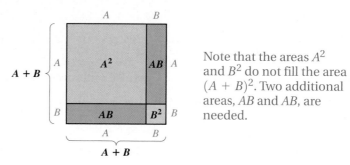

Note that the areas A^2 and B^2 do not fill the area $(A + B)^2$. Two additional areas, AB and AB, are needed.

Multiplications of Various Types

Recognizing patterns often helps when new problems are encountered. To simplify a new multiplication problem, always examine what type of product it is so that the best method for finding that product can be used. To do this, ask yourself questions similar to the following.

> **Multiplying Two Polynomials**
> 1. Is the multiplication the product of a monomial and a polynomial? If so, multiply each term of the polynomial by the monomial.
> 2. Is the multiplication the product of two binomials? If so:
>   a) Is it the product of the sum and the difference of the *same* two terms? If so, use the pattern
> $$(A + B)(A - B) = A^2 - B^2.$$
>   b) Is the product the square of a binomial? If so, use the pattern
> $$(A + B)(A + B) = (A + B)^2 = A^2 + 2AB + B^2,$$
>   or
> $$(A - B)(A - B) = (A - B)^2 = A^2 - 2AB + B^2.$$
>   c) If neither (a) nor (b) applies, use FOIL.
> 3. Is the multiplication the product of two polynomials other than those above? If so, multiply each term of one by every term of the other. Use columns if you wish.

EXAMPLE **5**   Multiply.

a) $(x + 3)(x - 3)$

b) $(t + 7)(t - 5)$

c) $(x + 7)(x + 7)$

d) $2x^3(9x^2 + x - 7)$

e) $(p + 3)(p^2 + 2p - 1)$

f) $\left(3x - \frac{1}{4}\right)^2$

SOLUTION

a) $(x + 3)(x - 3) = x^2 - 9$ This is the product of the sum and the difference of the same two terms.

b) $(t + 7)(t - 5) = t^2 - 5t + 7t - 35$ Using FOIL
$$= t^2 + 2t - 35$$

c) $(x + 7)(x + 7) = x^2 + 14x + 49$ This is the square of a binomial, $(x + 7)^2$.

d) $2x^3(9x^2 + x - 7) = 18x^5 + 2x^4 - 14x^3$ Multiplying each term of the trinomial by the monomial

e) We multiply each term of $p^2 + 2p - 1$ by every term of $p + 3$:
$$(p + 3)(p^2 + 2p - 1) = p^3 + 2p^2 - p \qquad \text{Multiplying by } p$$
$$+ 3p^2 + 6p - 3 \qquad \text{Multiplying by 3}$$
$$= p^3 + 5p^2 + 5p - 3.$$

f) $\left(3x - \frac{1}{4}\right)^2 = 9x^2 - 2(3x)\left(\frac{1}{4}\right) + \frac{1}{16}$ Squaring a binomial
$$= 9x^2 - \frac{3}{2}x + \frac{1}{16}$$

TRY EXERCISE 69

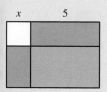

Visualizing
for Success

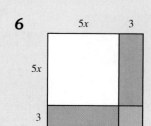

6

In each of Exercises 1–10, find two algebraic expressions for the shaded area of the figure from the list below.

A. $9 - 4x^2$

B. $x^2 - (x - 6)^2$

7

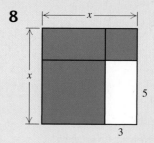

C. $(x + 3)(x - 3)$

D. $10^2 + 2^2$

E. $8x + 15$

F. $(x + 5)(x + 3) - x^2$

G. $x^2 - 6x + 9$

H. $(3 - 2x)^2 + 4x(3 - 2x)$

8

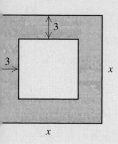

I. $(x + 3)^2$

J. $(5x + 3)^2 - 25x^2$

K. $(5 - 2x)^2 + 4x(5 - 2x)$

L. $x^2 - 9$

M. 104

N. $x^2 - 15$

9

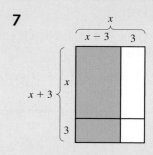

O. $12x - 36$

P. $30x + 9$

Q. $(x - 5)(x - 3) + 3(x - 5) + 5(x - 3)$

R. $(x - 3)^2$

S. $25 - 4x^2$

T. $x^2 + 6x + 9$

Answers on page A-18

An additional, animated version of this activity appears in MyMathLab. To use MyMathLab, you need a course ID and a student access code. Contact your instructor for more information.

10

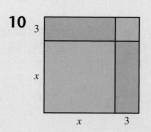

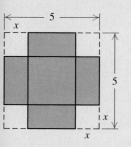

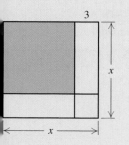

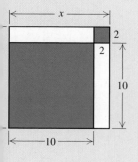

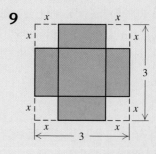

4.6 EXERCISE SET

For Extra Help

✎ *Concept Reinforcement* *Classify each statement as either true or false.*

1. FOIL is simply a memory device for finding the product of two binomials.

2. The square of a binomial cannot be found using FOIL.

3. Once FOIL is used, it is always possible to combine like terms.

4. The square of $A + B$ is not the sum of the squares of A and B.

Multiply.

5. $(x^2 + 2)(x + 3)$

6. $(x - 5)(x^2 - 6)$

7. $(t^4 - 2)(t + 7)$

8. $(n^3 + 8)(n - 4)$

9. $(y + 2)(y - 3)$

10. $(a + 2)(a + 2)$

11. $(3x + 2)(3x + 5)$

12. $(4x + 1)(2x + 7)$

13. $(5x - 3)(x + 4)$

14. $(4x - 5)(4x + 5)$

15. $(3 - 2t)(5 - t)$

16. $(7 - a)(4 - 3a)$

17. $(x^2 + 3)(x^2 - 7)$

18. $(x^2 + 2)(x^2 - 8)$

19. $\left(p - \frac{1}{4}\right)\left(p + \frac{1}{4}\right)$

20. $\left(q + \frac{3}{4}\right)\left(q + \frac{3}{4}\right)$

21. $(x - 0.3)(x - 0.3)$

22. $(x - 0.1)(x + 0.1)$

23. $(-3n + 2)(n + 7)$

24. $(-m + 5)(2m - 9)$

25. $(x + 10)(x + 10)$

26. $(x + 12)(x + 12)$

27. $(1 - 3t)(1 + 5t^2)$

28. $(1 + 2t)(1 - 3t^2)$

29. $(x^2 + 3)(x^3 - 1)$

30. $(x^4 - 3)(2x + 1)$

31. $(3x^2 - 2)(x^4 - 2)$

32. $(x^{10} + 3)(x^{10} - 3)$

33. $(2t^3 + 5)(2t^3 + 5)$

34. $(5t^2 + 1)(2t^2 + 3)$

35. $(8x^3 + 5)(x^2 + 2)$

36. $(5 - 4x^5)(5 + 4x^5)$

37. $(10x^2 + 3)(10x^2 - 3)$

38. $(7x - 2)(2x - 7)$

Multiply. Try to recognize the type of product before multiplying.

39. $(x + 8)(x - 8)$

40. $(x + 1)(x - 1)$

41. $(2x + 1)(2x - 1)$

42. $(4n + 7)(4n - 7)$

43. $(5m^2 + 4)(5m^2 - 4)$

44. $(3x^4 + 2)(3x^4 - 2)$

45. $(9a^3 + 1)(9a^3 - 1)$

46. $(t^2 - 0.2)(t^2 + 0.2)$

47. $(x^4 + 0.1)(x^4 - 0.1)$

48. $(a^3 + 5)(a^3 - 5)$

49. $\left(t - \frac{3}{4}\right)\left(t + \frac{3}{4}\right)$

50. $\left(m - \frac{2}{3}\right)\left(m + \frac{2}{3}\right)$

51. $(x + 3)^2$

52. $(2x - 1)^2$

53. $(7x^3 - 1)^2$

54. $(5x^3 + 2)^2$

55. $\left(a - \frac{2}{5}\right)^2$

56. $\left(t - \frac{1}{5}\right)^2$

57. $(t^4 + 3)^2$

58. $(a^3 + 6)^2$

59. $(2 - 3x^4)^2$

60. $(5 - 2t^3)^2$

61. $(5 + 6t^2)^2$

62. $(3p^2 - p)^2$

63. $(7x - 0.3)^2$

64. $(4a - 0.6)^2$

65. $7n^3(2n^2 - 1)$

66. $5m^3(4 - 3m^2)$

67. $(a - 3)(a^2 + 2a - 4)$

68. $(x^2 - 5)(x^2 + x -$

69. $(7 - 3x^4)(7 - 3x^4)$

70. $(x - 4x^3)^2$

71. $5x(x^2 + 6x - 2)$

72. $6x(-x^5 + 6x^2 + 9)$

73. $(q^5 + 1)(q^5 - 1)$

74. $(p^4 + 2)(p^4 - 2)$

75. $3t^2(5t^3 - t^2 + t)$

76. $-5x^3(x^2 + 8x - 9)$

77. $(6x^4 - 3x)^2$

78. $(8a^3 + 5)(8a^3 - 5)$

79. $(9a + 0.4)(2a^3 + 0.5)$

80. $(2a - 0.7)(8a^3 - 0.5$

81. $\left(\frac{1}{5} - 6x^4\right)\left(\frac{1}{5} + 6x^4\right)$

82. $\left(3 + \frac{1}{2}t^5\right)\left(3 + \frac{1}{2}t^5\right)$

83. $(a + 1)(a^2 - a + 1)$

84. $(x - 5)(x^2 + 5x + 25)$

Find the total area of all shaded rectangles.

85.

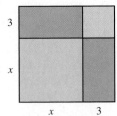

86.

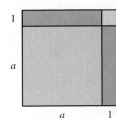

87.

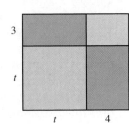

88.

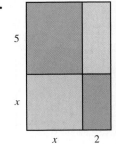

89.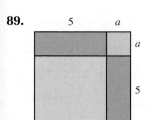

90.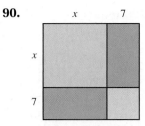

91.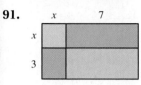

92.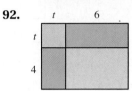

93.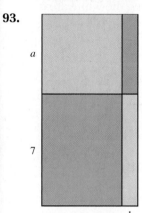

94.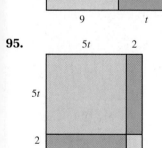

95.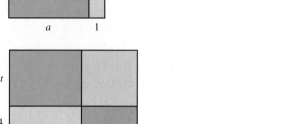

96.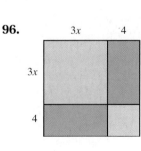

Draw and label rectangles similar to those in Exercises 85–96 to illustrate each of the following.

97. $(x + 5)^2$

98. $(x + 8)^2$

99. $(t + 9)^2$

100. $(a + 12)^2$

101. $(3 + x)^2$

102. $(7 + t)^2$

103. Kristi feels that since she can find the product of any two binomials using FOIL, she needn't study the other special products. What advice would you give her?

104. Under what conditions is the product of two binomials a binomial?

Skill Review

Review problem solving and solving a formula for a variable (Sections 2.3 and 2.5).

Solve. [2.5]

105. *Energy use.* Under typical use, a refrigerator, a freezer, and a washing machine together use 297 kilowatt-hours per month (kWh/mo). A refrigerator uses 21 times as much energy as a washing machine, and a freezer uses 11 times as much energy as a washing machine. How much energy is used by each appliance?

106. *Advertising.* North American advertisers spent $9.4 billion on search-engine marketing in 2006. This was a 62% increase over the amount spent in 2005. How much was spent in 2005?
Source: Search Engine Marketing Professional Organization

Solve. [2.3]

107. $5xy = 8$, for y

108. $3ab = c$, for a

109. $ax - by = c$, for x

110. $ax - by = c$, for y

Synthesis

111. By writing $19 \cdot 21$ as $(20 - 1)(20 + 1)$, Justin can find the product mentally. How do you think he does this?

112. The product $(A + B)^2$ can be regarded as the sum of the areas of four regions (as shown following Example 4). How might one visually represent $(A + B)^3$? Why?

Multiply.

Aha! **113.** $(4x^2 + 9)(2x + 3)(2x - 3)$

114. $(9a^2 + 1)(3a - 1)(3a + 1)$

Aha! **115.** $(3t - 2)^2(3t + 2)^2$

116. $(5a + 1)^2(5a - 1)^2$

117. $(t^3 - 1)^4(t^3 + 1)^4$

 118. $(32.41x + 5.37)^2$

Calculate as the difference of squares.

119. 18×22 [*Hint:* $(20 - 2)(20 + 2)$.]

120. 93×107

Solve.

121. $(x + 2)(x - 5) = (x + 1)(x - 3)$

122. $(2x + 5)(x - 4) = (x + 5)(2x - 4)$

Find a polynomial for the total shaded area in each figure.

123.

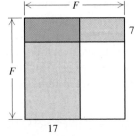

124.

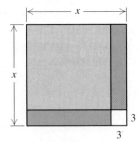

125.

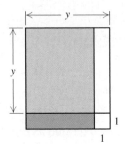

126. Find $(10 - 2x)^2$ by subtracting the white areas from 10^2.

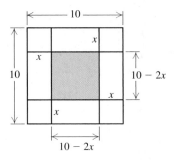

127. Find $(y - 2)^2$ by subtracting the white areas from y^2.

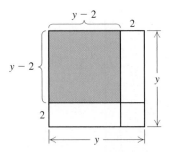

128. Find three consecutive integers for which the sum of the squares is 65 more than three times the square of the smallest integer.

129. Use a graphing calculator and the method developed on p. 258 to check your answers to Exercises 22, 47, and 83.

CONNECTING the CONCEPTS

When writing equivalent polynomial expressions, look first at the operation that you are asked to perform.

Operation	Procedure	Examples
Addition	Combine like terms.	$(2x^3 + 3x^2 - 5x - 7) + (9x^3 - 11x + 8)$ $= \underbrace{2x^3 + 9x^3} + 3x^2 \underbrace{- 5x - 11x} \underbrace{- 7 + 8}$ $= \underbrace{11x^3} + 3x^2 \quad \underbrace{-16x} \quad \underbrace{+ 1}$
Subtraction	Add the opposite of the polynomial being subtracted.	$(9x^4 - 3x^2 + x - 7) - (4x^3 - 8x^2 - 9x + 11)$ $= 9x^4 - 3x^2 + x - 7 + (-4x^3 + 8x^2 + 9x - 11)$ $= 9x^4 - 3x^2 + x - 7 - 4x^3 + 8x^2 + 9x - 11$ $= 9x^4 - 4x^3 + 5x^2 + 10x - 18$
Multiplication	Multiply each term of one polynomial by every term of the other.	$(x^2 - 5x)(3x^4 - 7x^3 + 1)$ $= x^2(3x^4 - 7x^3 + 1) - 5x(3x^4 - 7x^3 + 1)$ $= 3x^6 - 7x^5 + x^2 - 15x^5 + 35x^4 - 5x$ $= 3x^6 - 22x^5 + 35x^4 + x^2 - 5x$
	Special products: $(A + B)(A - B) = A^2 - B^2;$ $(A + B)^2 = A^2 + 2AB + B^2;$ $(A - B)^2 = A^2 - 2AB + B^2;$ $(A + B)(C + D)$ $\quad = AC + AD + BC + BD$	$(x + 5)(x - 5) = x^2 - 25;$ $(2x + 3)^2 = (2x)^2 + 2(2x)(3) + (3)^2 = 4x^2 + 12x + 9;$ $(x^2 - 1)^2 = (x^2)^2 - 2(x^2)(1) + (1)^2 = x^4 - 2x^2 + 1;$ $(x^2 + 3)(x - 2) = x^2(x) + x^2(-2) + 3(x) + 3(-2)$ $\quad\quad\quad\quad\quad = x^3 - 2x^2 + 3x - 6$

MIXED REVIEW

Identify the operation to be performed. Then simplify to form an equivalent expression.

1. $(3x^2 - 2x + 6) + (5x - 3)$

2. $(9x + 6) - (3x - 7)$

3. $6x^3(8x^2 - 7)$

4. $(3x + 2)(2x - 1)$

5. $(9x^3 - 7x + 3) - (5x^2 - 10)$

6. $(2x + 1)(x^2 + x - 3)$

7. $(9x + 1)(9x - 1)$

8. $(8x^3 + 5x) + (9x^4 - 6x^3 - 10x)$

Perform the indicated operation to form an equivalent expression.

9. $(4x^2 - x - 7) - (10x^2 - 3x + 5)$

10. $(3x + 8)(3x + 7)$

11. $8x^5(5x^4 - 6x^3 + 2)$

12. $(t^9 + 3t^6 - 8t^2) + (5t^7 - 3t^6 + 8t^2)$

13. $(2m - 1)^2$

14. $(x - 1)(x^2 + x + 1)$

15. $(5x^3 - 6x^2 - 2x) + (6x^2 + 2x + 3)$

16. $(c + 3)(c - 3)$

17. $(4y^3 + 7)^2$

18. $(3a^4 - 9a^3 - 7) - (4a^3 + 13a^2 - 3)$

19. $(4t^2 - 5)(4t^2 + 5)$

20. $(a^4 + 3)(a^4 - 8)$

4.7   Polynomials in Several Variables

Evaluating Polynomials ▪ Like Terms and Degree ▪ Addition and Subtraction ▪ Multiplication

Thus far, the polynomials that we have studied have had only one variable. Polynomials such as

$$5x + x^2y - 3y + 7, \qquad 9ab^2c - 2a^3b^2 + 8a^2b^3, \quad \text{and} \quad 4m^2 - 9n^2$$

contain two or more variables. In this section, we will add, subtract, multiply, and evaluate such **polynomials in several variables**.

Evaluating Polynomials

To evaluate a polynomial in two or more variables, we substitute numbers for the variables. Then we compute, using the rules for order of operations.

EXAMPLE 1   Evaluate the polynomial $4 + 3x + xy^2 + 8x^3y^3$ for $x = -2$ and $y = 5$.

SOLUTION   We substitute -2 for x and 5 for y:

$$4 + 3x + xy^2 + 8x^3y^3 = 4 + 3(-2) + (-2) \cdot 5^2 + 8(-2)^3 \cdot 5^3$$
$$= 4 - 6 - 50 - 8000 = -8052.$$

TRY EXERCISE 9

EXAMPLE 2   *Surface area of a right circular cylinder.*   The surface area of a right circular cylinder is given by the polynomial

$$2\pi rh + 2\pi r^2,$$

where h is the height and r is the radius of the base. A 12-oz can has a height of 4.7 in. and a radius of 1.2 in. Approximate its surface area to the nearest tenth of a square inch.

SOLUTION   We evaluate the polynomial for $h = 4.7$ in. and $r = 1.2$ in. If 3.14 is used to approximate π, we have

$$2\pi rh + 2\pi r^2 \approx 2(3.14)(1.2 \text{ in.})(4.7 \text{ in.}) + 2(3.14)(1.2 \text{ in.})^2$$
$$\approx 2(3.14)(1.2 \text{ in.})(4.7 \text{ in.}) + 2(3.14)(1.44 \text{ in}^2)$$
$$\approx 35.4192 \text{ in}^2 + 9.0432 \text{ in}^2 \approx 44.4624 \text{ in}^2.$$

If the π key of a calculator is used, we have

$$2\pi rh + 2\pi r^2 \approx 2(3.141592654)(1.2 \text{ in.})(4.7 \text{ in.})$$
$$+ 2(3.141592654)(1.2 \text{ in.})^2$$
$$\approx 44.48495197 \text{ in}^2.$$

Note that the unit in the answer (square inches) is a unit of area. The surface area is about 44.5 in^2 (square inches).

TRY EXERCISE 13

Like Terms and Degree

Recall that the degree of a monomial is the number of variable factors in the term. For example, the degree of $5x^2$ is 2 because there are two variable factors in $5 \cdot x \cdot x$. Similarly, the degree of $5a^2b^4$ is 6 because there are 6 variable factors in $5 \cdot a \cdot a \cdot b \cdot b \cdot b \cdot b$. Note that 6 can be found by adding the exponents 2 and 4.

As we learned in Section 4.3, the degree of a polynomial is the degree of the term of highest degree.

EXAMPLE 3

Identify the coefficient and the degree of each term and the degree of the polynomial

$$9x^2y^3 - 14xy^2z^3 + xy + 4y + 5x^2 + 7.$$

SOLUTION

Term	Coefficient	Degree	Degree of the Polynomial
$9x^2y^3$	9	5	
$-14xy^2z^3$	-14	6	6
xy	1	2	
$4y$	4	1	
$5x^2$	5	2	
7	7	0	

TRY EXERCISE 21

Note in Example 3 that although both xy and $5x^2$ have degree 2, they are *not* like terms. *Like*, or *similar*, *terms* either have exactly the same variables with exactly the same exponents or are constants. For example,

$8a^4b^7$ and $5b^7a^4$ are like terms

and

-17 and 3 are like terms,

but

$-2x^2y$ and $9xy^2$ are *not* like terms.

As always, combining like terms is based on the distributive law.

EXAMPLE 4

Combine like terms to form equivalent expressions.

a) $9x^2y + 3xy^2 - 5x^2y - xy^2$

b) $7ab - 5ab^2 + 3ab^2 + 6a^3 + 9ab - 11a^3 + b - 1$

SOLUTION

a) $9x^2y + 3xy^2 - 5x^2y - xy^2 = (9 - 5)x^2y + (3 - 1)xy^2$
$= 4x^2y + 2xy^2$ Try to go directly to this step.

b) $7ab - 5ab^2 + 3ab^2 + 6a^3 + 9ab - 11a^3 + b - 1$
$= -5a^3 - 2ab^2 + 16ab + b - 1$ We choose to write descending powers of a. Other, equivalent, forms can also be used.

TRY EXERCISE 25

Addition and Subtraction

The procedure used for adding polynomials in one variable is used to add polynomials in several variables.

EXAMPLE 5

Add.

a) $(-5x^3 + 3y - 5y^2) + (8x^3 + 4x^2 + 7y^2)$

b) $(5ab^2 - 4a^2b + 5a^3 + 2) + (3ab^2 - 2a^2b + 3a^3b - 5)$

SOLUTION

a) $(-5x^3 + 3y - 5y^2) + (8x^3 + 4x^2 + 7y^2)$

$= (-5 + 8)x^3 + 4x^2 + 3y + (-5 + 7)y^2$ Try to do this step mentally

$= 3x^3 + 4x^2 + 3y + 2y^2$

b) $(5ab^2 - 4a^2b + 5a^3 + 2) + (3ab^2 - 2a^2b + 3a^3b - 5)$

$= 8ab^2 - 6a^2b + 5a^3 + 3a^3b - 3$ ▶ TRY EXERCISE 33

STUDENT NOTES ——————

Always read the problem carefully. The difference between

$$(-5x^3 - 3y) + (8x^3 + 4x^2)$$

and

$$(-5x^3 - 3y)(8x^3 + 4x^2)$$

is enormous. To avoid wasting time working on an incorrectly copied exercise, be sure to double-check that you have written the correct problem in your notebook.

When subtracting a polynomial, remember to find the opposite of each term in that polynomial and then add.

EXAMPLE 6

Subtract: $(4x^2y + x^3y^2 + 3x^2y^3 + 6y) - (4x^2y - 6x^3y^2 + x^2y^2 - 5y)$.

SOLUTION

$(4x^2y + x^3y^2 + 3x^2y^3 + 6y) - (4x^2y - 6x^3y^2 + x^2y^2 - 5y)$

$= 4x^2y + x^3y^2 + 3x^2y^3 + 6y - 4x^2y + 6x^3y^2 - x^2y^2 + 5y$

$= 7x^3y^2 + 3x^2y^3 - x^2y^2 + 11y$ Combining like terms

▶ TRY EXERCISE 35

Multiplication

To multiply polynomials in several variables, multiply each term of one polynomial by every term of the other, just as we did in Sections 4.5 and 4.6.

EXAMPLE 7

Multiply: $(3x^2y - 2xy + 3y)(xy + 2y)$.

SOLUTION

$$
\begin{array}{r}
3x^2y - 2xy + 3y \\
xy + 2y \\
\hline
6x^2y^2 - 4xy^2 + 6y^2 \\
3x^3y^2 - 2x^2y^2 + 3xy^2 \\
\hline
3x^3y^2 + 4x^2y^2 - xy^2 + 6y^2
\end{array}
$$

Multiplying by $2y$
Multiplying by xy
Adding   ▶ TRY EXERCISE 51

The special products discussed in Section 4.6 can speed up our work.

EXAMPLE 8

Multiply.

a) $(p + 5q)(2p - 3q)$

b) $(3x + 2y)^2$

c) $(a^3 - 7a^2b)^2$

d) $(3x^2y + 2y)(3x^2y - 2y)$

e) $(-2x^3y^2 + 5t)(2x^3y^2 + 5t)$

f) $(2x + 3 - 2y)(2x + 3 + 2y)$

SOLUTION

$$\text{F} \quad \text{O} \quad \text{I} \quad \text{L}$$

a) $(p + 5q)(2p - 3q) = 2p^2 - 3pq + 10pq - 15q^2$

$\qquad\qquad\qquad\quad = 2p^2 + 7pq - 15q^2 \qquad$ Combining like terms

$$(A + B)^2 = A^2 + 2 \cdot A \cdot B + B^2$$
$$\downarrow \qquad \downarrow \qquad \downarrow \quad \downarrow \ \downarrow \ \downarrow \qquad \downarrow$$

b) $(3x + 2y)^2 = (3x)^2 + 2(3x)(2y) + (2y)^2 \qquad$ Using the pattern for squaring a binomial

$$= 9x^2 + 12xy + 4y^2$$

$$(A - B)^2 = A^2 - 2 \cdot A \cdot B + B^2$$
$$\downarrow \qquad \downarrow \qquad \downarrow \quad \downarrow \ \downarrow \ \downarrow \qquad \downarrow$$

c) $(a^3 - 7a^2b)^2 = (a^3)^2 - 2(a^3)(7a^2b) + (7a^2b)^2 \qquad$ Squaring a binomial

$$= a^6 - 14a^5b + 49a^4b^2 \qquad$$ Using the rules for exponents

$$(A + B)(A - B) = A^2 - B^2$$
$$\downarrow \quad \downarrow \quad \downarrow \quad \downarrow \qquad \downarrow \quad \downarrow$$

d) $(3x^2y + 2y)(3x^2y - 2y) = (3x^2y)^2 - (2y)^2 \qquad$ Using the pattern for multiplying the sum and the difference of two terms

$$= 9x^4y^2 - 4y^2 \qquad$$ Using the rules for exponents

e) $(-2x^3y^2 + 5t)(2x^3y^2 + 5t) = (5t - 2x^3y^2)(5t + 2x^3y^2) \qquad$ Using the commutative law for addition twice

$$= (5t)^2 - (2x^3y^2)^2 \qquad$$ Multiplying the sum and the difference of the same two terms

$$= 25t^2 - 4x^6y^4$$

$$(A - B)(A + B) = A^2 - B^2$$
$$\downarrow \qquad \downarrow \quad \downarrow \qquad \downarrow \quad \downarrow \qquad \downarrow$$

f) $(2x + 3 - 2y)(2x + 3 + 2y) = (2x + 3)^2 - (2y)^2 \qquad$ Multiplying a sum and a difference

$$= 4x^2 + 12x + 9 - 4y^2 \qquad$$ Squaring a binomial

> TRY EXERCISE ▶ 57

TECHNOLOGY CONNECTION

One way to evaluate the polynomial in Example 1 for $x = -2$ and $y = 5$ is to store -2 to X and 5 to Y and enter the polynomial.

```
-2 → X
                    -2
5 → Y
                     5
4+3X+XY²+8X^3Y^3
                 -8052
■
```

Evaluate.

1. $3x^2 - 2y^2 + 4xy + x$, for $x = -6$ and $y = 2.3$

2. $a^2b^2 - 8c^2 + 4abc + 9a$, for $a = 11, b = 15$, and $c = -7$

In Example 8, we recognized patterns that might elude some students, particularly in parts (e) and (f). In part (e), we *can* use FOIL, and in part (f), we *can* use long multiplication, but doing so is much slower. By carefully inspecting a problem before "jumping in," we can save ourselves considerable work. At least one instructor refers to this as "working smart" instead of "working hard."*

---

*Thanks to Pauline Kirkpatrick of Wharton County Junior College for this language.

4.7 EXERCISE SET

🔁 *Concept Reinforcement*   *Each of the expressions in Exercises 1–8 can be regarded as either* **(a)** *the square of a binomial,* **(b)** *the product of the sum and the difference of the same two terms, or* **(c)** *neither of the above. Select the appropriate choice for each expression.*

1. $(3x + 5y)^2$ 2. $(4x - 9y)(4x + 9y)$

3. $(5a + 6b)(-6b + 5a)$ 4. $(4a - 3b)(4a - 3b)$

5. $(r - 3s)(5r + 3s)$ 6. $(2x - 7y)(7y - 2x)$

7. $(4x - 9y)(4x - 9y)$ 8. $(2r + 9t)^2$

Evaluate each polynomial for $x = 5$ and $y = -2$.

9. $x^2 - 2y^2 + 3xy$ 10. $x^2 + 5y^2 - 4xy$

Evaluate each polynomial for $x = 2$, $y = -3$, and $z = -4$.

11. $xy^2z - z$ 12. $xy - x^2z + yz^2$

Lung capacity.   *The polynomial*
$$0.041h - 0.018A - 2.69$$
can be used to estimate the lung capacity, in liters, of a female with height h, in centimeters, and age A, in years.

13. Find the lung capacity of a 20-year-old woman who is 160 cm tall.

14. Find the lung capacity of a 40-year-old woman who is 165 cm tall.

15. *Female caloric needs.*   The number of calories needed each day by a moderately active woman who weighs w pounds, is h inches tall, and is a years old can be estimated by the polynomial
$$917 + 6w + 6h - 6a.$$
Rachel is moderately active, weighs 125 lb, is 64 in. tall, and is 27 yr old. What are her daily caloric needs?
Source: Parker, M., *She Does Math.* Mathematical Association of America

16. *Male caloric needs.*   The number of calories needed each day by a moderately active man who weighs w kilograms, is h centimeters tall, and is a years old can be estimated by the polynomial
$$19.18w + 7h - 9.52a + 92.4.$$
One of the authors of this text is moderately active, weighs 87 kg, is 185 cm tall, and is 59 yr old. What are his daily caloric needs?
Source: Parker, M., *She Does Math.* Mathematical Association of America

Surface area of a silo.   *A silo is a structure that is shaped like a right circular cylinder with a half sphere on top. The surface area of a silo of height h and radius r (including the area of the base) is given by the polynomial*
$$2\pi rh + \pi r^2.$$

17. A coffee grinder is shaped like a silo, with a height of 7 in. and a radius of $1\frac{1}{2}$ in. Find the surface area of the coffee grinder. Use 3.14 for π.

18. A $1\frac{1}{2}$-oz bottle of roll-on deodorant has a height of 4 in. and a radius of $\frac{3}{4}$ in. Find the surface area of the bottle if the bottle is shaped like a silo. Use 3.14 for π.

Altitude of a launched object.   *The altitude of an object in meters, is given by the polynomial*
$$h + vt - 4.9t^2,$$
where h is the height, in meters, at which the launch occurs, v is the initial upward speed (or velocity), in meters per second, and t is the number of seconds for which the object is airborne.

19. A bocce ball is thrown upward with an initial speed of 18 m/sec by a person atop the Leaning Tower of Pisa, which is 50 m above the ground. How high will the ball be 2 sec after it has been thrown?

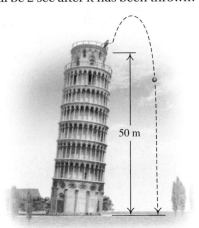

50 m

20. A golf ball is launched upward with an initial speed of 30 m/sec by a golfer atop the Washington Monument, which is 160 m above the ground. How high above the ground will the ball be after 3 sec?

Identify the coefficient and the degree of each term of each polynomial. Then find the degree of each polynomial.

21. $3x^2y - 5xy + 2y^2 - 11$

22. $xy^3 + 7x^3y^2 - 6xy^4 + 2$

23. $7 - abc + a^2b + 9ab^2$

24. $3p - pq - 7p^2q^3 - 8pq^6$

Combine like terms.

25. $3r + s - r - 7s$

26. $9a + b - 8a - 5b$

27. $5xy^2 - 2x^2y + x + 3x^2$

28. $m^3 + 2m^2n - 3m^2 + 3mn^2$

29. $6u^2v - 9uv^2 + 3vu^2 - 2v^2u + 11u^2$

30. $3x^2 + 6xy + 3y^2 - 5x^2 - 10xy$

31. $5a^2c - 2ab^2 + a^2b - 3ab^2 + a^2c - 2ab^2$

32. $3s^2t + r^2t - 9ts^2 - st^2 + 5t^2s - 7tr^2$

Add or subtract, as indicated.

33. $(6x^2 - 2xy + y^2) + (5x^2 - 8xy - 2y^2)$

34. $(7r^3 + rs - 5r^2) - (2r^3 - 3rs + r^2)$

35. $(3a^4 - 5ab + 6ab^2) - (9a^4 + 3ab - ab^2)$

36. $(2r^2t - 5rt + rt^2) - (7r^2t + rt - 5rt^2)$

37. $(5r^2 - 4rt + t^2) + (-6r^2 - 5rt - t^2) + (-5r^2 + 4rt - t^2)$

38. $(2x^2 - 3xy + y^2) + (-4x^2 - 6xy - y^2) + (4x^2 + 6xy + y^2)$

39. $(x^3 - y^3) - (-2x^3 + x^2y - xy^2 + 2y^3)$

40. $(a^3 + b^3) - (-5a^3 + 2a^2b - ab^2 + 3b^3)$

41. $(2y^4x^3 - 3y^3x) + (5y^4x^3 - y^3x) - (9y^4x^3 - y^3x)$

42. $(5a^2b - 7ab^2) - (3a^2b + ab^2) + (a^2b - 2ab^2)$

43. Subtract $7x + 3y$ from the sum of $4x + 5y$ and $-5x + 6y$.

44. Subtract $5a + 2b$ from the sum of $2a + b$ and $3a - 4b$.

Multiply.

45. $(4c - d)(3c + 2d)$

46. $(5x + y)(2x - 3y)$

47. $(xy - 1)(xy + 5)$

48. $(ab + 3)(ab - 5)$

49. $(2a - b)(2a + b)$

50. $(a - 3b)(a + 3b)$

51. $(5rt - 2)(4rt - 3)$

52. $(3xy - 1)(4xy + 2)$

53. $(m^3n + 8)(m^3n - 6)$

54. $(9 - u^2v^2)(2 - u^2v^2)$

55. $(6x - 2y)(5x - 3y)$

56. $(7a - 6b)(5a + 4b)$

57. $(pq + 0.1)(-pq + 0.1)$

58. $(rt + 0.2)(-rt + 0.2)$

59. $(x + h)^2$

60. $(a - r)^2$

61. $(4a - 5b)^2$

62. $(2x + 5y)^2$

63. $(ab + cd^2)(ab - cd^2)$

64. $(p^3 - 5q)(p^3 + 5q)$

65. $(2xy + x^2y + 3)(xy + y^2)$

66. $(5cd - c^2 - d^2)(2c - c^2d)$

Aha! **67.** $(a + b - c)(a + b + c)$

68. $(x + y + 2z)(x + y - 2z)$

69. $[a + b + c][a - (b + c)]$

70. $(a + b + c)(a - b - c)$

Find the total area of each shaded area.

71.

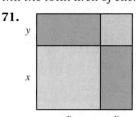

72.

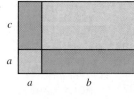

73.

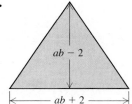

74.

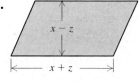

75.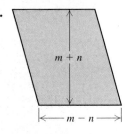

76.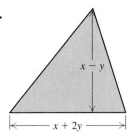

77.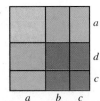

78.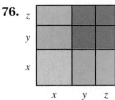

89.
$$5x^3 - 2x^2 + 1$$
$$-(5x^3 - 15x^2)$$

90.
$$2x^2 + 5x - 3$$
$$-(2x^2 + 6x)$$

Synthesis

 91. The concept of "leading term" was intentionally not discussed in this section. Why?

92. Explain how it is possible for the sum of two trinomials in several variables to be a binomial in one variable.

Draw and label rectangles similar to those in Exercises 71, 72, 75, and 76 to illustrate each product.

79. $(r + s)(u + v)$

80. $(m + r)(n + v)$

81. $(a + b + c)(a + d + f)$

82. $(r + s + t)^2$

83. Is it possible for a polynomial in 4 variables to have a degree less than 4? Why or why not?

84. A fourth-degree monomial is multiplied by a third-degree monomial. What is the degree of the product? Explain your reasoning.

Skill Review

To prepare for Section 4.8, review subtraction of polynomials using columns (Section 4.4).

Subtract. [4.4]

85.
$$x^2 - 3x - 7$$
$$-(\quad\; 5x - 3)$$

86.
$$2x^3 \qquad - x + 3$$
$$-(\quad\; x^2 \qquad - 1)$$

87.
$$3x^2 + x + 5$$
$$-(3x^2 + 3x)$$

88.
$$4x^3 - 3x^2 + x$$
$$-(4x^3 - 8x^2)$$

Find a polynomial for the shaded area. (Leave results in terms of π where appropriate.)

93.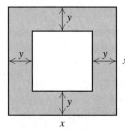

94.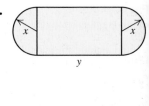

95.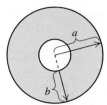

96.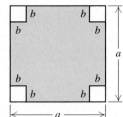

97. Find a polynomial for the total volume of the figure shown.

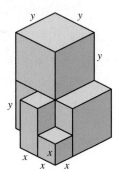

98. Find the shaded area in this figure using each of the approaches given below. Then check that both answers match.

a) Find the shaded area by subtracting the area of the unshaded square from the total area of the figure.

b) Find the shaded area by adding the areas of the three shaded rectangles.

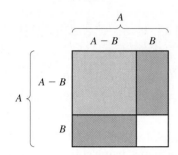

Find a polynomial for the surface area of each solid object shown. (Leave results in terms of π.)

99.   **100.**

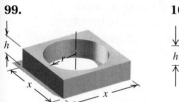

101. The observatory at Danville University is shaped like a silo that is 40 ft high and 30 ft wide (see Exercise 17). The Heavenly Bodies Astronomy Club is to paint the exterior of the observatory using paint that covers 250 ft² per gallon. How many gallons should they purchase? Explain your reasoning.

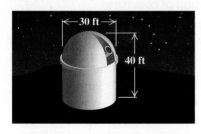

102. Multiply: $(x + a)(x - b)(x - a)(x + b)$.

The computer application Excel allows values for cells in a spreadsheet to be calculated from values in other cells. For example, if the cell C1 contains the formula

$$= A1 + 2*B1,$$

the value in C1 will be the sum of the value in A1 and twice the value in B1. This formula is a polynomial in the two variables A1 and B1.

103. The cell D4 contains the formula

$$= 2*A4 + 3*B4.$$

What is the value in D4 if the value in A4 is 5 and the value in B4 is 10?

104. The cell D6 contains the formula

$$= A1 - 0.2*B1 + 0.3*C1.$$

What is the value in D6 if the value in A1 is 10, the value in B1 is −3, and the value in C1 is 30?

105. *Interest compounded annually.* An amount of money P that is invested at the yearly interest rate r grows to the amount $P(1 + r)^t$ after t years. Find a polynomial that can be used to determine the amount to which P will grow after 2 yr.

106. *Yearly depreciation.* An investment P that drops in value at the yearly rate r drops in value to

$$P(1 - r)^t$$

after t years. Find a polynomial that can be used to determine the value to which P has dropped after 2 yr.

107. Suppose that $10,400 is invested at 8.5% compounded annually. How much is in the account at the end of 5 yr? (See Exercise 105.)

108. A $90,000 investment in computer hardware is depreciating at a yearly rate of 12.5%. How much is the investment worth after 4 yr? (See Exercise 106.)

CORNER

Finding the Magic Number

Focus: Evaluating polynomials in several variables

Time: 15–25 minutes

Group size: 3

Materials: A coin for each person

When a team nears the end of its schedule in first place, fans begin to discuss the team's "magic number." A team's magic number is the combined number of wins by that team and losses by the second-place team that guarantee the leading team a first-place finish. For example, if the Cubs' magic number is 3 over the Reds, any combination of Cubs wins and Reds losses that totals 3 will guarantee a first-place finish for the Cubs. A team's magic number is computed using the polynomial

$$G - P - L + 1,$$

where G is the length of the season, in games, P is the number of games that the leading team has played, and L is the total number of games that the second-place team has lost minus the total number of games that the leading team has lost.

ACTIVITY

1. The standings below are from a fictitious league. Each group should calculate the Jaguars' magic number with respect to the Catamounts as well as the Jaguars' magic number with respect to the Wildcats.

(Assume that the schedule is 162 games long.)

	W	L
Jaguars	92	64
Catamounts	90	66
Wildcats	89	66

2. Each group member should play the role of one of the teams, using coin tosses to simulate the remaining games. If a group member correctly predicts the side (heads or tails) that comes up, the coin toss represents a win for that team. Should the other side appear, the toss represents a loss. Assume that these games are against other (unlisted) teams in the league. Each group member should perform three coin tosses and then update the standings.

3. Recalculate the two magic numbers, using the updated standings from part (2).

4. Slowly—one coin toss at a time—play out the remainder of the season. Record all wins and losses, update the standings, and recalculate the magic numbers each time all three group members have completed a round of coin tosses.

5. Examine the work in part (4) and explain why a magic number of 0 indicates that a team has been eliminated from contention.

4.8 Division of Polynomials

Dividing by a Monomial ▪ Dividing by a Binomial

In this section, we study division of polynomials. We will find that polynomial division is similar to division in arithmetic.

Dividing by a Monomial

We first consider division by a monomial. When dividing a monomial by a monomial, we use the quotient rule of Section 4.1 to subtract exponents when bases are the same. For example,

$$\frac{15x^{10}}{3x^4} = 5x^{10-4}$$

$$= 5x^6$$

> **CAUTION!** The coefficients are divided but the exponents are subtracted.

and

$$\frac{42a^2b^5}{-3ab^2} = \frac{42}{-3}a^{2-1}b^{5-2} \qquad \text{Recall that } a^m/a^n = a^{m-n}.$$

$$= -14ab^3.$$

To divide a polynomial by a monomial, we note that since

$$\frac{A}{C} + \frac{B}{C} = \frac{A + B}{C},$$

it follows that

$$\frac{A + B}{C} = \frac{A}{C} + \frac{B}{C}. \qquad \text{Switching the left side and the right side of the equation}$$

This is actually how we perform divisions like $86 \div 2$. Although we might simply write

$$\frac{86}{2} = 43,$$

we are really saying

$$\frac{80 + 6}{2} = \frac{80}{2} + \frac{6}{2} = 40 + 3.$$

Similarly, to divide a polynomial by a monomial, we divide each term by the monomial:

$$\frac{80x^5 + 6x^7}{2x^3} = \frac{80x^5}{2x^3} + \frac{6x^7}{2x^3}$$

$$= \frac{80}{2}x^{5-3} + \frac{6}{2}x^{7-3} \qquad \text{Dividing coefficients and subtracting exponents}$$

$$= 40x^2 + 3x^4.$$

EXAMPLE 1 Divide $x^4 + 15x^3 - 6x^2$ by $3x$.

SOLUTION We divide each term of $x^4 + 15x^3 - 6x^2$ by $3x$:

$$\frac{x^4 + 15x^3 - 6x^2}{3x} = \frac{x^4}{3x} + \frac{15x^3}{3x} - \frac{6x^2}{3x}$$

$$= \frac{1}{3}x^{4-1} + \frac{15}{3}x^{3-1} - \frac{6}{3}x^{2-1} \qquad \text{Dividing coefficients and subtracting exponents}$$

$$= \frac{1}{3}x^3 + 5x^2 - 2x. \qquad \text{This is the quotient.}$$

To check, we multiply our answer by $3x$, using the distributive law:

$$3x\left(\frac{1}{3}x^3 + 5x^2 - 2x\right) = 3x \cdot \frac{1}{3}x^3 + 3x \cdot 5x^2 - 3x \cdot 2x$$

$$= x^4 + 15x^3 - 6x^2.$$

This is the polynomial that was being divided, so our answer, $\frac{1}{3}x^3 + 5x^2 - 2$ checks.

TRY EXERCISE 5

EXAMPLE **2**   Divide and check: $(10a^5b^4 - 2a^3b^2 + 6a^2b) \div (-2a^2b)$.

SOLUTION   We have

$$\frac{10a^5b^4 - 2a^3b^2 + 6a^2b}{-2a^2b} = \frac{10a^5b^4}{-2a^2b} - \frac{2a^3b^2}{-2a^2b} + \frac{6a^2b}{-2a^2b}$$

> We divide coefficients and subtract exponents.

$$= -\frac{10}{2}a^{5-2}b^{4-1} - \left(-\frac{2}{2}\right)a^{3-2}b^{2-1} + \left(-\frac{6}{2}\right)$$

$$= -5a^3b^3 + ab - 3.$$

Check: $-2a^2b(-5a^3b^3 + ab - 3)$

$$= -2a^2b(-5a^3b^3) + (-2a^2b)(ab) + (-2a^2b)(-3)$$

$$= 10a^5b^4 - 2a^3b^2 + 6a^2b$$

Our answer, $-5a^3b^3 + ab - 3$, checks.

TRY EXERCISE 7

Dividing by a Binomial

The divisors in Examples 1 and 2 have just one term. For divisors with more tha one term, we use long division, much as we do in arithmetic. Polynomials a written in descending order and any missing terms in the dividend are written i using 0 for the coefficients.

EXAMPLE **3**   Divide $x^2 + 5x + 6$ by $x + 3$.

SOLUTION   We begin by dividing x^2 by x:

> **Divide** the first term, x^2, by the first term in the divisor: $x^2/x = x$. Ignore the term 3 for the moment.

$$\begin{array}{r} x \\ x + 3 \overline{)x^2 + 5x + 6} \\ -(x^2 + 3x) \end{array}$$

Multiply $x + 3$ by x, using the distributive law.

$2x.$ **Subtract** both x^2 and $3x$:

$$x^2 + 5x - (x^2 + 3x) = 2x.$$

Now we "bring down" the next term—in this case, 6. The current remainde $2x + 6$, now becomes the focus of our division. We divide $2x$ by x.

$$\begin{array}{r} x \;\; + 2 \\ x + 3\,\overline{)\,x^2 + 5x + 6\,} \\ \underline{-(x^2 + 3x)} \\ 2x + 6 \end{array}$$

Divide $2x$ by x: $2x/x = 2$.

$-(2x + 6)$ ←— Multiply 2 by the divisor, $x + 3$, using the distributive law.

0 ←— Subtract $(2x + 6) - (2x + 6) = 0$.

The quotient is $x + 2$. The notation R 0 indicates a remainder of 0, although a remainder of 0 is generally not listed in an answer.

Check: To check, we multiply the quotient by the divisor and add any remainder to see if we get the dividend:

$$\underbrace{(x + 3)}_{\text{Divisor}}\;\underbrace{(x + 2)}_{\text{Quotient}}\; + \;\underbrace{0}_{\text{Remainder}}\; = \;\underbrace{x^2 + 5x + 6.}_{\text{Dividend}}$$

Our answer, $x + 2$, checks.

TRY EXERCISE 17

EXAMPLE **4**   Divide: $(2x^2 + 5x - 1) \div (2x - 1)$.

SOLUTION   We begin by dividing $2x^2$ by $2x$:

Divide the first term by the first term: $2x^2/(2x) = x$.

$$\begin{array}{r} x \\ 2x - 1\,\overline{)\,2x^2 + 5x - 1\,} \\ \underline{-(2x^2 - \;\; x)} \\ 6x \end{array}$$

Multiply $2x - 1$ by x.

Subtract by changing signs and adding: $(2x^2 + 5x) - (2x^2 - x) = 6x$.

Now, we bring down the -1 and divide $6x - 1$ by $2x - 1$.

$$\begin{array}{r} x \;\; + 3 \\ 2x - 1\,\overline{)\,2x^2 + 5x - 1\,} \\ \underline{-(2x^2 - \;\; x)} \\ 6x - 1 \\ \underline{-(6x - 3)} \\ 2 \end{array}$$

Divide $6x$ by $2x$: $6x/(2x) = 3$.

Multiply 3 by the divisor, $2x - 1$.

Subtract. Note that $-1 - (-3) = -1 + 3 = 2$.

The answer is $x + 3$ with R 2.

Another way to write $x + 3$ R 2 is as

$$\underbrace{x + 3}_{\text{Quotient}} + \underbrace{\frac{2}{2x - 1}}.$$ ←— Remainder

Divisor

(This is the way answers will be given at the back of the book.)

Check: To check, we multiply the divisor by the quotient and add the remainder:

$$(2x - 1)(x + 3) + 2 = 2x^2 + 5x - 3 + 2$$
$$= 2x^2 + 5x - 1.$$ Our answer checks.

TRY EXERCISE 29

Our division procedure ends when the degree of the remainder is less than that of the divisor. Check that this was indeed the case in Example 4.

EXAMPLE 5   Divide each of the following.

a) $(x^3 + 1) \div (x + 1)$ **b)** $(x^4 - 3x^2 + 4x - 3) \div (x^2 - 5)$

SOLUTION

a)

$$
\begin{array}{r}
x^2 - x + 1 \\
x + 1 \overline{)x^3 + 0x^2 + 0x + 1} \\
\end{array}
$$
$\longleftarrow$ Writing in the missing terms

$-(x^3 + x^2)$

$-x^2 + 0x$ $\longleftarrow$ Subtracting $x^3 + x^2$ from $x^3 + 0x^2$ and

$-(-x^2 - x)$ bringing down the $0x$

$x + 1$ $\longleftarrow$ Subtracting $-x^2 - x$ from $-x^2 + 0x$ and

$-(x + 1)$ bringing down the 1

0

The answer is $x^2 - x + 1$.

Check: $(x + 1)(x^2 - x + 1) = x^3 - x^2 + x + x^2 - x + 1$

$ = x^3 + 1.$

b)

$$
\begin{array}{r}
x^2 + 2 \\
x^2 - 5 \overline{)x^4 + 0x^3 - 3x^2 + 4x - 3} \\
\end{array}
$$
Writing in the missing term

$-(x^4 - 5x^2)$

$2x^2 + 4x - 3$ $\longleftarrow$ Subtracting $x^4 - 5x^2$ from

$-(2x^2 - 10)$ $x^4 - 3x^2$ and bringing down $4x - 3$

$4x + 7$ $\longleftarrow$ Subtracting $2x^2 - 10$ from

$2x^2 + 4x - 3$

Since the remainder, $4x + 7$, is of lower degree than the divisor, the division process stops. The answer is

$$x^2 + 2 + \frac{4x + 7}{x^2 - 5}.$$

Check: $(x^2 - 5)(x^2 + 2) + 4x + 7 = x^4 + 2x^2 - 5x^2 - 10 + 4x + 7$

$ = x^4 - 3x^2 + 4x - 3.$

TRY EXERCISE 35

4.8   **EXERCISE SET**

  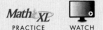
Divide and check.

1. $\dfrac{40x^6 - 25x^3}{5}$

2. $\dfrac{16a^5 - 24a^2}{8}$

3. $\dfrac{u - 2u^2 + u^7}{u}$

4. $\dfrac{50x^5 - 7x^4 + 2x}{x}$

5. $(18t^3 - 24t^2 + 6t) \div (3t)$

6. $(20t^3 - 15t^2 + 30t) \div (5t)$

7. $(42x^5 - 36x^3 + 9x^2) \div (6x^2)$

8. $(24x^6 + 18x^4 + 8x^3) \div (4x^3)$

9. $(32t^5 + 16t^4 - 8t^3) \div (-8t^3)$

10. $(36t^6 - 27t^5 - 9t^2) \div (-9t^2)$

1. $\dfrac{8x^2 - 10x + 1}{2x}$

2. $\dfrac{9x^2 + 3x - 2}{3x}$

3. $\dfrac{5x^3y + 10x^5y^2 + 15x^2y}{5x^2y}$

4. $\dfrac{12a^3b^2 + 4a^4b^5 + 16ab^2}{4ab^2}$

5. $\dfrac{9r^2s^2 + 3r^2s - 6rs^2}{-3rs}$

6. $\dfrac{4x^4y - 8x^6y^2 + 12x^8y^6}{4x^4y}$

7. $(x^2 - 8x + 12) \div (x - 2)$

8. $(x^2 + 2x - 15) \div (x + 5)$

9. $(t^2 - 10t - 20) \div (t - 5)$

10. $(t^2 + 8t - 15) \div (t + 4)$

11. $(2x^2 + 11x - 5) \div (x + 6)$

12. $(3x^2 - 2x - 13) \div (x - 2)$

13. $\dfrac{t^3 + 27}{t + 3}$ **24.** $\dfrac{a^3 + 8}{a + 2}$

15. $\dfrac{a^2 - 21}{a - 5}$ **26.** $\dfrac{t^2 - 13}{t - 4}$

17. $(5x^2 - 16x) \div (5x - 1)$

18. $(3x^2 - 7x + 1) \div (3x - 1)$

19. $(6a^2 + 17a + 8) \div (2a + 5)$

20. $(10a^2 + 19a + 9) \div (2a + 3)$

21. $\dfrac{2t^3 - 9t^2 + 11t - 3}{2t - 3}$

22. $\dfrac{8t^3 - 22t^2 - 5t + 12}{4t + 3}$

23. $(x^3 - x^2 + x - 1) \div (x - 1)$

24. $(t^3 - t^2 + t - 1) \div (t + 1)$

25. $(t^4 + 4t^2 + 3t - 6) \div (t^2 + 5)$

26. $(t^4 - 2t^2 + 4t - 5) \div (t^2 - 3)$

27. $(6x^4 - 3x^2 + x - 4) \div (2x^2 + 1)$

28. $(4x^4 - 4x^2 - 3) \div (2x^2 - 3)$

29. How is the distributive law used when dividing a polynomial by a binomial?

40. On an assignment, Emmy Lou *incorrectly* writes
$$\frac{12x^3 - 6x}{3x} = 4x^2 - 6x.$$
What mistake do you think she is making and how might you convince her that a mistake has been made?

Skill Review

Review graphing linear equations (Chapter 3).

Graph.

41. $3x - 4y = 12$ [3.3]   **42.** $y = -\frac{2}{3}x + 4$ [3.6]

43. $3y - 2 = 7$ [3.3]   **44.** $8x = 4y$ [3.2]

45. Find the slope of the line containing the points $(3, 2)$ and $(-7, 5)$. [3.5]

46. Find the slope and the y-intercept of the line given by $2y = 8x + 7$. [3.6]

47. Find the slope–intercept form of the line with slope -5 and y-intercept $(0, -10)$. [3.6]

48. Find the slope–intercept form of the line containing the points $(6, 3)$ and $(-2, -7)$. [3.7]

Synthesis

49. Explain how to form trinomials for which division by $x - 5$ results in a remainder of 3.

50. Under what circumstances will the quotient of two binomials have more than two terms?

Divide.

51. $(10x^{9k} - 32x^{6k} + 28x^{3k}) \div (2x^{3k})$

52. $(45a^{8k} + 30a^{6k} - 60a^{4k}) \div (3a^{2k})$

53. $(6t^{3h} + 13t^{2h} - 4t^h - 15) \div (2t^h + 3)$

54. $(x^4 + a^2) \div (x + a)$

55. $(5a^3 + 8a^2 - 23a - 1) \div (5a^2 - 7a - 2)$

56. $(15y^3 - 30y + 7 - 19y^2) \div (3y^2 - 2 - 5y)$

57. Divide the sum of $4x^5 - 14x^3 - x^2 + 3$ and $2x^5 + 3x^4 + x^3 - 3x^2 + 5x$ by $3x^3 - 2x - 1$.

58. Divide $5x^7 - 3x^4 + 2x^2 - 10x + 2$ by the sum of $(x - 3)^2$ and $5x - 8$.

If the remainder is 0 when one polynomial is divided by another, the divisor is a factor of the dividend. Find the value(s) of c for which $x - 1$ is a factor of each polynomial.

59. $x^2 - 4x + c$

60. $2x^2 - 3cx - 8$

61. $c^2x^2 + 2cx + 1$

Study Summary

SECTION 4.1: EXPONENTS AND THEIR PROPERTIES

(Assume that no denominators are 0 and that 0^0 is not considered.)

For any integers m and n:

1 as an exponent:	$a^1 = a$	$3^1 = 3$
0 as an exponent:	$a^0 = 1$	$3^0 = 1$
The Product Rule:	$a^m \cdot a^n = a^{m+n}$	$3^5 \cdot 3^9 = 3^{5+9} = 3^{14}$
The Quotient Rule:	$\dfrac{a^m}{a^n} = a^{m-n}$	$\dfrac{3^7}{3} = 3^{7-1} = 3^6$
The Power Rule:	$(a^m)^n = a^{mn}$	$(3^4)^2 = 3^{4 \cdot 2} = 3^8$
Raising a product to a power:	$(ab)^n = a^n b^n$	$(3x^5)^4 = 3^4(x^5)^4 = 81x^{20}$
Raising a quotient to a power:	$\left(\dfrac{a}{b}\right)^n = \dfrac{a^n}{b^n}$	$\left(\dfrac{3}{x}\right)^6 = \dfrac{3^6}{x^6}$

SECTION 4.2: NEGATIVE EXPONENTS AND SCIENTIFIC NOTATION

$$a^{-n} = \frac{1}{a^n};$$

$$\frac{a^{-n}}{b^{-m}} = \frac{b^m}{a^n};$$

$$\left(\frac{a}{b}\right)^{-n} = \left(\frac{b}{a}\right)^n$$

$$3^{-2} = \frac{1}{3^2} = \frac{1}{9};$$

$$\frac{3^{-7}}{x^{-5}} = \frac{x^5}{3^7};$$

$$\left(\frac{3}{x}\right)^{-2} = \left(\frac{x}{3}\right)^2$$

Scientific notation is given by $N \times 10^m$, where m is an integer, N is in decimal notation, and $1 \le N < 10$.

$$4100 = 4.1 \times 10^3;$$
$$5 \times 10^{-3} = 0.005$$

SECTION 4.3: POLYNOMIALS

A **polynomial** is a monomial or a sum of monomials.

When a polynomial is written as a sum of monomials, each monomial is a **term** of the polynomial.

The **degree of a term** of a polynomial is the number of variable factors in that term.

The **coefficient** of a term is the part of the term that is a constant factor.

The **leading term** of a polynomial is the term of highest degree.

The **leading coefficient** is the coefficient of the leading term.

The **degree of the polynomial** is the degree of the leading term.

Polynomial: $10x - x^3 - \frac{1}{2}x^2 + 3x^5 + 7$

Term	$10x$	$-x^3$	$-\frac{1}{2}x^2$	$3x^5$	7
Degree of term	1	3	2	5	0
Coefficient of term	10	-1	$-\frac{1}{2}$	3	7
Leading term	$3x^5$				
Leading coefficient	3				
Degree of polynomial	5				

A **monomial** has one term.

A **binomial** has two terms.

A **trinomial** has three terms.

Monomial (one term): $4x^3$

Binomial (two terms): $x^2 - 5$

Trinomial (three terms): $3t^3 + 2t - 10$

Like terms, or **similar terms**, are either constant terms or terms containing the same variable(s) raised to the same power(s). These can be **combined** within a polynomial.

Combine like terms: $3y^4 + 6y^2 - 7 - y^4 - 6y^2 + 8$.

$$3y^4 + 6y^2 - 7 - y^4 - 6y^2 + 8 = \underbrace{3y^4 - y^4}\ + \underbrace{6y^2 - 6y^2}\ \underbrace{- 7 + 8}$$
$$= \quad 2y^4 \quad + \quad 0 \quad + 1$$
$$= 2y^4 + 1$$

To **evaluate** a polynomial, replace the variable with a number. The **value** is calculated using the rules for order of operations.

Evaluate $t^3 - 2t^2 - 5t + 1$ *for* $t = -2$.
$$t^3 - 2t^2 - 5t + 1 = (-2)^3 - 2(-2)^2 - 5(-2) + 1$$
$$= -8 - 2(4) - (-10) + 1$$
$$= -8 - 8 + 10 + 1$$
$$= -5$$

SECTION 4.4: ADDITION AND SUBTRACTION OF POLYNOMIALS

Add polynomials by combining like terms.

$(2x^2 - 3x + 7) + (5x^3 + 3x - 9)$
$$= 2x^2 + (-3x) + 7 + 5x^3 + 3x + (-9)$$
$$= 5x^3 + 2x^2 - 2$$

Subtract polynomials by adding the opposite of the polynomial being subtracted.

$(2x^2 - 3x + 7) - (5x^3 + 3x - 9)$
$$= 2x^2 - 3x + 7 + (-5x^3 - 3x + 9)$$
$$= 2x^2 - 3x + 7 - 5x^3 - 3x + 9$$
$$= -5x^3 + 2x^2 - 6x + 16$$

SECTION 4.5: MULTIPLICATION OF POLYNOMIALS

Multiply polynomials by multiplying each term of one polynomial by each term of the other.

$(x + 2)(x^2 - x - 1)$
$$= x \cdot x^2 - x \cdot x - x \cdot 1 + 2 \cdot x^2 - 2 \cdot x - 2 \cdot 1$$
$$= x^3 - x^2 - x + 2x^2 - 2x - 2$$
$$= x^3 + x^2 - 3x - 2$$

SECTION 4.6: SPECIAL PRODUCTS

FOIL (First, Outer, Inner, Last):

$(A + B)(C + D) = AC + AD + BC + BD$

$$(x + 3)(x - 2) = x^2 - 2x + 3x - 6$$
$$= x^2 + x - 6$$

The product of a sum and a difference:

$$(A + B)(A - B) = A^2 - B^2$$

$A^2 - B^2$ is called a **difference of squares**.

$$(t^3 + 5)(t^3 - 5) = (t^3)^2 - 5^2$$
$$= t^6 - 25$$

The square of a binomial:
$$(A + B)^2 = A^2 + 2AB + B^2;$$
$$(A - B)^2 = A^2 - 2AB + B^2$$
$A^2 + 2AB + B^2$ and $A^2 - 2AB + B^2$ are called **perfect-square trinomials**.

$$(5x + 3)^2 = (5x)^2 + 2(5x)(3) + 3^2 = 25x^2 + 30x + 9;$$
$$(5x - 3)^2 = (5x)^2 - 2(5x)(3) + 3^2 = 25x^2 - 30x + 9$$

SECTION 4.7: POLYNOMIALS IN SEVERAL VARIABLES

To **evaluate** a polynomial, replace each variable with a number and simplify.

Evaluate $4 - 3xy + x^2y$ *for* $x = 5$ *and* $y = -1$.
$$4 - 3xy + x^2y = 4 - 3(5)(-1) + (5)^2(-1)$$
$$= 4 - (-15) + (-25)$$
$$= -6$$

The **degree** of a term is the number of variables in the term or the sum of the exponents of the variables.

The degree of $-19x^3yz^2$ is 6.

Add, subtract, and multiply polynomials in several variables in the same way as polynomials in one variable.

$$(3xy^2 - 4x^2y + 5xy) + (xy - 6x^2y) = 3xy^2 - 10x^2y + 6xy;$$
$$(3xy^2 - 4x^2y + 5xy) - (xy - 6x^2y) = 3xy^2 + 2x^2y + 4xy;$$
$$(2a^2b + 3a)(5a^2b - a) = 10a^4b^2 + 13a^3b - 3a^2$$

SECTION 4.8: DIVISION OF POLYNOMIALS

To divide a polynomial by a monomial, divide each term by the monomial. Divide coefficients and subtract exponents.

$$\frac{3t^5 - 6t^4 + 4t^2 + 9t}{3t} = \frac{3t^5}{3t} - \frac{6t^4}{3t} + \frac{4t^2}{3t} + \frac{9t}{3t}$$
$$= t^4 - 2t^3 + \tfrac{4}{3}t + 3$$

To divide a polynomial by a binomial, use long division.

Divide: $(x^2 + 5x - 2) \div (x - 3)$.

$$
\begin{array}{r}
x + 8 \\
x - 3 \overline{)x^2 + 5x - 2} \\
-(x^2 - 3x) \\
\hline
8x - 2 \\
-(8x - 24) \\
\hline
22
\end{array}
$$

$$(x^2 + 5x - 2) \div (x - 3) = x + 8 + \frac{22}{x - 3}$$

Review Exercises: Chapter 4

Concept Reinforcement *Classify each statement as either true or false.*

1. When two polynomials that are written in descending order are added, the result is generally written in descending order. [4.4]

2. The product of the sum and the difference of the same two terms is a difference of squares. [4.6]

3. When a binomial is squared, the result is a perfect-square trinomial. [4.6]

4. FOIL can be used whenever two polynomials are being multiplied. [4.6]

5. The degree of a polynomial cannot exceed the value of the polynomial's leading coefficient. [4.3]

6. Scientific notation is used only for extremely large numbers. [4.2]

7. FOIL can be used with polynomials in several variables. [4.7]

8. A positive number raised to a negative exponent can never represent a negative number. [4.2]

Simplify. [4.1]

9. $n^3 \cdot n^8 \cdot n$

10. $(7x)^8 \cdot (7x)^2$

11. $t^6 \cdot t^0$

12. $\dfrac{4^5}{4^2}$

13. $\dfrac{(a+b)^4}{(a+b)^4}$

14. $\dfrac{-18c^9 d^3}{2c^5 d}$

15. $(-2xy^2)^3$

16. $(2x^3)(-3x)^2$

17. $(a^2 b)(ab)^5$

18. $\left(\dfrac{2t^5}{3s^4}\right)^2$

19. Express using a positive exponent: 8^{-6}. [4.2]

20. Express using a negative exponent: $\dfrac{1}{a^9}$. [4.2]

Simplify. Do not use negative exponents in the answer. [4.2]

21. $4^5 \cdot 4^{-7}$

22. $\dfrac{6a^{-5}b}{3a^8 b^{-8}}$

23. $(w^3)^{-5}$

24. $(2x^{-3}y)^{-2}$

25. $\left(\dfrac{2x}{y}\right)^{-3}$

26. Convert to decimal notation: 4.7×10^8. [4.2]

27. Convert to scientific notation: 0.0000109. [4.2]

Multiply or divide and write scientific notation for the result. [4.2]

28. $(3.8 \times 10^4)(5.5 \times 10^{-1})$

29. $\dfrac{1.28 \times 10^{-8}}{2.5 \times 10^{-4}}$

Identify the terms of each polynomial. [4.3]

30. $8x^2 - x + \frac{2}{3}$

31. $-4y^5 + 7y^2 - 3y - 2$

List the coefficients of the terms in each polynomial. [4.3]

32. $9x^2 - x + 7$

33. $7n^4 - \frac{5}{6}n^2 - 4n + 10$

For each polynomial, **(a)** *list the degree of each term;* **(b)** *determine the leading term and the leading coefficient; and* **(c)** *determine the degree of the polynomial.* [4.3]

34. $4t^2 + 6 + 15t^5$

35. $-2x^5 + 7 - 3x^2 + x$

Classify each polynomial as a monomial, a binomial, a trinomial, or a polynomial with no special name. [4.3]

36. $4x^3 - 5x + 3$

37. $4 - 9t^3 - 7t^4 + 10t^2$

38. $7y^2$

Combine like terms and write in descending order. [4.3]

39. $3x - x^2 + 4x$

40. $\frac{3}{4}x^3 + 4x^2 - x^3 + 7$

41. $-4t^3 + 2t + 4t^3 + 8 - t - 9$

42. $-a + \frac{1}{3} + 20a^5 - 1 - 6a^5 - 2a^2$

Evaluate each polynomial for $x = -2$. [4.3]

43. $9x - 6$

44. $x^2 - 3x + 6$

Add or subtract. [4.4]

45. $(8x^4 - x^3 + x - 4) + (x^5 + 7x^3 - 3x - 5)$

46. $(5a^5 - 2a^3 - 9a^2) + (2a^5 + a^3) + (-a^5 - 3a^2)$

47. $(y^2 + 8y - 7) - (4y^2 - 10)$

48. $(3x^5 - 4x^4 + 2x^2 + 3) - (2x^5 - 4x^4 + 3x^3 + 4x^2 - 5)$

49. $\begin{aligned} -\tfrac{3}{4}x^4 &+ \tfrac{1}{2}x^3 &&&&+ \tfrac{7}{8} \\ &- \tfrac{1}{4}x^3 &- x^2 &- \tfrac{7}{4}x \\ +\tfrac{3}{2}x^4 &&+ \tfrac{2}{3}x^2 &&&&- \tfrac{1}{2} \end{aligned}$

50. $\begin{aligned} 2x^5 &&- x^3 &&+ x + 3 \\ -(3x^5 &- x^4 &+ 4x^3 &+ 2x^2 &- x + 3) \end{aligned}$

51. The length of a rectangle is 3 m greater than its width.

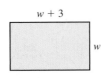

a) Find a polynomial for the perimeter. [4.4]
b) Find a polynomial for the area. [4.5]

Multiply.

52. $5x^2(-6x^3)$ [4.5]

53. $(7x + 1)^2$ [4.6]

54. $(a - 7)(a + 4)$ [4.6]

55. $(d - 8)(d + 8)$ [4.6]

56. $(4x^2 - 5x + 1)(3x - 2)$ [4.5]

57. $(x - 8)^2$ [4.6]

58. $3t^2(5t^3 - 2t^2 + 4t)$ [4.5]

59. $(2a + 9)(2a - 9)$ [4.6]

60. $(x - 0.8)(x - 0.5)$ [4.6]

61. $(x^4 - 2x + 3)(x^3 + x - 1)$ [4.5]

62. $(4y^3 - 5)^2$ [4.6]

63. $(2t^2 + 3)(t^2 - 7)$ [4.6]

64. $\left(a - \frac{1}{2}\right)\left(a + \frac{2}{3}\right)$ [4.6]

65. $(-7 + 2n)(7 + 2n)$ [4.6]

66. Evaluate $2 - 5xy + y^2 - 4xy^3 + x^6$ for $x = -1$ and $y = 2$. [4.7]

Identify the coefficient and the degree of each term of each polynomial. Then find the degree of each polynomial. [4.7]

67. $x^5y - 7xy + 9x^2 - 8$

68. $a^3b^8c^2 - c^{22} + a^5c^{10}$

Combine like terms. [4.7]

69. $u + 3v - 5u + v - 7$

70. $6m^3 + 3m^2n + 4mn^2 + m^2n - 5mn^2$

Add or subtract. [4.7]

71. $(4a^2 - 10ab - b^2) + (-2a^2 - 6ab + b^2)$

72. $(6x^3y^2 - 4x^2y - 6x) - (-5x^3y^2 + 4x^2y + 6x^2 - 6)$

Multiply. [4.7]

73. $(2x + 5y)(x - 3y)$

74. $(5ab - cd^2)^2$

75. Find a polynomial for the shaded area. [4.7]

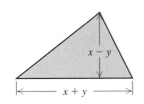

Divide. [4.8]

76. $(3y^5 - y^2 + 12y) \div (3y)$

77. $(6x^3 - 5x^2 - 13x + 13) \div (2x + 3)$

78. $\dfrac{t^4 + t^3 + 2t^2 - t - 3}{t + 1}$

Synthesis

79. Explain why $5x^3$ and $(5x)^3$ are not equivalent expressions. [4.1]

80. A binomial is squared and the result, written in descending order, is $x^2 - 6x + 9$. Is it possible to determine what binomial was squared? Why or why not? [4.6]

81. Determine, without performing the multiplications, the degree of each product. [4.5]
a) $(x^5 - 6x^2 + 3)(x^4 + 3x^3 + 7)$
b) $(x^7 - 4)^4$

82. Simplify:
$$(-3x^5 \cdot 3x^3 - x^6(2x)^2 + (3x^4)^2 + (2x^2)^4 - 20x^2(x^3)^2)^2. [4.1], [4.3]$$

83. A polynomial has degree 4. The x^2-term is missing. The coefficient of x^4 is two times the coefficient of x^3. The coefficient of x is 3 less than the coefficient of x^4. The remaining coefficient is 7 less than the coefficient of x. The sum of the coefficients is 15. Find the polynomial. [4.3]

Aha! 84. Multiply: $[(x - 5) - 4x^3][(x - 5) + 4x^3]$. [4.6]

85. Solve: $(x - 7)(x + 10) = (x - 4)(x - 6)$. [2.2], [4.6]

86. *Blood donors.* Every 4–6 weeks, Jordan donates 1.14×10^6 cubic millimeters (two pints) of whole blood, from which platelets are removed and the blood returned to the body. In one cubic millimeter of blood, there are about 2×10^5 platelets. Approximate the number of platelets in Jordan's typical donation. [4.2]

Simplify.

1. $x^7 \cdot x \cdot x^5$

2. $\dfrac{3^8}{3^7}$

3. $\dfrac{(3m)^4}{(3m)^4}$

4. $(t^5)^9$

5. $(5x^4y)(-2x^5y)^3$

6. $\dfrac{24a^7b^4}{20a^2b}$

7. Express using a positive exponent: y^{-7}.

8. Express using a negative exponent: $\dfrac{1}{5^6}$.

Simplify.

9. $t^{-4} \cdot t^{-5}$

10. $\dfrac{9x^3y^2}{3x^8y^{-3}}$

11. $(2a^3b^{-1})^{-4}$

12. $\left(\dfrac{ab}{c}\right)^{-3}$

13. Convert to scientific notation: 3,060,000,000.

14. Convert to decimal notation: 5×10^{-8}.

Multiply or divide and write scientific notation for the result.

15. $\dfrac{5.6 \times 10^6}{3.2 \times 10^{-11}}$

16. $(2.4 \times 10^5)(5.4 \times 10^{16})$

17. Classify $4x^2y - 7y^3$ as a monomial, a binomial, a trinomial, or a polynomial with no special name.

18. Identify the coefficient of each term of the polynomial:
$$3x^5 - x + \tfrac{1}{9}.$$

19. Determine the degree of each term, the leading term and the leading coefficient, and the degree of the polynomial:
$$2t^3 - t + 7t^5 + 4.$$

20. Evaluate $x^2 + 5x - 1$ for $x = -3$.

Combine like terms and write in descending order.

21. $4a^2 - 6 + a^2$

22. $y^2 - 3y - y + \tfrac{3}{4}y^2$

23. $3 - x^2 + 8x + 5x^2 - 6x - 2x + 4x^3$

Add or subtract.

24. $(3x^5 + 5x^3 - 5x^2 - 3) + (x^5 + x^4 - 3x^2 + 2x - 4)$

25. $\left(x^4 + \tfrac{2}{3}x + 5\right) + \left(4x^4 + 5x^2 + \tfrac{1}{3}x\right)$

26. $(5a^4 + 3a^3 - a^2 - 2a - 1) - (7a^4 - a^2 - a + 6)$

27. $(t^3 - 0.3t^2 - 20) - (t^4 - 1.5t^3 + 0.3t^2 - 11)$

Multiply.

28. $-2x^2(3x^2 - 3x - 5)$

29. $\left(x - \tfrac{1}{3}\right)^2$

30. $(5t - 7)(5t + 7)$

31. $(3b + 5)(2b - 1)$

32. $(x^6 - 4)(x^8 + 4)$

33. $(8 - y)(6 + 5y)$

34. $(2x + 1)(3x^2 - 5x - 3)$

35. $(8a^3 + 3)^2$

36. Evaluate $2x^2y - 3y^2$ for $x = -3$ and $y = 2$.

37. Combine like terms:
$$2x^3y - y^3 + xy^3 + 8 - 6x^3y - x^2y^2 + 11.$$

38. Subtract:
$$(8a^2b^2 - ab + b^3) - (-6ab^2 - 7ab - ab^3 + 5b^3).$$

39. Multiply: $(3x^5 - y)(3x^5 + y)$.

Divide.

40. $(12x^4 + 9x^3 - 15x^2) \div (3x^2)$

41. $(6x^3 - 8x^2 - 14x + 13) \div (3x + 2)$

Synthesis

42. The height of a box is 1 less than its length, and the length is 2 more than its width. Express the volume in terms of the length.

43. Solve: $x^2 + (x - 7)(x + 4) = 2(x - 6)^2$.

44. Simplify: $2^{-1} - 4^{-1}$.

45. Every day about 12.4 billion spam e-mails are sent. If each spam e-mail wastes 4 sec, how many hours are wasted each day due to spam?
Source: spam-filter-review.toptenreviews.com

Cumulative Review: Chapters 1–4

1. Evaluate $\dfrac{2x + y}{5}$ for $x = 12$ and $y = 6$. [1.1]

2. Evaluate $5x^2y - xy + y^2$ for $x = -1$ and $y = -2$. [4.7]

Simplify.

3. $\frac{1}{15} - \frac{2}{9}$ [1.3]

4. $2 - [10 - (5 + 12 \div 2^2 \cdot 3)]$ [1.8]

5. $2y - (y - 7) + 3$ [1.8]

6. $t^4 \cdot t^7 \cdot t$ [4.1]

7. $\dfrac{-100x^6y^8}{25xy^5}$ [4.1]

8. $(2a^2b)(5ab^3)^2$ [4.1]

9. Factor: $10a - 6b + 12$. [1.2]

10. Find the absolute value: $\left|\dfrac{11}{16}\right|$. [1.4]

11. Determine the degree of the polynomial
$-x^4 + 5x^3 + 3x^6 - 1$. [4.3]

12. Combine like terms and write in descending order:
$-\frac{1}{2}t^3 + 3t^2 + \frac{3}{4}t^3 + 0.1 - 8t^2 - 0.45$. [4.3]

13. In which quadrant is $(-2, 5)$ located? [3.1]

14. Graph on a number line: $x > -1$. [2.6]

Graph.

15. $3y + 2x = 0$ [3.2]

16. $3y - 2x = 12$ [3.3]

17. $3y = 2$ [3.3]

18. $3y = 2x + 9$ [3.6]

19. Find the slope and the y-intercept of the line given by $y = \frac{1}{10}x + \frac{3}{8}$. [3.6]

20. Find the slope of the line containing the points $(2, 3)$ and $(-6, 8)$. [3.5]

21. Write an equation of the line with slope $-\frac{2}{3}$ and y-intercept $(0, -10)$. [3.6]

22. Find the coordinates of the x- and y-intercepts of the graph of $2x + 5y = 8$. Do not graph. [3.3]

Solve.

23. $\frac{1}{6}n = -\frac{2}{3}$ [2.1]

24. $3 - 5x = 0$ [2.2]

25. $5y + 7 = 8y - 1$ [2.2]

26. $0.4t - 0.5 = 8.3$ [2.2]

27. $5(3 - x) = 2 + 7(x - 1)$ [2.2]

28. $2 - (x - 7) = 8 - 4(x + 5)$ [2.2]

29. $-\frac{1}{2}t \le 4$ [2.6]

30. $3x - 5 > 9x - 8$ [2.6]

31. Solve $c = \dfrac{5pq}{2t}$ for t. [2.3]

Add or subtract.

32. $(2u^2v - uv^2 + uv) + (3u^2 - v^2u + 5vu^2)$ [4.7]

33. $(3x^3 - 2x^2 + 6x) - (x^2 - 6x + 7)$ [4.4]

34. $(2x^5 - x^4 - x) - (x^5 - x^4 + x)$ [4.4]

Multiply.

35. $10(2a - 3b + 7)$ [1.2]

36. $8x^3(-2x^2 - 6x + 7)$ [4.5]

37. $(3a + 7)(2a - 1)$ [4.6]

38. $(x - 2)(x^2 + x - 5)$ [4.5]

39. $(4t^2 + 3)^2$ [4.6]

40. $\left(\frac{1}{2}x + 1\right)\left(\frac{1}{2}x - 1\right)$ [4.6]

41. $(2r^2 + s)(3r^2 - 4s)$ [4.7]

42. Divide: $(x^2 - x + 3) \div (x - 1)$. [4.8]

Simplify. Do not use negative exponents in the answer. [4.2]

43. 7^{-10}

44. $x^{-8} \cdot x$

45. $\left(\dfrac{4s}{3t^{-5}}\right)^{-2}$

46. $(3x^{-7}y^{-2})^{-1}$

Solve.

47. In 2007, Europe and the United States together had installed wind turbines capable of producing about 60 thousand megawatts of electricity. Europe's wind-turbine capacity was four times that of the United States. What was Europe's wind-turbine capacity in 2007? [2.5]

Source: BP Statistical Review of World Energy, 2007

48. In the first four months of 2007, U.S. electric utilities used coal to generate 644 megawatt hours of electricity. This was 49.6% of the total amount of electricity generated. How much electricity was generated in the first four months of 2007? [2.4]
Source: U.S. Energy Information Administration

49. Antonio's energy-efficient washer and dryer use a total of 70 kilowatt hours (kWh) of electricity each month. The dryer uses 10 more than twice as many kilowatt hours as the washer. How many kilowatt hours does each appliance use in a month? [2.5]

50. A typical two-person household will use 195 kWh of electricity each month to heat water. The usage increases to 315 kWh per month for a four-person household. [3.7]
Source: Lee County Electric Cooperative

a) Graph the data and determine an equation for the related line. Let w represent the number of kilowatt hours used each month and n represent the number of people in a household.

b) Use the equation of part (a) to estimate the number of kilowatt hours used each month by a five-person household.

51. Abrianna's contract specifies that she cannot work more than 40 hr per week. For the first 4 days of one week, she worked 8, 10, 7, and 9 hr. How many hours can she work on the fifth day without violating her contract? [2.7]

52. In 2006, Brazil owed about $240 billion in external debt. This amount was $\frac{3}{2}$ of Russia's debt. How much did Russia owe in 2006? [2.5]

53. In 2006, the average GPA of incoming freshmen at the University of South Carolina was 3.73. This was a 3.6% increase over the average GPA in 2001. What was the average GPA in 2001? [2.4]
Source: The Wall Street Journal, 11/10/06

54. U.S. retail losses due to crime have increased from $26 billion in 1998 to $38 billion in 2005. Find the rate of change of retail losses due to crime. [3.4]
Source: University of Florida

Synthesis

Solve. If no solution exists, state this.

55. $3x - 2(x + 6) = 4(x - 3)$ [2.2]

56. $x - (2x - 1) = 3x - 4(x + 1) + 10$ [2.2]

57. $(x - 2)(x + 3) = (4 - x)^2$ [2.2], [4.6]

58. Find the equation of a line with the same slope as $y = \frac{1}{2}x - 7$ and the same y-intercept as $2y = 5x + 8$. [3.6]

Simplify.

59. $7^{-1} + 8^0$ [4.2]

60. $-2x^5(x^7) + (x^3)^4 - (4x^5)^2(-x^2)$ [4.1], [4.3]

Polynomials and Factoring

Chris Gjersvik
:IPAL NETWORK ENGINEER
Upper Saddle River, New Jersey

he math skills we use in net-
vorking–telecommunications
help us in so many ways. For
instance, we use math when
ning the budgets for a com-
ter network or phone system
l when determining capacity
a network. We need to accu-
ately size network circuits so
y have enough bandwidth to
phone calls, Internet access,
streaming video, e-mail, and
er such applications. Finally,
e use math when we need to
ze network traffic and break
it down into its most basic
form, which uses the binary
numeral system.

AN APPLICATION

The number N, in millions, of
broadband cable and DSL subscribers
in the United States t years after 1998
can be approximated by

$$N = 0.3t^2 + 0.6t.$$

When will there be 36 million
broadband cable and DSL
subscribers?

Source: Based on information from Leichtman
Research Group

This problem appears as Exercise 19 in
Section 5.8.

n Chapter 1, we learned that *factoring* is multiplying reversed. Thus factoring polynomials requires a solid command of the multiplication methods learned in Chapter 4. Factoring is an important skill that will be used to solve equations and simplify other types of expressions found later in the study of algebra.

In Sections 5.1–5.6, we factor polynomials to find equivalent expressions that are products. In Sections 5.7 and 5.8, we use factoring to solve equations, including those that arise from real-world problems.

5.1 Introduction to Factoring

Factoring Monomials ▪ Factoring When Terms Have a Common Factor ▪
Factoring by Grouping ▪ Checking by Evaluating

Just as a number like 15 can be factored as $3 \cdot 5$, a polynomial like $x^2 + 7x$ can be factored as $x(x + 7)$. In both cases, we ask ourselves, "What was multiplied to obtain the given result?" The situation is much like a popular television game show in which an "answer" is given and participants must find the "question" to which the answer corresponds.

STUDY SKILLS ───────

You've Got Mail

Many students overlook an excellent opportunity to get questions answered—e-mail. If your instructor makes his or her e-mail address available, consider using it to get help. Often, just the act of writing out your question brings some clarity. If you do use e-mail, allow some time for your instructor to reply.

> ### Factoring
>
> To *factor* a polynomial is to find an equivalent expression that is a product. An equivalent expression of this type is called a *factorization* of the polynomial.

Factoring Monomials

To factor a monomial, we find two monomials whose product is equivalent to the original monomial. For example, $20x^2$ can be factored as $2 \cdot 10x^2, 4x \cdot 5x$, or $10x \cdot 2x$, as well as several other ways. To check, we multiply.

EXAMPLE **1** Find three factorizations of $15x^3$.

SOLUTION

a) $15x^3 = (3 \cdot 5)(x \cdot x^2)$ Thinking of how 15 and x^3 can be factored
$= (3x)(5x^2)$ The factors are $3x$ and $5x^2$. *Check*: $3x \cdot 5x^2 = 15x^3$

b) $15x^3 = (3 \cdot 5)(x^2 \cdot x)$
$= (3x^2)(5x)$ The factors are $3x^2$ and $5x$. *Check*: $3x^2 \cdot 5x = 15x^3$

c) $15x^3 = ((-5)(-3))x^3$
$= (-5)(-3x^3)$ The factors are -5 and $-3x^3$.
Check: $(-5)(-3x^3) = 15x^3$.

$(3x)(5x^2), (3x^2)(5x)$, and $(-5)(-3x^3)$ are all factorizations of $15x^3$. Other factorizations exist as well.

> TRY EXERCISE 9

Recall from Section 1.2 that the word "factor" can be a verb or a noun, depending on the context in which it appears.

Factoring When Terms Have a Common Factor

To multiply a polynomial of two or more terms by a monomial, we use the distributive law: $a(b + c) = ab + ac$. To factor a polynomial with two or more terms of the form $ab + ac$, we use the distributive law with the sides of the equation switched: $ab + ac = a(b + c)$.

Multiply   *Factor*

$3(x + 2y - z)$ $3x + 6y - 3z$

$\quad = 3 \cdot x + 3 \cdot 2y - 3 \cdot z$ $\quad = 3 \cdot x + 3 \cdot 2y - 3 \cdot z$

$\quad = 3x + 6y - 3z$ $\quad = 3(x + 2y - z)$

In the factorization on the right, note that since 3 appears as a factor of $3x$, $6y$, and $-3z$, it is a *common factor* for all the terms of the trinomial $3x + 6y - 3z$.

When we factor, we are forming an equivalent expression that is a product.

EXAMPLE **2**   Factor to form an equivalent expression: $10y + 15$.

SOLUTION   We write the prime factorization of both terms to determine any common factors:

The prime factorization of $10y$ is $2 \cdot 5 \cdot y$;

The prime factorization of 15 is $3 \cdot 5$.   5 is a common factor.

We "factor out" the common factor 5 using the distributive law:

> We can always check a factorization by multiplying.

$10y + 15 = 5 \cdot 2y + 5 \cdot 3$ Try to do this step mentally.

$\qquad\qquad = 5(2y + 3).$ Using the distributive law

Check: $5(2y + 3) = 5 \cdot 2y + 5 \cdot 3 = 10y + 15.$

The factorization of $10y + 15$ is $5(2y + 3)$.   **TRY EXERCISE** ▸ 15

We generally factor out the *largest* common factor.

EXAMPLE **3**   Factor: $8a - 12$.

SOLUTION   Lining up common factors in columns can help us determine the largest common factor:

The prime factorization of $8a$ is $2 \cdot 2 \cdot 2 \cdot \quad a$;

The prime factorization of 12 is $2 \cdot 2 \cdot \quad 3$.

Since both factorizations include two factors of 2, the largest common factor is $2 \cdot 2$, or 4:

$8a - 12 = 4 \cdot 2a - 4 \cdot 3$ 4 is a factor of $8a$ and of 12.

$8a - 12 = 4(2a - 3).$ Try to go directly to this step.

Check: $4(2a - 3) = 4 \cdot 2a - 4 \cdot 3 = 8a - 12$, as expected.

The factorization of $8a - 12$ is $4(2a - 3)$.   **TRY EXERCISE** ▸ 17

CAUTION! $2 \cdot 2 \cdot 2a - 2 \cdot 2 \cdot 3$ is a factorization of the *terms* of $8a - 12$ but not of the polynomial itself. The factorization of $8a - 12$ is $4(2a - 3)$.

A common factor may contain a variable.

EXAMPLE **4**

Factor: $24x^5 + 30x^2$.

SOLUTION

The prime factorization of $24x^5$ is $2 \cdot 2 \cdot 2 \cdot 3 \cdot \quad x \cdot x \cdot x \cdot x \cdot x.$
The prime factorization of $30x^2$ is $2 \cdot \qquad 3 \cdot 5 \cdot x \cdot x.$

The largest common factor is $2 \cdot 3 \cdot x \cdot x$, or $6x^2$.

$$24x^5 + 30x^2 = 6x^2 \cdot 4x^3 + 6x^2 \cdot 5 \qquad \text{Factoring each term}$$
$$= 6x^2(4x^3 + 5) \qquad \text{Factoring out } 6x^2$$

Check: $6x^2(4x^3 + 5) = 6x^2 \cdot 4x^3 + 6x^2 \cdot 5 = 24x^5 + 30x^2$, as expected.

The factorization of $24x^5 + 30x^2$ is $6x^2(4x^3 + 5)$. **TRY EXERCISE** 27

The largest common factor of a polynomial is the largest common factor of the coefficients times the largest common factor of the variable(s) in all the terms. Suppose in Example 4 that you did not recognize the *largest* common factor, and removed only part of it, as follows:

$$24x^5 + 30x^2 = 2x^2 \cdot 12x^3 + 2x^2 \cdot 15 \qquad 2x^2 \text{ is a common factor.}$$
$$= 2x^2(12x^3 + 15). \qquad 12x^3 + 15 \text{ itself contains a common factor.}$$

Note that $12x^3 + 15$ still has a common factor, 3. To find the largest common factor, continue factoring out common factors, as follows, until no more exist:

$$24x^5 + 30x^2 = 2x^2[3(4x^3 + 5)] \qquad \text{Factoring } 12x^3 + 15. \text{ Remember to rewrite the first common factor, } 2x^2.$$

$$= 6x^2(4x^3 + 5). \qquad \text{Using an associative law; } 2x^2 \cdot 3 = 6x^2$$

Since $4x^3 + 5$ cannot be factored any further, we say that we have factored *completely.* When we are directed simply to factor, it is understood that we should always factor completely.

EXAMPLE **5**

Factor: $12x^5 - 15x^4 + 27x^3$.

SOLUTION

The prime factorization of $12x^5$ is $2 \cdot 2 \cdot 3 \cdot \qquad x \cdot x \cdot x \cdot x \cdot x.$
The prime factorization of $15x^4$ is $\qquad 3 \cdot \qquad 5 \cdot x \cdot x \cdot x \cdot x.$
The prime factorization of $27x^3$ is $\qquad 3 \cdot 3 \cdot 3 \cdot \qquad x \cdot x \cdot x.$

The largest common factor is $3 \cdot x \cdot x \cdot x$, or $3x^3$.

$$12x^5 - 15x^4 + 27x^3 = 3x^3 \cdot 4x^2 - 3x^3 \cdot 5x + 3x^3 \cdot 9$$
$$= 3x^3(4x^2 - 5x + 9)$$

Since $4x^2 - 5x + 9$ has no common factor, we are done, except for a check:

$$3x^3(4x^2 - 5x + 9) = 3x^3 \cdot 4x^2 - 3x^3 \cdot 5x + 3x^3 \cdot 9$$
$$= 12x^5 - 15x^4 + 27x^3,$$

as expected. The factorization of $12x^5 - 15x^4 + 27x^3$ is $3x^3(4x^2 - 5x + 9)$.

TRY EXERCISE 31

Note in Examples 4 and 5 that the *largest* common variable factor is the *smallest* power of x in the original polynomial.

With practice, we can determine the largest common factor without writing the prime factorization of each term. Then, to factor, we write the largest common factor and parentheses and then fill in the parentheses. It is customary for the leading coefficient of the polynomial inside the parentheses to be positive.

EXAMPLE 6   Factor: **(a)** $8r^3s^2 + 16rs^3$; **(b)** $-3xy + 6xz - 3x$.

SOLUTION

a) $8r^3s^2 + 16rs^3 = 8rs^2(r^2 + 2s)$ Try to go directly to this step.

The largest common factor is $8rs^2$. $\longleftarrow$ $\begin{cases} 8r^3s^2 = 2 \cdot 2 \cdot 2 \cdot \quad r \cdot r^2 \cdot s^2 \\ 16rs^3 = 2 \cdot 2 \cdot 2 \cdot 2 \cdot r \cdot \quad s^2 \cdot s \end{cases}$

Check: $8rs^2(r^2 + 2s) = 8r^3s^2 + 16rs^3$.

b) $-3xy + 6xz - 3x = -3x(y - 2z + 1)$ Note that either $-3x$ or $3x$ can be the largest common factor.

We generally factor out a negative when the first coefficient is negative. The way we factor can depend on the situation in which we are working. We might also factor as follows:

$$-3xy + 6xz - 3x = 3x(-y + 2z - 1).$$

The checks are left to the student.

TRY EXERCISE 35

In some texts, the largest common factor is referred to as the *greatest* common factor. We have avoided this language because, as shown in Example 6(b), the largest common factor may represent a negative value that is actually *less* than other common factors.

> **Tips for Factoring**
> 1. Factor out the largest common factor, if one exists.
> 2. The common factor multiplies a polynomial with the same number of terms as the original polynomial.
> 3. Factoring can always be checked by multiplying. Multiplication should yield the original polynomial.

Factoring by Grouping

Sometimes algebraic expressions contain a common factor with two or more terms.

EXAMPLE 7   Factor: $x^2(x + 1) + 2(x + 1)$.

SOLUTION   The binomial $x + 1$ is a factor of both $x^2(x + 1)$ and $2(x + 1)$. Thus, $x + 1$ is a common factor:

$$x^2(x + 1) + 2(x + 1) = (x + 1)x^2 + (x + 1)2$$
  Using a commutative law twice. Try to do this step mentally.

$$= (x + 1)(x^2 + 2).$$
  Factoring out the common factor, $x + 1$

To check, we could simply reverse the above steps.
   The factorization is $(x + 1)(x^2 + 2)$.

TRY EXERCISE 37

In Example 7, the common binomial factor was clearly visible. How do we find such a factor in a polynomial like $5x^3 - x^2 + 15x - 3$? Although there is no factor, other than 1, common to all four terms, $5x^3 - x^2$ and $15x - 3$ can be grouped and factored separately:

$$5x^3 - x^2 = x^2(5x - 1) \quad \text{and} \quad 15x - 3 = 3(5x - 1).$$

Note that $5x^3 - x^2$ and $15x - 3$ share a common factor, $5x - 1$. This means that the original polynomial, $5x^3 - x^2 + 15x - 3$, can be factored:

$$5x^3 - x^2 + 15x - 3 = (5x^3 - x^2) + (15x - 3) \qquad \text{Each binomial has a common factor.}$$
$$= x^2(5x - 1) + 3(5x - 1) \qquad \text{Factoring each binomial}$$
$$= (5x - 1)(x^2 + 3). \qquad \text{Factoring out the common factor, } 5x - 1$$

Check: $(5x - 1)(x^2 + 3) = 5x \cdot x^2 + 5x \cdot 3 - 1 \cdot x^2 - 1 \cdot 3$
$$= 5x^3 - x^2 + 15x - 3.$$

If a polynomial can be split into groups of terms and the groups share a common factor, then the original polynomial can be factored. This method, known as **factoring by grouping**, can be tried on any polynomial with four or more terms.

EXAMPLE   8   Factor by grouping.

a) $2x^3 + 8x^2 + x + 4$ **b)** $8x^4 + 6x - 28x^3 - 21$

SOLUTION

a) $2x^3 + 8x^2 + x + 4 = (2x^3 + 8x^2) + (x + 4)$
$$= 2x^2(x + 4) + 1(x + 4) \qquad \text{Factoring } 2x^3 + 8x^2 \text{ to find a common binomial factor. Writing the 1 helps with the next step.}$$
$$= (x + 4)(2x^2 + 1) \qquad \text{Factoring out the common factor, } x + 4. \text{ The 1 is essential in the factor } 2x^2 + 1.$$

CAUTION! Be sure to include the term 1. The check below shows why it is essential.

Check: $(x + 4)(2x^2 + 1) = x \cdot 2x^2 + x \cdot 1 + 4 \cdot 2x^2 + 4 \cdot 1$ Using FOIL
$$= 2x^3 + x + 8x^2 + 4$$
$$= 2x^3 + 8x^2 + x + 4. \qquad \text{Using a commutative law}$$

The factorization is $(x + 4)(2x^2 + 1)$.

b) We have a choice of either

$$8x^4 + 6x - 28x^3 - 21 = (8x^4 + 6x) + (-28x^3 - 21)$$
$$= 2x(4x^3 + 3) + 7(-4x^3 - 3) \longleftarrow \text{No common factor}$$

or

$$8x^4 + 6x - 28x^3 - 21 = (8x^4 + 6x) + (-28x^3 - 21)$$
$$= 2x(4x^3 + 3) + (-7)(4x^3 + 3). \longleftarrow \text{Common factor}$$

Because of the common factor $4x^3 + 3$, we choose the latter:

$$8x^4 + 6x - 28x^3 - 21 = 2x(4x^3 + 3) + (-7)(4x^3 + 3)$$
$$= (4x^3 + 3)(2x + (-7)) \qquad \text{Try to do this step mentally.}$$
$$= (4x^3 + 3)(2x - 7). \qquad \text{The common factor } 4x^3 + 3 \text{ was factored out.}$$

Check: $(4x^3 + 3)(2x - 7) = 8x^4 - 28x^3 + 6x - 21$
$$= 8x^4 + 6x - 28x^3 - 21. \qquad \text{This is the original polynomial.}$$

The factorization is $(4x^3 + 3)(2x - 7)$.

> **TRY EXERCISE** 43

Although factoring by grouping can be useful, some polynomials, like $x^3 + x^2 + 2x - 2$, cannot be factored this way. Factoring polynomials of this type is beyond the scope of this text.

Checking by Evaluating

One way to check a factorization is to multiply. A second type of check, discussed toward the end of Section 4.5, uses the fact that equivalent expressions have the same value when evaluated for the same replacement. Thus a quick, partial check of Example 8(a) can be made by using a convenient replacement for x (say, 1) and evaluating both $2x^3 + 8x^2 + x + 4$ and $(x + 4)(2x^2 + 1)$:

$$2 \cdot 1^3 + 8 \cdot 1^2 + 1 + 4 = 2 + 8 + 1 + 4$$
$$= 15;$$
$$(1 + 4)(2 \cdot 1^2 + 1) = 5 \cdot 3$$
$$= 15.$$

Since the value of both expressions is the same, the factorization is probably correct.

Keep in mind the possibility that two expressions that are not equivalent may share the same value when evaluated at a certain value. Because of this, unless several values are used (at least one more than the degree of the polynomial, it turns out), evaluating offers only a partial check. Consult with your instructor before making extensive use of this type of check.

TECHNOLOGY CONNECTION

A partial check of a factorization can be performed using a table or a graph. To check Example 8(a), we let

$$y_1 = 2x^3 + 8x^2 + x + 4 \quad \text{and} \quad y_2 = (x + 4)(2x^2 + 1).$$

Then we set up a table in AUTO mode (see p. 88). If the factorization is correct, the values of y_1 and y_2 will be the same regardless of the table settings used.

ΔTBL = 1

X	Y₁	Y₂
0	4	4
1	15	15
2	54	54
3	133	133
4	264	264
5	459	459
6	730	730

X = 0

We can also graph $y_1 = 2x^3 + 8x^2 + x + 4$ and $y_2 = (x + 4)(2x^2 + 1)$. If the graphs appear to coincide, the factorization is probably correct. The TRACE feature can be used to confirm this.

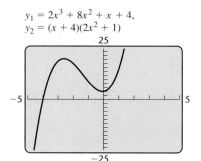

$y_1 = 2x^3 + 8x^2 + x + 4,$
$y_2 = (x + 4)(2x^2 + 1)$

Yscl = 2

Use a table or a graph to determine whether each factorization is correct.

1. $x^2 - 7x - 8 = (x - 8)(x + 1)$
2. $4x^2 - 5x - 6 = (4x + 3)(x - 2)$
3. $5x^2 + 17x - 12 = (5x + 3)(x - 4)$
4. $10x^2 + 37x + 7 = (5x - 1)(2x + 7)$
5. $12x^2 - 17x - 5 = (6x + 1)(2x - 5)$
6. $12x^2 - 17x - 5 = (4x + 1)(3x - 5)$
7. $x^2 - 4 = (x - 2)(x - 2)$
8. $x^2 - 4 = (x + 2)(x - 2)$

5.1   EXERCISE SET

Concept Reinforcement *In each of Exercises 1–8, match the phrase with the most appropriate choice from the column on the right.*

1. ____ A factorization of $35a^2b$

2. ____ A factor of $35a^2b$

3. ____ A common factor of $5x + 10$ and $4x + 8$

4. ____ A factorization of $3x^4 - 9x^2$

5. ____ A factorization of $9x^4 - 3x^2$

6. ____ A common factor of $2x + 10$ and $4x + 8$

7. ____ A factor of $3a + 6a^2$

8. ____ A factorization of $3a + 6a^2$

a) $3a(1 + 2a)$

b) $x + 2$

c) $3x^2(3x^2 - 1)$

d) $1 + 2a$

e) $3x^2(x^2 - 3)$

f) $5a^2$

g) 2

h) $7a \cdot 5ab$

Find three factorizations for each monomial. Answers may vary.

9. $14x^3$
10. $22x^3$
11. $-15a^4$

12. $-8t^5$
13. $25t^5$
14. $9a^4$

Factor. Remember to use the largest common factor and to check by multiplying. Factor out a negative factor if the first coefficient is negative.

15. $8x + 24$
16. $10x + 50$

17. $6x - 30$
18. $7x - 21$

19. $2x^2 + 2x - 8$
20. $6x^2 + 3x - 15$

21. $3t^2 + t$
22. $2t^2 + t$

23. $-5y^2 - 10y$
24. $-4y^2 - 12y$

25. $x^3 + 6x^2$
26. $5x^4 - x^2$

27. $16a^4 - 24a^2$

28. $25a^5 + 10a^3$

29. $-6t^6 + 9t^4 - 4t^2$

30. $-10t^5 + 15t^4 + 9t^3$

31. $6x^8 + 12x^6 - 24x^4 + 30x^2$

32. $10x^4 - 30x^3 - 50x - 20$

33. $x^5y^5 + x^4y^3 + x^3y^3 - x^2y^2$

34. $x^9y^6 - x^7y^5 + x^4y^4 + x^3y^3$

35. $-35a^3b^4 + 10a^2b^3 - 15a^3b^2$

36. $-21r^5t^4 - 14r^4t^6 + 21r^3t^6$

Factor.

37. $n(n - 6) + 3(n - 6)$

38. $b(b + 5) + 3(b + 5)$

39. $x^2(x + 3) - 7(x + 3)$

40. $3z^2(2z + 9) + (2z + 9)$

41. $y^2(2y - 9) + (2y - 9)$

42. $x^2(x - 7) - 3(x - 7)$

Factor by grouping, if possible, and check.

43. $x^3 + 2x^2 + 5x + 10$

44. $z^3 + 3z^2 + 7z + 21$

45. $5a^3 + 15a^2 + 2a + 6$

46. $3a^3 + 2a^2 + 6a + 4$

47. $9n^3 - 6n^2 + 3n - 2$

48. $10x^3 - 25x^2 + 2x - 5$

49. $4t^3 - 20t^2 + 3t - 15$

50. $8a^3 - 2a^2 + 12a - 3$

51. $7x^3 + 5x^2 - 21x - 15$

52. $5x^3 + 4x^2 - 10x - 8$

53. $6a^3 + 7a^2 + 6a + 7$

54. $7t^3 - 5t^2 + 7t - 5$

55. $2x^3 + 12x^2 - 5x - 30$

56. $x^3 - x^2 - 2x + 5$

57. $p^3 + p^2 - 3p + 10$

58. $w^3 + 7w^2 + 4w + 28$

59. $y^3 + 8y^2 - 2y - 16$

60. $3x^3 + 18x^2 - 5x - 25$

61. $2x^3 - 8x^2 - 9x + 36$

62. $20g^3 - 4g^2 - 25g + 5$

63. In answering a factoring problem, Taylor says the largest common factor is $-5x^2$ and Madison says the largest common factor is $5x^2$. Can they both be correct? Why or why not?

64. Write a two-sentence paragraph in which the word "factor" is used at least once as a noun and once as a verb.

Skill Review

To prepare for Section 5.2, review multiplying binomials using FOIL (Section 4.6).

Multiply. [4.6]

65. $(x + 2)(x + 7)$

66. $(x - 2)(x - 7)$

67. $(x + 2)(x - 7)$

68. $(x - 2)(x + 7)$

69. $(a - 1)(a - 3)$

70. $(t + 3)(t + 5)$

71. $(t - 5)(t + 10)$

72. $(a + 4)(a - 6)$

Synthesis

73. Azrah recognizes that evaluating provides only a partial check of her factoring. Because of this, she often performs a second check with a different replacement value. Is this a good idea? Why or why not?

74. Holly factors $12x^2y - 18xy^2$ as $6xy \cdot 2x - 6xy \cdot 3y$. Is this the factorization of the polynomial? Why or why not?

Factor, if possible.

75. $4x^5 + 6x^2 + 6x^3 + 9$

76. $x^6 + x^2 + x^4 + 1$

77. $2x^4 + 2x^3 - 4x^2 - 4x$

78. $x^3 + x^2 - 2x + 2$

Aha! **79.** $5x^5 - 5x^4 + x^3 - x^2 + 3x - 3$

Aha! **80.** $ax^2 + 2ax + 3a + x^2 + 2x + 3$

81. Write a trinomial of degree 7 for which $8x^2y^3$ is the largest common factor. Answers may vary.

5.2   Factoring Trinomials of the Type $x^2 + bx + c$

When the Constant Term Is Positive   ▪   When the Constant Term Is Negative   ▪
Prime Polynomials

We now learn how to factor trinomials like

$$x^2 + 5x + 4 \quad \text{or} \quad x^2 + 3x - 10,$$

for which no common factor exists and the leading coefficient is 1. Recall that
when factoring, we are writing an equivalent expression that is a product. For
these trinomials, the factors will be binomials.

As preparation for the factoring that follows, compare the following multiplications:

$$
\begin{array}{cccc}
\text{F} & \text{O} & \text{I} & \text{L} \\
\downarrow & \downarrow & \downarrow & \downarrow
\end{array}
$$

$$
\begin{aligned}
(x + 2)(x + 5) &= x^2 + 5x + 2x + 2 \cdot 5 \\
&= x^2 + \quad 7x \quad + \quad 10; \\
(x - 2)(x - 5) &= x^2 - 5x - 2x + (-2)(-5) \\
&= x^2 - \quad 7x \quad + \quad 10; \\
(x + 3)(x - 7) &= x^2 - 7x + 3x + 3(-7) \\
&= x^2 - \quad 4x \quad - \quad 21; \\
(x - 3)(x + 7) &= x^2 + 7x - 3x + (-3)7 \\
&= x^2 + \quad 4x \quad - \quad 21.
\end{aligned}
$$

Note that for all four products:

- The product of the two binomials is a trinomial.
- The coefficient of x in the trinomial is the sum of the constant terms in the
  binomials.
- The constant term in the trinomial is the product of the constant terms in the
  binomials.

These observations lead to a method for factoring certain trinomials. We first consider trinomials that have a positive constant term, just as in the first two multiplications above.

When the Constant Term Is Positive

To factor a polynomial like $x^2 + 7x + 10$, we think of FOIL in reverse. The x^2
resulted from x times x, which suggests that the first term of each binomial factor
is x. Next, we look for numbers p and q such that

$$x^2 + 7x + 10 = (x + p)(x + q).$$

To get the middle term and the last term of the trinomial, we need two numbers,
p and q, whose product is 10 and whose sum is 7. Those numbers are 2 and 5. Thus
the factorization is

$$(x + 2)(x + 5).$$

Check: $(x + 2)(x + 5) = x^2 + 5x + 2x + 10$
$$= x^2 + 7x + 10.$$

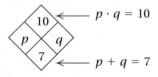

EXAMPLE 1

A GEOMETRIC APPROACH TO EXAMPLE 1

In Section 4.5, we saw that the product of two binomials can be regarded as the sum of the areas of four rectangles (see p. 264). Thus we can regard the factoring of $x^2 + 5x + 6$ as a search for p and q so that the sum of areas A, B, C, and D is $x^2 + 5x + 6$.

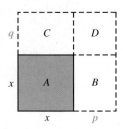

Note that area D is simply the product of p and q. In order for area D to be 6, p and q must be either 1 and 6 or 2 and 3. We illustrate both below.

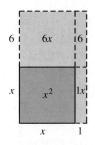

When p and q are 1 and 6, the total area is $x^2 + 7x + 6$, but when p and q are 2 and 3, as shown on the right, the total area is $x^2 + 5x + 6$, as desired. Thus the factorization of $x^2 + 5x + 6$ is $(x + 2)(x + 3)$.

Factor to form an equivalent expression: $x^2 + 5x + 6$.

SOLUTION   Think of FOIL in reverse. The first term of each factor is x:

$$(x + \quad)(x + \quad).$$

To complete the factorization, we need a constant term for each binomial. The constants must have a product of 6 and a sum of 5. We list some pairs of numbers that multiply to 6 and then check the sum of each pair of factors.

Pairs of Factors of 6	Sums of Factors
1, 6	7
2, 3	5 ←
−1, −6	−7
−2, −3	−5

The numbers we seek are 2 and 3.

One pair has a sum of 5.

Every pair has a product of 6.

Since

$$2 \cdot 3 = 6 \quad \text{and} \quad 2 + 3 = 5,$$

the factorization of $x^2 + 5x + 6$ is $(x + 2)(x + 3)$.

Check: $(x + 2)(x + 3) = x^2 + 3x + 2x + 6$
$$= x^2 + 5x + 6.$$

Thus, $(x + 2)(x + 3)$ is a product that is equivalent to $x^2 + 5x + 6$.

Note that since 5 and 6 are both positive, when factoring $x^2 + 5x + 6$ we need not consider negative factors of 6. Note too that changing the signs of the factors changes only the sign of the sum (see the table above).

TRY EXERCISE 7

At the beginning of this section, we considered the multiplication $(x - 2)(x - 5)$. For this product, the resulting trinomial, $x^2 - 7x + 10$, has a positive constant term but a negative coefficient of x. This is because the *product* of two negative numbers is always positive, whereas the *sum* of two negative numbers is always negative.

> ### To Factor $x^2 + bx + c$ When c Is Positive
>
> When the constant term c of a trinomial is positive, look for two numbers with the same sign. Select pairs of numbers with the sign of b, the coefficient of the middle term.
>
> $$x^2 - 7x + 10 = (x - 2)(x - 5);$$
>
>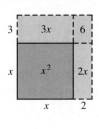
>
> $$x^2 + 7x + 10 = (x + 2)(x + 5)$$

EXAMPLE 2

Factor: $y^2 - 8y + 12$.

SOLUTION Since the constant term is positive and the coefficient of the middle term is negative, we look for a factorization of 12 in which both factors are negative. Their sum must be -8.

Pairs of Factors of 12	Sums of Factors
$-1, -12$	-13
$-2, -6$	-8 ← We need a sum of -8. The numbers we need are -2 and -6.
$-3, -4$	-7

STUDENT NOTES

It is important to be able to list *all* the pairs of factors of a number. See Example 1 on p. 21 for an organized approach for listing pairs of factors.

The factorization of $y^2 - 8y + 12$ is $(y - 2)(y - 6)$. The check is left to the student.

▶ **TRY EXERCISE** 13

When the Constant Term Is Negative

As we saw in two of the multiplications at the start of this section, the product of two binomials can have a negative constant term:

$$(x + 3)(x - 7) = x^2 - 4x - 21$$

and

$$(x - 3)(x + 7) = x^2 + 4x - 21.$$

It is important to note that when the signs of the constants in the binomials are reversed, only the sign of the middle term of the trinomial changes.

EXAMPLE 3

Factor: $x^2 - 8x - 20$.

SOLUTION The constant term, -20, must be expressed as the product of a negative number and a positive number. Since the sum of these two numbers must be negative (specifically, -8), the negative number must have the greater absolute value.

Pairs of Factors of -20	Sums of Factors
$1, -20$	-19
$2, -10$	-8 ← The numbers we need are 2 and -10.
$4, -5$	-1
$5, -4$	1
$10, -2$	8
$20, -1$	19

Because in these three pairs, the positive number has the greater absolute value, these sums are all positive. For this problem, these pairs can be eliminated even before calculating the sum.

The numbers that we are looking for are 2 and -10.

Check: $(x + 2)(x - 10) = x^2 - 10x + 2x - 20$
$$= x^2 - 8x - 20.$$

The factorization of $x^2 - 8x - 20$ is $(x + 2)(x - 10)$.

▶ **TRY EXERCISE** 21

> ### To Factor $x^2 + bx + c$ When c Is Negative
>
> When the constant term c of a trinomial is negative, look for a positive number and a negative number that multiply to c. Select pairs of numbers for which the number with the larger absolute value has the same sign as b, the coefficient of the middle term.
>
> $$x^2 - 4x - 21 = (x + 3)(x - 7);$$
>
> $$x^2 + 4x - 21 = (x - 3)(x + 7)$$

EXAMPLE **4**

Factor: $t^2 - 24 + 5t$.

SOLUTION   It helps to first write the trinomial in descending order: $t^2 + 5t - 24$. The factorization of the constant term, -24, must have one factor positive and one factor negative. The sum must be 5, so the positive factor must have the larger absolute value. Thus we consider only pairs of factors in which the positive factor has the larger absolute value.

Pairs of Factors of -24	Sums of Factors
$-1, 24$	23
$-2, 12$	10
$-3, \ 8$	5 ← The numbers we need are -3 and 8.
$-4, \ 6$	2

The factorization is $(t - 3)(t + 8)$. The check is left to the student.

> TRY EXERCISE ▸ 23

Polynomials in two or more variables, such as $a^2 + 4ab - 21b^2$, are factored in a similar manner.

EXAMPLE **5**

Factor: $a^2 + 4ab - 21b^2$.

SOLUTION   It may help to write the trinomial in the equivalent form

$$a^2 + 4ba - 21b^2.$$

We now regard $-21b^2$ as the "constant" term and $4b$ as the "coefficient" of a. Then we try to express $-21b^2$ as a product of two factors whose sum is $4b$. Those factors are $-3b$ and $7b$.

Check: $(a - 3b)(a + 7b) = a^2 + 7ab - 3ba - 21b^2$
$$= a^2 + 4ab - 21b^2.$$

The factorization of $a^2 + 4ab - 21b^2$ is $(a - 3b)(a + 7b)$.

> TRY EXERCISE ▸ 55

Prime Polynomials

EXAMPLE **6**

Factor: $x^2 - x + 5$.

SOLUTION   Since 5 has very few factors, we can easily check all possibilities.

Pairs of Factors of 5	Sums of Factors
5, 1	6
−5, −1	−6

Since there are no factors whose sum is −1, the polynomial is *not* factorable into binomials.

> **TRY EXERCISE** 37

In this text, a polynomial like $x^2 - x + 5$ that cannot be factored further is said to be **prime**. In more advanced courses, other types of numbers are considered. There, polynomials like $x^2 - x + 5$ can be factored and are not considered prime.

Often factoring requires two or more steps. Remember, when told to factor, we should *factor completely*. This means that the final factorization should contain only prime polynomials.

EXAMPLE **7**

Factor: $-2x^3 + 20x^2 - 50x$.

SOLUTION   *Always* look first for a common factor. Since the leading coefficient is negative, we begin by factoring out $-2x$:

$$-2x^3 + 20x^2 - 50x = -2x(x^2 - 10x + 25).$$

Now consider $x^2 - 10x + 25$. Since the constant term is positive and the coefficient of the middle term is negative, we look for a factorization of 25 in which both factors are negative. Their sum must be −10.

STUDENT NOTES ———————

Whenever a new set of parentheses is created while factoring, check the expression inside the parentheses to see if it can be factored further.

Pairs of Factors of 25	Sums of Factors
−25, −1	−26
−5, −5	−10 ←

The numbers we need are −5 and −5.

The factorization of $x^2 - 10x + 25$ is $(x - 5)(x - 5)$, or $(x - 5)^2$.

> *CAUTION!*   When factoring involves more than one step, be careful to write out the *entire* factorization.

Check: $-2x(x - 5)(x - 5) = -2x[x^2 - 10x + 25]$ Multiplying binomials
$$= -2x^3 + 20x^2 - 50x.$$ Using the distributive law

The factorization of $-2x^3 + 20x^2 - 50x$ is $-2x(x - 5)(x - 5)$, or $-2x(x - 5)^2$.

> **TRY EXERCISE** 27

Once any common factors have been factored out, the following summary can be used to factor $x^2 + bx + c$.

> **To Factor $x^2 + bx + c$**
>
> 1. Find a pair of factors that have c as their product and b as their sum.
>
>   a) If c is positive, both factors will have the same sign as b.
>   b) If c is negative, one factor will be positive and the other will be negative. Select the factors such that the factor with the larger absolute value has the same sign as b.
>
> 2. Check by multiplying.

Note that each polynomial has a unique factorization (except for the order in which the factors are written).

| 5.2 | **EXERCISE SET** | For Extra Help | MyMathLab | Math XL PRACTICE | WATCH | DOWNLOAD |

Concept Reinforcement *For Exercises 1–6, assume that a polynomial of the form $x^2 + bx + c$ can be factored as $(x + p)(x + q)$. Complete each sentence by replacing each blank with either "positive" or "negative."*

1. If b is positive and c is positive, then p will be _____ and q will be _____.

2. If b is negative and c is positive, then p will be _____ and q will be _____.

3. If p is negative and q is negative, then b must be _____ and c must be _____.

4. If p is positive and q is positive, then b must be _____ and c must be _____.

5. If b, c, and p are all negative, then q must be _____.

6. If b and c are negative and p is positive, then q must be _____.

Factor completely. Remember to look first for a common factor. Check by multiplying. If a polynomial is prime, state this.

7. $x^2 + 8x + 16$

8. $x^2 + 9x + 20$

9. $x^2 + 11x + 10$

10. $y^2 + 8y + 7$

11. $x^2 + 10x + 21$

12. $x^2 + 6x + 9$

13. $t^2 - 9t + 14$

14. $a^2 - 9a + 20$

15. $b^2 - 5b + 4$

16. $x^2 - 10x + 25$

17. $a^2 - 7a + 12$

18. $z^2 - 8z + 7$

19. $d^2 - 7d + 10$

20. $x^2 - 8x + 15$

21. $x^2 - 2x - 15$

22. $x^2 - x - 42$

23. $x^2 + 2x - 15$

24. $x^2 + x - 42$

25. $2x^2 - 14x - 36$

26. $3y^2 - 9y - 84$

27. $-x^3 + 6x^2 + 16x$

28. $-x^3 + x^2 + 42x$

29. $4y - 45 + y^2$

30. $7x - 60 + x^2$

31. $x^2 - 72 + 6x$

32. $-2x - 99 + x^2$

33. $-5b^2 - 35b + 150$

34. $-c^4 - c^3 + 56c^2$

35. $x^5 - x^4 - 2x^3$

36. $2a^2 - 4a - 70$

37. $x^2 + 5x + 10$

38. $x^2 + 11x + 18$

39. $32 + 12t + t^2$

40. $y^2 - y + 1$

41. $x^2 + 20x + 99$

42. $x^2 + 20x + 100$

43. $3x^3 - 63x^2 - 300x$

44. $2x^3 - 40x^2 + 192x$

45. $-2x^2 + 42x + 144$

46. $-4x^2 - 40x - 100$

47. $y^2 - 20y + 96$

48. $144 - 25t + t^2$

49. $-a^6 - 9a^5 + 90a^4$

50. $-a^4 - a^3 + 132a^2$

51. $t^2 + \frac{2}{3}t + \frac{1}{9}$

52. $x^2 - \frac{2}{5}x + \frac{1}{25}$

53. $11 + w^2 - 4w$

54. $6 + p^2 + 2p$

55. $p^2 - 7pq + 10q^2$

56. $a^2 - 2ab - 3b^2$

57. $m^2 + 5mn + 5n^2$

58. $x^2 - 11xy + 24y^2$

59. $s^2 - 4st - 12t^2$

60. $b^2 + 8bc - 20c^2$

61. $6a^{10} + 30a^9 - 84a^8$

62. $5a^8 - 20a^7 - 25a^6$

63. Without multiplying $(x - 17)(x - 18)$, explain why it cannot possibly be a factorization of $x^2 + 35x + 306$.

64. Shari factors $x^3 - 8x^2 + 15x$ as $(x^2 - 5x)(x - 3)$. Is she wrong? Why or why not? What advice would you offer?

Skill Review

To prepare for Section 5.3, review multiplying binomials using FOIL (Section 4.6).

Multiply. [4.6]

65. $(2x + 3)(3x + 4)$ **66.** $(2x + 3)(3x - 4)$

67. $(2x - 3)(3x + 4)$ **68.** $(2x - 3)(3x - 4)$

69. $(5x - 1)(x - 7)$ **70.** $(x + 6)(3x - 5)$

Synthesis

71. When searching for a factorization, why do we list pairs of numbers with the correct *product* instead of pairs of numbers with the correct *sum*?

72. When factoring $x^2 + bx + c$ with a large value of c, Riley begins by writing out the prime factorization of c. What is the advantage of doing this?

73. Find all integers b for which $a^2 + ba - 50$ can be factored.

74. Find all integers m for which $y^2 + my + 50$ can be factored.

Factor completely.

75. $y^2 - 0.2y - 0.08$ **76.** $x^2 + \frac{1}{2}x - \frac{3}{16}$

77. $-\frac{1}{3}a^3 + \frac{1}{3}a^2 + 2a$ **78.** $-a^7 + \frac{25}{7}a^5 + \frac{30}{7}a^6$

79. $x^{2m} + 11x^m + 28$ **80.** $-t^{2n} + 7t^n - 10$

Aha! **81.** $(a + 1)x^2 + (a + 1)3x + (a + 1)2$

82. $ax^2 - 5x^2 + 8ax - 40x - (a - 5)9$
(*Hint*: See Exercise 81.)

83. Find the volume of a cube if its surface area is $6x^2 + 36x + 54$ square meters.

Find a polynomial in factored form for the shaded area in each figure. (Use π in your answers where appropriate.)

84.

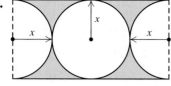

85.

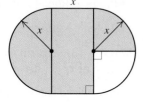

86.

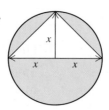

87.

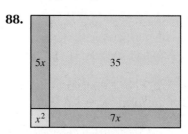

88.

$5x$	35
x^2	$7x$

89.

$4x$	20
x^2	$5x$

90. A census taker asks a woman, "How many children do you have?"

   "Three," she answers.

   "What are their ages?"

   She responds, "The product of their ages is 36. The sum of their ages is the house number next door."

   The math-savvy census taker walks next door, reads the house number, appears puzzled, and returns to the woman, asking, "Is there something you forgot to tell me?"

   "Oh yes," says the woman. "I'm sorry. The oldest child is at the park."

   The census taker records the three ages, thanks the woman for her time, and leaves.

   How old is each child? Explain how you reached this conclusion. (*Hint*: Consider factorizations.)

Source: Adapted from Anita Harnadek, *Classroom Quickies*. Pacific Grove, CA: Critical Thinking Press and Software

COLLABORATIVE

CORNER

Visualizing Factoring

Focus: Visualizing factoring

Time: 20–30 minutes

Group size: 3

Materials: Graph paper and scissors

The product $(x + 2)(x + 3)$ can be regarded as the area of a rectangle with width $x + 2$ and length $x + 3$. Similarly, factoring a polynomial like $x^2 + 5x + 6$ can be thought of as determining the length and the width of a rectangle that has area $x^2 + 5x + 6$. This is the approach used below.

ACTIVITY

1. **a)** To factor $x^2 + 11x + 10$ geometrically, the group needs to cut out shapes like those below to represent x^2, $11x$, and 10. This can be done by either tracing the figures below or by selecting a value for x, say 4, and using the squares on the graph paper to cut out the following:

   x^2:   Using the value selected for x, cut out a square that is x units on each side.

   $11x$: Using the value selected for x, cut out a rectangle that is 1 unit wide and x units long. Repeat this to form 11 such strips.

   10:   Cut out two rectangles with whole-number dimensions and an area of 10. One should be 2 units by 5 units and the other 1 unit by 10 units.

   b) The group, working together, should then attempt to use one of the two rectangles with area 10, along with all of the other shapes, to piece together one large rectangle. Only one of the rectangles with area 10 will work.

   c) From the large rectangle formed in part (b), use the length and the width to determine the factorization of $x^2 + 11x + 10$. Where do the dimensions of the rectangle representing 10 appear in the factorization?

2. Repeat step (1) above, but this time use the other rectangle with area 10, and use only 7 of the 11 strips, along with the x^2-shape. Piece together the shapes to form one large rectangle. What factorization do the dimensions of this rectangle suggest?

3. Cut out rectangles with area 12 and use the above approach to factor $x^2 + 8x + 12$. What dimensions should be used for the rectangle with area 12?

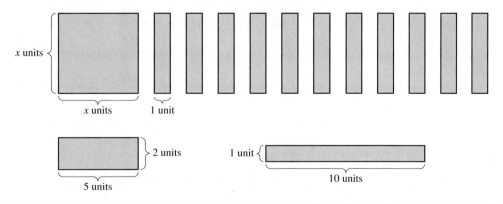

5.3 Factoring Trinomials of the Type $ax^2 + bx + c$

Factoring with FOIL ▪ The Grouping Method

In Section 5.2, we learned a FOIL-based method for factoring trinomials of the type $x^2 + bx + c$. Now we learn to factor trinomials in which the leading, or x^2, coefficient is not 1. First we will use another FOIL-based method and then we will use an alternative method that involves factoring by grouping. Use the method that you prefer or the one recommended by your instructor.

Factoring with FOIL

Before factoring trinomials of the type $ax^2 + bx + c$, consider the following:

$$\overset{\text{F} \quad \text{O} \quad \text{I} \quad \text{L}}{(2x + 5)(3x + 4) = 6x^2 + 8x + 15x + 20}$$
$$= 6x^2 + \quad 23x \quad + 20.$$

To factor $6x^2 + 23x + 20$, we could reverse the multiplication and look for two binomials whose product is this trinomial. We see from the multiplication above that:

- the product of the First terms must be $6x^2$;
- the product of the Outer terms plus the product of the Inner terms must be $23x$; and
- the product of the Last terms must be 20.

How can such a factorization be found without first seeing the corresponding multiplication? Our first approach relies on trial and error and FOIL.

To Factor $ax^2 + bx + c$ Using FOIL

1. Make certain that all common factors have been removed. If any remain, factor out the largest common factor.
2. Find two First terms whose product is ax^2:

$$(\blacksquare x + \quad)(\blacksquare x + \quad) = ax^2 + bx + c.$$
$$\underline{\qquad\qquad}\text{FOIL}$$

3. Find two Last terms whose product is c:

$$(\quad x + \blacksquare)(\quad x + \blacksquare) = ax^2 + bx + c.$$
$$\underline{\qquad\qquad}\text{FOIL}$$

4. Check by multiplying to see if the sum of the Outer and Inner products is bx. If necessary, repeat steps 2 and 3 until the correct combination is found.

$$(\blacksquare x + \blacksquare)(\blacksquare x + \blacksquare) = ax^2 + bx + c.$$

If no correct combination exists, state that the polynomial is prime.

EXAMPLE   **1**   Factor: $3x^2 - 10x - 8$.

SOLUTION

1. First, check for a common factor. In this case, there is none (other than 1 or -1).

2. Find two **First** terms whose product is $3x^2$.
   The only possibilities for the **First** terms are $3x$ and x:

   $$(3x + \quad)(x + \quad).$$

3. Find two **Last** terms whose product is -8. There are four pairs of factors of -8 and each can be listed in two ways:

$-1,\ \ 8$		$8, -1$
$1, -8$	and	$-8,\ \ 1$
$-2,\ \ 4$		$4, -2$
$2, -4$		$-4,\ \ 2.$

   Important! Since the First terms are not identical, we must consider the pairs of factors in both orders.

4. Knowing that all **First** and **Last** products will check, systematically inspect the **Outer** and **Inner** products resulting from steps (2) and (3). Look for the combination in which the sum of the products is the middle term, $-10x$. Our search ends as soon as the correct combination is found. If none exists, we state that the polynomial is prime.

Pair of Factors	*Corresponding Trial*	*Product*	
$-1,\ \ 8$	$(3x - 1)(x + 8)$	$3x^2 + 24x - x - 8$ $= 3x^2 + 23x - 8$	Wrong middle term
$1, -8$	$(3x + 1)(x - 8)$	$3x^2 - 24x + x - 8$ $= 3x^2 - 23x - 8$	Wrong middle term
$-2,\ \ 4$	$(3x - 2)(x + 4)$	$3x^2 + 12x - 2x - 8$ $= 3x^2 + 10x - 8$	Wrong middle term
$2, -4$	$(3x + 2)(x - 4)$	$3x^2 - 12x + 2x - 8$ $= 3x^2 - 10x - 8$	Correct middle term!
$8, -1$	$(3x + 8)(x - 1)$	$3x^2 - 3x + 8x - 8$ $= 3x^2 + 5x - 8$	Wrong middle term
$-8,\ \ 1$	$(3x - 8)(x + 1)$	$3x^2 + 3x - 8x - 8$ $= 3x^2 - 5x - 8$	Wrong middle term
$4, -2$	$(3x + 4)(x - 2)$	$3x^2 - 6x + 4x - 8$ $= 3x^2 - 2x - 8$	Wrong middle term
$-4,\ \ 2$	$(3x - 4)(x + 2)$	$3x^2 + 6x - 4x - 8$ $= 3x^2 + 2x - 8$	Wrong middle term

The correct factorization is $(3x + 2)(x - 4)$.

TRY EXERCISE   5

Two observations can be made from Example 1. First, we listed all possible trials even though we generally stop after finding the correct factorization. We did this to show that **each trial differs only in the middle term of the product**. Second, note that as in Section 5.2, **only the sign of the middle term changes when the signs in the binomials are reversed**.

EXAMPLE **2**   Factor: $10x^2 + 37x + 7$.

SOLUTION

1. There is no factor (other than 1 or -1) common to a three terms.

2. Because $10x^2$ factors as $10x \cdot x$ or $5x \cdot 2x$, we have two possibilities:

$$(10x + \quad)(x + \quad) \quad \text{or} \quad (5x + \quad)(2x + \quad).$$

3. There are two pairs of factors of 7 and each can be listed in two ways:

$$\begin{matrix} 1, & 7 \\ -1, & -7 \end{matrix} \quad \text{and} \quad \begin{matrix} 7, & 1 \\ -7, & -1. \end{matrix}$$

4. Look for **O**uter and **I**nner products for which the sum is th middle term. Because all coefficients in $10x^2 + 37x +$ are positive, we need consider only those combination involving positive factors of 7.

Trial	*Product*	
$(10x + 1)(x + 7)$	$10x^2 + 70x + 1x + 7$	
	$= 10x^2 + 71x + 7$	Wrong middle term
$(10x + 7)(x + 1)$	$10x^2 + 10x + 7x + 7$	
	$= 10x^2 + 17x + 7$	Wrong middle term
$(5x + 7)(2x + 1)$	$10x^2 + 5x + 14x + 7$	
	$= 10x^2 + 19x + 7$	Wrong middle term
$(5x + 1)(2x + 7)$	$10x^2 + 35x + 2x + 7$	
	$= 10x^2 + 37x + 7$	Correct middl term!

The correct factorization is $(5x + 1)(2x + 7)$.

TRY EXERCISE 9

A GEOMETRIC APPROACH TO EXAMPLE 2

The factoring of $10x^2 + 37x + 7$ can be regarded as a search for r and s so that the sum of areas A, B, C, and D is $10x^2 + 37x + 7$.

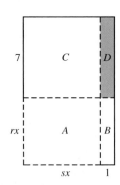

Because A must be $10x^2$, the product rs must be 10. Only when r is 2 and s is 5 will the sum of areas B and C be $37x$ (see below).

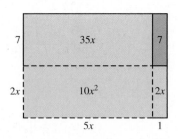

EXAMPLE **3**   Factor: $24x^3 - 76x^2 + 40x$.

SOLUTION

1. First, we factor out the largest common factor, $4x$:

$$4x(6x^2 - 19x + 10).$$

2. Next, we factor $6x^2 - 19x + 10$. Since $6x^2$ can be factored as $3x \cdot 2x$ or $6x \cdot$ we have two possibilities:

$$(3x + \quad)(2x + \quad) \quad \text{or} \quad (6x + \quad)(x + \quad).$$

3. There are four pairs of factors of 10 and each can be listed in two ways:

$$\begin{matrix} 1, & 10 \\ -1, & -10 \\ 2, & 5 \\ -2, & -5 \end{matrix} \quad \text{and} \quad \begin{matrix} 10, & 1 \\ -10, & -1 \\ 5, & 2 \\ -5, & -2. \end{matrix}$$

4. The two possibilities from step (2) and the eight possibilities from step (3 give $2 \cdot 8$, or 16 possibilities for factorizations. With careful consideration

we can eliminate some possibilities without multiplying. Since the sign of the middle term, $-19x$, is negative, but the sign of the last term, 10, is positive, the two factors of 10 must both be negative. This means only four pairings from step (3) need be considered. We first try these factors with $(3x + \quad)(2x + \quad)$, looking for **O**uter and **I**nner products for which the sum is $-19x$. If none gives the correct factorization, then we will consider $(6x + \quad)(x + \quad)$.

Trial	Product	
$(3x - 1)(2x - 10)$	$6x^2 - 30x - 2x + 10$	
	$= 6x^2 - 32x + 10$	Wrong middle term
$(3x - 10)(2x - 1)$	$6x^2 - 3x - 20x + 10$	
	$= 6x^2 - 23x + 10$	Wrong middle term
$(3x - 2)(2x - 5)$	$6x^2 - 15x - 4x + 10$	
	$= 6x^2 - 19x + 10$	Correct middle term!
$(3x - 5)(2x - 2)$	$6x^2 - 6x - 10x + 10$	
	$= 6x^2 - 16x + 10$	Wrong middle term

Since we have a correct factorization, we need not consider

$(6x + \quad)(x + \quad)$.

Look again at the possibility $(3x - 5)(2x - 2)$. Without multiplying, we can reject such a possibility. To see why, note that

$(3x - 5)(2x - 2) = (3x - 5)2(x - 1)$.

The expression $2x - 2$ has a common factor, 2. But we removed the *largest* common factor in step (1). If $2x - 2$ were one of the factors, then 2 would be *another* common factor in addition to the original, $4x$. Thus, $(2x - 2)$ cannot be part of the factorization of $6x^2 - 19x + 10$. Similar reasoning can be used to reject $(3x - 1)(2x - 10)$ as a possible factorization.

Once the largest common factor is factored out, none of the remaining factors can have a common factor.

The factorization of $6x^2 - 19x + 10$ is $(3x - 2)(2x - 5)$, but do not forget the common factor! The factorization of $24x^3 - 76x^2 + 40x$ is

$4x(3x - 2)(2x - 5)$. ▸ TRY EXERCISE 15

STUDENT NOTES

Keep your work organized so that you can see what you have already considered. For example, when factoring $6x^2 - 19x + 10$, we can list all possibilities and cross out those in which a common factor appears:

$(3x - 1)(2x - 10)$
$(3x - 10)(2x - 1)$
$(3x - 2)(2x - 5)$
$(3x - 5)(2x - 2)$
$(6x - 1)(x - 10)$
$(6x - 10)(x - 1)$
$(6x - 2)(x - 5)$
$(6x - 5)(x - 2)$

By being organized and not erasing, we can see that there are only four possible factorizations.

Tips for Factoring $ax^2 + bx + c$

To factor $ax^2 + bx + c \,(a > 0)$:

- Make sure that any common factor has been factored out.
- Once the largest common factor has been factored out of the original trinomial, no binomial factor can contain a common factor (other than 1 or -1).
- If c is positive, then the signs in both binomial factors must match the sign of b.
- Reversing the signs in the binomials reverses the sign of the middle term of their product.
- Organize your work so that you can keep track of which possibilities you have checked.
- Remember to include the largest common factor—if there is one—in the final factorization.
- Always check by multiplying.

EXAMPLE **4**

Factor: $10x + 8 - 3x^2$.

SOLUTION An important problem-solving strategy is to find a way to make new problems look like problems we already know how to solve. The factoring tips above apply only to trinomials of the form $ax^2 + bx + c$, with $a > 0$. This leads us to rewrite $10x + 8 - 3x^2$ in descending order:

$$10x + 8 - 3x^2 = -3x^2 + 10x + 8.$$ Using the commutative law to write descending order

Although $-3x^2 + 10x + 8$ looks similar to the trinomials we have factored, the tips above require a positive leading coefficient. This can be found by factoring out -1:

$$-3x^2 + 10x + 8 = -1(3x^2 - 10x - 8)$$ Factoring out -1 changes the signs of the coefficients.

$$= -1(3x + 2)(x - 4).$$ Using the result from Example 1

The factorization of $10x + 8 - 3x^2$ is $-1(3x + 2)(x - 4)$. **TRY EXERCISE** 31

EXAMPLE **5**

Factor: $6r^2 - 13rs - 28s^2$.

SOLUTION In order for the product of the first terms to be $6r^2$ and the product of the last terms to be $-28s^2$, the binomial factors will be of the form

$$(\blacksquare r + \blacksquare s)(\blacksquare r + \blacksquare s).$$

We verify that no common factor exists and then examine the first term, $6r^2$. There are two possibilities:

$$(2r + \quad)(3r + \quad) \quad \text{or} \quad (6r + \quad)(r + \quad).$$

The last term, $-28s^2$, has the following pairs of factors:

$$
\begin{array}{ll}
s, -28s & -28s, \quad s \\
-s, \quad 28s & 28s, \quad -s \\
2s, -14s & -14s, \quad 2s \\
-2s, \quad 14s & 14s, -2s \\
4s, \quad -7s & -7s, \quad 4s \\
-4s, \quad 7s & 7s, -4s.
\end{array}
$$
and

Note that listing the pairs of factors of $-28s^2$ is just like listing the pairs of factors of -28, except that each factor also contains a factor of s.

Some trials, like $(2r + 28s)(3r - s)$ and $(2r + 14s)(3r - 2s)$, cannot be correct because both $(2r + 28s)$ and $(2r + 14s)$ contain a common factor, 2. We try $(2r + 7s)(3r - 4s)$:

$$(2r + 7s)(3r - 4s) = 6r^2 - 8rs + 21rs - 28s^2$$
$$= 6r^2 + 13rs - 28s^2.$$

Our trial is incorrect, but only because of the sign of the middle term. To correctly factor $6r^2 - 13rs - 28s^2$, we simply change the signs in the binomials:

$$(2r - 7s)(3r + 4s) = 6r^2 + 8rs - 21rs - 28s^2$$
$$= 6r^2 - 13rs - 28s^2.$$

The correct factorization of $6r^2 - 13rs - 28s^2$ is $(2r - 7s)(3r + 4s)$.

TRY EXERCISE 67

The Grouping Method

Another method of factoring trinomials of the type $ax^2 + bx + c$ is known as the *grouping method*. The grouping method relies on rewriting $ax^2 + bx + c$ in the form $ax^2 + px + qx + c$ and then factoring by grouping. To develop this method, consider the following*:

$$(2x + 5)(3x + 4) = 2x \cdot 3x + 2x \cdot 4 + 5 \cdot 3x + 5 \cdot 4 \qquad \text{Using FOIL}$$
$$= 2 \cdot 3 \cdot x^2 + 2 \cdot 4x + 5 \cdot 3x + 5 \cdot 4$$
$$= 2 \cdot 3 \cdot x^2 + (2 \cdot 4 + 5 \cdot 3)x + 5 \cdot 4$$

$$\underset{a}{\uparrow} \qquad\qquad\qquad \underset{b}{\uparrow} \qquad\qquad \underset{c}{\uparrow}$$

$$= 6x^2 \quad + \quad 23x \quad + \quad 20.$$

Note that reversing these steps shows that $6x^2 + 23x + 20$ can be rewritten as $6x^2 + 8x + 15x + 20$ and then factored by grouping. Note that the numbers that add to b (in this case, $2 \cdot 4$ and $5 \cdot 3$) also multiply to ac (in this case, $2 \cdot 3 \cdot 5 \cdot 4$).

To Factor $ax^2 + bx + c$, Using the Grouping Method

1. Factor out the largest common factor, if one exists.
2. Multiply the leading coefficient a and the constant c.
3. Find a pair of factors of ac whose sum is b.
4. Rewrite the middle term, bx, as a sum or a difference using the factors found in step (3).
5. Factor by grouping.
6. Include any common factor from step (1) and check by multiplying.

EXAMPLE **6** Factor: $3x^2 - 10x - 8$.

SOLUTION

1. First, we note that there is no common factor (other than 1 or -1).
2. We multiply the leading coefficient, 3, and the constant, -8:

$$3(-8) = -24.$$

3. We next look for a factorization of -24 in which the sum of the factors is the coefficient of the middle term, -10.

Pairs of Factors of -24	Sums of Factors
1, -24	-23
-1, 24	23
2, -12	-10 ← $\qquad$ 2 + (−12) = −10
-2, 12	10
3, -8	-5
-3, 8	5
4, -6	-2
-4, 6	2

We normally stop listing pairs of factors once we have found the one we are after.

---

*This discussion was inspired by a lecture given by Irene Doo at Austin Community College.

4. Next, we express the middle term as a sum or a difference using the factor found in step (3):

$$-10x = 2x - 12x.$$

5. We now factor by grouping as follows:

$$3x^2 - 10x - 8 = 3x^2 + 2x - 12x - 8 \qquad \text{Substituting } 2x - 12x \text{ for } -10x. \text{ We could also use } -12x + 2x.$$

$$= x(3x + 2) - 4(3x + 2) \qquad \text{Factoring by grouping; see Section 5.1}$$

$$= (3x + 2)(x - 4). \qquad \text{Factoring out the common factor, } 3x + 2$$

6. *Check:* $(3x + 2)(x - 4) = 3x^2 - 12x + 2x - 8 = 3x^2 - 10x - 8.$

The factorization of $3x^2 - 10x - 8$ is $(3x + 2)(x - 4)$.   **TRY EXERCISE** ▶ 51

EXAMPLE   7   Factor: $8x^3 + 22x^2 - 6x.$

SOLUTION

1. We factor out the largest common factor, $2x$:

$$8x^3 + 22x^2 - 6x = 2x(4x^2 + 11x - 3).$$

2. To factor $4x^2 + 11x - 3$ by grouping, we multiply the leading coefficient, 4, and the constant term, -3:

$$4(-3) = -12.$$

3. We next look for factors of -12 that add to 11.

Pairs of Factors of -12	Sums of Factors
1, -12	-11
-1, 12	11 ←
.	.
.	.
.	.

Since $-1 + 12 = 11$, there is no need to list other pairs of factors.

4. We then rewrite the $11x$ in $4x^2 + 11x - 3$ using

$$11x = -1x + 12x, \quad \text{or} \quad 11x = 12x - 1x.$$

5. Next, we factor by grouping:

$$4x^2 + 11x - 3 = 4x^2 - 1x + 12x - 3 \qquad \text{Rewriting the middle term; } 12x - 1x \text{ could also be used.}$$

$$= x(4x - 1) + 3(4x - 1) \qquad \text{Factoring by grouping. Note the common factor, } 4x - 1.$$

$$= (4x - 1)(x + 3). \qquad \text{Factoring out the common factor}$$

6. The factorization of $4x^2 + 11x - 3$ is $(4x - 1)(x + 3)$. But don't forget the common factor, $2x$. The factorization of the original trinomial is

$$2x(4x - 1)(x + 3).$$

TRY EXERCISE ▶ 57

5.3	**EXERCISE SET**

➡ **Concept Reinforcement** *In each of Exercises 1–4, match the polynomial with the correct factorization from the column on the right.*

1. _____ $12x^2 + 16x - 3$ **a)** $(7x - 1)(2x + 3)$

2. _____ $14x^2 + 19x - 3$ **b)** $(6x + 1)(2x - 3)$

3. _____ $14x^2 - 19x - 3$ **c)** $(6x - 1)(2x + 3)$

4. _____ $12x^2 - 16x - 3$ **d)** $(7x + 1)(2x - 3)$

Factor completely. If a polynomial is prime, state this.

5. $2x^2 + 7x - 4$ **6.** $3x^2 + x - 4$

7. $3x^2 - 17x - 6$ **8.** $5x^2 - 19x - 4$

9. $4t^2 + 12t + 5$ **10.** $6t^2 + 17t + 7$

11. $15a^2 - 14a + 3$ **12.** $10a^2 - 11a + 3$

13. $6x^2 + 17x + 12$ **14.** $6x^2 + 19x + 10$

15. $6x^2 - 10x - 4$ **16.** $5t^3 - 21t^2 + 18t$

17. $7t^3 + 15t^2 + 2t$ **18.** $15t^2 + 20t - 75$

19. $10 - 23x + 12x^2$ **20.** $-20 + 31x - 12x^2$

21. $-35x^2 - 34x - 8$ **22.** $28x^2 + 38x - 6$

23. $4 + 6t^2 - 13t$ **24.** $9 + 8t^2 - 18t$

25. $25x^2 + 40x + 16$ **26.** $49t^2 + 42t + 9$

27. $20y^2 + 59y - 3$ **28.** $25a^2 - 23a - 2$

29. $14x^2 + 73x + 45$ **30.** $35x^2 - 57x - 44$

31. $-2x^2 + 15 + x$ **32.** $2t^2 - 19 - 6t$

33. $-6x^2 - 33x - 15$ **34.** $-12x^2 - 28x + 24$

35. $10a^2 - 8a - 18$ **36.** $20y^2 - 25y + 5$

37. $12x^2 + 68x - 24$ **38.** $6x^2 + 21x + 15$

39. $4x + 1 + 3x^2$ **40.** $-9 + 18x^2 + 21x$

Factor. Use factoring by grouping even though it would seem reasonable to first combine like terms.

41. $x^2 + 3x - 2x - 6$ **42.** $x^2 + 4x - 2x - 8$

43. $8t^2 - 6t - 28t + 21$

44. $35t^2 - 40t + 21t - 24$

45. $6x^2 + 4x + 15x + 10$ **46.** $3x^2 - 2x + 3x - 2$

47. $2y^2 + 8y - y - 4$ **48.** $7n^2 + 35n - n - 5$

49. $6a^2 - 8a - 3a + 4$ **50.** $10a^2 - 4a - 5a + 2$

Factor completely. If a polynomial is prime, state this.

51. $16t^2 + 23t + 7$ **52.** $9t^2 + 14t + 5$

53. $-9x^2 - 18x - 5$ **54.** $-16x^2 - 32x - 7$

55. $10x^2 + 30x - 70$ **56.** $10a^2 + 25a - 15$

57. $18x^3 + 21x^2 - 9x$ **58.** $6x^3 - 4x^2 - 10x$

59. $89x + 64 + 25x^2$ **60.** $47 - 42y + 9y^2$

61. $168x^3 + 45x^2 + 3x$

62. $144x^5 - 168x^4 + 48x^3$

63. $-14t^4 + 19t^3 + 3t^2$

64. $-70a^4 + 68a^3 - 16a^2$

65. $132y + 32y^2 - 54$ **66.** $220y + 60y^2 - 225$

67. $2a^2 - 5ab + 2b^2$ **68.** $3p^2 - 16pq - 12q^2$

69. $8s^2 + 22st + 14t^2$ **70.** $10s^2 + 4st - 6t^2$

71. $27x^2 - 72xy + 48y^2$

72. $-30a^2 - 87ab - 30b^2$

73. $-24a^2 + 34ab - 12b^2$ **74.** $15a^2 - 5ab - 20b^2$

75. $19x^3 - 3x^2 + 14x^4$ **76.** $10x^5 - 2x^4 + 22x^3$

77. $18a^7 + 8a^6 + 9a^8$ **78.** $40a^8 + 16a^7 + 25a^9$

79. Asked to factor $2x^2 - 18x + 36$, Kay *incorrectly* answers

$$2x^2 - 18x + 36 = 2(x^2 + 9x + 18)$$
$$= 2(x + 3)(x + 6).$$

If this were a 10-point quiz question, how many points would you take off? Why?

80. Asked to factor $4x^2 + 28x + 48$, Herb *incorrectly* answers

$$4x^2 + 28x + 48 = (2x + 6)(2x + 8)$$
$$= 2(x + 3)(x + 4).$$

If this were a 10-point quiz question, how many points would you take off? Why?

Skill Review

To prepare for Section 5.4, review the special products in Section 4.6.

Multiply. [4.6]

81. $(x - 2)^2$ **82.** $(x + 2)^2$

83. $(x + 2)(x - 2)$ **84.** $(5t - 3)^2$

85. $(4a + 1)^2$

86. $(2n + 7)(2n - 7)$

87. $(3c - 10)^2$

88. $(1 - 5a)^2$

89. $(8n + 3)(8n - 3)$

90. $(9 - y)(9 + y)$

Synthesis

91. Explain how you would prove to a fellow student that a given trinomial is prime.

92. For the trinomial $ax^2 + bx + c$, suppose that a is the product of three different prime factors and c is the product of another two prime factors. How many possible factorizations (like those in Example 1) exist? Explain how you determined your answer.

Factor. If a polynomial is prime, state this.

93. $18x^2y^2 - 3xy - 10$

94. $8x^2y^3 + 10xy^2 + 2y$

95. $9a^2b^3 + 25ab^2 + 16$

96. $-9t^{10} - 12t^5 - 4$

97. $16t^{10} - 8t^5 + 1$

98. $9a^2b^2 - 15ab - 2$

99. $-15x^{2m} + 26x^m - 8$

100. $-20x^{2n} - 16x^n - 3$

101. $3a^{6n} - 2a^{3n} - 1$

102. $a^{2n+1} - 2a^{n+1} + a$

103. $7(t - 3)^{2n} + 5(t - 3)^n - 2$

104. $3(a + 1)^{n+1}(a + 3)^2 - 5(a + 1)^n(a + 3)^3$

CONNECTING the CONCEPTS

In Sections 5.1–5.3, we have considered factoring out a common factor, factoring by grouping, and factoring with FOIL. The following is a good strategy to follow when you encounter a mixed set of factoring problems.

1. Factor out any common factor.
2. Try factoring by grouping for polynomials with four terms.
3. Try factoring with FOIL for trinomials. If the leading coefficient of the trinomial is not 1, you may instead try factoring by grouping.

Polynomial	Number of Terms	Factorization
$12y^5 - 6y^4 + 30y^2$	3	There is a common factor: $6y^2$. $12y^5 - 6y^4 + 30y^2 = 6y^2(2y^3 - y^2 + 5)$. The trinomial in the parentheses cannot be factored further.
$t^4 - 5t^3 - 3t + 15$	4	There is no common factor. We factor by grouping. $t^4 - 5t^3 - 3t + 15 = t^3(t - 5) - 3(t - 5)$ $= (t - 5)(t^3 - 3)$
$-4x^4 + 4x^3 + 80x^2$	3	There is a common factor: $-4x^2$. $-4x^4 + 4x^3 + 80x^2 = -4x^2(x^2 - x - 20)$ The trinomial in the parentheses can be factored: $-4x^4 + 4x^3 + 80x^2 = -4x^2(x^2 - x - 20)$ $= -4x^2(x + 4)(x - 5)$.
$10n^2 - 17n + 3$	3	There is no common factor. We factor with FOIL or by grouping. $10n^2 - 17n + 3 = (2n - 3)(5n - 1)$

MIXED REVIEW

Factor completely. If a polynomial is prime,
state this.

1. $6x^5 - 18x^2$

2. $x^2 + 10x + 16$

3. $2x^2 + 13x - 7$

4. $x^3 + 3x^2 + 2x + 6$

5. $5x^2 + 40x - 100$

6. $x^2 - 2x - 5$

7. $7x^2y - 21xy - 28y$

8. $15a^4 - 27a^2b^2 + 21a^2b$

9. $b^2 - 14b + 49$

10. $12x^2 - x - 1$

11. $c^3 + c^2 - 4c - 4$

12. $2x^2 + 30x - 200$

13. $t^2 + t - 10$

14. $15d^2 - 30d + 75$

15. $15p^2 + 16pq + 4q^2$

16. $-2t^3 - 10t^2 - 12t$

17. $x^2 + 4x - 77$

18. $10c^2 + 20c + 10$

19. $5 + 3x - 2x^2$

20. $2m^3n - 10m^2n - 6mn + 30n$

5.4 | Factoring Perfect-Square Trinomials and Differences of Squares

Recognizing Perfect-Square Trinomials ▪ Factoring Perfect-Square Trinomials ▪
Recognizing Differences of Squares ▪ Factoring Differences of Squares ▪ Factoring Completely

In Section 4.6, we studied special products of certain binomials. Reversing these rules provides shortcuts for factoring certain polynomials.

Recognizing Perfect-Square Trinomials

Some trinomials are squares of binomials. For example, $x^2 + 10x + 25$ is the square of the binomial $x + 5$, because

$$(x + 5)^2 = x^2 + 2 \cdot x \cdot 5 + 5^2 = x^2 + 10x + 25.$$

A trinomial that is the square of a binomial is called a **perfect-square trinomial**.
    In Section 4.6, we considered squaring binomials as a special-product rule:

$$(A + B)^2 = A^2 + 2AB + B^2;$$
$$(A - B)^2 = A^2 - 2AB + B^2.$$

Reading the right-hand sides first, we can use these equations to factor perfect-square trinomials. Note that in order for a trinomial to be the square of a binomial, it must have the following:

1. Two terms, A^2 and B^2, must be squares, such as

    $4, \quad x^2, \quad 81m^2, \quad 16t^2.$

2. Neither A^2 nor B^2 is being subtracted.

3. The remaining term is either $2 \cdot A \cdot B$ or $-2 \cdot A \cdot B$, where A and B are the square roots of A^2 and B^2.

EXAMPLE 1

Determine whether each of the following is a perfect-square trinomial.

a) $x^2 + 6x + 9$ **b)** $t^2 - 8t - 9$ **c)** $16x^2 + 49 - 56x$

SOLUTION

a) To see if $x^2 + 6x + 9$ is a perfect-square trinomial, note that:

1. Two terms, x^2 and 9, are squares.
2. Neither x^2 nor 9 is being subtracted.
3. The remaining term, $6x$, is $2 \cdot x \cdot 3$, where x and 3 are the square roots of x^2 and 9.

Thus, $x^2 + 6x + 9$ *is* a perfect-square trinomial.

b) To see if $t^2 - 8t - 9$ is a perfect-square trinomial, note that:

1. Both t^2 and 9, are squares. But:
2. Since 9 is being subtracted, $t^2 - 8t - 9$ *is not* a perfect-square trinomial.

c) To see if $16x^2 + 49 - 56x$ is a perfect-square trinomial, it helps to first write it in descending order:

$$16x^2 - 56x + 49.$$

Next, note that:

1. Two terms, $16x^2$ and 49, are squares.
2. There is no minus sign before $16x^2$ or 49.
3. Twice the product of the square roots, $2 \cdot 4x \cdot 7$, is $56x$. The remaining term, $-56x$, is the opposite of this product.

Thus, $16x^2 + 49 - 56x$ *is* a perfect-square trinomial.   ▶ TRY EXERCISE   11

Factoring Perfect–Square Trinomials

Either of the factoring methods discussed in Section 5.3 can be used to factor perfect-square trinomials, but a faster method is to recognize the following patterns.

> ### Factoring a Perfect-Square Trinomial
> $$A^2 + 2AB + B^2 = (A + B)^2; \qquad A^2 - 2AB + B^2 = (A - B)^2$$

Each factorization uses the square roots of the squared terms and the sign of the remaining term. To verify these equations, you should compute $(A + B)(A + B)$ and $(A - B)(A - B)$.

EXAMPLE 2

Factor: **(a)** $x^2 + 6x + 9$; **(b)** $t^2 + 49 - 14t$; **(c)** $16x^2 - 40x + 25$.

SOLUTION

a) $x^2 + 6x + 9 = x^2 + 2 \cdot x \cdot 3 + 3^2 = (x + 3)^2$ The sign of the middle
                                                                     term is positive.
$$\underbrace{A^2}\ +\ \underbrace{2}\ \underbrace{A}\ \underbrace{B}\ +\ \underbrace{B^2}\ =\ \underbrace{(A\ +\ B)^2}$$

b) $t^2 + 49 - 14t = t^2 - 14t + 49$ Using a commutative law to write
                                               in descending order
$$= t^2 - 2 \cdot t \cdot 7 + 7^2 = (t - 7)^2$$
$$\underbrace{A^2}\ -\ \underbrace{2}\ \underbrace{A}\ \underbrace{B}\ +\ \underbrace{B^2}\ =\ \underbrace{(A\ -\ B)^2}$$

c) $16x^2 - 40x + 25 = (4x)^2 - 2 \cdot 4x \cdot 5 + 5^2 = (4x - 5)^2$ Recall that $(4x)^2 = 16x^2$.

$$A^2 \quad -2 \quad A \quad B + B^2 = (A - B)^2$$ **TRY EXERCISE** 19

Polynomials in more than one variable can also be perfect-square trinomials.

EXAMPLE **3**   Factor: $4p^2 - 12pq + 9q^2$.

SOLUTION   We have

$$4p^2 - 12pq + 9q^2 = (2p)^2 - 2(2p)(3q) + (3q)^2$$ Recognizing the perfect-square trinomial

$$= (2p - 3q)^2.$$ The sign of the middle term is negative.

Check: $(2p - 3q)(2p - 3q) = 4p^2 - 12pq + 9q^2.$

The factorization is $(2p - 3q)^2$.   **TRY EXERCISE** 43

EXAMPLE **4**   Factor: $-75m^3 - 60m^2 - 12m$.

SOLUTION   *Always* look first for a common factor. This time there is one. We factor out $-3m$ so that the leading coefficient of the polynomial inside the parentheses is positive:

Factor out the common factor.

$$-75m^3 - 60m^2 - 12m = -3m[25m^2 + 20m + 4]$$
$$= -3m[(5m)^2 + 2(5m)(2) + 2^2]$$ Recognizing the perfect-square trinomial. Try to do this mentally.

Factor the perfect-square trinomial.

$$= -3m(5m + 2)^2.$$

Check: $-3m(5m + 2)^2 = -3m(5m + 2)(5m + 2)$
$$= -3m(25m^2 + 20m + 4)$$
$$= -75m^3 - 60m^2 - 12m.$$

The factorization is $-3m(5m + 2)^2$.   **TRY EXERCISE** 31

Recognizing Differences of Squares

Some binomials represent the difference of two squares. For example, the binomial $16x^2 - 9$ is a difference of two expressions, $16x^2$ and 9, that are squares. To see this, note that $16x^2 = (4x)^2$ and $9 = 3^2$.

Any expression, like $16x^2 - 9$, that can be written in the form $A^2 - B^2$ is called a **difference of squares**. Note that in order for a binomial to be a difference of squares, it must have the following.

   1. There must be two expressions, both squares, such as

$$25, \quad t^2, \quad 4x^2, \quad 1, \quad x^6, \quad 49y^8, \quad 100x^2y^2.$$

   2. The terms in the binomial must have different signs.

Note that in order for an expression to be a square, its coefficient must be a perfect square and the power(s) of the variable(s) must be even.

EXAMPLE 5   Determine whether each of the following is a difference of squares.

a) $9x^2 - 64$ **b)** $25 - t^3$ **c)** $-4x^{10} + 36$

SOLUTION

a) To see if $9x^2 - 64$ is a difference of squares, note that:

  1. The first expression is a square: $9x^2 = (3x)^2$.
     The second expression is a square: $64 = 8^2$.
  2. The terms have different signs.

Thus, $9x^2 - 64$ is a difference of squares, $(3x)^2 - 8^2$.

b) To see if $25 - t^3$ is a difference of squares, note that:

  1. The expression t^3 is not a square.

Thus, $25 - t^3$ is not a difference of squares.

c) To see if $-4x^{10} + 36$ is a difference of squares, note that:

  1. The expressions $4x^{10}$ and 36 are squares: $4x^{10} = (2x^5)^2$ and $36 = 6^2$.
  2. The terms have different signs.

Thus, $-4x^{10} + 36$ is a difference of squares, $6^2 - (2x^5)^2$. It is often useful t
rewrite $-4x^{10} + 36$ in the equivalent form $36 - 4x^{10}$.   **TRY EXERCISE 51**

Factoring Differences of Squares

To factor a difference of squares, we reverse a pattern from Section 4.6.

> ### Factoring a Difference of Squares
> $$A^2 - B^2 = (A + B)(A - B)$$

Once we have identified the expressions that are playing the roles of A and B
the factorization can be written directly. To verify this equation, simply multip
$(A + B)(A - B)$.

EXAMPLE 6   Factor: **(a)** $x^2 - 4$; **(b)** $1 - 9p^2$; **(c)** $s^6 - 16t^{10}$; **(d)** $50x^2 - 8x^8$.

SOLUTION

a) $x^2 - 4 = x^2 - 2^2 = (x + 2)(x - 2)$
$$A^2 - B^2 = (A + B)(A - B)$$

b) $1 - 9p^2 = 1^2 - (3p)^2 = (1 + 3p)(1 - 3p)$
$$A^2 - B^2 = (A + B)(A - B)$$

c) $s^6 - 16t^{10} = (s^3)^2 - (4t^5)^2$ Using the rules for powers
$$A^2 - B^2$$

$= (s^3 + 4t^5)(s^3 - 4t^5)$ Try to go directly to this step.
$$(A + B)(A - B)$$

d) *Always* look first for a common factor. This time there is one, $2x^2$:

Factor out the common factor.

$$50x^2 - 8x^8 = 2x^2(25 - 4x^6)$$
$$= 2x^2[5^2 - (2x^3)^2] \quad \text{Recognizing } A^2 - B^2.$$
$$\text{Try to do this mentally.}$$

Factor the difference of squares.

$$= 2x^2(5 + 2x^3)(5 - 2x^3).$$

Check: $2x^2(5 + 2x^3)(5 - 2x^3) = 2x^2(25 - 4x^6)$
$$= 50x^2 - 8x^8.$$

The factorization of $50x^2 - 8x^8$ is $2x^2(5 + 2x^3)(5 - 2x^3)$.

TRY EXERCISE 57

CAUTION! Note in Example 6 that a difference of squares is *not* the square of the difference; that is,

$$A^2 - B^2 \neq (A - B)^2. \quad \begin{array}{l}\text{To see this, note that} \\ (A - B)^2 = A^2 - 2AB + B^2.\end{array}$$

Factoring Completely

Sometimes, as in Examples 4 and 6(d), a *complete* factorization requires two or more steps. Factoring is complete when no factor can be factored further.

EXAMPLE 7   Factor: $y^4 - 16$.

SOLUTION   We have

Factor a difference of squares.

$$y^4 - 16 = (y^2)^2 - 4^2 \quad \text{Recognizing } A^2 - B^2$$
$$= (y^2 + 4)(y^2 - 4) \quad \text{Note that } y^2 - 4 \text{ is not prime.}$$

Factor another difference of squares.

$$= (y^2 + 4)(y + 2)(y - 2). \quad \begin{array}{l}\text{Note that } y^2 - 4 \text{ is itself a} \\ \text{difference of squares.}\end{array}$$

Check: $(y^2 + 4)(y + 2)(y - 2) = (y^2 + 4)(y^2 - 4)$
$$= y^4 - 16.$$

The factorization is $(y^2 + 4)(y + 2)(y - 2)$.

TRY EXERCISE 79

Note in Example 7 that the factor $y^2 + 4$ is a *sum* of squares that cannot be factored further.

CAUTION! There is no general formula for factoring a sum of squares. In particular,

$$A^2 + B^2 \neq (A + B)^2.$$

As you proceed through the exercises, these suggestions may prove helpful.

> **Tips for Factoring**
> 1. Always look first for a common factor! If there is one, factor it out.
> 2. Be alert for perfect-square trinomials and for binomials that are differences of squares. Once recognized, they can be factored without trial and error.
> 3. Always factor completely.
> 4. Check by multiplying.

5.4   EXERCISE SET

For Extra Help   **MyMathLab**   PRACTICE   WATCH   DOWNLOAD

🐚 *Concept Reinforcement   Identify each of the following as a perfect-square trinomial, a difference of squares, a prime polynomial, or none of these.*

1. $4x^2 + 49$
2. $x^2 - 64$
3. $t^2 - 100$
4. $x^2 - 5x + 4$
5. $9x^2 + 6x + 1$
6. $a^2 - 8a + 16$
7. $2t^2 + 10t + 6$
8. $-25x^2 - 9$
9. $16t^2 - 25$
10. $4r^2 + 20r + 25$

Determine whether each of the following is a perfect-square trinomial.

11. $x^2 + 18x + 81$
12. $x^2 - 16x + 64$
13. $x^2 - 10x - 25$
14. $x^2 - 14x - 49$
15. $x^2 - 3x + 9$
16. $x^2 + 4x + 4$
17. $9x^2 + 25 - 30x$
18. $36x^2 + 16 - 24x$

Factor completely. Remember to look first for a common factor and to check by multiplying. If a polynomial is prime, state this.

19. $x^2 + 16x + 64$
20. $x^2 + 10x + 25$
21. $x^2 - 10x + 25$
22. $x^2 - 16x + 64$
23. $5p^2 + 20p + 20$
24. $3p^2 - 12p + 12$
25. $1 - 2t + t^2$
26. $1 + t^2 + 2t$
27. $18x^2 + 12x + 2$
28. $25x^2 + 10x + 1$
29. $49 - 56y + 16y^2$
30. $75 - 60m + 12m^2$
31. $-x^5 + 18x^4 - 81x^3$
32. $-2x^2 + 40x - 200$
33. $2n^3 + 40n^2 + 200n$
34. $x^3 + 24x^2 + 144x$

35. $20x^2 + 100x + 125$
36. $27m^2 - 36m + 12$
37. $49 - 42x + 9x^2$
38. $64 - 112x + 49x^2$
39. $16x^2 + 24x + 9$
40. $2a^2 + 28a + 98$
41. $2 + 20x + 50x^2$
42. $9x^2 + 30x + 25$
43. $9p^2 + 12pq + 4q^2$
44. $x^2 - 3xy + 9y^2$
45. $a^2 - 12ab + 49b^2$
46. $25m^2 - 20mn + 4n^2$
47. $-64m^2 - 16mn - n^2$
48. $-81p^2 + 18pq - q^2$
49. $-32s^2 + 80st - 50t^2$
50. $-36a^2 - 96ab - 64b^2$

Determine whether each of the following is a difference of squares.

51. $x^2 - 100$
52. $x^2 + 49$
53. $n^4 + 1$
54. $n^4 - 81$
55. $-1 + 64t^2$
56. $-12 + 25t^2$

Factor completely. Remember to look first for a common factor. If a polynomial is prime, state this.

57. $x^2 - 25$
58. $x^2 - 36$
59. $p^2 - 9$
60. $q^2 + 1$
61. $-49 + t^2$
62. $-64 + m^2$
63. $6a^2 - 24$
64. $x^2 - 8x + 16$
65. $49x^2 - 14x + 1$
66. $3t^2 - 3$
67. $200 - 2t^2$
68. $98 - 8w^2$

69. $-80a^2 + 45$

70. $25x^2 - 4$

71. $5t^2 - 80$

72. $-4t^2 + 64$

73. $8x^2 - 162$

74. $24x^2 - 54$

75. $36x - 49x^3$

76. $16x - 81x^3$

77. $49a^4 - 20$

78. $25a^4 - 9$

79. $t^4 - 1$

80. $x^4 - 16$

81. $-3x^3 + 24x^2 - 48x$

82. $-2a^4 + 36a^3 - 162a^2$

83. $75t^3 - 27t$

84. $80s^4 - 45s^2$

85. $a^8 - 2a^7 + a^6$

86. $x^8 - 8x^7 + 16x^6$

87. $10a^2 - 10b^2$

88. $6p^2 - 6q^2$

89. $16x^4 - y^4$

90. $98x^2 - 32y^2$

91. $18t^2 - 8s^2$

92. $a^4 - 81b^4$

93. Explain in your own words how to determine whether a polynomial is a perfect-square trinomial.

94. Explain in your own words how to determine whether a polynomial is a difference of squares.

Skill Review

To prepare for Section 5.5, review the product and power rules for exponents and multiplication of polynomials (Sections 4.1 and 4.5).

Simplify. [4.1]

95. $(2x^2y^4)^3$

96. $(-5x^2y)^3$

Multiply. [4.5]

97. $(x + 1)(x + 1)(x + 1)$

98. $(x - 1)^3$

99. $(p + q)^3$

100. $(p - q)^3$

Synthesis

101. Leon concludes that since $x^2 - 9 = (x - 3)(x + 3)$, it must follow that $x^2 + 9 = (x + 3)(x - 3)$. What mistake(s) is he making?

102. Write directions that would enable someone to construct a polynomial that contains a perfect-square trinomial, a difference of squares, and a common factor.

Factor completely. If a polynomial is prime, state this.

103. $x^8 - 2^8$

104. $3x^2 - \frac{1}{3}$

105. $18x^3 - \frac{8}{25}x$

106. $0.81t - t^3$

107. $(y - 5)^4 - z^8$

108. $x^2 - \left(\frac{1}{x}\right)^2$

109. $-x^4 + 8x^2 + 9$

110. $-16x^4 + 96x^2 - 144$

Aha! **111.** $(y + 3)^2 + 2(y + 3) + 1$

112. $49(x + 1)^2 - 42(x + 1) + 9$

113. $27p^3 - 45p^2 - 75p + 125$

114. $a^{2n} - 49b^{2n}$

115. $81 - b^{4k}$

116. $9b^{2n} + 12b^n + 4$

117. Subtract $(x^2 + 1)^2$ from $x^2(x + 1)^2$.

Factor by grouping. Look for a grouping of three terms that is a perfect-square trinomial.

118. $t^2 + 4t + 4 - 25$

119. $y^2 + 6y + 9 - x^2 - 8x - 16$

Find c such that each polynomial is the square of a binomial.

120. $cy^2 + 6y + 1$

121. $cy^2 - 24y + 9$

122. Find the value of a if $x^2 + a^2x + a^2$ factors into $(x + a)^2$.

123. Show that the difference of the squares of two consecutive integers is the sum of the two integers. (*Hint*: Use x for the smaller number.)

5.5 Factoring Sums or Differences of Cubes

Formulas for Factoring Sums or Differences of Cubes ▪ Using the Formulas

Formulas for Factoring Sums or Differences of Cubes

We have seen that a difference of two squares can always be factored, but a *sum* of two squares is usually prime. The situation is different with cubes: The difference *or sum* of two cubes can always be factored. To see this, consider the following products:

$$(A + B)(A^2 - AB + B^2) = A(A^2 - AB + B^2) + B(A^2 - AB + B^2)$$
$$= A^3 - A^2B + AB^2 + A^2B - AB^2 + B^3$$
$$= A^3 + B^3 \qquad \text{Combining like terms}$$

and

$$(A - B)(A^2 + AB + B^2) = A(A^2 + AB + B^2) - B(A^2 + AB + B^2)$$
$$= A^3 + A^2B + AB^2 - A^2B - AB^2 - B^3$$
$$= A^3 - B^3. \qquad \text{Combining like terms}$$

These products allow us to factor a sum or a difference of two cubes. Observe how the location of the + and − signs changes.

> **Factoring a Sum or a Difference of Two Cubes**
> $$A^3 + B^3 = (A + B)(A^2 - AB + B^2);$$
> $$A^3 - B^3 = (A - B)(A^2 + AB + B^2)$$

Using the Formulas

Remembering this list of cubes may prove helpful when factoring.

N	0.2	0.1	0	1	2	3	4	5	6
N^3	0.008	0.001	0	1	8	27	64	125	216

We say that 2 is the *cube root* of 8, that 3 is the cube root of 27, and so on.

EXAMPLE 1   Write an equivalent expression by factoring: $x^3 + 27$.

SOLUTION   We first observe that

$$x^3 + 27 = x^3 + 3^3. \qquad \text{This is a sum of cubes.}$$

Next, in one set of parentheses, we write the first cube root, x, plus the second cube root, 3:

$$(x + 3)(\qquad).$$

To get the other factor, we think of $x + 3$ and do the following:

Square the first term: x^2.
Multiply the terms and then change the sign: $-3x$.
Square the second term: 3^2, or 9.

$$(x + 3)(x^2 - 3x + 9).$$

Check: $(x + 3)(x^2 - 3x + 9) = x^3 - 3x^2 + 9x + 3x^2 - 9x + 27$
$$= x^3 + 27.   \text{Combining like terms}$$

Thus, $x^3 + 27 = (x + 3)(x^2 - 3x + 9)$.

TRY EXERCISE ▶ 13

In Example 2, you will see that the pattern used to write the trinomial factor in Example 1 can be used when factoring a *difference* of two cubes as well.

EXAMPLE 2

Factor.

a) $125x^3 - y^3$

b) $m^6 + 64$

c) $128y^7 - 250x^6y$

d) $r^6 - s^6$

SOLUTION

a) We have

$$125x^3 - y^3 = (5x)^3 - y^3.   \text{This is a difference of cubes.}$$

In one set of parentheses, we write the cube root of the first term, $5x$, minus the cube root of the second term, y:

$$(5x - y)(   ).   \text{This can be regarded as } 5x \text{ plus the cube root of } (-y)^3, \text{since } -y^3 = (-y)^3.$$

If you think of $A^3 - B^3$ as $A^3 + (-B)^3$, it is then sufficient to remember only the pattern for factoring a sum of two cubes. Be sure to simplify your result if you do this.

To get the other factor, we think of $5x + y$ and do the following:

Square the first term: $(5x)^2$, or $25x^2$.
Multiply the terms and then change the sign: $5xy$.
Square the second term: $(-y)^2 = y^2$.

$$(5x - y)(25x^2 + 5xy + y^2).$$

Check:
$$(5x - y)(25x^2 + 5xy + y^2) = 125x^3 + 25x^2y + 5xy^2 - 25x^2y - 5xy^2 - y^3$$
$$= 125x^3 - y^3.   \text{Combining like terms}$$

Thus, $125x^3 - y^3 = (5x - y)(25x^2 + 5xy + y^2)$.

b) We have

$$m^6 + 64 = (m^2)^3 + 4^3.   \text{Rewriting as a sum of quantities cubed}$$

Next, we reuse the pattern used in Example 1:

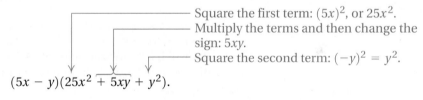

$$A^3 + B^3 = (A + B)(A^2 - A \cdot B + B^2)$$
$$(m^2)^3 + 4^3 = (m^2 + 4)((m^2)^2 - m^2 \cdot 4 + 4^2)$$
$$= (m^2 + 4)(m^4 - 4m^2 + 16).   \text{The check is left to the student.}$$

c) We have

$$128y^7 - 250x^6y = 2y(64y^6 - 125x^6)$$

Remember: *Always* look for a common factor.

$$= 2y[(4y^2)^3 - (5x^2)^3].$$

Rewriting as a difference of quantities cubed

To factor $(4y^2)^3 - (5x^2)^3$, we reuse the pattern in part (a) above:

$$A^3 \quad - \quad B^3 \quad = (A \quad - \quad B)(\quad A^2 \quad + \quad A \cdot B \quad + \quad B^2)$$

$$(4y^2)^3 - (5x^2)^3 = (4y^2 - 5x^2)((4y^2)^2 + 4y^2 \cdot 5x^2 + (5x^2)^2)$$

$$= (4y^2 - 5x^2)(16y^4 + 20x^2y^2 + 25x^4).$$

The check is left to the student. We have

$$128y^7 - 250x^6y = 2y(4y^2 - 5x^2)(16y^4 + 20x^2y^2 + 25x^4).$$

d) We have

$$r^6 - s^6 = (r^3)^2 - (s^3)^2$$

$$= (r^3 + s^3)(r^3 - s^3)$$

Factoring a difference of two *squares*

$$= (r + s)(r^2 - rs + s^2)(r - s)(r^2 + rs + s^2).$$

Factoring the sum and the difference of two cubes

To check, read the steps in reverse order and inspect the multiplication.

> **TRY EXERCISES** 31 and 41

In Example 2(d), suppose we first factored $r^6 - s^6$ as a difference of two cubes

$$(r^2)^3 - (s^2)^3 = (r^2 - s^2)(r^4 + r^2s^2 + s^4)$$

$$= (r + s)(r - s)(r^4 + r^2s^2 + s^4).$$

In this case, we might have missed some factors; $r^4 + r^2s^2 + s^4$ can be factored as $(r^2 - rs + s^2)(r^2 + rs + s^2)$, but we probably would never have suspected that such a factorization exists. Given a choice, it is generally better to factor as a difference of squares before factoring as a sum or a difference of cubes.

Useful Factoring Facts

Sum of cubes: $\qquad A^3 + B^3 = (A + B)(A^2 - AB + B^2)$

Difference of cubes: $\quad A^3 - B^3 = (A - B)(A^2 + AB + B^2)$

Difference of squares: $\quad A^2 - B^2 = (A + B)(A - B)$

There is no formula for factoring a sum of two squares.

5.5   **EXERCISE SET**

↪ *Concept Reinforcement   Classify each binomial as either a sum of cubes, a difference of cubes, a difference of squares, or none of these.*

1. $x^3 - 1$

2. $8 + t^3$

3. $9x^4 - 25$

4. $9x^2 + 25$

5. $1000t^3 + 1$

6. $x^3y^3 - 27z^3$

7. $25x^2 + 8x$

8. $100y^8 - 25x^4$

9. $s^{21} - t^{15}$

10. $14x^3 - 2x$

Factor completely.

11. $x^3 - 64$

12. $t^3 - 27$

13. $z^3 + 1$

14. $x^3 + 8$

15. $t^3 - 1000$

16. $m^3 + 125$

17. $27x^3 + 1$

18. $8a^3 + 1$

19. $64 - 125x^3$

20. $27 - 8t^3$

21. $x^3 - y^3$

22. $y^3 - z^3$

23. $a^3 + \frac{1}{8}$

24. $x^3 + \frac{1}{27}$

25. $8t^3 - 8$

26. $2y^3 - 128$

27. $54x^3 + 2$

28. $8a^3 + 1000$

29. $rs^4 + 64rs$

30. $ab^5 + 1000ab^2$

31. $5x^3 - 40z^3$

32. $2y^3 - 54z^3$

33. $y^3 - \frac{1}{1000}$

34. $x^3 - \frac{1}{8}$

35. $x^3 + 0.001$

36. $y^3 + 0.125$

37. $64x^6 - 8t^6$

38. $125c^6 - 8d^6$

39. $54y^4 - 128y$

40. $3z^5 - 3z^2$

41. $z^6 - 1$

42. $t^6 + 1$

43. $t^6 + 64y^6$

44. $p^6 - q^6$

45. $x^{12} - y^3z^{12}$

46. $a^9 + b^{12}c^{15}$

47. How could you use factoring to convince someone that $x^3 + y^3 \neq (x + y)^3$?

48. Is the following statement true or false and why? If A^3 and B^3 have a common factor, then A and B have a common factor.

Skill Review

Review graphing linear equations (Chapter 3).

49. Find the slope of the line containing the points $(-2, -5)$ and $(3, -6)$. [3.5]

50. Find the slope of the line given by $y - 3 = \frac{1}{4}x$. [3.6]

Graph.

51. $2x - 5y = 10$ [3.3]

52. $-5x = 10$ [3.3]

53. $y = \frac{2}{3}x - 1$ [3.6]

54. $y - 2 = -2(x + 4)$ [3.7]

Synthesis

55. Explain how the geometric model below can be used to verify the formula for factoring $a^3 - b^3$.

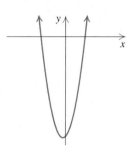

56. Explain how someone could construct a binomial that is both a difference of two cubes and a difference of two squares.

Factor.

57. $x^{6a} - y^{3b}$

58. $2x^{3a} + 16y^{3b}$

Aha! 59. $(x + 5)^3 + (x - 5)^3$

60. $\frac{1}{16}x^{3a} + \frac{1}{2}y^{6a}z^{9b}$

61. $5x^3y^6 - \frac{5}{8}$

62. $x^3 - (x + y)^3$

63. $x^{6a} - (x^{2a} + 1)^3$

64. $(x^{2a} - 1)^3 - x^{6a}$

65. $t^4 - 8t^3 - t + 8$

<table>
<tr><td>**5.6**</td><td>## Factoring: A General Strategy</td></tr>
</table>

Choosing the Right Method

Thus far, each section in this chapter has examined one or two different methods for factoring polynomials. In practice, when the need for factoring a polynomial arises, we must decide on our own which method to use. Regardless of the polynomial with which we are faced, the guidelines listed below can always be used.

To Factor a Polynomial

A. Always look for a common factor first. If there is one, factor out the largest common factor. Be sure to include it in your final answer.

B. Then look at the number of terms.

Two terms: Try factoring as a difference of squares first: $A^2 - B^2 = (A + B)(A - B)$. Next, try factoring as a sum or a difference of cubes: $A^3 + B^3 = (A + B)(A^2 - AB + B^2)$ and $A^3 - B^3 = (A - B)(A^2 + AB + B^2)$.

Three terms: If the trinomial is a perfect-square trinomial, factor accordingly: $A^2 + 2AB + B^2 = (A + B)^2$ or $A^2 - 2AB + B^2 = (A - B)^2$. If it is not a perfect-square trinomial, try using FOIL or grouping.

Four terms: Try factoring by grouping.

C. Always *factor completely*. When a factor can itself be factored, be sure to factor it. Remember that some polynomials, like $x^2 + 9$, are prime.

D. Check by multiplying.

Choosing the Right Method

EXAMPLE **1**

Factor: $5t^4 - 80$.

SOLUTION

A. We look for a common factor:

$$5t^4 - 80 = 5(t^4 - 16). \qquad \text{5 is the largest common factor.}$$

B. The factor $t^4 - 16$ is a difference of squares: $(t^2)^2 - 4^2$. We factor it, being careful to rewrite the 5 from step (A):

$$5t^4 - 80 = 5(t^2 + 4)(t^2 - 4). \qquad t^4 - 16 = (t^2 + 4)(t^2 - 4)$$

C. Since $t^2 - 4$ is a difference of squares, we continue factoring:

$$5t^4 - 80 = 5(t^2 + 4)(t^2 - 4) = 5(t^2 + 4)(t - 2)(t + 2).$$

This is a sum of squares, which cannot be factored.

D. *Check:* $5(t^2 + 4)(t - 2)(t + 2) = 5(t^2 + 4)(t^2 - 4)$
$$= 5(t^4 - 16) = 5t^4 - 80.$$

The factorization is $5(t^2 + 4)(t - 2)(t + 2)$.

▶ TRY EXERCISE ▶ 5

EXAMPLE **2**

Factor: $2x^3 + 10x^2 + x + 5$.

SOLUTION

A. We look for a common factor. There is none.

B. Because there are four terms, we try factoring by grouping:

$$2x^3 + 10x^2 + x + 5$$
$$= (2x^3 + 10x^2) + (x + 5) \quad \text{Separating into two binomials}$$
$$= 2x^2(x + 5) + 1(x + 5) \quad \text{Factoring out the largest common factor from each binomial. The 1 serves as an aid.}$$
$$= (x + 5)(2x^2 + 1). \quad \text{Factoring out the common factor, } x + 5$$

C. Nothing can be factored further, so we have factored completely.

D. *Check:* $(x + 5)(2x^2 + 1) = 2x^3 + x + 10x^2 + 5$
$$= 2x^3 + 10x^2 + x + 5.$$

The factorization is $(x + 5)(2x^2 + 1)$.   **TRY EXERCISE** 13

EXAMPLE **3**

Factor: $-n^5 + 2n^4 + 35n^3$.

SOLUTION

A. We note that there is a common factor, $-n^3$:

$$-n^5 + 2n^4 + 35n^3 = -n^3(n^2 - 2n - 35).$$

B. The factor $n^2 - 2n - 35$ is not a perfect-square trinomial. We factor it using trial and error:

$$-n^5 + 2n^4 + 35n^3 = -n^3(n^2 - 2n - 35)$$
$$= -n^3(n - 7)(n + 5).$$

C. Nothing can be factored further, so we have factored completely.

D. *Check:* $-n^3(n - 7)(n + 5) = -n^3(n^2 - 2n - 35)$
$$= -n^5 + 2n^4 + 35n^3.$$

The factorization is $-n^3(n - 7)(n + 5)$.   **TRY EXERCISE** 21

EXAMPLE **4**

Factor: $x^2 - 20x + 100$.

SOLUTION

A. We look first for a common factor. There is none.

B. This polynomial is a perfect-square trinomial. We factor it accordingly:

$$x^2 - 20x + 100 = x^2 - 2 \cdot x \cdot 10 + 10^2 \quad \text{Try to do this step mentally.}$$
$$= (x - 10)^2.$$

C. Nothing can be factored further, so we have factored completely.

D. *Check:* $(x - 10)(x - 10) = x^2 - 20x + 100.$

The factorization is $(x - 10)(x - 10)$, or $(x - 10)^2$.   **TRY EXERCISE** 7

EXAMPLE 5

Factor: $6x^2y^4 - 21x^3y^5 + 3x^2y^6$.

SOLUTION

A. We first factor out the largest common factor, $3x^2y^4$:

$$6x^2y^4 - 21x^3y^5 + 3x^2y^6 = 3x^2y^4(2 - 7xy + y^2).$$

B. The constant term in $2 - 7xy + y^2$ is not a square, so we do not have perfect-square trinomial. Note that x appears only in $-7xy$. The product of form like $(1 - y)(2 - y)$ has no x in the middle term. Thus, $2 - 7xy + y^2$ can not be factored.

C. Nothing can be factored further, so we have factored completely.

D. *Check:* $3x^2y^4(2 - 7xy + y^2) = 6x^2y^4 - 21x^3y^5 + 3x^2y^6$.

The factorization is $3x^2y^4(2 - 7xy + y^2)$.

> **TRY EXERCISE** ▸ 33

EXAMPLE 6

Factor: $x^6 - 64$.

SOLUTION

A. We look first for a common factor. There is none (other than 1 or -1).

B. There are two terms, a difference of squares: $(x^3)^2 - (8)^2$. We factor:

$$x^6 - 64 = (x^3 + 8)(x^3 - 8).\qquad \text{Note that } x^6 = (x^3)^2.$$

C. One factor is a sum of two cubes, and the other factor is a difference of tw cubes. We factor both:

$$x^6 - 64 = (x + 2)(x^2 - 2x + 4)(x - 2)(x^2 + 2x + 4).$$

The factorization is complete because no factor can be factored further.

D. *Check:* $(x + 2)(x^2 - 2x + 4)(x - 2)(x^2 + 2x + 4) = (x^3 + 8)(x^3 - 8)$

$$= x^6 - 64.$$

The factorization is $(x + 2)(x^2 - 2x + 4)(x - 2)(x^2 + 2x + 4)$.

> **TRY EXERCISE** ▸ 31

EXAMPLE 7

Factor: $-25m^2 - 20mn - 4n^2$.

SOLUTION

A. We look first for a common factor. Since all the terms are negative, we facto out a -1:

$$-25m^2 - 20mn - 4n^2 = -1(25m^2 + 20mn + 4n^2).$$

B. There are three terms in the parentheses. Note that the first term and the las term are squares: $25m^2 = (5m)^2$ and $4n^2 = (2n)^2$. We see that twice the prod uct of $5m$ and $2n$ is the middle term,

$$2 \cdot 5m \cdot 2n = 20mn,$$

so the trinomial is a perfect square. To factor, we write a binomial squared:

$$-25m^2 - 20mn - 4n^2 = -1(25m^2 + 20mn + 4n^2)$$

$$= -1(5m + 2n)^2.$$

C. Nothing can be factored further, so we have factored completely.

D. *Check:* $-1(5m + 2n)^2 = -1(25m^2 + 20mn + 4n^2)$

$$= -25m^2 - 20mn - 4n^2.$$

The factorization is $-1(5m + 2n)^2$, or $-(5m + 2n)^2$.

> **TRY EXERCISE** ▸ 59

EXAMPLE 8   Factor: $x^2y^2 + 7xy + 12$.

SOLUTION

A. We look first for a common factor. There is none.

B. Since only one term is a square, we do not have a perfect-square trinomial. We use trial and error, thinking of the product xy as a single variable:

$$(xy + \quad)(xy + \quad).$$

We factor the last term, 12. All the signs are positive, so we consider only positive factors. Possibilities are 1, 12 and 2, 6 and 3, 4. The pair 3, 4 gives a sum of 7 for the coefficient of the middle term. Thus,

$$x^2y^2 + 7xy + 12 = (xy + 3)(xy + 4).$$

C. Nothing can be factored further, so we have factored completely.

D. *Check:* $(xy + 3)(xy + 4) = x^2y^2 + 7xy + 12.$

The factorization is $(xy + 3)(xy + 4)$.

> **TRY EXERCISE** 61

Compare the variables appearing in Example 7 with those in Example 8. Note that if the leading term contains one variable and a different variable is in the last term, as in Example 7, each binomial contains two variable terms. When two variables appear in the leading term and no variables appear in the last term, as in Example 8, each binomial contains one term that has two variables and one term that is a constant.

EXAMPLE 9   Factor: $a^4 - 16b^4$.

SOLUTION

A. We look first for a common factor. There is none.

B. There are two terms. Since $a^4 = (a^2)^2$ and $16b^4 = (4b^2)^2$, we see that we have a difference of squares. Thus,

$$a^4 - 16b^4 = (a^2 + 4b^2)(a^2 - 4b^2).$$

C. The factor $(a^2 - 4b^2)$ is itself a difference of squares. Thus,

$$a^4 - 16b^4 = (a^2 + 4b^2)(a + 2b)(a - 2b). \qquad \text{Factoring } a^2 - 4b^2$$

D. *Check:* $(a^2 + 4b^2)(a + 2b)(a - 2b) = (a^2 + 4b^2)(a^2 - 4b^2)$
$$= a^4 - 16b^4.$$

The factorization is $(a^2 + 4b^2)(a + 2b)(a - 2b)$.

> **TRY EXERCISE** 53

5.6   **EXERCISE SET**

↪ *Concept Reinforcement*   *In each of Exercises 1–4, complete the sentence.*

1. As a first step when factoring polynomials, always check for a _____.

2. When factoring a trinomial, if two terms are not squares, it cannot be a _____.

3. If a polynomial has four terms and no common factor, it may be possible to factor by _____.

4. It is always possible to check a factorization by _____.

Factor completely. If a polynomial is prime, state this.

5. $5a^2 - 125$

6. $10c^2 - 810$

7. $y^2 + 49 - 14y$

8. $a^2 + 25 + 10a$

9. $3t^2 + 16t + 21$

10. $8t^2 + 31t - 4$

11. $x^3 + 18x^2 + 81x$

12. $x^3 - 24x^2 + 144x$

13. $x^3 - 5x^2 - 25x + 125$

14. $x^3 + 3x^2 - 4x - 12$

15. $27t^3 - 3t$

16. $98t^2 - 18$

17. $9x^3 + 12x^2 - 45x$

18. $20x^3 - 4x^2 - 72x$

19. $t^2 + 25$

20. $4x^2 + 20x - 144$

21. $6y^2 + 18y - 240$

22. $4n^2 + 81$

23. $-2a^6 + 8a^5 - 8a^4$

24. $-x^5 - 14x^4 - 49x^3$

25. $5x^5 - 80x$

26. $4x^4 - 64$

27. $t^4 - 9$

28. $9 + t^8$

29. $-x^6 + 2x^5 - 7x^4$

30. $-x^5 + 4x^4 - 3x^3$

31. $x^3 - y^3$

32. $8t^3 + 1$

33. $ax^2 + ay^2$

34. $12n^2 + 24n^3$

35. $2\pi rh + 2\pi r^2$

36. $4\pi r^2 + 2\pi r$

Aha! **37.** $(a + b)5a + (a + b)3b$

38. $5c(a^3 + b) - (a^3 + b)$

39. $x^2 + x + xy + y$

40. $n^2 + 2n + np + 2p$

41. $a^2 - 2a - ay + 2y$

42. $2x^2 - 4x + xz - 2z$

43. $3x^2 + 13xy - 10y^2$

44. $-x^2 - y^2 - 2xy$

45. $8m^3n - 32m^2n^2 + 24mn$

46. $a^2 - 7a - 6$

47. $4b^2 + a^2 - 4ab$

48. $7p^4 - 7q^4$

49. $16x^2 + 24xy + 9y^2$

50. $6a^2b^3 + 12a^3b^2 - 3a^4b^2$

51. $m^2 - 5m + 8$

52. $25z^2 + 10zy + y^2$

53. $a^4b^4 - 16$

54. $a^5 - 4a^4b - 5a^3b^2$

55. $80cd^2 - 36c^2d + 4c^3$

56. $2p^2 + pq + q^2$

57. $64t^6 - 1$

58. $m^6 - 1$

59. $-12 - x^2y^2 - 8xy$

60. $m^2n^2 - 4mn - 32$

61. $5p^2q^2 + 25pq - 30$

62. $a^4b^3 + 2a^3b^2 - 15a^2b$

63. $54a^4 + 16ab^3$

64. $54x^3y - 250y^4$

65. $x^6 + x^5y - 2x^4y^2$

66. $2s^6t^2 + 10s^3t^3 + 12t^4$

67. $36a^2 - 15a + \frac{25}{16}$

68. $a^2 + 2a^2bc + a^2b^2c^2$

69. $\frac{1}{81}x^2 - \frac{8}{27}x + \frac{16}{9}$

70. $\frac{1}{4}a^2 + \frac{1}{3}ab + \frac{1}{9}b^2$

71. $1 - 16x^{12}y^{12}$

72. $b^4a - 81a^5$

73. $4a^2b^2 + 12ab + 9$

74. $9c^2 + 6cd + d^2$

75. $z^4 + 6z^3 - 6z^2 - 36z$

76. $t^5 - 2t^4 + 5t^3 - 10t^2$

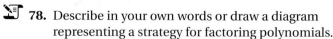 **77.** Kelly factored $16 - 8x + x^2$ as $(x - 4)^2$, while Tony factored it as $(4 - x)^2$. Are they both correct? Why o~~r~~ why not?

78. Describe in your own words or draw a diagram representing a strategy for factoring polynomials.

Skill Review

To prepare for Section 5.7, review solving equations (Section 2.2).

Solve. [2.2]

79. $8x - 9 = 0$

80. $3x + 5 = 0$

81. $2x + 7 = 0$

82. $4x - 1 = 0$

83. $3 - x = 0$

84. $22 - 2x = 0$

85. $2x - 5 = 8x + 1$

86. $3(x - 1) = 9 - x$

Synthesis

87. There are third-degree polynomials in x that we are not yet able to factor, despite the fact that they are not prime. Explain how such a polynomial could be created.

88. Describe a method that could be used to find a binomial of degree 16 that can be expressed as the product of prime binomial factors.

Factor.

89. $-(x^5 + 7x^3 - 18x)$

90. $18 + a^3 - 9a - 2a^2$

91. $-x^4 + 7x^2 + 18$

92. $-3a^4 + 15a^2 - 12$

Aha! **93.** $y^2(y + 1) - 4y(y + 1) - 21(y + 1)$

94. $y^2(y - 1) - 2y(y - 1) + (y - 1)$

95. $(y + 4)^2 + 2x(y + 4) + x^2$

96. $6(x - 1)^2 + 7y(x - 1) - 3y^2$

97. $2(a + 3)^4 - (a + 3)^3(b - 2) - (a + 3)^2(b - 2)^2$

98. $5(t - 1)^5 - 6(t - 1)^4(s - 1) + (t - 1)^3(s - 1)^2$

99. $49x^4 + 14x^2 + 1 - 25x^6$

COLLABORATIVE

CORNER

Matching Factorizations*

Focus: Factoring

Time: 20 minutes

Group size: Begin with the entire class. If there is an odd number of students, the instructor should participate.

Materials: Prepared sheets of paper, pins or tape. On half of the sheets, the instructor writes a polynomial. On the remaining sheets, the instructor writes the factorization of those polynomials. The polynomials and factorizations should be similar; for example,

$$x^2 - 2x - 8, \quad (x - 2)(x - 4),$$
$$x^2 - 6x + 8, \quad (x - 1)(x - 8),$$
$$x^2 - 9x + 8, \quad (x + 2)(x - 4).$$

ACTIVITY

1. As class members enter the room, the instructor pins or tapes either a polynomial or a factorization to the back of each student. Class members are told only whether their sheet of paper contains a polynomial or a factorization.

2. After all students are wearing a sheet of paper, they should mingle with one another, attempting to match up their factorization with the appropriate polynomial or vice versa. They may ask questions of one another that relate to factoring and polynomials. Answers to the questions should be yes or no. For example, a legitimate question might be "Is my last term negative?" or "Do my factors have opposite signs?"

3. The game is over when all factorization/polynomial pairs have "found" one another.

*Thanks to Jann MacInnes of Florida Community College at Jacksonville–Kent Campus for suggesting this activity.

5.7   Solving Polynomial Equations by Factoring

The Principle of Zero Products   ●   Factoring to Solve Equations

When we factor a polynomial, we are forming an *equivalent expression*. We now use our factoring skills to *solve equations*. We already know how to solve linear equations like $x + 2 = 7$ and $2x = 9$. The equations we will learn to solve in this section contain a variable raised to a power greater than 1 and will usually have more than one solution.

Whenever two polynomials are set equal to each other, we have a *polynomial equation*. The degree of a polynomial equation is the same as the highest degree of any term in the equation. Second-degree equations like $4t^2 - 9 = 0$ and $x^2 + 6x + 5 = 0$ are called **quadratic equations**.

> ### Quadratic Equation
>
> A *quadratic equation* is an equation equivalent to one of the form
>
> $$ax^2 + bx + c = 0,$$
>
> where a, b, and c are constants, with $a \neq 0$.

In order to solve quadratic equations, we need to develop a new principle.

The Principle of Zero Products

Suppose we are told that the product of two numbers is 6. On the basis of this information, it is impossible to know the value of either number—the product could be $2 \cdot 3, 6 \cdot 1, 12 \cdot \frac{1}{2}$, and so on. However, if we are told that the product of two numbers is 0, we know that at least one of the two factors must itself be 0. For example, if $(x + 3)(x - 2) = 0$, we can conclude that either $x + 3$ is 0 or $x - 2$ is 0.

> ### The Principle of Zero Products
> An equation $AB = 0$ is true if and only if $A = 0$ or $B = 0$, or both.
> (A product is 0 if and only if at least one factor is 0.)

EXAMPLE **1**

Solve: $(x + 3)(x - 2) = 0$.

SOLUTION   We are looking for all values of x that will make the equation true. The equation tells us that the product of $x + 3$ and $x - 2$ is 0. In order for the product to be 0, at least one factor must be 0. Thus we look for any value of x for which $x + 3 = 0$, as well as any value of x for which $x - 2 = 0$, that is, either

$$x + 3 = 0 \quad or \quad x - 2 = 0.$$ Using the principle of zero products. There are two equations to solve.

We solve each equation:

$$x + 3 = 0 \quad or \quad x - 2 = 0$$
$$x = -3 \quad or \quad x = 2.$$

Both -3 and 2 should be checked in the original equation.

Check: For -3:

$$\frac{(x + 3)(x - 2) = 0}{(-3 + 3)(-3 - 2) \;\bigm|\; 0}$$
$$0(-5)$$
The factor $x + 3$ is 0 when $x = -3$.
$$0 \stackrel{?}{=} 0 \quad \text{TRUE}$$

For 2:

$$\frac{(x + 3)(x - 2) = 0}{(2 + 3)(2 - 2) \;\bigm|\; 0}$$
$$5(0)$$
The factor $x - 2$ is 0 when $x = 2$.
$$0 \stackrel{?}{=} 0 \quad \text{TRUE}$$

The solutions are -3 and 2.

TRY EXERCISE 5

When we are using the principle of zero products, the word "or" is meant to emphasize that any one of the factors could be the one that represents 0.

EXAMPLE **2**

Solve: $3(5x + 1)(x - 7) = 0$.

SOLUTION   The factors in this equation are 3, $5x + 1$, and $x - 7$. Since the factor 3 is constant, the only way in which $3(5x + 1)(x - 7)$ can be 0 is for one of the other factors to be 0, that is,

$$5x + 1 = 0 \quad or \quad x - 7 = 0$$ Using the principle of zero products
$$5x = -1 \quad or \quad x = 7$$ Solving the two equations separately
$$x = -\tfrac{1}{5} \quad or \quad x = 7.$$ $5x + 1 = 0$ when $x = -\frac{1}{5}$; $x - 7 = 0$ when $x = 7$

Check: For $-\frac{1}{5}$:

$$\begin{array}{c|c} 3(5x + 1)(x - 7) = 0 \\ \hline 3\left(5\left(-\frac{1}{5}\right) + 1\right)\left(-\frac{1}{5} - 7\right) & 0 \\ 3(-1 + 1)\left(-7\frac{1}{5}\right) \\ 3(0)\left(-7\frac{1}{5}\right) \\ 0 \stackrel{?}{=} 0 & \text{TRUE} \end{array}$$

For 7:

$$\begin{array}{c|c} 3(5x + 1)(x - 7) = 0 \\ \hline 3(5(7) + 1)(7 - 7) & 0 \\ 3(35 + 1)0 \\ 0 \stackrel{?}{=} 0 & \text{TRUE} \end{array}$$

The solutions are $-\frac{1}{5}$ and 7.   **TRY EXERCISE** ▶ 9

The constant factor 3 in Example 2 is never 0 and is not a solution of the equation. However, a variable factor such as x or t *can* equal 0, and must be considered when using the principle of zero products.

EXAMPLE 3

Solve: $7t(t - 5) = 0$.

SOLUTION   We have

$$7 \cdot t(t - 5) = 0 \qquad \text{The factors are 7, } t\text{, and } t - 5.$$
$$t = 0 \quad or \quad t - 5 = 0 \qquad \text{Using the principle of zero products}$$
$$t = 0 \quad or \qquad t = 5. \qquad \text{Solving. Note that the constant factor, 7, is never 0.}$$

The solutions are 0 and 5. The check is left to the student.   **TRY EXERCISE** ▶ 15

Factoring to Solve Equations

By factoring and using the principle of zero products, we can now solve a variety of quadratic equations.

EXAMPLE 4

Solve: $x^2 + 5x + 6 = 0$.

SOLUTION   This equation differs from those solved in Chapter 2. There are no like terms to combine, and there is a squared term. We first factor the polynomial. Then we use the principle of zero products:

$$x^2 + 5x + 6 = 0$$
$$(x + 2)(x + 3) = 0 \qquad \text{Factoring}$$
$$x + 2 = 0 \quad or \quad x + 3 = 0 \qquad \text{Using the principle of zero products}$$
$$x = -2 \quad or \qquad x = -3.$$

Check: For -2:

$$\begin{array}{c|c} x^2 + 5x + 6 = 0 \\ \hline (-2)^2 + 5(-2) + 6 & 0 \\ 4 - 10 + 6 \\ -6 + 6 \\ 0 \stackrel{?}{=} 0 & \text{TRUE} \end{array}$$

For -3:

$$\begin{array}{c|c} x^2 + 5x + 6 = 0 \\ \hline (-3)^2 + 5(-3) + 6 & 0 \\ 9 - 15 + 6 \\ -6 + 6 \\ 0 \stackrel{?}{=} 0 & \text{TRUE} \end{array}$$

The solutions are -2 and -3.   **TRY EXERCISE** ▶ 21

The principle of zero products applies even when there is a common factor.

EXAMPLE | **5**

STUDENT NOTES

Checking for a common factor is an important step that is often overlooked. In Example 5, the equation must be factored. If we "divide both sides by x," we will not find the solution 0.

Solve: $x^2 + 7x = 0$.

SOLUTION   Although there is no constant term, because of the x^2-term, the equation is still quadratic. The methods of Chapter 2 are not sufficient, so we try factoring:

$$x^2 + 7x = 0$$
$$x(x + 7) = 0 \qquad \text{Factoring out the largest common factor, } x$$
$$x = 0 \quad or \quad x + 7 = 0 \qquad \text{Using the principle of zero products}$$
$$x = 0 \quad or \qquad x = -7.$$

The solutions are 0 and -7. The check is left to the student.

TRY EXERCISE 27

> *CAUTION!*   We *must* have 0 on one side of the equation before the principle of zero products can be used. Get all nonzero terms on one side and 0 on the other.

EXAMPLE | **6**

Solve: **(a)** $x^2 - 8x = -16$; **(b)** $4t^2 = 25$.

SOLUTION

a) We first add 16 to get 0 on one side:

$$x^2 - 8x = -16$$
$$x^2 - 8x + 16 = 0 \qquad \text{Adding 16 to both sides to get 0 on one side}$$
$$(x - 4)(x - 4) = 0 \qquad \text{Factoring}$$
$$x - 4 = 0 \quad or \quad x - 4 = 0 \qquad \text{Using the principle of zero products}$$
$$x = 4 \quad or \qquad x = 4.$$

There is only one solution, 4. The check is left to the student.

b) We have

$$4t^2 = 25$$
$$4t^2 - 25 = 0 \qquad \text{Subtracting 25 from both sides to get 0 on one side}$$
$$(2t - 5)(2t + 5) = 0 \qquad \text{Factoring a difference of squares}$$
$$\left.\begin{array}{rcl} 2t - 5 = 0 & or & 2t + 5 = 0 \\ 2t = 5 & or & 2t = -5 \\ t = \tfrac{5}{2} & or & t = -\tfrac{5}{2}. \end{array}\right\} \begin{array}{l} \text{Solving the two equations} \\ \text{separately} \end{array}$$

The solutions are $\frac{5}{2}$ and $-\frac{5}{2}$. The check is left to the student.

TRY EXERCISE 41

When solving quadratic equations by factoring, remember that a factorization is not useful unless 0 is on the other side of the equation.

EXAMPLE | **7**

Solve: $(x + 3)(2x - 1) = 9$.

SOLUTION   Be careful with an equation like this! Since we need 0 on one side, we first multiply out the product on the left and then subtract 9 from both sides.

$$(x + 3)(2x - 1) = 9$$ This is not a product equal to 0.

$$2x^2 + 5x - 3 = 9$$ Multiplying on the left

$$2x^2 + 5x - 3 - 9 = 9 - 9$$ Subtracting 9 from both sides to get 0 on one side

$$2x^2 + 5x - 12 = 0$$ Combining like terms

$$(2x - 3)(x + 4) = 0$$ Factoring. Now we have a product equal to 0.

$$2x - 3 = 0 \quad or \quad x + 4 = 0$$ Using the principle of zero products

$$2x = 3 \quad or \qquad x = -4$$

$$x = \tfrac{3}{2} \quad or \qquad x = -4$$

Check: For $\tfrac{3}{2}$:

$$\frac{(x + 3)(2x - 1) = 9}{\left(\tfrac{3}{2} + 3\right)\left(2 \cdot \tfrac{3}{2} - 1\right) \,\Big|\, 9}$$
$$\left(\tfrac{9}{2}\right)(2)$$
$$9 \overset{?}{=} 9 \quad \text{TRUE}$$

For -4:

$$\frac{(x + 3)(2x - 1) = 9}{(-4 + 3)(2(-4)-1) \,\Big|\, 9}$$
$$(-1)(-9)$$
$$9 \overset{?}{=} 9 \quad \text{TRUE}$$

The solutions are $\tfrac{3}{2}$ and -4.

$\boxed{\text{TRY EXERCISE}}$ 43

We can use the principle of zero products to solve polynomials with degree greater than 2, if they can be factored.

EXAMPLE 8

Solve: $3x^3 - 30x = 9x^2$.

SOLUTION   We have

$$3x^3 - 30x = 9x^2$$

$$3x^3 - 9x^2 - 30x = 0$$ Getting 0 on one side and writing in descending order

$$3x(x^2 - 3x - 10) = 0$$ Factoring out a common factor

$$3x(x + 2)(x - 5) = 0$$ Factoring the trinomial

$$3x = 0 \quad or \quad x + 2 = 0 \quad or \quad x - 5 = 0$$ Using the principle of zero products

$$x = 0 \quad or \qquad x = -2 \quad or \qquad x = 5.$$

Check:

$$\frac{3x^3 - 30x = 9x^2}{3 \cdot 0^3 - 30 \cdot 0 \,\Big|\, 9 \cdot 0^2}$$
$$0 - 0 \,\Big|\, 9 \cdot 0$$
$$0 \overset{?}{=} 0 \qquad \text{TRUE}$$

$$\frac{3x^3 - 30x = 9x^2}{3(-2)^3 - 30(-2) \,\Big|\, 9(-2)^2}$$
$$3(-8) + 60 \,\Big|\, 9 \cdot 4$$
$$-24 + 60 \,\Big|\, 36$$
$$36 \overset{?}{=} 36 \qquad \text{TRUE}$$

$$\frac{3x^3 - 30x = 9x^2}{3 \cdot 5^3 - 30 \cdot 5 \,\Big|\, 9 \cdot 5^2}$$
$$3 \cdot 125 - 150 \,\Big|\, 9 \cdot 25$$
$$375 - 150 \,\Big|\, 225$$
$$225 \overset{?}{=} 225 \qquad \text{TRUE}$$

The solutions are 0, -2, and 5.

$\boxed{\text{TRY EXERCISE}}$ 53

ALGEBRAIC–GRAPHICAL CONNECTION

When graphing equations in Chapter 3, we found the x-intercept by replacing y with 0 and solving for x. This procedure is also used to find the x-intercepts when graphing equations of the form $y = ax^2 + bx + c$. Although the details of creating such graphs is left for Chapter 11, we consider them briefly here from the standpoint of finding x-intercepts. The graphs are shaped as shown. Note that each x-intercept represents a solution of $ax^2 + bx + c = 0$.

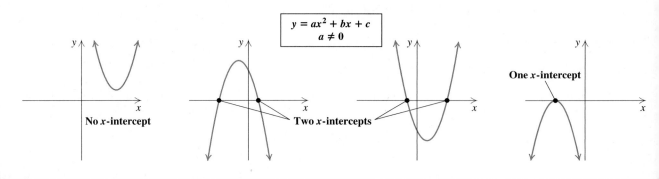

$$y = ax^2 + bx + c$$
$$a \neq 0$$

No x-intercept   Two x-intercepts   One x-intercept

EXAMPLE **9**   Find the x-intercepts for the graph of the equation shown. (The grid is intentionally not included.)

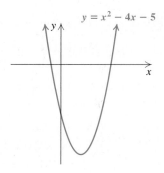

$$y = x^2 - 4x - 5$$

SOLUTION   To find the x-intercepts, we let $y = 0$ and solve for x:

$$0 = x^2 - 4x - 5 \qquad \text{Substituting 0 for } y$$
$$0 = (x - 5)(x + 1) \qquad \text{Factoring}$$
$$x - 5 = 0 \quad or \quad x + 1 = 0 \qquad \text{Using the principle of zero products}$$
$$x = 5 \quad or \qquad x = -1. \qquad \text{Solving for } x$$

The x-intercepts are $(5, 0)$ and $(-1, 0)$.

TRY EXERCISE 61

TECHNOLOGY CONNECTION

A graphing calculator allows us to solve polynomial equations even when an equation cannot be solved by factoring. For example, to solve $x^2 - 3x - 5 = 0$, we can let $y_1 = x^2 - 3x - 5$ and $y_2 = 0$. Selecting a bold line type to the left of y_2 in the Y= window makes the line easier to see. Using the INTERSECT option of the CALC menu, we select the two graphs in which we are interested, along with a guess. The graphing calculator displays the point of intersection.

An alternative method uses only y_1 and the ZERO option of the CALC menu. This option requires you to enter an x-value to the left of each x-intercept as a LEFT BOUND. An x-value to the right of the x-intercept is then entered as a RIGHT BOUND. Finally, a GUESS value between the two bounds is entered and the x-intercept, or ZERO, is displayed.

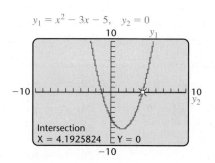

$y_1 = x^2 - 3x - 5, \quad y_2 = 0$

Intersection
X = 4.1925824   Y = 0

Use a graphing calculator to find the solutions, if they exist, accurate to two decimal places.

1. $x^2 + 4x - 3 = 0$
2. $x^2 - 5x - 2 = 0$
3. $x^2 + 13.54x + 40.95 = 0$
4. $x^2 - 4.43x + 6.32 = 0$
5. $1.235x^2 - 3.409x = 0$

5.7 EXERCISE SET

For Extra Help   MyMathLab   Math XL PRACTICE   WATCH   DOWNLOAD

➡ *Concept Reinforcement* *For each of Exercises 1–4, match the phrase with the most appropriate choice from the column on the right.*

1. ____ The name of equations of the type $ax^2 + bx + c = 0$, with $a \neq 0$

2. ____ The maximum number of solutions of quadratic equations

3. ____ The idea that $A \cdot B = 0$ if and only if $A = 0$ or $B = 0$

4. ____ The number that a product must equal before the principle of zero products is used

a) 2

b) 0

c) Quadratic

d) The principle of zero products

Solve using the principle of zero products.

5. $(x + 2)(x + 9) = 0$

6. $(x + 3)(x + 10) = 0$

7. $(2t - 3)(t + 6) = 0$

8. $(5t - 8)(t - 1) = 0$

9. $4(7x - 1)(10x - 3) = 0$

10. $6(4x - 3)(2x + 9) = 0$

11. $x(x - 7) = 0$

12. $x(x + 2) = 0$

13. $\left(\frac{2}{3}x - \frac{12}{11}\right)\left(\frac{7}{4}x - \frac{1}{12}\right) = 0$

14. $\left(\frac{1}{9} - 3x\right)\left(\frac{1}{5} + 2x\right) = 0$

15. $6n(3n + 8) = 0$

16. $10n(4n - 5) = 0$

17. $(20 - 0.4x)(7 - 0.1x) = 0$

18. $(1 - 0.05x)(1 - 0.3x) = 0$

19. $(3x - 2)(x + 5)(x - 1) = 0$

20. $(2x + 1)(x + 3)(x - 5) = 0$

Solve by factoring and using the principle of zero products.

21. $x^2 - 7x + 6 = 0$ **22.** $x^2 - 6x + 5 = 0$

23. $x^2 + 4x - 21 = 0$ **24.** $x^2 - 7x - 18 = 0$

25. $n^2 + 11n + 18 = 0$ **26.** $n^2 + 8n + 15 = 0$

27. $x^2 - 10x = 0$ **28.** $x^2 + 8x = 0$

29. $6t + t^2 = 0$ **30.** $3t - t^2 = 0$

31. $x^2 - 36 = 0$ **32.** $x^2 - 100 = 0$

33. $4t^2 = 49$ **34.** $9t^2 = 25$

35. $0 = 25 + x^2 + 10x$ **36.** $0 = 6x + x^2 + 9$

37. $64 + x^2 = 16x$ **38.** $x^2 + 1 = 2x$

39. $4t^2 = 8t$ **40.** $12t = 3t^2$

41. $4y^2 = 7y + 15$ **42.** $12y^2 - 5y = 2$

43. $(x - 7)(x + 1) = -16$

44. $(x + 2)(x - 7) = -18$

45. $15z^2 + 7 = 20z + 7$

46. $14z^2 - 3 = 21z - 3$

47. $36m^2 - 9 = 40$

48. $81x^2 - 5 = 20$

49. $(x + 3)(3x + 5) = 7$

50. $(x - 1)(5x + 4) = 2$

51. $3x^2 - 2x = 9 - 8x$

52. $x^2 - 2x = 18 + 5x$

53. $x^2(2x - 1) = 3x$

54. $x^2 = x(10 - 3x^2)$

55. $(2x - 5)(3x^2 + 29x + 56) = 0$

56. $(4x + 9)(15x^2 - 7x - 2) = 0$

57. Use this graph to solve $x^2 - 3x - 4 = 0$.

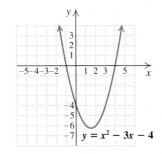

58. Use this graph to solve $x^2 + x - 6 = 0$.

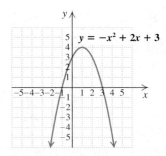

59. Use this graph to solve $-x^2 - x + 6 = 0$.

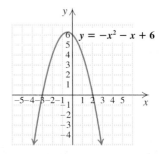

60. Use this graph to solve $-x^2 + 2x + 3 = 0$.

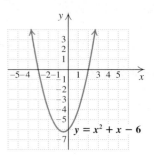

Find the x-intercepts for the graph of each equation. Grid are intentionally not included.

61. $y = x^2 - x - 6$ **62.** $y = x^2 + 3x - 4$

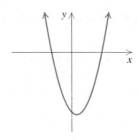 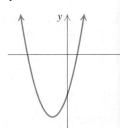

63. $y = x^2 + 2x - 8$ **64.** $y = x^2 - 2x - 15$

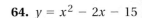

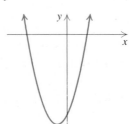 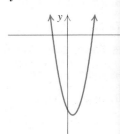

5. $y = 2x^2 + 3x - 9$ **66.** $y = 2x^2 + x - 10$

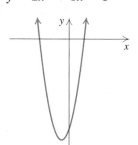   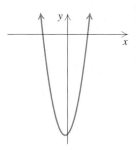

7. The equation $x^2 + 1 = 0$ has no real-number solutions. What implications does this have for the graph of $y = x^2 + 1$?

8. What is the difference between a quadratic polynomial and a quadratic equation?

Skill Review

o prepare for Section 5.8, review solving problems using ne five-step strategy (Section 2.5).

ranslate to an algebraic expression. [1.1]

9. The square of the sum of two numbers

0. The sum of the squares of two numbers

1. The product of two consecutive integers

olve. [2.5]

2. In 2005, shoppers spent $22.8 billion on gifts for Mother's Day and for Father's Day combined. They spent $4.8 billion more for Mother's Day than for Father's Day. How much did shoppers spend for each holiday?
Source: National Retail Federation

3. The first angle of a triangle is four times as large as the second. The measure of the third angle is 30° less than that of the second. How large are the angles?

4. A rectangular table top is twice as long as it is wide. The perimeter of the table is 192 in. What are the dimensions of the table?

Synthesis

75. What is wrong with solving $x^2 = 3x$ by dividing both sides of the equation by x?

76. When the principle of zero products is used to solve a quadratic equation, will there always be two different solutions? Why or why not?

77. Find an equation with integer coefficients that has the given numbers as solutions. For example, 3 and -2 are solutions to $x^2 - x - 6 = 0$.

a) $-4, 5$ b) $-1, 7$ c) $\frac{1}{4}, 3$
d) $\frac{1}{2}, \frac{1}{3}$ e) $\frac{2}{3}, \frac{3}{4}$ f) $-1, 2, 3$

Solve.

78. $16(x - 1) = x(x + 8)$

79. $a(9 + a) = 4(2a + 5)$

80. $(t - 5)^2 = 2(5 - t)$

81. $-x^2 + \frac{9}{25} = 0$

82. $a^2 = \frac{49}{100}$

Aha!   **83.** $(t + 1)^2 = 9$

84. $\frac{27}{25}x^2 = \frac{1}{3}$

85. For each equation on the left, find an equivalent equation on the right.

a) $x^2 + 10x - 2 = 0$ $4x^2 + 8x + 36 = 0$
b) $(x - 6)(x + 3) = 0$ $(2x + 8)(2x - 5) = 0$
c) $5x^2 - 5 = 0$ $9x^2 - 12x + 24 = 0$
d) $(2x - 5)(x + 4) = 0$ $(x + 1)(5x - 5) = 0$
e) $x^2 + 2x + 9 = 0$ $x^2 - 3x - 18 = 0$
f) $3x^2 - 4x + 8 = 0$ $2x^2 + 20x - 4 = 0$

86. Explain how to construct an equation that has seven solutions.

87. Explain how the graph in Exercise 59 can be used to visualize the solutions of
$$-x^2 - x + 6 = 4.$$

Use a graphing calculator to find the solutions of each equation. Round solutions to the nearest hundredth.

88. $-x^2 + 0.63x + 0.22 = 0$

89. $x^2 - 9.10x + 15.77 = 0$

90. $6.4x^2 - 8.45x - 94.06 = 0$

91. $x^2 + 13.74x + 42.00 = 0$

92. $0.84x^2 - 2.30x = 0$

93. $1.23x^2 + 4.63x = 0$

94. $x^2 + 1.80x - 5.69 = 0$

CONNECTING ↕ the CONCEPTS

Recall that an *equation* is a statement that two *expressions* are equal. When we simplify expressions, combine expressions, and form equivalent expressions, each result is an expression. When we are asked to solve an equation, the result is one or more numbers. Remember to read the directions to an exercise carefully so you do not attempt to "solve" an expression.

MIXED REVIEW

For Exercises 1–6, tell whether each is an example of an expression or an equation.

1. $x^2 - 25$

2. $x^2 - 25 = 0$

3. $x^2 + 2x = 5$

4. $(x + 3)(2x - 1)$

5. $x(x + 3) - 2(2x - 7) - (x - 5)$

6. $x = 10$

7. Add the expressions:
$$(2x^3 - 5x + 1) + (x^2 - 3x - 1).$$

8. Subtract the expressions:
$$(x^2 - x - 5) - (3x^2 - x + 6).$$

9. Solve the equation: $t^2 - 100 = 0$.

10. Multiply the expressions: $(3a - 2)(2a - 5)$.

11. Factor the expression: $n^2 - 10n + 9$.

12. Solve the equation: $x^2 + 16 = 10x$.

13. Solve: $4t^2 + 20t + 25 = 0$.

14. Add: $(3x^3 - 5x + 1) + (4x^3 + 7x - 8)$.

15. Factor: $16x^2 - 81$.

16. Solve: $y^2 - 5y - 24 = 0$.

17. Subtract: $(a^2 - 2) - (5a^2 + a + 9)$.

18. Factor: $18x^4 - 24x^3 + 20x^2$.

19. Solve: $3x^2 + 5x + 2 = 0$.

20. Multiply: $4x^2(2x^3 - 5x^2 + 3)$.

5.8   Solving Applications

Applications   •   The Pythagorean Theorem

Applications

We can use the five-step problem-solving process and our new methods of solving quadratic equations to solve new types of problems.

EXAMPLE 1

Race numbers.   Terry and Jody each entered a boat in the Lakeport Race. The racing numbers of their boats were consecutive numbers, the product of which was 156. Find the numbers.

SOLUTION

1. **Familiarize.** Consecutive numbers are one apart, like 49 and 50. Let $x =$ the first boat number; then $x + 1 =$ the next boat number.

2. **Translate.** We reword the problem before translating:

Rewording:	The first boat number	times	the next boat number	is	156.
Translating:	x	$\cdot$	$(x + 1)$	$=$	156

3. **Carry out.** We solve the equation as follows:

$$x(x + 1) = 156$$
$$x^2 + x = 156 \qquad \text{Multiplying}$$
$$x^2 + x - 156 = 0 \qquad \text{Subtracting 156 to get 0 on one side}$$
$$(x - 12)(x + 13) = 0 \qquad \text{Factoring}$$
$$x - 12 = 0 \quad or \quad x + 13 = 0 \qquad \text{Using the principle of zero products}$$
$$x = 12 \quad or \qquad x = -13. \qquad \text{Solving each equation}$$

4. **Check.** The solutions of the equation are 12 and -13. Since race numbers are not negative, -13 must be rejected. On the other hand, if x is 12, then $x + 1$ is 13 and $12 \cdot 13 = 156$. Thus the solution 12 checks.

5. **State.** The boat numbers for Terry and Jody were 12 and 13.

> **TRY EXERCISE** 5

EXAMPLE 2

Manufacturing.   Wooden Work, Ltd., builds cutting boards that are twice as long as they are wide. The most popular board that Wooden Work makes has an area of 800 cm². What are the dimensions of the board?

SOLUTION

1. **Familiarize.** We first make a drawing. Recall that the area of any rectangle i
Length · Width. We let $x =$ the width of the board, in centimeters. The lengt
is then $2x$, since the board is twice as long as it is wide.

$2x$ x

2. **Translate.** We reword and translate as follows:

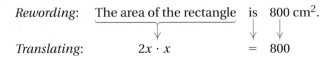

Rewording: The area of the rectangle   is   800 cm^2.

Translating: $2x \cdot x$ $=$ 800

3. **Carry out.** We solve the equation as follows:

$$2x \cdot x = 800$$
$$2x^2 = 800$$

$2x^2 - 800 = 0$ Subtracting 800 to get 0 on one side of the equation

$2(x^2 - 400) = 0$ Factoring out a common factor of 2

$2(x - 20)(x + 20) = 0$ Factoring a difference of squares

$(x - 20)(x + 20) = 0$ Dividing both sides by 2

$x - 20 = 0$ *or* $x + 20 = 0$ Using the principle of zero products

$x = 20$ *or* $x = -20.$ Solving each equation

4. **Check.** The solutions of the equation are 20 and -20. Since the width mu
be positive, -20 cannot be a solution. To check 20 cm, we note that
the width is 20 cm, then the length is $2 \cdot 20$ cm $= 40$ cm and the area
20 cm $\cdot$ 40 cm $= 800$ cm^2. Thus the solution 20 checks.

5. **State.** The cutting board is 20 cm wide and 40 cm long.   ▶ **TRY EXERCISE**   9

EXAMPLE   **3**   *Dimensions of a leaf.*   Each leaf of one particular *Philodendron* species is ap
proximately a triangle. A typical leaf has an area of 320 in^2. If the leaf
12 in. longer than it is wide, find the length and the width of the leaf.

SOLUTION

1. **Familiarize.** The formula for the area of a triangle is Area
$\frac{1}{2} \cdot$ (base) $\cdot$ (height). We let $b =$ the width, in inches, of the triangle
base and $b + 12 =$ the height, in inches.

2. **Translate.** We reword and translate as follows:

Rewording: The area of the leaf   is   320 in^2.

Translating: $\frac{1}{2} \cdot b(b + 12)$ $=$ 320

3. **Carry out.** We solve the equation as follows:

$$\frac{1}{2} \cdot b \cdot (b + 12) = 320$$

$$\frac{1}{2}(b^2 + 12b) = 320 \qquad \text{Multiplying}$$

$$b^2 + 12b = 640 \qquad \text{Multiplying by 2 to clear fractions}$$

$$b^2 + 12b - 640 = 0 \qquad \text{Subtracting 640 to get 0 on one side}$$

$$(b + 32)(b - 20) = 0 \qquad \text{Factoring}$$

$$b + 32 = 0 \quad or \quad b - 20 = 0 \qquad \text{Using the principle of zero products}$$

$$b = -32 \quad or \qquad b = 20.$$

4. **Check.** The width must be positive, so -32 cannot be a solution. Suppose the base is 20 in. The height would be $20 + 12$, or 32 in., and the area $\frac{1}{2}(20)(32)$, or 320 in². These numbers check in the original problem.

5. **State.** The leaf is 32 in. long and 20 in. wide.

> **TRY EXERCISE** 13

EXAMPLE 4

Medicine. For certain people suffering an extreme allergic reaction, the drug epinephrine (adrenaline) is sometimes prescribed. The number of micrograms N of epinephrine in an adult's bloodstream t minutes after 250 micrograms have been injected can be approximated by

$$-10t^2 + 100t = N.$$

How long after an injection will there be about 210 micrograms of epinephrine in the bloodstream?

Source: Based on information in Chohan, Naina, Rita M. Doyle, and Patricia Nayle (eds.), *Nursing Handbook*, 21st ed. Springhouse, PA: Springhouse Corporation, 2001

SOLUTION

1. **Familiarize.** To familiarize ourselves with this problem, we could calculate N for different choices of t. We leave this for the student. Note that there may be two solutions, one on each side of the time at which the drug's effect peaks.

2. **Translate.** To find the length of time after injection when 210 micrograms are in the bloodstream, we replace N with 210 in the formula above:

$$-10t^2 + 100t = 210. \qquad \text{Substituting 210 for } N. \text{ This is now an equation in one variable.}$$

3. **Carry out.** We solve the equation as follows:

$$-10t^2 + 100t = 210$$

$$-10t^2 + 100t - 210 = 0 \qquad \text{Subtracting 210 from both sides to get 0 on one side}$$

$$-10(t^2 - 10t + 21) = 0 \qquad \text{Factoring out the largest common factor, } -10$$

$$-10(t - 3)(t - 7) = 0 \qquad \text{Factoring}$$

$$t - 3 = 0 \quad or \quad t - 7 = 0 \qquad \text{Using the principle of zero products}$$

$$t = 3 \quad or \qquad t = 7.$$

4. **Check.** Since $-10 \cdot 3^2 + 100 \cdot 3 = -90 + 300 = 210$, the number 3 checks. Since $-10 \cdot 7^2 + 100 \cdot 7 = -490 + 700 = 210$, the number 7 also checks.

5. **State.** There will be 210 micrograms of epinephrine in the bloodstream approximately 3 minutes and 7 minutes after injection.

> **TRY EXERCISE** 17

The Pythagorean Theorem

The following problems involve the Pythagorean theorem, which relates the lengths of the sides of a *right* triangle. A triangle is a **right triangle** if it has a 90°, or *right*, angle. The side opposite the 90° angle is called the **hypotenuse**. The other sides are called **legs**.

The Pythagorean Theorem

In any right triangle, if a and b are the lengths of the legs and c is the length of the hypotenuse, then

$$a^2 + b^2 = c^2, \quad \text{or}$$

$$(\text{Leg})^2 + (\text{Other leg})^2 = (\text{Hypotenuse})^2.$$

The equation $a^2 + b^2 = c^2$ is called the **Pythagorean equation**.*

The Pythagorean theorem is named for the Greek mathematician Pythagoras (569?–500? B.C.). We can think of this relationship as adding areas.

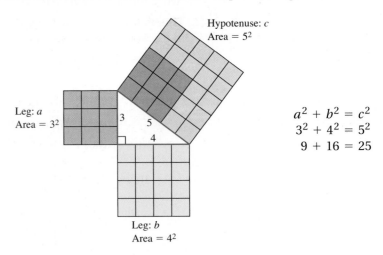

If we know the lengths of any two sides of a right triangle, we can use the Pythagorean equation to determine the length of the third side.

---

*The *converse* of the Pythagorean theorem is also true. That is, if $a^2 + b^2 = c^2$, then the triangle is a right triangle.

EXAMPLE 5   *Travel.*   A zipline canopy tour in Alaska includes a cable that slopes downward from a height of 135 ft to a height of 100 ft. The trees that the cable connects are 120 ft apart. Find the minimum length of the cable.

SOLUTION

    1. Familiarize. We first make a drawing or visualize the situation. The difference in height between the platforms is 35 ft. Note that the cable must have some extra length to allow for the rider's movement, but we will approximate its length as the hypotenuse of a right triangle, as shown.

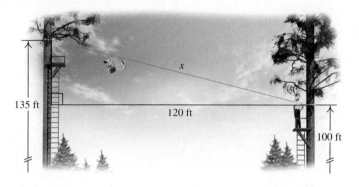

    2. Translate. Since a right triangle is formed, we can use the Pythagorean theorem:

$$a^2 + b^2 = c^2$$
$$35^2 + 120^2 = x^2. \qquad \text{Substituting}$$

    3. Carry out. We solve the equation as follows:

$1225 + 14{,}400 = x^2$	Squaring 35 and 120
$15{,}625 = x^2$	Adding
$0 = x^2 - 15{,}625$	Subtracting 15,625 from both sides
$0 = (x + 125)(x - 125)$	Note that $15{,}625 = 125^2$. A calculator would be helpful here.
$x + 125 = 0 \quad or \quad x - 125 = 0$	Using the principle of zero products
$x = -125 \quad or \quad x = 125.$	

    4. Check. Since the length of the cable must be positive, -125 is not a solution. If the length is 125 ft, we have $35^2 + 120^2 = 1225 + 14{,}400 = 15{,}625$, which is 125^2. Thus the solution 125 checks.

    5. State. The minimum length of the cable is 125 ft.

▸ TRY EXERCISE ▸ 27

EXAMPLE   **6**   *Bridge design.* A 50-ft diagonal brace on a bridge connects a support at the center of the bridge to a side support on the bridge. The horizontal distance that it spans is 10 ft longer than the height that it reaches on the side of the bridge. Find both distances.

SOLUTION

1. **Familiarize.** We first make a drawing. The diagonal brace and the missing distances form the hypotenuse and the legs of a right triangle. We let x = the length of the vertical leg. Then $x + 10$ = the length of the horizontal leg. The hypotenuse has length 50 ft.

2. **Translate.** Since the triangle is a right triangle, we can use the Pythagorean theorem:

$$a^2 + b^2 = c^2$$
$$x^2 + (x + 10)^2 = 50^2. \qquad \text{Substituting}$$

3. **Carry out.** We solve the equation as follows:

$x^2 + (x^2 + 20x + 100) = 2500$	Squaring
$2x^2 + 20x + 100 = 2500$	Combining like terms
$2x^2 + 20x - 2400 = 0$	Subtracting 2500 to get 0 on one side
$2(x^2 + 10x - 1200) = 0$	Factoring out a common factor
$2(x + 40)(x - 30) = 0$	Factoring. A calculator would be helpful here.
$x + 40 = 0 \quad or \quad x - 30 = 0$	Using the principle of zero products
$x = -40 \quad or \qquad x = 30.$	

4. **Check.** The integer -40 cannot be a length of a side because it is negative. the length is 30 ft, $x + 10 = 40$, and $30^2 + 40^2 = 900 + 1600 = 2500$, which is 50^2. So the solution 30 checks.

5. **State.** The height that the brace reaches on the side of the bridge is 30 ft, and the distance that it reaches to the middle of the bridge is 40 ft.

TRY EXERCISE 31

1. Angle measures. The measures of the angles of a triangle are three consecutive integers. Find the measures of the angles.

2. Rectangle dimensions. The area of a rectangle is 3604 ft². The length is 15 ft longer than the width. Find the dimensions of the rectangle.

3. Sales tax. Claire paid $3604 for a used pickup truck. This included 6% for sales tax. How much did the truck cost before tax?

4. Wire cutting. A 180-m wire is cut into three pieces. The third piece is 2 m longer than the first. The second is two-thirds as long as the first. How long is each piece?

5. Perimeter. The perimeter of a rectangle is 240 ft. The length is 2 ft greater than the width. Find the length and the width.

Translating for Success

Translate each word problem to an equation and select a correct translation from equations A–O.

A. $2x \cdot x = 288$

B. $x(x + 60) = 7021$

C. $59 = x \cdot 60$

D. $x^2 + (x + 15)^2 = 3604$

E. $x^2 + (x + 70)^2 = 130^2$

F. $0.06x = 3604$

G. $2(x + 2) + 2x = 240$

H. $\frac{1}{2}x(x - 1) = 1770$

I. $x + \frac{2}{3}x + (x + 2) = 180$

J. $0.59x = 60$

K. $x + 0.06x = 3604$

L. $2x^2 + x = 288$

M. $x(x + 15) = 3604$

N. $x^2 + 60 = 7021$

O. $x + (x + 1) + (x + 2) = 180$

Answers on page A-22

An additional, animated version of this activity appears in MyMathLab. To use MyMathLab, you need a course ID and a student access code. Contact your instructor for more information.

6. Cell-phone tower. A guy wire on a cell-phone tower is 130 ft long and is attached to the top of the tower. The height of the tower is 70 ft longer than the distance from the point on the ground where the wire is attached to the bottom of the tower. Find the height of the tower.

7. Sales meeting attendance. PTQ Corporation holds a sales meeting in Tucson. Of the 60 employees, 59 of them attend the meeting. What percent attend the meeting?

8. Dimensions of a pool. A rectangular swimming pool is twice as long as it is wide. The area of the surface is 288 ft². Find the dimensions of the pool.

9. Dimensions of a triangle. The height of a triangle is 1 cm less than the length of the base. The area of the triangle is 1770 cm². Find the height and the length of the base.

10. Width of a rectangle. The length of a rectangle is 60 ft longer than the width. Find the width if the area of the rectangle is 7021 ft².

Solve. Use the five-step problem-solving approach.

1. A number is 6 less than its square. Find all such numbers.

2. A number is 30 less than its square. Find all such numbers.

3. One leg of a right triangle is 2 m longer than the other leg. The length of the hypotenuse is 10 m. Find the length of each side.

4. One leg of a right triangle is 7 cm shorter than the other leg. The length of the hypotenuse is 13 cm. Find the length of each side.

5. *Parking-space numbers.* The product of two consecutive parking spaces is 132. Find the parking-space numbers.

6. *Page numbers.* The product of the page numbers on two facing pages of a book is 420. Find the page numbers.

7. The product of two consecutive even integers is 168. Find the integers.

8. The product of two consecutive odd integers is 195. Find the integers.

9. *Construction.* The front porch on Trent's new home is five times as long as it is wide. If the area of the porch is 180 ft², find the dimensions.

5w

w

10. *Furnishings.* The work surface of Anita's desk is a rectangle that is twice as long as it is wide. If the area

w   2w

of the desktop is 18 ft², find the length and the width of the desk.

11. *Design.* The screen of the TI-84 Plus graphing calculator is nearly rectangular. The length of the rectangle is 2 cm more than the width. If the area of the rectangle is 24 cm², find the length and the width.

w + 2

12. *Area of a garden.* The length of a rectangular garden is 4 m greater than the width. The area of the garden is 96 m². Find the length and the width.

w   w + 4

13. *Dimensions of a triangle.* The height of a triangle is 3 in. less than the length of the base. If the area of the triangle is 54 in², find the height and the length of the base.

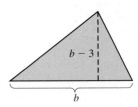

b − 3

b

14. *Dimensions of a triangle.* A triangle is 10 cm wider than it is tall. The area is 48 cm². Find the height and the base.

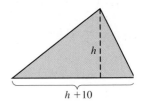

h

h + 10

5. *Dimensions of a sail.* The height of the jib sail on a Lightning sailboat is 5 ft greater than the length of its "foot." If the area of the sail is 42 ft², find the length of the foot and the height of the sail.

6. *Road design.* A triangular traffic island has a base half as long as its height. Find the base and the height if the island has an area of 64 m².

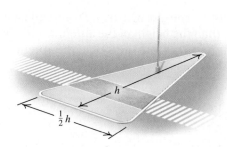

7. *Medicine.* For many people suffering from constricted bronchial muscles, the drug Albuterol is prescribed. The number of micrograms A of Albuterol in a person's bloodstream t minutes after 200 micrograms have been inhaled can be approximated by

$$A = -50t^2 + 200t.$$

How long after an inhalation will there be about 150 micrograms of Albuterol in the bloodstream?
Source: Based on information in Chohan, Naina, Rita M. Doyle, and Patricia Nayle (eds.), *Nursing Handbook*, 21st ed. Springhouse, PA: Springhouse Corporation, 2001

8. *Medicine.* For adults with certain heart conditions, the drug Primacor (milrinone lactate) is prescribed. The number of milligrams M of Primacor in the bloodstream of a 132-lb patient t hours after a 3-mg dose has been injected can be approximated by

$$M = -\frac{1}{2}t^2 + \frac{5}{2}t.$$

How long after an injection will there be about 2 mg in the bloodstream?
Source: Based on information in Chohan, Naina, Rita M. Doyle, and Patricia Nayle (eds.), *Nursing Handbook*, 21st ed. Springhouse, PA: Springhouse Corporation, 2001

19. *High-speed Internet.* The number N, in millions, of broadband cable and DSL subscribers in the United States t years after 1998 can be approximated by

$$N = 0.3t^2 + 0.6t.$$

When will there be 36 million broadband cable and DSL subscribers?
Source: Based on information from Leichtman Research Group

20. *Wave height.* The height of waves in a storm depends on the speed of the wind. Assuming the wind has no obstructions for a long distance, the maximum wave height H for a wind speed x can be approximated by

$$H = 0.006x^2 + 0.6x.$$

Here H is in feet and x is in knots (nautical miles per hour). For what wind speed would the maximum wave height be 6.6 ft?
Source: Based on information from cimss.ssec.wisc.edu

Games in a league's schedule. In a sports league of x teams in which all teams play each other twice, the total number N of games played is given by

$$x^2 - x = N.$$

Use this formula for Exercises 21 and 22.

21. The Colchester Youth Soccer League plays a total of 240 games, with all teams playing each other twice. How many teams are in the league?

22. The teams in a women's softball league play each other twice, for a total of 132 games. How many teams are in the league?

Number of handshakes. The number of possible handshakes H within a group of n people is given by $H = \frac{1}{2}(n^2 - n)$. Use this formula for Exercises 23–26.

23. At a meeting, there are 12 people. How many handshakes are possible?

24. At a party, there are 25 people. How many handshakes are possible?

25. *High-fives.* After winning the championship, all San Antonio Spurs teammates exchanged "high-fives." Altogether there were 66 high-fives. How many players were there?

26. *Toasting.* During a toast at a party, there were 105 "clicks" of glasses. How many people took part in the toast?

27. *Construction.* The diagonal braces in a lookout tower are 15 ft long and span a horizontal distance of 12 ft. How high does each brace reach vertically?

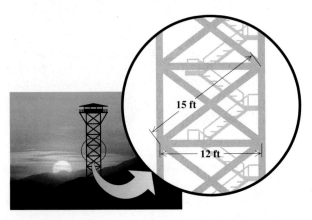

28. *Reach of a ladder.* Twyla has a 26-ft ladder leaning against her house. If the bottom of the ladder is 10 ft from the base of the house, how high does the ladder reach?

29. *Roadway design.* Elliott Street is 24 ft wide when it ends at Main Street in Brattleboro, Vermont. A 40-ft long diagonal crosswalk allows pedestrians to cross Main Street to or from either corner of Elliott Street (see the figure). Determine the width of Main Street.

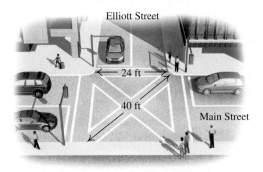

30. *Aviation.* Engine failure forced Robbin to pilot her Cessna 150 to an emergency landing. To land, Robbin's plane glided 17,000 ft over a 15,000-ft stretch of deserted highway. From what altitude did the descent begin?

31. *Archaeology.* Archaeologists have discovered that the 18th-century garden of the Charles Carroll House in Annapolis, Maryland, was a right triangle. One leg of the triangle was formed by a 400-ft long sea wall. The hypotenuse of the triangle was 200 ft longer than the other leg. What were the dimensions of the garden?
Source: www.bsos.umd.edu

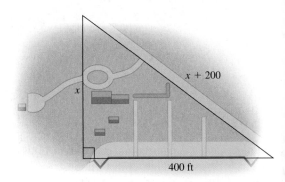

32. *Guy wire.* The guy wire on a TV antenna is 1 m longer than the height of the antenna. If the guy wire is anchored 3 m from the foot of the antenna, how tall is the antenna?

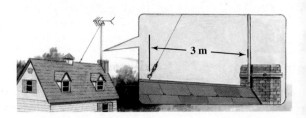

33. *Architecture.* An architect has allocated a rectangular space of 264 ft² for a square dining room and a 10-ft wide kitchen, as shown in the figure. Find the dimensions of each room.

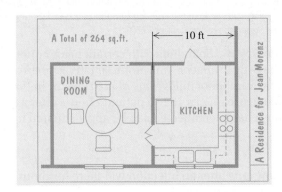

34. *Design.*   A window panel for a sun porch consists of a 7-ft high rectangular window stacked above a square window. The windows have the same width. If the total area of the window panel is 18 ft², find the dimensions of each window.

7 ft

Height of a rocket.   *For Exercises 35–38, assume that a water rocket is launched upward with an initial velocity of 48 ft/sec. Its height h, in feet, after t seconds, is given by h = 48t − 16t².*

35. Determine the height of the rocket $\frac{1}{2}$ sec after it has been launched.

36. Determine the height of the rocket 2.5 sec after it has been launched.

37. When will the rocket be exactly 32 ft above the ground?

38. When will the rocket crash into the ground?

39. Do we now have the ability to solve *any* problem that translates to a quadratic equation? Why or why not?

40. Write a problem for a classmate to solve such that only one of two solutions of a quadratic equation can be used as an answer.

Skill Review

To prepare for Chapter 6, review addition, subtraction, multiplication, and division using fraction notation (Sections 1.3, 1.5, 1.6, and 1.7).

Simplify.

41. $-\dfrac{3}{5} \cdot \dfrac{4}{7}$ [1.7]

42. $-\dfrac{3}{5} \div \dfrac{4}{7}$ [1.7]

43. $-\dfrac{5}{6} - \dfrac{1}{6}$ [1.6]

44. $\dfrac{3}{4} + \left(-\dfrac{5}{2}\right)$ [1.5]

45. $-\dfrac{3}{8} \cdot \left(-\dfrac{10}{15}\right)$ [1.7]

46. $\dfrac{-\dfrac{8}{15}}{-\dfrac{2}{3}}$ [1.7]

47. $\dfrac{5}{24} + \dfrac{3}{28}$ [1.3]

48. $\dfrac{5}{6} - \left(-\dfrac{2}{9}\right)$ [1.6]

Synthesis

The converse of the Pythagorean theorem is also true. That is, if a² + b² = c², then the triangle is a right triangle (where a and b are the lengths of the legs and c is the length of the hypotenuse). Use this result to answer Exercises 49 and 50.

49. An archaeologist has measuring sticks of 3 ft, 4 ft, and 5 ft. Explain how she could draw a 7-ft by 9-ft rectangle on a piece of land being excavated.

50. Explain how measuring sticks of 5 cm, 12 cm, and 13 cm can be used to draw a right triangle that has two 45° angles.

51. *Sailing.*   The mainsail of a Lightning sailboat is a right triangle in which the hypotenuse is called the leech. If a 24-ft tall mainsail has a leech length of 26 ft and if Dacron® sailcloth costs $1.50 per square foot, find the cost of the fabric for a new mainsail.

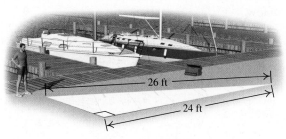

26 ft

24 ft

52. *Roofing.*   A *square* of shingles covers 100 ft² of surface area. How many squares will be needed to re-shingle the house shown?

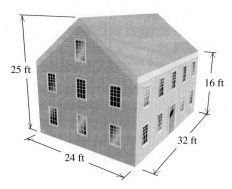

25 ft

16 ft

24 ft

32 ft

53. Solve for *x*.

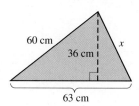

60 cm

36 cm

x

63 cm

54. *Pool sidewalk.* A cement walk of uniform width is built around a 20-ft by 40-ft rectangular pool. The total area of the pool and the walk is 1500 ft². Find the width of the walk.

55. *Folding sheet metal.* An open rectangular gutter is made by turning up the sides of a piece of metal 20 in. wide, as shown. The area of the cross-section of the gutter is 48 in². Find the possible depths of the gutter.

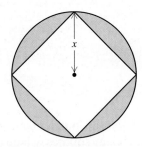

48 in²

← 20 in. →

56. Find a polynomial for the shaded area in the figure below.

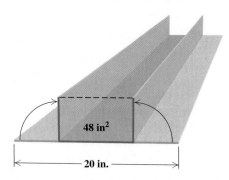

x

57. *Telephone service.* Use the information in the figure below to determine the height of the telephone pole.

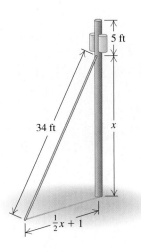

5 ft

34 ft

x

$\frac{1}{2}x + 1$

58. *Dimensions of a closed box.* The total surface area of a closed box is 350 m². The box is 9 m high and has a square base and lid. Find the length of a side of the base.

Medicine. For certain people with acid reflux, the drug Pepcid (famotidine) is used. The number of milligrams N of Pepcid in an adult's bloodstream t hours after a 20-mg tablet has been swallowed can be approximated by

$$N = -0.009t\,(t - 12)^3.$$

Use a graphing calculator with the window $[-1, 13, -1, 2]$ *and the* TRACE *feature to answer Exercises 59–61.*

Source: Based on information in Chohan, Naina, Rita M. Doyle, and Patricia Nayle (eds.), *Nursing Handbook*, 21st ed. Springhouse, PA: Springhouse Corporation, 2001

59. Approximately how long after a tablet has been swallowed will there be 18 mg in the bloodstream?

60. Approximately how long after a tablet has been swallowed will there be 10 mg in the bloodstream?

61. Approximately how long after a tablet has been swallowed will the peak dosage in the bloodstream occur?

Study Summary

KEY TERMS AND CONCEPTS	EXAMPLES

SECTION 5.1: INTRODUCTION TO FACTORING

To **factor** a polynomial means to write it as a product. Always begin by factoring out the **largest common factor**.

Factor: $12x^4 - 30x^3$.
$$12x^4 - 30x^3 = 6x^3(2x - 5)$$

Some polynomials with four terms can be **factored by grouping**.

Factor: $3x^3 - x^2 - 6x + 2$.
$$3x^3 - x^2 - 6x + 2 = x^2(3x - 1) - 2(3x - 1)$$
$$= (3x - 1)(x^2 - 2)$$

SECTION 5.2: FACTORING TRINOMIALS OF THE TYPE $x^2 + bx + c$

Some trinomials of the type $x^2 + bx + c$ can be factored by reversing the steps of FOIL.

Factor: $x^2 - 11x + 18$.

Pairs of Factors of 18	Sums of Factors
$-1, -18$	-19
$-2, \ -9$	-11

18 is positive and -11 is negative, so both factors will be negative.

←The numbers we need are -2 and -9.

The factorization is $(x - 2)(x - 9)$.

SECTION 5.3: FACTORING TRINOMIALS OF THE TYPE $ax^2 + bx + c$

One method for factoring trinomials of the type $ax^2 + bx + c$ is a FOIL-based method.

Factor: $6x^2 - 5x - 6$.

The factors will be in the form $(3x + \ )(2x + \ )$ or $(6x + \ )(x + \ )$. We list all pairs of factors of -6, and check possible products by multiplying any possibilities that do not contain a common factor.

$(3x - 2)(2x + 3) = 6x^2 + 5x - 6$,
$(3x + 2)(2x - 3) = 6x^2 - 5x - 6$. ←This is the correct product, so we stop here.

The factorization is $(3x + 2)(2x - 3)$.

Another method for factoring trinomials of the type $ax^2 + bx + c$ involves factoring by grouping.

Factor: $6x^2 - 5x - 6$.

Multiply the leading coefficient and the constant term: $6(-6) = -36$. Look for factors of -36 that add to -5.

Pairs of Factors of -36	Sums of Factors
$1, -36$	-35
$2, -18$	-16
$3, -12$	-9
$4, \ -9$	-5

-5 is negative, so the negative factor must have the greater absolute value.

←The numbers we want are 4 and -9.

Rewrite $-5x$ as $4x - 9x$ and factor by grouping:
$$6x^2 - 5x - 6 = 6x^2 + 4x - 9x - 6$$
$$= 2x(3x + 2) - 3(3x + 2)$$
$$= (3x + 2)(2x - 3).$$

SECTION 5.4: FACTORING PERFECT-SQUARE TRINOMIALS AND DIFFERENCES OF SQUARES

Factoring a perfect-square trinomial

$$A^2 + 2AB + B^2 = (A + B)^2;$$
$$A^2 - 2AB + B^2 = (A - B)^2$$

Factor: $y^2 + 100 - 20y$.

$$A^2 - 2AB + B^2 = (A - B)^2$$

$$y^2 + 100 - 20y = y^2 - 20y + 100 = (y - 10)^2$$

Factoring a difference of squares

$$A^2 - B^2 = (A + B)(A - B)$$

Factor: $9t^2 - 1$.

$$A^2 - B^2 = (A + B)(A - B)$$

$$9t^2 - 1 = (3t + 1)(3t - 1)$$

SECTION 5.5: FACTORING SUMS OR DIFFERENCES OF CUBES

Factoring a sum or a difference of cubes

$$A^3 + B^3 = (A + B)(A^2 - AB + B^2)$$
$$A^3 - B^3 = (A - B)(A^2 + AB + B^2)$$

$$x^3 + 1000 = (x + 10)(x^2 - 10x + 100)$$
$$z^6 - 8w^3 = (z^2 - 2w)(z^4 + 2wz^2 + 4w^2)$$

SECTION 5.6: FACTORING: A GENERAL STRATEGY

To factor a polynomial:

A. Factor out the largest common factor.

B. Look at the number of terms.

Two terms: If a difference of squares, use $A^2 - B^2 = (A + B)(A - B)$.
If a sum of cubes, use
$A^3 + B^3 = (A + B)(A^2 - AB + B^2)$.
If a difference of cubes, use
$A^3 - B^3 = (A - B)(A^2 + AB + B^2)$.

Three terms: If a trinomial square, use
$A^2 + 2AB + B^2 = (A + B)^2$ or
$A^2 - 2AB + B^2 = (A - B)^2$.
Otherwise, try FOIL or grouping.

Four terms: Try factoring by grouping.

C. Factor completely.

D. Check by multiplying.

Factor: $5x^5 - 80x$.

$$5x^5 - 80x = 5x(x^4 - 16)$$ 5x is the largest common factor.

$$= 5x(x^2 + 4)(x^2 - 4)$$ $x^4 - 16$ is a difference of squares.

$$= 5x(x^2 + 4)(x + 2)(x - 2)$$ $x^2 - 4$ is also a difference of squares.

Check: $5x(x^2 + 4)(x + 2)(x - 2) = 5x(x^2 + 4)(x^2 - 4)$
$$= 5x(x^4 - 16) = 5x^5 - 80x.$$

Factor: $-x^2y^2 - 3xy + 10$.

$$-x^2y^2 - 3xy + 10 = -(x^2y^2 + 3xy - 10)$$ Factor out −1 to make the leading coefficient positive.

$$= -(xy + 5)(xy - 2)$$

Check: $-(xy + 5)(xy - 2) = -(x^2y^2 + 3xy - 10)$
$$= -x^2y^2 - 3xy + 10.$$

SECTION 5.7: SOLVING POLYNOMIAL EQUATIONS BY FACTORING

The Principle of Zero Products

An equation $AB = 0$ is true if and only if $A = 0$ or $B = 0$, or both.

Solve: $x^2 + 7x = 30$.

$$x^2 + 7x = 30$$
$$x^2 + 7x - 30 = 0$$ Getting 0 on one side
$$(x + 10)(x - 3) = 0$$ Factoring
$$x + 10 = 0 \quad or \quad x - 3 = 0$$ Using the principle of zero products

$$x = -10 \quad or \quad x = 3$$

The solutions are −10 and 3.

SECTION 5.8: SOLVING APPLICATIONS

The Pythagorean Theorem

In any right triangle, if a and b are the lengths of the legs and c is the length of the hypotenuse, then

$a^2 + b^2 = c^2$, or
$(\text{Leg})^2 + (\text{Other leg})^2 = (\text{Hypotenuse})^2$.

Aaron has a 25-ft ladder leaning against his house. The height that the ladder reaches on the house is 17 ft more than the distance that the bottom of the ladder is from the house. Find both distances.

$$x^2 + (x + 17)^2 = 25^2$$
$$x^2 + x^2 + 34x + 289 = 625 \qquad \text{Squaring}$$
$$2x^2 + 34x - 336 = 0$$
$$2(x + 24)(x - 7) = 0 \qquad \text{Factoring}$$
$$x + 24 = 0 \qquad or \quad x - 7 = 0 \qquad \text{Using the principle of zero products}$$
$$x = -24 \quad or \qquad x = 7.$$

Since -24 cannot be a length, we check 7. When $x = 7$, $x + 17 = 24$, and $7^2 + 24^2 = 49 + 576 = 625 = 25^2$.

The ladder reaches 24 ft up the side of the house, and the bottom of the ladder is 7 ft from the house.

Review Exercises: Chapter 5

➥ *Concept Reinforcement* *Classify each statement as either true or false.*

1. The largest common variable factor is the largest power of the variable in the polynomial. [5.1]

2. A prime polynomial has no common factor other than 1 or -1. [5.2]

3. Every perfect-square trinomial can be expressed as a binomial squared. [5.4]

4. Every binomial can be regarded as a difference of squares. [5.4]

5. Every quadratic equation has two different solutions. [5.7]

6. The principle of zero products can be applied whenever a product equals 0. [5.7]

7. In a right triangle, the hypotenuse is always longer than either leg. [5.8]

8. The Pythagorean theorem can be applied to any triangle that has an angle measuring at least 90°. [5.8]

Find three factorizations of each monomial. [5.1]

9. $20x^3$

10. $-18x^5$

Factor completely. If a polynomial is prime, state this.

11. $12x^4 - 18x^3$ [5.1]

12. $8a^2 - 12a$ [5.1]

13. $100t^2 - 1$ [5.4]

14. $x^2 + x - 12$ [5.2]

15. $x^2 + 14x + 49$ [5.4]

16. $12x^3 + 12x^2 + 3x$ [5.4]

17. $6x^3 + 9x^2 + 2x + 3$ [5.1]

18. $6a^2 + a - 5$ [5.3]

19. $25t^2 + 9 - 30t$ [5.4]

20. $48t^2 - 28t + 6$ [5.1]

21. $81a^4 - 1$ [5.4]

22. $9x^3 + 12x^2 - 45x$ [5.3]

23. $2x^3 - 250$ [5.5]

24. $x^4 + 4x^3 - 2x - 8$ [5.1]

25. $a^2b^4 - 64$ [5.4]

26. $-8x^6 + 32x^5 - 4x^4$ [5.1]

27. $75 + 12x^2 - 60x$ [5.4]

28. $y^2 + 9$ [5.4]

29. $-t^3 + t^2 + 42t$ [5.2]

30. $4x^2 - 25$ [5.4]

31. $n^2 - 60 - 4n$ [5.2]

32. $5z^2 - 30z + 10$ [5.1]

33. $4t^2 + 13t + 10$ [5.3]

34. $2t^2 - 7t - 4$ [5.3]

35. $7x^3 + 35x^2 + 28x$ [5.2]

36. $8y^3 + 27x^6$ [5.5]

37. $20x^2 - 20x + 5$ [5.4]

38. $-6x^3 + 150x$ [5.4]

39. $15 - 8x + x^2$ [5.2]

40. $3x + x^2 + 5$ [5.2]

41. $x^2y^2 + 6xy - 16$ [5.2]

42. $12a^2 + 84ab + 147b^2$ [5.4]

43. $m^2 + 5m + mt + 5t$ [5.1]

44. $32x^4 - 128y^4z^4$ [5.4]

45. $6m^2 + 2mn + n^2 + 3mn$ [5.1], [5.3]

46. $6r^2 + rs - 15s^2$ [5.3]

Solve. [5.7]

47. $(x - 9)(x + 11) = 0$

48. $x^2 + 2x - 35 = 0$

49. $16x^2 = 9$

50. $3x^2 + 2 = 5x$

51. $2x^2 - 7x = 30$

52. $(x + 1)(x - 2) = 4$

53. $9t - 15t^2 = 0$

54. $3x^2 + 3 = 6x$

55. The square of a number is 12 more than the number. Find all such numbers. [5.8]

56. The formula $x^2 - x = N$ can be used to determine the total number of games played, N, in a league of x teams in which all teams play each other twice. Serena referees for a soccer league in which all teams play each other twice and a total of 90 games is played. How many teams are in the league? [5.8]

57. Find the x-intercepts for the graph of $y = 2x^2 - 3x - 5$.
[5.7]

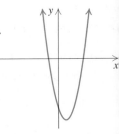

58. The front of a house is a triangle that is as wide as it is tall. Its area is 98 ft². Find the height and the base. [5.8]

59. Josh needs to add a diagonal brace to his LEGO® robot. The brace must span a height of 8 holes and a width of 6 holes. How long should the brace be?
[5.8]

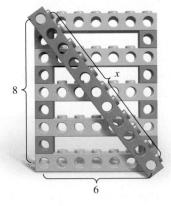

Synthesis

60. On a quiz, Celia writes the factorization of $4x^2 - 100$ as $(2x - 10)(2x + 10)$. If this were a 10-point question, how many points would you give Celia? Why?
[5.4]

61. How do the equations solved in this chapter differ from those solved in previous chapters? [5.7]

Solve.

62. The pages of a book measure 15 cm by 20 cm. Margins of equal width surround the printing on each page and constitute one half of the area of the page. Find the width of the margins. [5.8]

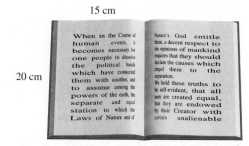

15 cm

20 cm

63. The cube of a number is the same as twice the square of the number. Find the number. [5.8]

64. The length of a rectangle is two times its width. When the length is increased by 20 cm and the width is decreased by 1 cm, the area is 160 cm². Find the original length and width. [5.8]

65. The length of each side of a square is increased by 5 cm to form a new square. The area of the new square is $2\frac{1}{4}$ times the area of the original square. Find the area of each square. [5.8]

Solve. [5.7]

66. $(x - 2)2x^2 + x(x - 2) - (x - 2)15 = 0$

Aha! **67.** $x^2 + 25 = 0$

Test: Chapter 5

CHAPTER Test Prep VIDEO CD

Step-by-step test solutions are found on the video CD in the front of this book.

1. Find three factorizations of $12x^4$.

Factor completely. If a polynomial is prime, state this.

2. $x^2 - 13x + 36$

3. $x^2 + 25 - 10x$

4. $6y^2 - 8y^3 + 4y^4$

5. $x^3 + x^2 + 2x + 2$

6. $t^7 - 3t^5$

7. $a^3 + 3a^2 - 4a$

8. $28x - 48 + 10x^2$

9. $4t^2 - 25$

10. $x^2 - x - 6$

11. $-6m^3 - 9m^2 - 3m$

12. $3r^3 - 3$

13. $45r^2 + 60r + 20$

14. $3x^4 - 48$

15. $49t^2 + 36 + 84t$

16. $x^4 + 2x^3 - 3x - 6$

17. $x^2 + 3x + 6$

18. $4x^2 - 4x - 15$

19. $6t^3 + 9t^2 - 15t$

20. $3m^2 - 9mn - 30n^2$

Solve.

21. $x^2 - 6x + 5 = 0$

22. $2x^2 - 7x = 15$

23. $4t - 10t^2 = 0$

24. $25t^2 = 1$

25. $x(x - 1) = 20$

26. Find the x-intercepts for the graph of $y = 3x^2 - 5x - 8$.

27. The length of a rectangle is 6 m more than the width. The area of the rectangle is 40 m². Find the length and the width.

28. The number of possible handshakes H within a group of n people is given by $H = \frac{1}{2}(n^2 - n)$. At a meeting, everyone shook hands once with everyone else. If there were 45 handshakes, how many people were at the meeting?

29. A mason wants to be sure she has a right corner in a building's foundation. She marks a point 3 ft from the corner along one wall and another point 4 ft from the corner along the other wall. If the corner is a right angle, what should the distance be between the two marked points?

Synthesis

30. *Dimensions of an open box.* A rectangular piece of cardboard is twice as long as it is wide. A 4-cm square is cut out of each corner, and the sides

are turned up to make a box with an open top. The volume of the box is 616 cm³. Find the original dimensions of the cardboard.

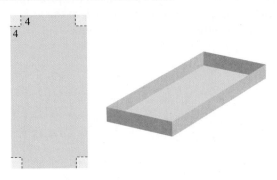

31. Factor: $(a + 3)^2 - 2(a + 3) - 35$.

32. Solve: $20x(x + 2)(x - 1) = 5x^3 - 24x - 14x^2$.

Cumulative Review: Chapters 1–5

Simplify. Do not use negative exponents in the answer.

1. $\frac{3}{8} \div \frac{3}{4}$ [1.3]

2. $\frac{3}{8} \cdot \frac{3}{4}$ [1.3]

3. $\frac{3}{8} + \frac{3}{4}$ [1.3]

4. $-2 + (20 \div 4)^2 - 6 \cdot (-1)^3$ [1.8]

5. $(3x^2y^3)^{-2}$ [4.2]

6. $(t^2)^3 \cdot t^4$ [4.1]

7. $(3x^4 - 2x^2 + x - 7) + (5x^3 + 2x^2 - 3)$ [4.4]

8. $(a^2b - 2ab^2 + 3b^3) - (4a^2b - ab^2 + b^3)$ [4.7]

9. $\dfrac{3t^3s^{-1}}{12t^{-5}s}$ [4.2]

10. $\left(\dfrac{-2x^2y}{3z^4}\right)^3$ [4.1]

11. Evaluate $-x$ for $x = -8$. [1.6]

12. Evaluate $-(-x)$ for $x = -8$. [1.6]

13. Determine the leading term of the polynomial
$4x^3 - 6x^2 - x^4 + 7$. [4.3]

14. Divide: $(8x^4 - 20x^3 + 2x^2 - 4x) \div (4x)$. [4.8]

Multiply.

15. $-4t^8(t^3 - 2t - 5)$ [4.5]

16. $(3x - 5)^2$ [4.6]

17. $(10x^5 + y)(10x^5 - y)$ [4.7]

18. $(x - 1)(x^2 - x - 1)$ [4.5]

Factor completely.

19. $c^2 - 1$ [5.4]

20. $5x + 5y + 10x^2 + 10xy$ [5.1]

21. $4r^2 - 4rt + t^2$ [5.4]

22. $6x^2 - 19x + 10$ [5.3]

23. $10y^2 + 40$ [5.1]

24. $x^2y - 3xy + 2y$ [5.2]

25. $12x^2 - 5xy - 2y^2$ [5.3]

26. $125a^3 + 64b^3$ [5.5]

Solve.

27. $\frac{1}{3} + 2x = \frac{1}{2}$ [2.2]

$3(t - 1) = 2 - (t + 1)$ [2.2]

$8y - 6(y - 2) = 3(2y + 7)$ [2.2]

$3x - 7 \geq 4 - 8x$ [2.6]

$(x - 1)(x + 3) = 0$ [5.7]

$x^2 + x = 12$ [5.7]

$3x^2 = 12$ [5.7]

$3x^2 = 12x$ [5.7]

Solve $a = bc + dc$ for c. [2.3]

Find the slope of the line containing the points $(6, 7)$ and $(-2, 7)$. [3.5]

Find the slope and the y-intercept of the line given by $2x + y = 5$. [3.6]

Write the slope–intercept equation for the line with slope 5 and y-intercept $\left(0, -\frac{1}{3}\right)$. [3.6]

Write the slope–intercept equation for the line with slope 5 that contains the point $\left(-\frac{1}{3}, 0\right)$. [3.7]

aph.

$4(x + 1) = 8$ [3.3]

41. $x + y = 5$ [3.3]

$y = \frac{3}{2}x - 2$ [3.6]

43. $3x + 5y = 10$ [3.6]

Use a grid 10 squares wide and 10 squares high to plot $(5, 40)$, $(18, -60)$, and $(30, -22)$. Choose the scale carefully. [3.1]

lve.

On average, men talk 97 min more per month on cell phones than do women. The sum of men's average minutes and women's average minutes is 647 min. What is the average number of minutes per month that men talk on cell phones? [2.5]
Source: *International Communications Research for Cingular Wireless*

The number of cell-phone subscribers increased from 680,000 in 1986 to 233,000,000 in 2006. What was the average rate of increase? [3.4]
Source: CTIA – The Wireless Association

In 2007, there were 1.2 billion Internet users worldwide. Of these, 5% spoke French. How many Internet users spoke French? [2.4]
Source: Internetworldstats.com

The number of people in the United States, in thousands, who are on a waiting list for an organ transplant can be approximated by the polynomial $2.38t + 77.38$, where t is the number of years since 2000. Estimate the number of people on a waiting list for an organ transplant in 2010. [4.3]
Source: Based on information from The Organ Procurement and Transplantation Network

49. A 13-ft ladder is placed against a building in such a way that the distance from the top of the ladder to the ground is 7 ft more than the distance from the bottom of the ladder to the building. Find both distances. [5.8]

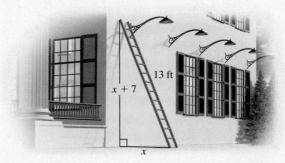

50. A rectangular table in Arlo's House of Tunes is six times as long as it is wide. If the area of the table is 24 ft^2, find the length and the width of the table. [5.8]

51. Donna's quiz grades are 8, 3, 5, and 10. What scores on the fifth quiz will make her average quiz grade at least 7? [2.7]

52. The average amount of sodium in a serving of Chef Boyardee foods dropped from 1100 mg in 2003 to 900 mg in 2007. [3.7]
Source: *The Indianapolis Star*, 11/25/07

a) Graph the data and determine an equation for the related line. Let s represent the average amount of sodium per serving and t the number of years after 2000.

b) Use the equation of part (a) to estimate the average amount of sodium in a serving of Chef Boyardee foods in 2006.

Synthesis

53. Solve $x = \dfrac{abx}{2 - b}$ for b. [2.3]

54. Write an equation of the line parallel to the x-axis and passing through $(-6, -8)$. [3.3]

55. a) Multiply: $(3y + 2 + x)(3y + 2 - x)$. [4.6]
b) Factor: $9y^2 + 12y + 4 - x^2$. [5.4]

56. Solve: $6x^3 + 4x^2 = 2x$. [5.7]

7.5 Formulas, Applications, and Variation

Formulas ▪ Direct Variation ▪ Inverse Variation ▪ Joint Variation and Combined Variation

Formulas

Formulas occur frequently as mathematical models. Many formulas conta[in] rational expressions, and to solve such formulas for a specified letter, we procee[d] as when solving rational equations.

EXAMPLE 1

Electronics.   The formula

$$\frac{1}{R} = \frac{1}{r_1} + \frac{1}{r_2}$$

is used by electricians to determine the resistance R of two resistors r_1 and r_2 connected in parallel.* Solve for r_1.

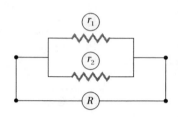

SOLUTION   We use the same approach as in Section 6.6:

$$Rr_1r_2 \cdot \frac{1}{R} = Rr_1r_2 \cdot \left(\frac{1}{r_1} + \frac{1}{r_2}\right) \qquad \text{Multiplying both sides by the LC[D]} \atop \text{to clear fractions}$$

$$Rr_1r_2 \cdot \frac{1}{R} = Rr_1r_2 \cdot \frac{1}{r_1} + Rr_1r_2 \cdot \frac{1}{r_2} \qquad \text{Multiplying to remove parenthes[es]}$$

$$r_1r_2 = Rr_2 + Rr_1. \qquad \text{Simplifying by removing factors}$$

equal to 1: $\dfrac{R}{R} = 1; \dfrac{r_1}{r_1} = 1; \dfrac{r_2}{r_2} = 1$

At this point it is tempting to multiply by $1/r_2$ to get r_1 alone on the left, b[ut] note that there is an r_1 on the right. We must get all the terms involving r_1 on th[e] *same side* of the equation.

$$r_1r_2 - Rr_1 = Rr_2 \qquad \text{Subtracting } Rr_1 \text{ from both sides}$$

$$r_1(r_2 - R) = Rr_2 \qquad \text{Factoring out } r_1 \text{ in order to combine like term[s]}$$

$$r_1 = \frac{Rr_2}{r_2 - R} \qquad \text{Dividing both sides by } r_2 - R \text{ to get } r_1 \text{ alone}$$

This formula can be used to calculate r_1 whenever R and r_2 are known.

 17

EXAMPLE 2

Astronomy.   The formula

$$\frac{V^2}{R^2} = \frac{2g}{R + h}$$

is used to find a satellite's *escape velocity V*, where R is a planet's radius, h is th[e] satellite's height above the planet, and g is the planet's gravitational constar[t]. Solve for h.

---

*Recall that the subscripts 1 and 2 merely indicate that r_1 and r_2 are different variables representing similar quantities.

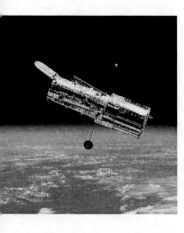

SOLUTION   We first multiply by the LCD, $R^2(R + h)$, to clear fractions:

$$\frac{V^2}{R^2} = \frac{2g}{R + h}$$

$$R^2(R + h)\frac{V^2}{R^2} = R^2(R + h)\frac{2g}{R + h} \qquad \text{Multiplying to clear fractions}$$

$$\frac{R^2(R + h)V^2}{R^2} = \frac{R^2(R + h)2g}{R + h}$$

$$(R + h)V^2 = R^2 \cdot 2g. \qquad \text{Removing factors equal to 1:}$$
$$\frac{R^2}{R^2} = 1 \text{ and } \frac{R + h}{R + h} = 1$$

Remember: We are solving for h. Although we *could* distribute V^2, since h appears only within the factor $R + h$, it is easier to divide both sides by V^2:

$$\frac{(R + h)V^2}{V^2} = \frac{2R^2g}{V^2} \qquad \text{Dividing both sides by } V^2$$

$$R + h = \frac{2R^2g}{V^2} \qquad \text{Removing a factor equal to 1: } \frac{V^2}{V^2} = 1$$

$$h = \frac{2R^2g}{V^2} - R. \qquad \text{Subtracting } R \text{ from both sides}$$

The last equation can be used to determine the height of a satellite above a planet when the planet's radius and gravitational constant, along with the satellite's escape velocity, are known.   **TRY EXERCISE** 29

EXAMPLE 3

Acoustics (the Doppler Effect).   The formula

$$f = \frac{sg}{s + v}$$

is used to determine the frequency f of a sound that is moving at velocity v toward a listener who hears the sound as frequency g. Here s is the speed of sound in a particular medium. Solve for s.

UDENT NOTES

e steps used to solve equations
precisely the same steps used
solve formulas. If you feel "rusty"
his regard, study the earlier sec-
n in which this type of equation
t appeared. Then make sure that
can consistently solve those
ations before returning to the
rk with formulas.

SOLUTION   We first clear fractions by multiplying by the LCD, $s + v$:

$$f \cdot (s + v) = \frac{sg}{s + v}(s + v)$$

$$fs + fv = sg. \qquad \text{The variable for which we are solving, } s,$$
$$\text{appears on both sides, forcing us to}$$
$$\text{distribute on the left side.}$$

Next, we must get all terms containing s on one side:

$$fv = sg - fs \qquad \text{Subtracting } fs \text{ from both sides}$$
$$fv = s(g - f) \qquad \text{Factoring out } s. \text{ This is like combining like terms.}$$
$$\frac{fv}{g - f} = s. \qquad \text{Dividing both sides by } g - f$$

Since s is isolated on one side, we have solved for s. This last equation can be use
to determine the speed of sound whenever f, v, and g are known.

> TRY EXERCISE 19

To Solve a Rational Equation for a Specified Variable

1. Multiply both sides by the LCD to clear fractions, if necessary.
2. Multiply to remove parentheses, if necessary.
3. Get all terms with the specified variable alone on one side.
4. Factor out the specified variable if it is in more than one term.
5. Multiply or divide on both sides to isolate the specified variable.

Variation

To extend our study of formulas and functions, we now examine three real-wor
situations: direct variation, inverse variation, and combined variation.

DIRECT VARIATION

A computer technician earns $22 per hour. In 1 hr, $22 is earned. In 2 hr, $44
earned. In 3 hr, $66 is earned, and so on. This gives rise to a set of ordered pairs:

$$(1, 22), (2, 44), (3, 66), (4, 88), \quad \text{and so on.}$$

Note that the ratio of earnings E to time t is $\frac{22}{1}$ in every case.

If a situation is modeled by pairs for which the ratio is constant, we say the
is **direct variation**. Here earnings *vary directly* as the time:

We have $\dfrac{E}{t} = 22$, so $E = 22t$ or, using function notation, $E(t) = 22t$.

Direct Variation

When a situation is modeled by a linear function of the form $f(x) = kx$,
or $y = kx$, where k is a nonzero constant, we say that there is *direct variation*, that y *varies directly* as x, or that y *is proportional to* x. The number k is called the *variation constant*, or *constant of proportionality*.

Note that for $k > 0$, any equation of the form $y = kx$ indicates that as x i
creases, y increases as well.

EXAMPLE 4

Find the variation constant and an equation of variation if y varies directly as x, and $y = 32$ when $x = 2$.

SOLUTION   We know that $(2, 32)$ is a solution of $y = kx$. Therefore,

$$32 = k \cdot 2 \qquad \text{Substituting}$$

$$\frac{32}{2} = k, \quad \text{or} \quad k = 16. \qquad \text{Solving for } k$$

The variation constant is 16. The equation of variation is $y = 16x$. The notation $y(x) = 16x$ or $f(x) = 16x$ is also used.   TRY EXERCISE 43

EXAMPLE 5

Ocean waves.   The speed v of a train of ocean waves varies directly as the swell period t, or time between successive waves. Waves with a swell period of 12 sec are traveling 21 mph. How fast are waves traveling that have a swell period of 20 sec?

Source: www.rodntube.com

SOLUTION

1. **Familiarize.** Because of the phrase "v . . . varies directly as . . . t," we express the speed of the wave v, in miles per hour, as a function of the swell period t, in seconds. Thus, $v(t) = kt$, where k is the variation constant. Because we are using ratios, we can use the units "seconds" and "miles per hour" without converting sec to hr or hr to sec. Knowing that waves with a swell period of 12 sec are traveling 21 mph, we have $v(12) = 21$.

2. **Translate.** We find the variation constant using the data and then use it to write the equation of variation:

$$v(t) = kt$$

$$v(12) = k \cdot 12 \qquad \text{Replacing } t \text{ with } 12$$

$$21 = k \cdot 12 \qquad \text{Replacing } v(12) \text{ with } 21$$

$$\frac{21}{12} = k \qquad \text{Solving for } k$$

$$1.75 = k. \qquad \text{This is the variation constant.}$$

The equation of variation is $v(t) = 1.75t$. This is the translation.

3. **Carry out.** To find the speed of waves with a swell period of 20 sec, we compute $v(20)$:

$$v(t) = 1.75t$$

$$v(20) = 1.75(20) \qquad \text{Substituting 20 for } t$$

$$= 35.$$

4. **Check.** To check, we could reexamine all our calculations. Note that our answer seems reasonable since the ratios 21/12 and 35/20 are both 1.75.

5. **State.** Waves with a swell period of 20 sec are traveling 35 mph.

          TRY EXERCISE 55

INVERSE VARIATION

Suppose a bus travels 20 mi. At 20 mph, the trip takes 1 hr. At 40 mph, it takes $\frac{1}{2}$ hr. At 60 mph, it takes $\frac{1}{3}$ hr, and so on. This gives pairs of numbers, all having the same product:

$$(20, 1), \left(40, \tfrac{1}{2}\right), \left(60, \tfrac{1}{3}\right), \left(80, \tfrac{1}{4}\right), \quad \text{and so on.}$$

Note that the product of each pair is 20. When a situation is modeled by pa[irs] for which the product is constant, we say that there is **inverse variation**. Sin[ce] $r \cdot t = 20$, we have

$$t = \frac{20}{r} \quad \text{or, using function notation,} \quad t(r) = \frac{20}{r}.$$

Inverse Variation

When a situation is modeled by a rational function of the form $f(x) = k/x$, or $y = k/x$, where k is a nonzero constant, we say that there is *inverse variation*, that *y varies inversely as x*, or that *y is inversely proportional to x*. The number k is called the *variation constant*, or *constant of proportionality*.

Note that for $k > 0$, any equation of the form $y = k/x$ indicates that as [x] increases, y decreases.

EXAMPLE 6   Find the variation constant and an equation of variation if y varies inversely as [x] and $y = 32$ when $x = 0.2$.

SOLUTION   We know that $(0.2, 32)$ is a solution of

$$y = \frac{k}{x}.$$

Therefore,

$$32 = \frac{k}{0.2} \qquad \text{Substituting}$$

$$(0.2)32 = k$$

$$6.4 = k. \qquad \text{Solving for } k$$

The variation constant is 6.4. The equation of variation is

$$y = \frac{6.4}{x}.$$

> TRY EXERCISE 4[9]

There are many real-life quantities that vary inversely.

EXAMPLE 7   *Movie downloads.*   The time t that it takes to download a movie file vari[es] inversely as the transfer speed s of the Internet connection. A typical full-leng[th] movie file will transfer in 48 min at a transfer speed of 256 KB/s (kilobytes per se[c]ond). How long will it take to transfer the same movie file at a transfer spe[ed] of 32 KB/s?

Source: www.xsvidmovies.com

SOLUTION

1. **Familiarize.** Because of the phrase ". . . varies inversely as the transf[er] speed," we express the download time t, in minutes, as a function of t[he] transfer speed s, in kilobytes per second. Thus, $t(s) = k/s$.

2. **Translate.** We use the given information to solve for k. We will then use that result to write the equation of variation.

$$t(s) = \frac{k}{s}$$

$$t(256) = \frac{k}{256} \qquad \text{Replacing } s \text{ with } 256$$

$$48 = \frac{k}{256} \qquad \text{Replacing } t(256) \text{ with } 48$$

$$12{,}288 = k.$$

The equation of variation is $t(s) = 12{,}288/s$. This is the translation.

3. **Carry out.** To find the download time at a transfer speed of 32 KB/s, we calculate $t(32)$:

$$t(32) = \frac{12{,}288}{32} = 384.$$

4. **Check.** Note that, as expected, as the transfer speed goes *down*, the download time goes *up*. Also, the products $48 \cdot 256$ and $32 \cdot 384$ are both 12,288.

5. **State.** At a transfer speed of 32 KB/s, it will take 384 min, or 6 hr 24 min, to download the movie file.

> TRY EXERCISE 57

JOINT VARIATION AND COMBINED VARIATION

When a variable varies directly with more than one other variable, we say that there is *joint variation*. For example, in the formula for the volume of a right circular cylinder, $V = \pi r^2 h$, we say that V varies *jointly* as h and the square of r.

> ### Joint Variation
> y varies *jointly* as x and z if, for some nonzero constant k, $y = kxz$.

EXAMPLE 8 Find an equation of variation if y varies jointly as x and z, and $y = 30$ when $x = 2$ and $z = 3$.

SOLUTION We have

$$y = kxz,$$

so

$$30 = k \cdot 2 \cdot 3$$

$$k = 5. \qquad \text{The variation constant is 5.}$$

The equation of variation is $y = 5xz$.

> TRY EXERCISE 73

Joint variation is one form of *combined variation*. In general, when a variable varies directly and/or inversely, at the same time, with more than one other variable, there is **combined variation**. Examples 8 and 9 are both examples of combined variation.

EXAMPLE **9** Find an equation of variation if y varies jointly as x and z and inversely as the square of w, and $y = 105$ when $x = 3$, $z = 20$, and $w = 2$.

SOLUTION The equation of variation is of the form

$$y = k \cdot \frac{xz}{w^2},$$

so, substituting, we have

$$105 = k \cdot \frac{3 \cdot 20}{2^2}$$
$$105 = k \cdot 15$$
$$k = 7.$$

Thus,

$$y = 7 \cdot \frac{xz}{w^2}.$$

TRY EXERCISE 75

7.5 EXERCISE SET

Concept Reinforcement *Match each statement with the correct term that completes it from the list on the right.*

1. To clear fractions, we can multiply both sides of an equation by the _____.

2. With direct variation, pairs of numbers have a constant _____.

3. With inverse variation, pairs of numbers have a constant _____.

4. If $y = k/x$, then y varies _____ as x.

5. If $y = kx$, then y varies _____ as x.

6. If $y = kxz$, then y varies _____ as x and z.

a) Directly

b) Inversely

c) Jointly

d) LCD

e) Product

f) Ratio

Determine whether each situation represents direct variation or inverse variation.

7. Two painters can scrape a house in 9 hr, whereas three painters can scrape the house in 6 hr.

8. Andres planted 5 bulbs in 20 min and 7 bulbs in 28 min.

9. Salma swam 2 laps in 7 min and 6 laps in 21 min.

10. It took 2 band members 80 min to set up for a show with 4 members working, it took 40 min.

11. It took 3 hr for 4 volunteers to wrap the campus' collection of Toys for Tots, but only 1.5 hr with 8 volunteers working.

12. Ayana's air conditioner cooled off 1000 ft^3 in 10 min and 3000 ft^3 in 30 min.

lve each formula for the specified variable.

3. $f = \dfrac{L}{d}$; d

14. $\dfrac{W_1}{W_2} = \dfrac{d_1}{d_2}$; W_1

5. $s = \dfrac{(v_1 + v_2)t}{2}$; v_1

16. $s = \dfrac{(v_1 + v_2)t}{2}$; t

7. $\dfrac{t}{a} + \dfrac{t}{b} = 1$; b

18. $\dfrac{1}{R} = \dfrac{1}{r_1} + \dfrac{1}{r_2}$; R

9. $R = \dfrac{gs}{g + s}$; g

20. $K = \dfrac{rt}{r - t}$; t

1. $I = \dfrac{nE}{R + nr}$; n

22. $I = \dfrac{nE}{R + nr}$; r

3. $\dfrac{1}{p} + \dfrac{1}{q} = \dfrac{1}{f}$; q

24. $\dfrac{1}{p} + \dfrac{1}{q} = \dfrac{1}{f}$; p

5. $S = \dfrac{H}{m(t_1 - t_2)}$; t_1

26. $S = \dfrac{H}{m(t_1 - t_2)}$; H

7. $\dfrac{E}{e} = \dfrac{R + r}{r}$; r

28. $\dfrac{E}{e} = \dfrac{R + r}{R}$; R

9. $S = \dfrac{a}{1 - r}$; r

30. $S = \dfrac{a - ar^n}{1 - r}$; a

1. $c = \dfrac{f}{(a + b)c}$; $a + b$

2. $d = \dfrac{g}{d(c + f)}$; $c + f$

3. *Interest.* The formula

$$P = \frac{A}{1 + r}$$

is used to determine what principal P should be invested for one year at $(100 \cdot r)\%$ simple interest in order to have A dollars after a year. Solve for r.

4. *Taxable interest.* The formula

$$I_t = \frac{I_f}{1 - T}$$

gives the *taxable interest rate* I_t equivalent to the *tax-free interest rate* I_f for a person in the $(100 \cdot T)\%$ tax bracket. Solve for T.

5. *Average speed.* The formula

$$v = \frac{d_2 - d_1}{t_2 - t_1}$$

gives an object's average speed v when that object has traveled d_1 miles in t_1 hours and d_2 miles in t_2 hours. Solve for t_1.

36. *Average acceleration.* The formula

$$a = \frac{v_2 - v_1}{t_2 - t_1}$$

gives a vehicle's *average acceleration* when its velocity changes from v_1 at time t_1 to v_2 at time t_2. Solve for t_2.

37. *Work rate.* The formula

$$\frac{1}{t} = \frac{1}{a} + \frac{1}{b}$$

gives the total time t required for two workers to complete a job, if the workers' individual times are a and b. Solve for t.

38. *Planetary orbits.* The formula

$$\frac{x^2}{a^2} + \frac{y^2}{b^2} = 1$$

can be used to plot a planet's elliptical orbit of width $2a$ and length $2b$ (see p. 869 in Section 10.2). Solve for b^2.

39. *Semester average.* The formula

$$A = \frac{2Tt + Qq}{2T + Q}$$

gives a student's average A after T tests and Q quizzes, where each test counts as 2 quizzes, t is the test average, and q is the quiz average. Solve for Q.

40. *Astronomy.* The formula

$$L = \frac{dR}{D - d},$$

where D is the diameter of the sun, d is the diameter of the earth, R is the earth's distance from the sun, and L is some fixed distance, is used in calculating when lunar eclipses occur. Solve for D.

41. *Body-fat percentage.* The YMCA calculates men's body-fat percentage p using the formula

$$p = \frac{-98.42 + 4.15c - 0.082w}{w},$$

where c is the waist measurement, in inches, and w is the weight, in pounds. Solve for w.
Source: YMCA guide to Physical Fitness Assessment

42. *Preferred viewing distance.* Researchers model the distance D from which an observer prefers to watch television in "picture heights"—that is, multiples of the height of the viewing screen. The preferred viewing distance is given by

$$D = \frac{3.55H + 0.9}{H},$$

where D is in picture heights and H is in meters. Solve for H.

Source: www.tid.es, Telefonica Investigación y Desarrollo, S.A. Unipersonal

Find the variation constant and an equation of variation if y varies directly as x and the following conditions apply.

43. $y = 30$ when $x = 5$

44. $y = 80$ when $x = 16$

45. $y = 3.4$ when $x = 2$

46. $y = 2$ when $x = 5$

47. $y = 2$ when $x = \frac{1}{5}$

48. $y = 0.9$ when $x = 0.5$

Find the variation constant and an equation of variation in which y varies inversely as x, and the following conditions exist.

49. $y = 5$ when $x = 20$

50. $y = 40$ when $x = 8$

51. $y = 11$ when $x = 4$

52. $y = 9$ when $x = 10$

53. $y = 27$ when $x = \frac{1}{3}$

54. $y = 81$ when $x = \frac{1}{9}$

55. *Hooke's law.* Hooke's law states that the distance d that a spring is stretched by a hanging object varies directly as the mass m of the object. If the distance is 20 cm when the mass is 3 kg, what is the distance when the mass is 5 kg?

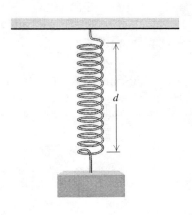

56. *Ohm's law.* The electric current I, in amperes, in a circuit varies directly as the voltage V. When 15 volts are applied, the current is 5 amperes. What is the current when 18 volts are applied?

57. *Work rate.* The time T required to do a job varies inversely as the number of people P working. It takes 5 hr for 7 volunteers to pick up rubbish from 1 mi of roadway. How long would it take 10 volunteers to complete the job?

58. *Pumping rate.* The time t required to empty a tank varies inversely as the rate r of pumping. If a Briggs and Stratton pump can empty a tank in 45 min at the rate of 600 kL/min, how long will it take the pump to empty the tank at 1000 kL/min?

59. *Water from melting snow.* The number of centimeters W of water produced from melting snow varies directly as the number of centimeters S of snow. Meteorologists know that under certain conditions, 150 cm of snow will melt to 16.8 cm of water. The average annual snowfall in Alta, Utah, is 500 in. Assuming the above conditions, how much water will replace the 500 in. of snow?

60. *Gardening.* The number of calories burned by a gardener is directly proportional to the time spent gardening. It takes 30 min to burn 180 calories. How long would it take to burn 240 calories when gardening?

Source: www.healthstatus.com

Aha! **61.** *Mass of water in a human.* The number of kilograms W of water in a human body varies directly as the mass of the body. A 96-kg person contains 64 kg of water. How many kilograms of water are in a 48-kg person?

62. *Weight on Mars.* The weight M of an object on Mars varies directly as its weight E on Earth. A person who weighs 95 lb on Earth weighs 38 lb on Mars. How much would a 100-lb person weigh on Mars?

3. *String length and frequency.* The frequency of a string is inversely proportional to its length. A violin string that is 33 cm long vibrates with a frequency of 260 Hz. What is the frequency when the string is shortened to 30 cm?

4. *Wavelength and frequency.* The wavelength W of a radio wave varies inversely as its frequency F. A wave with a frequency of 1200 kilohertz has a length of 300 meters. What is the length of a wave with a frequency of 800 kilohertz?

5. *Ultraviolet index.* At an ultraviolet, or UV, rating of 4, those people who are less sensitive to the sun will burn in 75 min. Given that the number of minutes it takes to burn, t, varies inversely with the UV rating, u, how long will it take less sensitive people to burn when the UV rating is 14?
Source: *The Electronic Textbook of Dermatology* at www.telemedicine.org

6. *Current and resistance.* The current I in an electrical conductor varies inversely as the resistance R of the conductor. If the current is $\frac{1}{2}$ ampere when the resistance is 240 ohms, what is the current when the resistance is 540 ohms?

7. *Air pollution.* The average U.S. household of 2.6 people released 0.94 ton of carbon monoxide into the environment in a recent year. How many tons were released nationally? Use 305,000,000 as the U.S. population.
Sources: Based on data from the U.S. Environmental Protection Agency and the U.S. Census Bureau

8. *Relative aperture.* The relative aperture, or f-stop, of a 23.5-mm lens is directly proportional to the focal length F of the lens. If a lens with a 150-mm focal length has an f-stop of 6.3, find the f-stop of a 23.5-mm lens with a focal length of 80 mm.

Find an equation of variation in which:

69. y varies directly as the square of x, and $y = 50$ when $x = 10$.

70. y varies directly as the square of x, and $y = 0.15$ when $x = 0.1$.

71. y varies inversely as the square of x, and $y = 50$ when $x = 10$.

72. y varies inversely as the square of x, and $y = 0.15$ when $x = 0.1$.

73. y varies jointly as x and z, and $y = 105$ when $x = 14$ and $z = 5$.

74. y varies jointly as x and z, and $y = \frac{3}{2}$ when $x = 2$ and $z = 10$.

75. y varies jointly as w and the square of x and inversely as z, and $y = 49$ when $w = 3$, $x = 7$, and $z = 12$.

76. y varies directly as x and inversely as w and the square of z, and $y = 4.5$ when $x = 15$, $w = 5$, and $z = 2$.

77. *Stopping distance of a car.* The stopping distance d of a car after the brakes have been applied varies directly as the square of the speed r. Once the brakes are applied, a car traveling 60 mph can stop in 138 ft. What stopping distance corresponds to a speed of 40 mph?
Source: Based on data from Edmunds.com

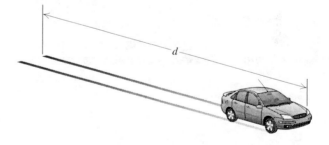

78. *Reverberation time.* A sound's reverberation time T is the time it takes for the sound level to decrease by 60 dB (decibels) after the sound has been turned off. Reverberation time varies directly as the volume V of a room and inversely as the sound absorption A of the room. A given sound has a reverberation time of 1.5 sec in a room with a volume of 90 m³ and a sound absorption of 9.6. What is the reverberation time of the same sound in a room with a volume of 84 m³ and a sound absorption of 10.5?
Source: www.isover.co.uk

79. *Volume of a gas.*   The volume V of a given mass of a gas varies directly as the temperature T and inversely as the pressure P. If $V = 231$ cm^3 when $T = 300°$K (Kelvin) and $P = 20$ lb/cm^2, what is the volume when $T = 320°$K and $P = 16$ lb/cm^2?

80. *Intensity of a signal.*   The intensity I of a television signal varies inversely as the square of the distance d from the transmitter. If the intensity is 25 W/m^2 at a distance of 2 km, what is the intensity 6.25 km from the transmitter?

81. *Atmospheric drag.*   Wind resistance, or atmospheric drag, tends to slow down moving objects. Atmospheric drag W varies jointly as an object's surface area A and velocity v. If a car traveling at a speed of 40 mph with a surface area of 37.8 ft^2 experiences a drag of 222 N (Newtons), how fast must a car with 51 ft^2 of surface area travel in order to experience a drag force of 430 N?

82. *Drag force.*   The drag force F on a boat varies jointly as the wetted surface area A and the square of the velocity of the boat. If a boat traveling 6.5 mph experiences a drag force of 86 N when the wetted surface area is 41.2 ft^2, find the wetted surface area of a boat traveling 8.2 mph with a drag force of 94 N.

83. If y varies directly as x, does doubling x cause y to be doubled as well? Why or why not?

84. Which exercise did you find easier to work: Exercise 15 or Exercise 19? Why?

Skill Review

To prepare for Chapter 8, review solving an equation for y and translating phrases to algebraic expressions (Sections 1.1 and 2.3).

Solve. [2.3]

85. $x - 6y = 3$, for y

86. $3x - 8y = 5$, for y

87. $5x + 2y = -3$, for y

88. $x + 8y = 4$, for y

Translate each of the following. Do not solve. [1.1]

89. Five more than twice a number is 49.

90. Three less than half of some number is 57.

91. The sum of two consecutive integers is 145.

92. The difference between a number and its opposite is 20.

Synthesis

93. Suppose that the number of customer complaints is inversely proportional to the number of employees hired. Will a firm reduce the number of complaints more by expanding from 5 to 10 employees, or from 20 to 25? Explain. Consider using a graph to help justify your answer.

94. Why do you think subscripts are used in Exercises 15 and 25 but not in Exercises 27 and 28?

95. *Escape velocity.*   A satellite's escape velocity is 6.5 mi/sec, the radius of the earth is 3960 mi, and the earth's gravitational constant is 32.2 ft/sec^2. How far is the satellite from the surface of the earth? (See Example 2.)

96. The *harmonic mean* of two numbers a and b is a number M such that the reciprocal of M is the average of the reciprocals of a and b. Find a formula for the harmonic mean.

97. *Health-care.*   Young's rule for determining the size of a particular child's medicine dosage c is

$$c = \frac{a}{a + 12} \cdot d,$$

where a is the child's age and d is the typical adult dosage. If a child's age is doubled, the dosage increases. Find the ratio of the larger dosage to the smaller dosage. By what percent does the dosage increase?
Source: Olsen, June Looby, Leon J. Ablon, and Anthony Patrick Giangrasso, *Medical Dosage Calculations*, 6th ed.

98. Solve for x:

$$x^2\left(1 - \frac{2pq}{x}\right) = \frac{2p^2q^3 - pq^2x}{-q}.$$

99. *Average acceleration.*   The formula

$$a = \frac{\dfrac{d_4 - d_3}{t_4 - t_3} - \dfrac{d_2 - d_1}{t_2 - t_1}}{t_4 - t_2}$$

can be used to approximate average acceleration, where the d's are distances and the t's are the corresponding times. Solve for t_1.

100. If y varies inversely as the cube of x and x is multiplied by 0.5, what is the effect on y?

1. *Intensity of light.* The intensity I of light from a bulb varies directly as the wattage of the bulb and inversely as the square of the distance d from the bulb. If the wattage of a light source and its distance from reading matter are both doubled, how does the intensity change?

2. Describe in words the variation represented by $W = \dfrac{km_1M_1}{d^2}$. Assume k is a constant.

3. *Tension of a musical string.* The tension T on a string in a musical instrument varies jointly as the string's mass per unit length m, the square of its length l, and the square of its fundamental frequency f. A 2-m long string of mass 5 gm/m with a fundamental frequency of 80 has a tension of 100 N (Newtons). How long should the same string be if its tension is going to be changed to 72 N?

4. *Volume and cost.* A peanut butter jar in the shape of a right circular cylinder is 4 in. high and 3 in. in diameter and sells for $1.20. If we assume that cost is proportional to volume, how much should a jar 6 in. high and 6 in. in diameter cost?

105. *Golf distance finder.* A device used in golf to estimate the distance d to a hole measures the size s that the 7-ft pin *appears* to be in a viewfinder. The viewfinder uses the principle, diagrammed here, that s gets bigger when d gets smaller. If $s = 0.56$ in. when $d = 50$ yd, find an equation of variation that expresses d as a function of s. What is d when $s = 0.40$ in.?

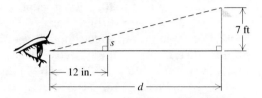

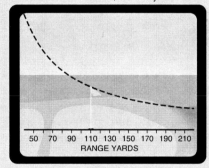

HOW IT WORKS:

Just sight the flagstick through the viewfinder...
fit flag between top dashed line and the solid line below...
...read the distance, 50 – 220 yards.

Nothing to focus.
·
Gives you exact distance that your ball
lies from the flagstick.
·
Choose proper club on every approach shot.
·
Figure new pin placement instantly.
·
Train your naked eye for formal and tournament play.
·
Eliminate the need to remember every stake,
tree, and bush on the course.

Photo Credits

A   Mean, Median, and Mode

Mean   ■   Median   ■   Mode

One way to analyze data is to look for a single representative number, called a **center point** or **measure of central tendency**. Those most often used are the **mean** (or **average**), the **median**, and the **mode**.

Mean

Let's first consider the *mean*, or *average*.

> ### Mean, or Average
>
> The *mean*, or *average*, of a set of numbers is the sum of the numbers divided by the number of addends.

EXAMPLE   **1**   Consider the following data on revenue, in billions of dollars, for Starbucks Corporation in five recent years:

$$\$2.2, \quad \$2.6, \quad \$3.3, \quad \$4.1, \quad \$5.3.$$

What is the mean of the numbers?

SOLUTION   First, we add the numbers:

$$2.2 + 2.6 + 3.3 + 4.1 + 5.3 = 17.5.$$

Then we divide by the number of addends, 5:

$$\frac{(2.2 + 2.6 + 3.3 + 4.1 + 5.3)}{5} = \frac{17.5}{5} = 3.5.$$

The mean, or average, revenue of Starbucks for those five years is $3.5 billion.

Note that $3.5 + 3.5 + 3.5 + 3.5 + 3.5 = 17.5$. If we use this center point, 3.5, repeatedly as the addend, we get the same sum that we do when adding individual data numbers.

Median

The *median* is useful when we wish to de-emphasize extreme scores. For exam-ple, suppose five workers in a technology company manufactured the followi number of computers during one day's work:

Sarah: 88
Matt: 92
Pat: 66
Jen: 94
Mark: 91

Let's first list the scores in order from smallest to largest:

66   88   91   92   94.
              ↑
          Middle number

The middle number—in this case, 91—is the **median**.

> ### Median
>
> Once a set of data has been arranged from smallest to largest, the *median* of the set of data is the middle number if there is an odd num-ber of data numbers. If there is an even number of data numbers, then there are two middle numbers and the median is the *average* of the two middle numbers.

EXAMPLE 2   Find the median of the following set of household incomes:

$76,000, $58,000, $87,000, $32,500, $64,800, $62,500.

SOLUTION   We first rearrange the numbers in order from smallest to largest.

$32,500, $58,000, $62,500, $64,800, $76,000, $87,000
                          ↑
                       Median

There is an even number of numbers. We look for the middle two, which a $62,500 and $64,800. The median is the average of $62,500 and $64,800:

$$\frac{\$62,500 + \$64,800}{2} = \$63,650.$$

Mode

The last center point we consider is called the *mode*. A number that occurs most c ten in a set of data is sometimes considered a representative number or center poi

> ### Mode
>
> The *mode* of a set of data is the number or numbers that occur most often. If each number occurs the same number of times, then there is *no* mode.

EXAMPLE   3   Find the mode of the following data:

23, 24, 27, 18, 19, 27.

SOLUTION   The number that occurs most often is 27. Thus the mode is 27.

It is easier to find the mode of a set of data if the data are ordered.

EXAMPLE   4   Find the mode of the following data:

83, 84, 84, 84, 85, 86, 87, 87, 87, 88, 89, 90.

SOLUTION   There are two numbers that occur most often, 84 and 87. Thus the modes are 84 and 87.

EXAMPLE   5   Find the mode of the following data:

115, 117, 211, 213, 219.

SOLUTION   Each number occurs the same number of times. The set of data has *no* mode.

A   EXERCISE SET

r each set of numbers, find the mean (average), the ?dian, and any modes that exist.

. 13, 21, 18, 13, 20

. 5, 2, 8, 10, 7, 1, 9

. 3, 8, 20, 3, 20, 10

. 19, 19, 8, 16, 8, 7

. 4.7, 2.3, 4.6, 4.9, 3.8

. 13.4, 13.4, 12.6, 42.9

. 234, 228, 234, 228, 234, 278

. $29.95, $28.79, $30.95, $29.95

. *Hurricanes.*   The following bar graph shows the number of hurricanes that struck the United States

Answers to Exercises 1–8 can be found on p. IA-37.

by month from 1851 to 2006. What is the average number for the 8 months given? the median? the mode?   Average: 34.875; median: 22; mode: 0

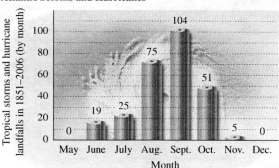

Atlantic Storms and Hurricanes

Source: Atlantic Oceanographic and Meteorological Laboratory

10.   *iPod prices.*   A price comparison showed the following online prices for an Apple iPod Nano:

$199, $197.97, $249.99, $179, $197.97.

What was the average price? the median price? the mode?

Average: $204.79; median: $197.97; mode: $197.97

11. *NBA tall men.* The following lists the heights, in inches, of the tallest men in the NBA in a recent year. Find the mean, the median, and the mode.

Zydrunas Ilgauskas	87
Yao Ming	90
Dikembe Mutombo	86
Kosta Perovic	86

Source: National Basketball Association
Mean: 87.25; median: 86.5; mode: 86

12. *Coffee consumption.* The following lists the annual coffee consumption, in number of cups per person, for various countries. Find the mean, the median, and the mode.

Germany	1113
United States	610
Switzerland	1215
France	798
Italy	750

Source: Beverage Marketing Corporation
Mean: 897.2; median: 798; mode: none

13. *PBA scores.* Kelly Kulick rolled scores of 254, 202, 184, 269, 151, 223, 258, 222, and 202 in a recent tour trial for the Professional Bowlers Association. What was her average? her median? her mode?

Source: Professional Bowlers Association
Average: 218.3; median: 222; mode: 202

14. *Salmon prices.* The following prices per pound of Atlantic salmon were found at six fish markets:

$8.99, $8.49, $8.99, $9.99, $9.49, $7.99.

What was the average price per pound? the median price? the mode?
Average: $8.99; median: $8.99; mode: $8.99

Synthesis

15. *Hank Aaron.* Hank Aaron averaged $34\frac{7}{22}$ home runs per year over a 22-yr career. After 21 yr, Aaron had averaged $35\frac{10}{21}$ home runs per year. How many home runs did Aaron hit in his final year?
10 home runs

16. *Length of pregnancy.* Marta was pregnant 270 days, 259 days, and 272 days for her first three pregnancies. In order for Marta's average length of pregnancy to equal the worldwide average of 266 days, how long must her fourth pregnancy last?
Source: David Crystal (ed.), *The Cambridge Factfinder.* Cambridge CB2 1RP: Cambridge University Press, 1993, p. 84.
263 days

17. The ordered set of data 18, 21, 24, a, 36, 37, b has a median of 30 and an average of 32. Find a and b.
$a = 30, b = 58$

18. *Male height.* Jason's brothers are 174 cm, 180 cm, 179 cm, and 172 cm tall. The average male is 176.5 cm tall. How tall is Jason if he and his brothers have an average height of 176.5 cm? 177.5 cm

---

B	Sets

Naming Sets ∎ Membership ∎ Subsets ∎ Intersections ∎ Unions

A **set** is a collection of objects. In mathematics the objects, or **elements**, of a set are generally numbers. This section provides an introduction to sets and how combine them.

Naming Sets

To name the set of whole numbers less than 6, we can use *roster notation*, as follows:

$$\{0, 1, 2, 3, 4, 5\}.$$

The set of real numbers x for which x is less than 6 cannot be named by listing all its members because there is an infinite number of them. We name such a set using *set-builder notation*, as follows:

$$\{x \mid x < 6\}.$$

This is read

"The set of all x such that x is less than 6."

See Section 2.6 for more on this notation.

Membership

The symbol $\in$ means *is a member of* or *belongs to*, or *is an element of*. Thus,

$$x \in A$$

means

x is a member of A,   or x belongs to A,   or x is an element of A.

EXAMPLE 1   Classify each of the following as true or false.

a) $1 \in \{1, 2, 3\}$

b) $1 \in \{2, 3\}$

c) $4 \in \{x \mid x \text{ is an even whole number}\}$

d) $5 \in \{x \mid x \text{ is an even whole number}\}$

SOLUTION

a) Since 1 is listed as a member of the set, $1 \in \{1, 2, 3\}$ is true.

b) Since 1 is *not* a member of $\{2, 3\}$, the statement $1 \in \{2, 3\}$ is false.

c) Since 4 is an even whole number, $4 \in \{x \mid x \text{ is an even whole number}\}$ is true.

d) Since 5 is *not* even, $5 \in \{x \mid x \text{ is an even whole number}\}$ is false.

 TRY EXERCISE 7

Set membership can be illustrated with a diagram, as shown below.

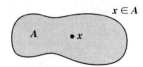

Subsets

If every element of A is also an element of B, then A is a *subset* of B. This is denoted $A \subseteq B$.

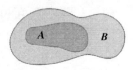

The set of whole numbers is a subset of the set of integers. The set of ration numbers is a subset of the set of real numbers.

EXAMPLE 2 Classify each of the following as true or false.

a) $\{1, 2\} \subseteq \{1, 2, 3, 4\}$

b) $\{p, q, r, w\} \subseteq \{a, p, r, z\}$

c) $\{x \mid x < 6\} \subseteq \{x \mid x \leq 11\}$

SOLUTION

a) Since every element of $\{1, 2\}$ is in the set $\{1, 2, 3, 4\}$, it follows th $\{1, 2\} \subseteq \{1, 2, 3, 4\}$ is true.

b) Since $q \in \{p, q, r, w\}$, but $q \notin \{a, p, r, z\}$, it follows that $\{p, q, r, w\} \subseteq \{a, p, r,$ is false.

c) Since every number that is less than 6 is also less than 11, the stateme $\{x \mid x < 6\} \subseteq \{x \mid x \leq 11\}$ is true.

TRY EXERCISE 15

Intersections

The *intersection* of sets A and B, denoted $A \cap B$, is the set of members common both sets.

EXAMPLE 3 Find each intersection.

a) $\{0, 1, 3, 5, 25\} \cap \{2, 3, 4, 5, 6, 7, 9\}$

b) $\{a, p, q, w\} \cap \{p, q, t\}$

SOLUTION

a) $\{0, 1, 3, 5, 25\} \cap \{2, 3, 4, 5, 6, 7, 9\} = \{3, 5\}$

b) $\{a, p, q, w\} \cap \{p, q, t\} = \{p, q\}$

TRY EXERCISE 19

Set intersection can be illustrated with a diagram, as shown below.

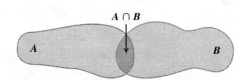

The set without members is known as the *empty set*, and is written $\varnothing$ an sometimes $\{\ \}$. Each of the following is a description of the empty set:

The set of all 12-ft–tall people;

$\{2, 3\} \cap \{5, 6, 7\}$;

$\{x \mid x \text{ is an even natural number}\} \cap \{x \mid x \text{ is an odd natural number}\}$.

Unions

Two sets A and B can be combined to form a set that contains the members both A and B. The new set is called the *union* of A and B, denoted $A \cup B$.

EXAMPLE 4 Find each union.

a) $\{0, 5, 7, 13, 27\} \cup \{0, 2, 3, 4, 5\}$

b) $\{a, c, e, g\} \cup \{b, d, f\}$

SOLUTION

a) $\{0, 5, 7, 13, 27\} \cup \{0, 2, 3, 4, 5\} = \{0, 2, 3, 4, 5, 7, 13, 27\}$

Note that the 0 and the 5 are *not* listed twice in the solution.

b) $\{a, c, e, g\} \cup \{b, d, f\} = \{a, b, c, d, e, f, g\}$ **TRY EXERCISE** 25

Set union can be illustrated with a diagram, as shown below.

$A \cup B$ is shaded.

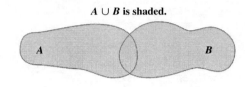

B   EXERCISE SET

...me each set using the roster method.

. The set of whole numbers 8 through 11 $\{8, 9, 10, 11\}$

. The set of whole numbers 83 through 89
$\{83, 84, 85, 86, 87, 88, 89\}$

. The set of odd numbers between 40 and 50
$\{41, 43, 45, 47, 49\}$

. The set of multiples of 5 between 10 and 40
$\{15, 20, 25, 30, 35\}$

. $\{x \mid$ the square of x is 9$\}$ $\{-3, 3\}$

. $\{x \mid x$ is the cube of $\frac{1}{2}\}$ $\{\frac{1}{8}\}$

...assify each statement as either true or false.

. $5 \in \{x \mid x$ is an odd number$\}$ True

. $8 \in \{x \mid x$ is an odd number$\}$ False

. Skiing $\in$ The set of all sports   True

. Pharmacist $\in$ The set of all professions requiring a
college degree   True

. $3 \in \{-4, -3, 0, 1\}$ False

. $0 \in \{-4, -3, 0, 1\}$ True

. $\frac{2}{3} \in \{x \mid x$ is a rational number$\}$ True

. $\frac{2}{3} \in \{x \mid x$ is a real number$\}$ True

. $\{-1, 0, 1\} \subseteq \{-3, -2, -1, 1\,2, 3\}$ False

. The set of vowels $\subseteq$ The set of consonants   False

. The set of integers $\subseteq$ The set of rational numbers
True

. $\{2, 4, 6\} \subseteq \{1, 2, 3, 4, 5, 6, 7\}$ True

...nd each intersection.

. $\{a, b, c, d, e\} \cap \{c, d, e, f, g\}$ $\{c, d, e\}$

. $\{a, e, i, o, u\} \cap \{q, u, i, c, k\}$ $\{u, i\}$

21. $\{1, 2, 3, 4, 6, 12\} \cap \{1, 2, 3, 6, 9, 18\}$ $\{1, 2, 3, 6\}$

22. $\{1, 2, 3, 4, 6, 12\} \cap \{1, 5, 7, 35\}$ $\{1\}$

23. $\{2, 4, 6, 8\} \cap \{1, 3, 5, 7\}$ $\varnothing$

24. $\{a, e, i, o, u\} \cap \{m, n, f, g, h\}$ $\varnothing$

Find each union.

25. $\{a, e, i, o, u\} \cup \{q, u, i, c, k\}$ $\{a, e, i, o, u, q, c, k\}$

26. $\{a, b, c, d, e\} \cup \{c, d, e, f, g\}$ $\{a, b, c, d, e, f, g\}$

27. $\{1, 2, 3, 4, 6, 12\} \cup \{1, 2, 3, 6, 9, 18\}$
$\{1, 2, 3, 4, 6, 9, 12, 18\}$

28. $\{1, 2, 3, 4, 6, 12\} \cup \{1, 5, 7, 35\}$ $\{1, 2, 3, 4, 5, 6, 7, 12, 35\}$

29. $\{2, 4, 6, 8\} \cup \{1, 3, 5, 7\}$ $\{1, 2, 3, 4, 5, 6, 7, 8\}$

30. $\{a, e, i, o, u\} \cup \{m, n, f, g, h\}$ $\{a, e, i, o, u, m, n, f, g, h\}$

31. What advantage(s) does set-builder notation have
over roster notation?

32. What advantage(s) does roster notation have over
set-builder notation?

Synthesis

33. Find the union of the set of integers and the set of
whole numbers.   The set of integers

34. Find the intersection of the set of odd integers and
the set of even integers. $\varnothing$

35. Find the union of the set of rational numbers and
the set of irrational numbers.   The set of real numbers

36. Find the intersection of the set of even integers and
the set of positive rational numbers.
The set of positive even integers

37. Find the intersection of the set of rational numbers and the set of irrational numbers. ○

38. Find the union of the set of negative integers, the set of positive integers, and the set containing 0.
The set of integers

39. For a set A, find each of the following.

   a) $A \cup \varnothing$ A

   b) $A \cup A$ A

   c) $A \cap A$ A

   d) $A \cap \varnothing$ ○

Classify each statement as either true or false.

40. The empty set can be written $\varnothing$, { }, or {0}.   False

41. For any set A, $\varnothing \subseteq A$.   True

42. For any set A, $A \subseteq A$.   True

43. For any sets A and B, $A \cap B \subseteq A$.   True

44. A set is *closed* under an operation if, when the operation is performed on its members, the result is in the set. For example, the set of real numbers is closed under the operation of addition since the sum of any two real numbers is a real number.

   a) Is the set of even numbers closed under addition? Yes   No

   b) Is the set of odd numbers closed under addition?

   c) Is the set {0, 1} closed under addition?   No

   d) Is the set {0, 1} closed under multiplication?   Ye

   e) Is the set of real numbers closed under multiplication?   Yes

   f) Is the set of integers closed under division?   No

45. Experiment with sets of various types and determine whether the following distributive law for sets is true: True

$$A \cap (B \cup C) = (A \cap B) \cup (A \cap C).$$

C   Synthetic Division

Streamlining Long Division ▪ The Remainder Theorem

Streamlining Long Division

To divide a polynomial by a binomial of the type $x - a$, we can streamline the usual procedure to develop a process called *synthetic division*.

Compare the following. In each stage, we attempt to write less than in the previous stage, while retaining enough essentials to solve the problem.

STAGE 1

When a polynomial is written in descending order, the coefficients provide the essential information:

$$
\begin{array}{r}
4x^2 + 5x + 11 \\
x - 2 \overline{)\,4x^3 - 3x^2 + x + 7} \\
\underline{4x^3 - 8x^2} \\
5x^2 + x \\
\underline{5x^2 - 10x} \\
11x + 7 \\
\underline{11x - 22} \\
29
\end{array}
\qquad
\begin{array}{r}
4 + 5 + 11 \\
1 - 2 \overline{)\,4 - 3 + 1 + 7} \\
\underline{4 - 8} \\
5 + 1 \\
\underline{5 - 10} \\
11 + 7 \\
\underline{11 - 22} \\
29
\end{array}
$$

Because the leading coefficient in $x - 2$ is 1, each time we multiply it by a term in the answer, the leading coefficient of that product duplicates a coefficient in the answer. In the next stage, rather than duplicate these numbers we focus on where -2 is used and drop the 1 from the divisor.

STAGE 2

$$
\begin{array}{r}
4x^2 + 5x + 11 \\
x - 2\overline{)4x^3 - 3x^2 + x + 7} \\
\underline{4x^3 - 8x^2} \\
5x^2 + x \\
\underline{5x^2 - 10x} \\
11x + 7 \\
\underline{11x - 22} \\
29
\end{array}
$$

$$
\begin{array}{r}
4 + 5 + 11 \\
-2\overline{)4 - 3 + 1 + 7} \\
- 8 \\
\underline{5 + 1} \\
- 10 \\
\underline{11 + 7} \\
- 22 \\
\underline{29}
\end{array}
$$

— Multiply: $-2 \cdot 4 = -8.$
Subtract: $-3 - (-8) = 5.$
Multiply: $-2 \cdot 5 = -10.$
Subtract: $1 - (-10) = 11.$
Multiply: $-2 \cdot 11 = -22.$
Subtract: $7 - (-22) = 29.$

To simplify further, we now reverse the sign of the -2 in the divisor and, in exchange, *add* at each step in the long division.

STAGE 3

$$
\begin{array}{r}
4x^2 + 5x + 11 \\
x - 2\overline{)4x^3 - 3x^2 + x + 7} \\
\underline{4x^3 - 8x^2} \\
5x^2 + x \\
\underline{5x^2 - 10x} \\
11x + 7 \\
\underline{11x - 22} \\
29
\end{array}
$$

$$
\begin{array}{r}
4 + 5 + 11 \\
2\overline{)4 - 3 + 1 + 7} \\
8 \\
\underline{5 + 1} \\
10 \\
\underline{11 + 7} \\
22 \\
\underline{29}
\end{array}
$$

Replace the -2 with 2.
Multiply: $2 \cdot 4 = 8.$
Add: $-3 + 8 = 5.$
Multiply: $2 \cdot 5 = 10.$
Add: $1 + 10 = 11.$
Multiply: $2 \cdot 11 = 22.$
Add: $7 + 22 = 29.$

The blue numbers can be eliminated if we look at the red numbers instead.

STAGE 4

$$
\begin{array}{r}
4x^2 + 5x + 11 \\
x - 2\overline{)4x^3 - 3x^2 + x + 7} \\
\underline{4x^3 - 8x^2} \\
5x^2 + x \\
\underline{5x^2 - 10x} \\
11x + 7 \\
\underline{11x - 22} \\
29
\end{array}
$$

$$
\begin{array}{r}
4 \quad 5 \quad 11 \\
2\overline{)4 \quad -3 \quad 1 \quad 7} \\
8 \quad 10 \quad 22 \\
\underline{5 \quad 11 \quad 29}
\end{array}
$$

STUDENT NOTES

You will not need to write out all the stages when performing synthetic division on your own. We show the steps to help you understand the reasoning behind the method.

Note that the 5 and the 11 preceding the remainder 29 coincide with the 5 and the 11 following the 4 on the top line. By writing a 4 to the left of 5 on the bottom line, we can eliminate the top line in stage 4 and read our answer from the bottom line. This final stage is commonly called **synthetic division**.

STAGE 5

$$
\begin{array}{r}
4 \quad 5 \quad 11 \\
2\overline{)4 \quad -3 \quad 1 \quad 7} \\
8 \quad 10 \quad 22 \\
\underline{5 \quad 11 \quad 29}
\end{array}
$$

$$
\begin{array}{r}
\underline{2}\ |\ 4 \quad -3 \quad 1 \quad 7 \\
8 \quad 10 \quad 22 \\
4 \quad 5 \quad 11\ |\ 29
\end{array}
$$

— This is the remainder.
This is the zero-degree coefficient.
This is the first-degree coefficient.
This is the second-degree coefficient.

The quotient is $4x^2 + 5x + 11$ with a remainder of 29.

Remember that for this method to work, the divisor must be of the form $x - a$, that is, a variable minus a constant.

EXAMPLE 1   Use synthetic division to divide: $(x^3 + 6x^2 - x - 30) \div (x - 2)$.

SOLUTION

$$
\begin{array}{r|rrrr}
2 & 1 & 6 & -1 & -30 \\
  &   &   &   &   \\
\hline
  & 1 &   &   &   \\
\end{array}
$$
Write the 2 of $x - 2$ and the coefficients of the dividend.

Bring down the first coefficient.

$$
\begin{array}{r|rrrr}
2 & 1 & 6 & -1 & -30 \\
  &   & 2 &   &   \\
\hline
  & 1 & 8 &   &   \\
\end{array}
$$
Multiply 1 by 2 to get 2.

Add 6 and 2.

$$
\begin{array}{r|rrrr}
2 & 1 & 6 & -1 & -30 \\
  &   & 2 & 16 &   \\
\hline
  & 1 & 8 & 15 &   \\
\end{array}
$$
Multiply 8 by 2.

Add -1 and 16.

$$
\begin{array}{r|rrrr}
2 & 1 & 6 & -1 & -30 \\
  &   & 2 & 16 & 30 \\
\hline
  & 1 & 8 & 15 & 0 \\
\end{array}
$$
Multiply 15 by 2 and add.

The answer is $x^2 + 8x + 15$ with R 0, or just $x^2 + 8x + 15$.

TRY EXERCISE 7

EXAMPLE 2   Use synthetic division to divide.

a) $(2x^3 + 7x^2 - 5) \div (x + 3)$

b) $(10x^2 - 13x + 3x^3 - 20) \div (4 + x)$

SOLUTION

a) $(2x^3 + 7x^2 - 5) \div (x + 3)$

The dividend has no x-term, so we need to write 0 as the coefficient of x. Note that $x + 3 = x - (-3)$, so we write -3 inside the ⌋.

$$
\begin{array}{r|rrrr}
-3 & 2 & 7 & 0 & -5 \\
   &   & -6 & -3 & 9 \\
\hline
   & 2 & 1 & -3 & \,|\,4 \\
\end{array}
$$

The answer is $2x^2 + x - 3$, with R 4, or $2x^2 + x - 3 + \dfrac{4}{x + 3}$.

b) We first rewrite $(10x^2 - 13x + 3x^3 - 20) \div (4 + x)$ in descending order:

$$(3x^3 + 10x^2 - 13x - 20) \div (x + 4).$$

Next, we use synthetic division. Note that $x + 4 = x - (-4)$.

$$
\begin{array}{r|rrrr}
-4 & 3 & 10 & -13 & -20 \\
   &   & -12 & 8 & 20 \\
\hline
   & 3 & -2 & -5 & \,|\,0 \\
\end{array}
$$

The answer is $3x^2 - 2x - 5$.

TRY EXERCISE 15

Teaching Tip
You may wish to emphasize that synthetic division requires a divisor of the form $x - a$.

The Remainder Theorem

Because the remainder is 0, Example 1 shows that $x - 2$ is a factor of $x^3 + 6x^2 - x - 30$ and that $x^3 + 6x^2 - x - 30 = (x - 2)(x^2 + 8x + 15)$. Thus if $f(x) = x^3 + 6x^2 - x - 30$, then $f(2) = 0$ (since $x - 2$ is a factor of $f(x)$). Similarly, from Example 2(b), we know that if $g(x) = 10x^2 - 13x + 3x^3 - 20$, then $x + 4$ is a factor of $g(x)$ and $g(-4) = 0$. In both examples, the remainder from the division, 0, can serve as a function value. Remarkably, this pattern extends to nonzero remainders. For example, the remainder in Example 2(a) is 4, and if $f(x) = 2x^3 + 7x^2 - 5$, then $f(-3)$ is also 4 (you should check this). The fact that the remainder and the function value coincide is predicted by the remainder theorem.

> ### The Remainder Theorem
> The remainder obtained by dividing $P(x)$ by $x - r$ is $P(r)$.

A proof of this result is outlined in Exercise 31.

EXAMPLE 3   Let $f(x) = 8x^5 - 6x^3 + x - 8$. Use synthetic division to find $f(2)$.

SOLUTION   The remainder theorem tells us that $f(2)$ is the remainder when $f(x)$ is divided by $x - 2$. We use synthetic division to find that remainder:

$$
\begin{array}{r|rrrrrr}
2 & 8 & 0 & -6 & 0 & 1 & -8 \\
  &   & 16 & 32 & 52 & 104 & 210 \\
\hline
  & 8 & 16 & 26 & 52 & 105 & 202
\end{array}
$$

Although the bottom line can be used to find the quotient for the division $(8x^5 - 6x^3 + x - 8) \div (x - 2)$, what we are really interested in is the remainder. It tells us that $f(2) = 202$.

TRY EXERCISE ▶ 21

The remainder theorem is often used to check division. Thus Example 2(a) can be checked by computing $P(-3) = 2(-3)^3 + 7(-3)^2 - 5$. Since $P(-3) = 4$ and the remainder in Example 2(a) is also 4, our division was probably correct.

C   EXERCISE SET

◆ *Concept Reinforcement*   *Classify each statement either true or false.*

1. If $x - 2$ is a factor of some polynomial $P(x)$, then $P(2) = 0$.   True

2. If $p(3) = 0$ for some polynomial $p(x)$, then $x - 3$ is a factor of $p(x)$.   True

3. If $P(-5) = 39$ and $P(x) = x^3 + 7x^2 + 3x + 4$, then

$$
\begin{array}{r|rrrr}
-5 & 1 & 7 & 3 & 4 \\
   &   & -5 & -10 & 35 \\
\hline
   & 1 & 2 & -7 & 39
\end{array}
$$
    True

4. In order for $f(x)/g(x)$ to exist, $g(x)$ must be 0.   False

5. In order to use synthetic division, we must be sure that the divisor is of the form $x - a$.   True

6. Synthetic division can be used in problems in which long division could not be used.   False

---

Use synthetic division to divide.

7. $(x^3 - 4x^2 - 2x + 5) \div (x - 1)$ $x^2 - 3x - 5$

8. $(x^3 - 4x^2 + 5x - 6) \div (x - 3)$ $x^2 - x + 2$

9. $(a^2 + 8a + 11) \div (a + 3)$ $a + 5 + \dfrac{-4}{a + 3}$

10. $(a^2 + 8a + 11) \div (a + 5)$ $a + 3 + \dfrac{-4}{a + 5}$

11. $(2x^3 - x^2 - 7x + 14) \div (x + 2)$ $2x^2 - 5x + 3 + \dfrac{8}{x + 2}$

12. $(3x^3 - 10x^2 - 9x + 15) \div (x - 4)$
$$3x^2 + 2x - 1 + \frac{11}{x - 4}$$

13. $(a^3 - 10a + 12) \div (a - 2)$ $a^2 + 2a - 6$

14. $(a^3 - 14a + 15) \div (a - 3)$ $a^2 + 3a - 5$

15. $(3y^3 - 7y^2 - 20) \div (y - 3)$ $3y^2 + 2y + 6 + \dfrac{-2}{y - 3}$

16. $(2x^3 - 3x^2 + 8) \div (x + 2)$ $2x^2 - 7x + 14 + \dfrac{-20}{x + 2}$

17. $(x^5 - 32) \div (x - 2)$ $x^4 + 2x^3 + 4x^2 + 8x + 16$

18. $(y^5 - 1) \div (y - 1)$ $y^4 + y^3 + y^2 + y + 1$

19. $(3x^3 + 1 - x + 7x^2) \div \left(x + \frac{1}{3}\right)$ $3x^2 + 6x - 3 + \dfrac{2}{x + \frac{1}{3}}$

20. $(8x^3 - 1 + 7x - 6x^2) \div \left(x - \frac{1}{2}\right)$ $8x^2 - 2x + 6 + \dfrac{2}{x - \frac{1}{2}}$

Use synthetic division to find the indicated function value.

21. $f(x) = 5x^4 + 12x^3 + 28x + 9$; $f(-3)$ 6

22. $g(x) = 3x^4 - 25x^2 - 18$; $g(3)$ 0

23. $P(x) = 2x^4 - x^3 - 7x^2 + x + 2$; $P(-3)$ 125

24. $F(x) = 3x^4 + 8x^3 + 2x^2 - 7x - 4$; $F(-2)$ 2

25. $f(x) = x^4 - 6x^3 + 11x^2 - 17x + 20$; $f(4)$ 0

26. $p(x) = x^4 + 7x^3 + 11x^2 - 7x - 12$; $p(2)$ 90

27. Why is it that we *add* when performing synthetic division, but *subtract* when performing long division?

28. Explain how synthetic division could be useful when attempting to factor a polynomial.

Synthesis

29. Let $Q(x)$ be a polynomial function with $p(x)$ a factor of $Q(x)$. If $p(3) = 0$, does it follow that $Q(3) = 0$? Why or why not? If $Q(3) = 0$, does it follow that $p(3) = 0$? Why or why not?

▣ Answer to Exercise 31 can be found on p. IA-37.

30. What adjustments must be made if synthetic division is to be used to divide a polynomial by a binomial of the form $ax + b$, with $a > 1$?

31. To prove the remainder theorem, note that any polynomial $P(x)$ can be rewritten as $(x - r) \cdot Q(x) + R$, where $Q(x)$ is the quotient polynomial that arises when $P(x)$ is divided by $x - r$, and R is some constant (the remainder).

a) How do we know that R must be a constant?   ▣
b) Show that $P(r) = R$ (this says that $P(r)$ is the remainder when $P(x)$ is divided by $x - r$).   ▣

32. Let $f(x) = 6x^3 - 13x^2 - 79x + 140$. Find $f(4)$ and then solve the equation $f(x) = 0$. $0; -\frac{7}{2}, \frac{5}{3}, 4$

33. Let $f(x) = 4x^3 + 16x^2 - 3x - 45$. Find $f(-3)$ and then solve the equation $f(x) = 0$. $0; -3, -\frac{5}{2}, \frac{3}{2}$

34. Use the TRACE feature on a graphing calculator to check your answer to Exercise 32.

35. Use the TRACE feature on a graphing calculator to check your answer to Exercise 33.

Nested evaluation.   One way to evaluate a polynomial function like $P(x) = 3x^4 - 5x^3 + 4x^2 - 1$ is to successively factor out x as shown:
$$P(x) = x(x(x(3x - 5) + 4) + 0) - 1.$$
Computations are then performed using this "nested" form of $P(x)$.

36. Use nested evaluation to find $f(4)$ in Exercise 32. Note the similarities to the calculations performed with synthetic division.   0

37. Use nested evaluation to find $f(-3)$ in Exercise 33. Note the similarities to the calculations performed with synthetic division.   0

LE 1   Fraction and Decimal Equivalents

Fraction Notation	$\frac{1}{10}$	$\frac{1}{8}$	$\frac{1}{6}$	$\frac{1}{5}$	$\frac{1}{4}$	$\frac{3}{10}$	$\frac{1}{3}$	$\frac{3}{8}$	$\frac{2}{5}$	$\frac{1}{2}$
Decimal Notation	0.1	0.125	$0.16\overline{6}$	0.2	0.25	0.3	$0.333\overline{3}$	0.375	0.4	0.5
Percent Notation	10%	12.5%, or $12\frac{1}{2}\%$	$16.6\overline{6}\%$, or $16\frac{2}{3}\%$	20%	25%	30%	$33.3\overline{3}\%$, or $33\frac{1}{3}\%$	37.5%, or $37\frac{1}{2}\%$	40%	50%
Fraction Notation	$\frac{3}{5}$	$\frac{5}{8}$	$\frac{2}{3}$	$\frac{7}{10}$	$\frac{3}{4}$	$\frac{4}{5}$	$\frac{5}{6}$	$\frac{7}{8}$	$\frac{9}{10}$	$\frac{1}{1}$
Decimal Notation	0.6	0.625	$0.666\overline{6}$	0.7	0.75	0.8	$0.83\overline{3}$	0.875	0.9	1
Percent Notation	60%	62.5%, or $62\frac{1}{2}\%$	$66.6\overline{6}\%$, or $66\frac{2}{3}\%$	70%	75%	80%	$83.3\overline{3}\%$, or $83\frac{1}{3}\%$	87.5%, or $87\frac{1}{2}\%$	90%	100%

TABLE 2 Squares and Square Roots with Approximations to Three Decimal Places

N	$\sqrt{N}$	N^2	N	$\sqrt{N}$	N^2	N	$\sqrt{N}$	N^2	N	$\sqrt{N}$	N^2
1	1	1	26	5.099	676	51	7.141	2601	76	8.718	5776
2	1.414	4	27	5.196	729	52	7.211	2704	77	8.775	5929
3	1.732	9	28	5.292	784	53	7.280	2809	78	8.832	6084
4	2	16	29	5.385	841	54	7.348	2916	79	8.888	6241
5	2.236	25	30	5.477	900	55	7.416	3025	80	8.944	6400
6	2.449	36	31	5.568	961	56	7.483	3136	81	9	6561
7	2.646	49	32	5.657	1024	57	7.550	3249	82	9.055	6724
8	2.828	64	33	5.745	1089	58	7.616	3364	83	9.110	6889
9	3	81	34	5.831	1156	59	7.681	3481	84	9.165	7056
10	3.162	100	35	5.916	1225	60	7.746	3600	85	9.220	7225
11	3.317	121	36	6	1296	61	7.810	3721	86	9.274	7396
12	3.464	144	37	6.083	1369	62	7.874	3844	87	9.327	7569
13	3.606	169	38	6.164	1444	63	7.937	3969	88	9.381	7744
14	3.742	196	39	6.245	1521	64	8	4096	89	9.434	7921
15	3.873	225	40	6.325	1600	65	8.062	4225	90	9.487	8100
16	4	256	41	6.403	1681	66	8.124	4356	91	9.539	8281
17	4.123	289	42	6.481	1764	67	8.185	4489	92	9.592	8464
18	4.243	324	43	6.557	1849	68	8.246	4624	93	9.644	8649
19	4.359	361	44	6.633	1936	69	8.307	4761	94	9.695	8836
20	4.472	400	45	6.708	2025	70	8.367	4900	95	9.747	9025
21	4.583	441	46	6.782	2116	71	8.426	5041	96	9.798	9216
22	4.690	484	47	6.856	2209	72	8.485	5184	97	9.849	9409
23	4.796	529	48	6.928	2304	73	8.544	5329	98	9.899	9604
24	4.899	576	49	7	2401	74	8.602	5476	99	9.950	9801
25	5	625	50	7.071	2500	75	8.660	5625	100	10	10,000

Answers

e complete step-by-step solutions for the exercises listed below can be found in the *Student's Solutions nual*, ISBN 0-321-58623-9/978-0-321-58623-0, which can be purchased online or at your bookstore.

APTER 1

chnology Connection, p. 7

3438   **2.** 47,531

nslating for Success, p. 9

H   **2.** E   **3.** K   **4.** B   **5.** O   **6.** L   **7.** M   **8.** C
D   **10.** F

ercise Set 1.1, pp. 10–12

Expression   **2.** Equation   **3.** Equation
Expression   **5.** Equation   **6.** Equation
Expression   **8.** Equation   **9.** Equation
Expression   **11.** Expression   **12.** Expression
45   **15.** 8   **17.** 5   **19.** 4   **21.** 5   **23.** 3
24 ft^2 **27.** 15 cm^2 **29.** 0.345   **31.** Let r represent
's age; $r + 5$, or $5 + r$ **33.** $6b$, or $b \cdot 6$ **35.** $c - 9$
$6 + q$, or $q + 6$ **39.** Let m represent Mai's speed;
, or $m \cdot 8$ **41.** $y - x$ **43.** $x \div w$, or $\dfrac{x}{w}$ **45.** Let l
resent the length of the box and h represent the height;
h, or $h + l$ **47.** $9 \cdot 2m$, or $2m \cdot 9$ **49.** Let y
resent "some number"; $\dfrac{1}{4}y - 13$, or $\dfrac{y}{4} - 13$ **51.** Let a
b represent the two numbers; $5(a - b)$ **53.** Let w
resent the number of women attending; 64% of w,
$0.64w$ **55.** Yes   **57.** No   **59.** Yes   **61.** Yes
Let x represent the unknown number; $73 + x = 201$
Let x represent the unknown number; $42x = 2352$
Let s represent the number of unoccupied squares;
$19 = 64$ **69.** Let w represent the amount of solid
ste generated, in millions of tons; 32% of $w = 79$, or
$2w = 79$ **71.** (f)   **73.** (d)   **75.** (g)   **77.** (e)
🖩   **81.** 🖩   **83.** $450   **85.** 2   **87.** 6   **89.** $w + 4$
$l + w + l + w$, or $2l + 2w$ **93.** $t + 8$ **95.** 🖩

ercise Set 1.2, pp. 18–20

Commutative   **2.** Associative   **3.** Associative
Commutative   **5.** Distributive   **6.** Associative
Associative   **8.** Commutative   **9.** Commutative
Distributive   **11.** $t + 11$ **13.** $8x + 4$
$3y + 9x$ **17.** $5(1 + a)$ **19.** $x \cdot 7$ **21.** ts

23. $5 + ba$ **25.** $(a + 1)5$ **27.** $x + (8 + y)$
29. $(u + v) + 7$ **31.** $ab + (c + d)$ **33.** $8(xy)$
35. $(2a)b$ **37.** $(3 \cdot 2)(a + b)$
39. $(s + t) + 6$; $(t + 6) + s$ **41.** $17(ab)$; $b(17a)$
43. $(1 + x) + 2 = (x + 1) + 2$ Commutative law
$\qquad\qquad\quad = x + (1 + 2)$ Associative law
$\qquad\qquad\quad = x + 3$ Simplifying
45. $(m \cdot 3)7 = m(3 \cdot 7)$ Associative law
$\qquad\qquad\quad = m \cdot 21$ Simplifying
$\qquad\qquad\quad = 21m$ Commutative law
47. $2x + 30$ **49.** $4 + 4a$ **51.** $24 + 8y$
53. $90x + 60$ **55.** $5r + 10 + 15t$ **57.** $2a + 2b$
59. $5x + 5y + 10$ **61.** $x, xyz, 1$ **63.** $2a, \dfrac{a}{3b}, 5b$
65. x, y **67.** $4x, 4y$ **69.** $2(a + b)$ **71.** $7(1 + y)$
73. $4(8x + 1)$ **75.** $5(x + 2 + 3y)$ **77.** $7(a + 5b)$
79. $11(4x + y + 2z)$ **81.** $5, n$ **83.** $3, (x + y)$
85. $7, a, b$ **87.** $(a - b), (x - y)$ **89.** 🖩   **91.** Let k
represent Kara's salary; $\dfrac{1}{2}k$, or $\dfrac{k}{2}$ **92.** $2(m + 3)$, or
$2(3 + m)$ **93.** 🖩   **95.** Yes; distributive law
97. No; for example, let $m = 1$. Then $7 \div 3 \cdot 1 = \frac{7}{3}$ and
$1 \cdot 3 \div 7 = \frac{3}{7}$.   **99.** No; for example, let $x = 1$ and
$y = 2$. Then $30 \cdot 2 + 1 \cdot 15 = 60 + 15 = 75$ and
$5[2(1 + 3 \cdot 2)] = 5[2(7)] = 5 \cdot 14 = 70$.   **101.** 🖩

Exercise Set 1.3, pp. 27–29

1. (b)   **2.** (c)   **3.** (d)   **4.** (a)   **5.** Composite
7. Prime   **9.** Composite   **11.** Prime   **13.** Neither
15. $1 \cdot 50$; $2 \cdot 25$; $5 \cdot 10$; 1, 2, 5, 10, 25, 50
17. $1 \cdot 42$; $2 \cdot 21$; $3 \cdot 14$; $6 \cdot 7$; 1, 2, 3, 6, 7, 14, 21, 42
19. $3 \cdot 13$ **21.** $2 \cdot 3 \cdot 5$ **23.** $3 \cdot 3 \cdot 3$ **25.** $2 \cdot 3 \cdot 5 \cdot 5$
27. $2 \cdot 2 \cdot 2 \cdot 5$ **29.** Prime   **31.** $2 \cdot 3 \cdot 5 \cdot 7$ **33.** $5 \cdot 23$
35. $\frac{3}{5}$ **37.** $\frac{2}{7}$ **39.** $\frac{1}{4}$ **41.** 4   **43.** $\frac{1}{4}$ **45.** 6
47. $\frac{21}{25}$ **49.** $\frac{60}{41}$ **51.** $\frac{15}{7}$ **53.** $\frac{3}{10}$ **55.** 6   **57.** $\frac{1}{2}$
59. $\frac{7}{6}$ **61.** $\dfrac{3b}{7a}$ **63.** $\dfrac{10}{n}$ **65.** $\frac{5}{6}$ **67.** 1   **69.** $\frac{5}{18}$
71. 0   **73.** $\frac{35}{18}$ **75.** $\frac{10}{3}$ **77.** 27   **79.** 1   **81.** $\frac{6}{35}$
83. 18   **85.** 🖩   **87.** $5(3 + x)$; answers may vary
88. $7 + (b + a)$, or $(a + b) + 7$ **89.** 🖩
91. Row 1: 7, 2, 36, 14, 8, 8; row 2: 9, 18, 2, 10, 12, 21
93. $\frac{2}{5}$ **95.** $\dfrac{5q}{t}$ **97.** $\frac{6}{25}$ **99.** $\dfrac{5ap}{2cm}$ **101.** $\dfrac{23r}{18t}$

103. $\frac{28}{45}$ m^2 **105.** $14\frac{2}{9}$ m   **107.** $27\frac{3}{5}$ cm

Technology Connection, p. 33

1. 2.236067977   **2.** 2.645751311   **3.** 3.605551275
4. 5.196152423   **5.** 6.164414003   **6.** 7.071067812

Exercise Set 1.4, pp. 35–37

1. Repeating   **2.** Terminating   **3.** Integer
4. Whole number   **5.** Rational number
6. Irrational number   **7.** Natural number
8. Absolute value   **9.** $-10,500, 27,482$ **11.** $136, -4$
13. $-554, 499.19$ **15.** $650, -180$ **17.** $8, -5$
19. [number line: $\frac{10}{3}$]   **21.** [number line: -4.3]

23. [number line]   **25.** 0.875   **27.** -0.75
29. $-1.1\overline{6}$ **31.** $0.\overline{6}$ **33.** -0.5 **35.** $0.\overline{13}$
37. [number line: $\sqrt{5}$]   **39.** [number line: $-\sqrt{22}$]
41. $>$ **43.** $<$ **45.** $<$ **47.** $>$ **49.** $<$ **51.** $<$
53. $x < -2$ **55.** $y \geq 10$ **57.** True   **59.** False
61. True   **63.** 58   **65.** 12.2   **67.** $\sqrt{2}$ **69.** $\frac{9}{7}$ **71.** 0
73. 8   **75.** $-83, -4.7, 0, \frac{5}{9}, 2.1\overline{6}, 62$ **77.** $-83, 0, 62$
79. $-83, -4.7, 0, \frac{5}{9}, 2.1\overline{6}, \pi, \sqrt{17}, 62$ **81.** ✍   **83.** 42
84. $ba + 5$, or $5 + ab$ **85.** ✍   **87.** ✍
89. $-23, -17, 0, 4$ **91.** $-\frac{4}{3}, \frac{4}{9}, \frac{4}{8}, \frac{4}{6}, \frac{4}{5}, \frac{4}{3}, \frac{4}{2}$ **93.** $<$ **95.** $=$
97. $-19, 19$ **99.** $-4, -3, 3, 4$ **101.** $\frac{3}{3}$ **103.** $\frac{70}{9}$
105. $x \leq 0$ **107.** $|t| \geq 20$ **109.** ✍

Exercise Set 1.5, pp. 41–43

1. (f)   **2.** (d)   **3.** (e)   **4.** (a)   **5.** (b)   **6.** (c)
7. -3 **9.** 4   **11.** -7 **13.** -8 **15.** -35 **17.** -8
19. 0   **21.** -41 **23.** 0   **25.** 9   **27.** -2 **29.** 11
31. -43 **33.** 0   **35.** 18   **37.** -45 **39.** 0   **41.** 16
43. -0.8 **45.** -9.1 **47.** $\frac{3}{5}$ **49.** $\frac{-6}{7}$ **51.** $-\frac{1}{15}$
53. $\frac{2}{9}$ **55.** -3 **57.** 0   **59.** The price rose 29¢.
61. Her new balance was \$95.   **63.** The total gain was 20 yd.
65. The lake rose $\frac{3}{10}$ ft.   **67.** Logan owes \$85.   **69.** $17a$
71. $9x$ **73.** $25t$ **75.** $-2m$ **77.** $-10y$ **79.** $1 - 2x$
81. $12x + 17$ **83.** $7r + 8t + 16$ **85.** $18n + 16$
87. ✍   **89.** $21z + 14y + 7$ **90.** $\frac{28}{3}$ **91.** ✍
93. \$451.70   **95.** $-5y$ **97.** $-7m$ **99.** $-7t, -23$
101. 1 under par

Exercise Set 1.6, pp. 48–51

1. (d)   **2.** (g)   **3.** (f)   **4.** (h)   **5.** (a)   **6.** (c)
7. (b)   **8.** (e)   **9.** Six minus ten
11. Two minus negative twelve   **13.** Nine minus the
opposite of t **15.** The opposite of x minus y
17. Negative three minus the opposite of n **19.** -51
21. $\frac{11}{3}$ **23.** 3.14   **25.** 45   **27.** $\frac{14}{3}$ **29.** -0.101

31. 37   **33.** $-\frac{2}{5}$ **35.** 1   **37.** -15 **39.** -3 **41.** -6
43. -3 **45.** -7 **47.** -6 **49.** 0   **51.** -5
53. -10 **55.** -11 **57.** 0   **59.** 0   **61.** 8   **63.** -11
65. 16   **67.** -19 **69.** 1   **71.** 17   **73.** 3   **75.** -3
77. -21 **79.** 10   **81.** -8 **83.** -60 **85.** -23
87. -7.3 **89.** 1.1   **91.** -5.5 **93.** -0.928 **95.** $-\frac{7}{11}$
97. $-\frac{4}{5}$ **99.** $\frac{5}{17}$ **101.** $3.8 - (-5.2); 9$
103. $114 - (-79); 193$ **105.** -40 **107.** 43   **109.** 32
111. -62 **113.** -139 **115.** 0   **117.** $-3y, -8x$
119. $9, -5t, -3st$ **121.** $-3x$ **123.** $-5a + 4$
125. $-n - 9$ **127.** $-3x - 6$ **129.** $-8t - 7$
131. $-12x + 3y + 9$ **133.** $8x + 66$ **135.** 214°F
137. 30,347 ft   **139.** 116 m   **141.** ✍   **143.** 432 ft^2
144. $2 \cdot 2 \cdot 2 \cdot 2 \cdot 2 \cdot 3 \cdot 3 \cdot 3$ **145.** ✍
147. 11:00 P.M., August 14   **149.** False. For example,
let $m = -3$ and $n = -5$. Then $-3 > -5$, but
$-3 + (-5) = -8 \not> 0$.   **151.** True. For example, for
$m = 4$ and $n = -4$, $4 = -(-4)$ and $4 + (-4) = 0$; for
$m = -3$ and $n = 3$, $-3 = -3$ and $-3 + 3 = 0$.
153. (-) 9 - (-) 7 ENTER

Exercise Set 1.7, pp. 56–58

1. 1   **2.** 0   **3.** 0   **4.** 1   **5.** 0   **6.** 1   **7.** 1   **8.** 0
9. 1   **10.** 0   **11.** -40 **13.** -56 **15.** -40 **17.** 72
19. -42 **21.** 45   **23.** 190   **25.** -132 **27.** 1200
29. -126 **31.** 11.5   **33.** 0   **35.** $-\frac{2}{7}$ **37.** $\frac{1}{12}$
39. -11.13 **41.** $-\frac{5}{12}$ **43.** 252   **45.** 0   **47.** $\frac{1}{28}$
49. 150   **51.** 0   **53.** -720 **55.** $-30,240$ **57.** -9
59. -4 **61.** -7 **63.** 4   **65.** -9 **67.** 5.1   **69.** $\frac{100}{11}$
71. -8 **73.** Undefined   **75.** -4 **77.** 0   **79.** 0
81. $-\frac{8}{3}; \frac{8}{-3}$ **83.** $-\frac{29}{35}; \frac{-29}{35}$ **85.** $\frac{-7}{3}; \frac{7}{-3}$ **87.** $-\frac{x}{2}; \frac{x}{-2}$
89. $-\frac{5}{4}$ **91.** $-\frac{10}{51}$ **93.** $-\frac{1}{10}$ **95.** $\frac{1}{4.3}$, or $\frac{10}{43}$ **97.** $-\frac{4}{9}$
99. Does not exist   **101.** $\frac{21}{20}$ **103.** -1 **105.** 1
107. $\frac{3}{11}$ **109.** $-\frac{7}{4}$ **111.** 1   **113.** $\frac{1}{10}$ **115.** $-\frac{7}{6}$
117. Undefined   **119.** $-\frac{14}{15}$ **121.** ✍   **123.** $\frac{22}{39}$
124. $12x - y - 9$ **125.** ✍   **127.** $\dfrac{1}{a + b}$
129. $-(a + b)$ **131.** $x = -x$ **133.** For 2 and 3,
the reciprocal of the sum is $1/(2 + 3)$, or $1/5$. But
$1/5 \neq 1/2 + 1/3$.   **135.** 5°F   **137.** Positive
139. Positive   **141.** Positive   **143.** Distributive law;
law of opposites; multiplicative property of zero

Connecting the Concepts, p. 59

1. -10 **2.** 16   **3.** 4   **4.** -6 **5.** -120 **6.** -7
7. -23 **8.** -3 **9.** -1 **10.** -3 **11.** -0.8
12. -3.77 **13.** -7 **14.** -4.1 **15.** -12 **16.** $\frac{5}{3}$
17. 100   **18.** 77   **19.** 180   **20.** -52

Exercise Set 1.8, pp. 66–68

1. (a) Division; **(b)** subtraction; **(c)** addition;
(d) multiplication; **(e)** subtraction; **(f)** multiplication

(a) Multiplication; **(b)** subtraction; **(c)** addition;
subtraction; **(e)** division; **(f)** multiplication
x^6 **5.** $(-5)^3$ **7.** $(3t)^5$ **9.** $2n^4$ **11.** 16   **13.** 9
-9 **17.** 64   **19.** 625   **21.** 7   **23.** -32
$81t^4$ **27.** $-343x^3$ **29.** 26   **31.** 51   **33.** -6
1   **37.** 298   **39.** 11   **41.** -36 **43.** 1291
152   **47.** 36   **49.** 1   **51.** -44 **53.** 41   **55.** -10
-5 **59.** -19 **61.** -3 **63.** -75 **65.** 9   **67.** 30
6   **71.** -17 **73.** $-9x - 1$ **75.** $7n - 8$
$-4a + 3b - 7c$ **79.** $-3x^2 - 5x + 1$ **81.** $2x - 7$
$-9x + 6$ **85.** $21t - r$ **87.** $9y - 25z$ **89.** $x^2 + 6$
$-t^3 + 4t$ **93.** $37a^2 - 23ab + 35b^2$
$-22t^3 - t^2 + 9t$ **97.** $2x - 25$ **99.** ✍   **101.** Let n
represent the number; $2n - 9$ **102.** Let m and n represent
two numbers; $\frac{1}{2}(m + n)$ **103.** ✍
$-6r - 5t + 21$ **107.** $-2x - f$ **109.** ✍
. True   **113.** False   **115.** 0   **117.** 17
. 39,000   **121.** $44x^3$

view Exercises: Chapter 1, pp. 73–74

True   **2.** True   **3.** False   **4.** True   **5.** False
False   **7.** True   **8.** False   **9.** False   **10.** True
24   **12.** 4   **13.** -16 **14.** -15 **15.** $y - 7$
$xz + 10$, or $10 + xz$ **17.** Let b represent Brandt's
ed and w represent the wind speed; $15(b - w)$
No   **19.** Let d represent the number of digital prints,
illions, made in 2006; $14.1 = d + 3.2$ **20.** $t \cdot 3 + 5$
$2x + (y + z)$ **22.** $(4x)y, 4(yx), (4y)x$; answers
y vary   **23.** $18x + 30y$ **24.** $40x + 24y + 16$
$3(7x + 5y)$ **26.** $11(2a + 9b + 1)$ **27.** $2 \cdot 2 \cdot 2 \cdot 7$
$\frac{5}{12}$ **29.** $\frac{9}{4}$ **30.** $\frac{19}{24}$ **31.** $\frac{3}{16}$ **32.** $\frac{3}{5}$ **33.** $\frac{27}{25}$
$-3600, 1350$ **35.**

$$\xleftarrow{\hspace{0.5em}}\overset{\overset{\frac{-1}{3}}{\big\downarrow}}{\underset{-5\ -4\ -3\ -2\ -1\ \ 0\ \ 1\ \ 2\ \ 3\ \ 4\ \ 5}{+\!\!+\!\!+\!\!+\!\!+\!\!+\!\!+\!\!+\!\!+\!\!+\!\!+}}\xrightarrow{\hspace{0.5em}}$$

$x > -3$ **37.** True   **38.** False   **39.** $-0.\overline{4}$ **40.** 1
-12 **42.** -10 **43.** $-\frac{7}{12}$ **44.** 0   **45.** -5 **46.** 8
$-\frac{7}{5}$ **48.** -7.9 **49.** 63   **50.** -9.18 **51.** $-\frac{2}{7}$
-140 **53.** -7 **54.** -3 **55.** $\frac{9}{4}$ **56.** 48
168   **58.** $\frac{21}{8}$ **59.** 18   **60.** 53   **61.** $\frac{103}{17}$
$7a - b$ **63.** $-4x + 5y$ **64.** 7   **65.** $-\frac{1}{7}$
$(2x)^4$ **67.** $-125x^3$ **68.** $-3a + 9$ **69.** $11b - 27$
$3x^4 + 10x$ **71.** $17n^2 + m^2 + 20mn$ **72.** $5x + 28$
73. ✍ The value of a constant never varies. A variable can
present a variety of numbers.   **74.** ✍ A term is one of
parts of an expression that is separated from the other
rts by plus signs. A factor is part of a product.   **75.** ✍
e distributive law is used in factoring algebraic expres-
ns, multiplying algebraic expressions, combining like
ms, finding the opposite of a sum, and subtracting alge-
ic expressions.   **76.** ✍ A negative number raised to an
even power is positive; a negative number raised to an
d power is negative.   **77.** 25,281   **78. (a)** $\frac{3}{11}$; **(b)** $\frac{10}{11}$
$-\frac{5}{8}$ **80.** -2.1 **81.** (i)   **82.** (j)   **83.** (a)
(h)   **85.** (k)   **86.** (b)   **87.** (c)   **88.** (e)
(d)   **90.** (f)   **91.** (g)

Test: Chapter 1, p. 75

1. [1.1] 4   **2.** [1.1] Let x and y represent the numbers;
$xy - 9$ **3.** [1.1] $240\,\text{ft}^2$ **4.** [1.2] $q + 3p$
5. [1.2] $(x - 4) \cdot y$ **6.** [1.1] No   **7.** [1.1] Let p represent
the maximum production capability; $p - 4250 = 45{,}950$
8. [1.2] $35 + 7x$ **9.** [1.7] $-5y + 10$
10. [1.2] $11(1 + 4x)$ **11.** [1.2] $7(x + 1 + 7y)$
12. [1.3] $2 \cdot 2 \cdot 3 \cdot 5 \cdot 5$ **13.** [1.3] $\frac{3}{7}$ **14.** [1.4] $<$
15. [1.4] $>$ **16.** [1.4] $\frac{9}{4}$ **17.** [1.4] 3.8   **18.** [1.6] $\frac{2}{3}$
19. [1.7] $-\frac{7}{4}$ **20.** [1.6] 10   **21.** [1.4] $-5 \geq x$
22. [1.6] 7.8   **23.** [1.5] -8 **24.** [1.6] -2.5 **25.** [1.6] $-\frac{7}{8}$
26. [1.7] -48 **27.** [1.7] $\frac{2}{9}$ **28.** [1.7] -6 **29.** [1.7] $\frac{3}{4}$
30. [1.7] -9.728 **31.** [1.8] -173 **32.** [1.6] 15
33. [1.8] -64 **34.** [1.8] 448   **35.** [1.6] $21a + 22y$
36. [1.8] $16x^4$ **37.** [1.8] $x + 7$ **38.** [1.8] $9a - 12b - 7$
39. [1.8] $-y - 16$ **40.** [1.1] 5
41. [1.8] $9 - (3 - 4) + 5 = 15$ **42.** [1.8] 15
43. [1.8] $4a$ **44.** [1.8] False

CHAPTER 2

Exercise Set 2.1, pp. 83–85

1. (c)   **2.** (b)   **3.** (f)   **4.** (a)   **5.** (d)   **6.** (e)   **7.** (d)
8. (b)   **9.** (c)   **10.** (a)   **11.** 11   **13.** -25 **15.** -31
17. 41   **19.** 19   **21.** -6 **23.** $\frac{7}{3}$ **25.** $-\frac{1}{10}$ **27.** $\frac{41}{24}$
29. $-\frac{1}{20}$ **31.** 9.1   **33.** -5 **35.** 7   **37.** 12   **39.** -38
41. 8   **43.** -7 **45.** 8   **47.** 88   **49.** 20   **51.** -54
53. $-\frac{5}{9}$ **55.** 1   **57.** $\frac{9}{2}$ **59.** -7.6 **61.** -2.5 **63.** -15
65. -5 **67.** $-\frac{7}{6}$ **69.** -128 **71.** $-\frac{1}{2}$ **73.** -15 **75.** 9
77. 310.756   **79.** ✍   **81.** -6 **82.** 2   **83.** 1
84. -16 **85.** ✍   **87.** 11.6   **89.** 2   **91.** $-23, 23$
93. 9000   **95.** 250

Technology Connection, p. 88

1. 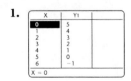   **2.**

3. 4; not reliable because, depending on the choice of ΔTbl, it
is easy to scroll past a solution without realizing it.

Exercise Set 2.2, pp. 91–92

1. (c)   **2.** (e)   **3.** (a)   **4.** (f)   **5.** (b)   **6.** (d)   **7.** 8
9. 7   **11.** 5   **13.** $\frac{10}{3}$ **15.** -7 **17.** -5 **19.** -4
21. 19   **23.** -2.8 **25.** 3   **27.** 15   **29.** -6 **31.** $-\frac{25}{2}$
33. All real numbers; identity   **35.** -3 **37.** -6 **39.** 2
41. 0   **43.** 6   **45.** No solution; contradiction   **47.** $-\frac{1}{2}$
49. 0   **51.** 10   **53.** 4   **55.** 0   **57.** No solution;
contradiction   **59.** $\frac{5}{2}$ **61.** -8 **63.** $\frac{1}{6}$
65. All real numbers; identity   **67.** 2   **69.** $\frac{16}{3}$ **71.** $\frac{2}{5}$
73. 1   **75.** -4 **77.** $1.\overline{6}$ **79.** $-\frac{60}{37}$ **81.** 11   **83.** 8
85. $\frac{16}{15}$ **87.** $-\frac{1}{31}$ **89.** 2   **91.** ✍   **93.** -7 **94.** 15

95. -15 **96.** -28 **97.** 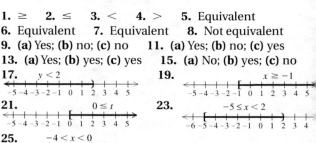   **99.** $\frac{1136}{909}$, or $1.\overline{2497}$
101. No solution; contradiction   **103.** $\frac{2}{3}$ **105.** 0
107. $\frac{52}{45}$ **109.** All real numbers; identity

Technology Connection, p. 94

1. 800

Exercise Set 2.3, pp. 97–100

1. 309.6 m   **3.** 1423 students   **5.** 8.4734 **7.** 255 mg
9. $b = \dfrac{A}{h}$ **11.** $r = \dfrac{d}{t}$ **13.** $P = \dfrac{I}{rt}$ **15.** $m = 65 - H$
17. $l = \dfrac{P - 2w}{2}$, or $l = \dfrac{P}{2} - w$ **19.** $\pi = \dfrac{A}{r^2}$
21. $h = \dfrac{2A}{b}$ **23.** $c^2 = \dfrac{E}{m}$ **25.** $d = 2Q - c$
27. $b = 3A - a - c$ **29.** $r = wf$ **31.** $C = \frac{5}{9}(F - 32)$
33. $y = 2x - 1$ **35.** $y = -\frac{2}{5}x + 2$ **37.** $y = \frac{4}{3}x - 2$
39. $y = -\frac{9}{8}x + \frac{1}{2}$ **41.** $y = \frac{3}{5}x - \frac{8}{5}$
43. $x = \dfrac{z - 13}{2} - y$, or $x = \dfrac{z - 13 - 2y}{2}$
45. $l = 4(t - 27) + w$ **47.** $t = \dfrac{A}{a + b}$ **49.** $h = \dfrac{2A}{a + b}$
51. $L = W - \dfrac{N(R - r)}{400}$, or $L = \dfrac{400W - NR + Nr}{400}$
53.   **55.** -10 **56.** -196 **57.** 0 **58.** -32
59. -13 **60.** 65 **61.**   **63.** 40 yr   **65.** 27 in^3
67. $a = \dfrac{w}{c} \cdot d$ **69.** $c = \dfrac{d}{a - b}$ **71.** $a = \dfrac{c}{3 + b + d}$
73. $K = 9.632w + 19.685h - 10.54a + 102.3$

Exercise Set 2.4, pp. 104–108

1. (d)   **2.** (c)   **3.** (e)   **4.** (b)   **5.** (c)   **6.** (d)   **7.** (f)
8. (a)   **9.** (b)   **10.** (e)   **11.** 0.49 **13.** 0.01
15. 0.041 **17.** 0.2 **19.** 0.0625 **21.** 0.002 **23.** 1.75
25. 38% **27.** 3.9% **29.** 45% **31.** 70% **33.** 0.09%
35. 106% **37.** 180% **39.** 60% **41.** 32% **43.** 25%
45. 26% **47.** $46\frac{2}{3}$, or $\frac{140}{3}$ **49.** 2.5 **51.** $10,000$
53. 125% **55.** 0.8 **57.** 50% **59.** $33.\overline{3}\%$, or $33\frac{1}{3}\%$
61. 2.85 million Americans   **63.** 23.37 million Americans
65. 75 credits   **67.** 595 at bats   **69.** (a) 16%; (b) $\$29$
71. $33.\overline{3}\%$, or $33\frac{1}{3}\%$; $66.\overline{6}\%$, or $66\frac{2}{3}\%$ **73.** $\$168$
75. 285 women   **77.** $\$19.20$ an hour   **79.** The actual
cost was 43.7% more than the estimate.   **81.** $\$45$
83. $\$148.50$ **85.** About 31.5 lb   **87.** About 2.45 billion
pieces of mail   **89.** About 165 calories   **91.**
93. Let l represent the length and w represent the width;
$2l + 2w$ **94.** $0.05 \cdot 180$ **95.** Let p represent the number
of points Tino scored; $p - 5$ **96.** $15 + 1.5x$ **97.** $10\left(\frac{1}{2}a\right)$
98. Let n represent the number; $3n + 10$ **99.** Let l
represent the length and w represent the width; $w = l - 2$
100. Let x represent the first number and y represent the
second number; $x = 4y$ **101.**   **103.** $18,500$ people
105. About 6 ft 7 in.   **107.** About 27% **109.**

Exercise Set 2.5, pp. 116–121

1. 11 **3.** $\frac{11}{2}$ **5.** $\$150$ **7.** $\$130$ **9.** About 78.4 mi
11. 160 mi   **13.** 1204 and 1205 **15.** 285 and 287
17. $32, 33, 34$ **19.** Man: 103 yr; woman: 101 yr
21. Non-spam: 25 billion messages; spam: 100 billion
messages   **23.** 140 and 141 **25.** Width: 100 ft; length:
160 ft; area: $16,000$ ft^2 **27.** Width: 21 m; length: 25 m
29. $1\frac{3}{4}$ in. by $3\frac{1}{2}$ in.   **31.** $30°, 90°, 60°$ **33.** $70°$
35. Bottom: 144 ft; middle: 72 ft; top: 24 ft   **37.** 8.75 mi,
or $8\frac{3}{4}$ mi   **39.** $128\frac{1}{3}$ mi   **41.** $65°, 25°$ **43.** $140°, 40°$
45. Length: 27.9 cm; width: 21.6 cm   **47.** $\$6600$
49. 830 points   **51.** $\$125,000$ **53.** 160 chirps per
minute   **55.**   **57.** $<$ **58.** $>$ **59.** $>$ **60.** $<$
61. $-4 \leq x$ **62.** $5 > x$ **63.** $y < 5$ **64.** $t \geq -10$
65.   **67.** $\$37$ **69.** 20 **71.** Half-dollars: 5;
quarters: 10; dimes: 20; nickels: 60   **73.** $\$95.99$
75. 5 DVDs   **77.** 6 mi   **79.**   **81.** Width: 23.31 cm;
length: 27.56 cm

Exercise Set 2.6, pp. 128–130

1. $\geq$ **2.** $\leq$ **3.** $<$ **4.** $>$ **5.** Equivalent
6. Equivalent   **7.** Equivalent   **8.** Not equivalent
9. (a) Yes; (b) no; (c) no   **11.** (a) Yes; (b) no; (c) yes
13. (a) Yes; (b) yes; (c) yes   **15.** (a) No; (b) yes; (c) no
17. $y < 2$
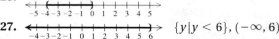
19. $x \geq -1$

21. $0 \leq t$ **23.** $-5 \leq x < 2$

25. $-4 < x < 0$

27. $\{y \mid y < 6\}, (-\infty, 6)$
29. $\{x \mid x \geq -4\}, [-4, \infty)$
31. $\{t \mid t > -3\}, (-3, \infty)$
33. $\{x \mid x \leq -7\}, (-\infty, -7]$
35. $\{x \mid x > -4\}, (-4, \infty)$ **37.** $\{x \mid x \leq 2\}, (-\infty, 2]$
39. $\{x \mid x < -1\}, (-\infty, -1)$ **41.** $\{x \mid x \geq 0\}, [0, \infty)$
43. $\{y \mid y > 3\}, (3, \infty)$
45. $\{n \mid n < 17\}, (-\infty, 17)$,
47. $\{x \mid x \leq -9\}, (-\infty, -9]$,
49. $\{y \mid y \leq \frac{1}{2}\}, \left(-\infty, \frac{1}{2}\right]$,
51. $\{t \mid t > \frac{5}{8}\}, \left(\frac{5}{8}, \infty\right)$,
53. $\{x \mid x < 0\}, (-\infty, 0)$,
55. $\{t \mid t < 23\}, (-\infty, 23)$
57. $\{y \mid y \geq 22\}, [22, \infty)$,
59. $\{x \mid x < 7\}, (-\infty, 7)$
61. $\{t \mid t < -3\}, (-\infty, -3)$,

$\{n|n \geq -1.5\}, [-1.5, \infty)$,

$\{y|y \geq -\frac{1}{10}\}, \left[-\frac{1}{10}, \infty\right)$
$\{x|x < -\frac{4}{5}\}, \left(-\infty, -\frac{4}{5}\right)$

$\{x|x < 6\}$, or $(-\infty, 6)$ **71.** $\{t|t \leq 7\}$, or $(-\infty, 7]$
$\{x|x > -4\}$, or $(-4, \infty)$ **75.** $\{y|y < -\frac{10}{3}\}$, or
$\infty, -\frac{10}{3})$ **77.** $\{x|x > -10\}$, or $(-10, \infty)$
$\{y|y < 0\}$, or $(-\infty, 0)$ **81.** $\{y|y \geq \frac{3}{2}\}$, or $\left[\frac{3}{2}, \infty\right)$
$\{x|x > -4\}$, or $(-4, \infty)$ **85.** $\{t|t > 1\}$, or $(1, \infty)$
$\{x|x \leq -9\}$, or $(-\infty, -9]$ **89.** $\{t|t < 14\}$, or
$\infty, 14)$ **91.** $\{y|y \leq -4\}$, or $(-\infty, -4]$
$\{t|t < -\frac{5}{3}\}$, or $\left(-\infty, -\frac{5}{3}\right)$ **95.** $\{r|r > -3\}$, or $(-3, \infty)$
$\{x|x \leq 7\}$, or $(-\infty, 7]$ **99.** $\{x|x > -\frac{5}{32}\}$, or $\left(-\frac{5}{32}, \infty\right)$
. ✍ **103.** $17x - 6$ **104.** $2m - 16n$
. $7x - 8y - 46$ **106.** $-47t + 1$
. $35a - 20b - 17$ **108.** $-21x + 32$ **109.** ✍
. $\{x|x \text{ is a real number}\}$, or $(-\infty, \infty)$
. $\{x|x \leq \frac{5}{6}\}$, or $\left(-\infty, \frac{5}{6}\right]$
. $\{x|x \leq -4a\}$, or $(-\infty, -4a]$
. $\left\{x\middle|x > \dfrac{y - b}{a}\right\}$, or $\left(\dfrac{y - b}{a}, \infty\right)$
. $\{x|x \text{ is a real number}\}$, or $(-\infty, \infty)$

nnecting the Concepts, pp. 130–131

21 **2.** $\{x|x \leq 21\}$, or $(-\infty, 21]$ **3.** -6
$\{x|x > -6\}$, or $(-6, \infty)$ **5.** $\{x|x < 6\}$, or $(-\infty, 6)$
  7. $-\frac{1}{3}$ **8.** $\{y|y < 3\}$, or $(-\infty, 3)$
$\{t|t \leq -16\}$, or $(-\infty, -16]$ **10.** $\frac{11}{2}$
$\{a|a < -1\}$, or $(-\infty, -1)$ **12.** $\{x|x < 10.75\}$, or
$\infty, 10.75)$ **13.** $\{x|x \geq -11\}$, or $[-11, \infty)$
105 **15.** -4.24 **16.** 15 **17.** $\{y|y \geq 3\}$, or $[3, \infty)$
$\frac{14}{3}$ **19.** $\{x|x > \frac{22}{5}\}$, or $\left(\frac{22}{5}, \infty\right)$
$\{a|a \geq 0\}$, or $[0, \infty)$

nslating for Success, p. 134

F **2.** I **3.** C **4.** E **5.** D **6.** J **7.** O **8.** M
B **10.** L

ercise Set 2.7, pp. 135–138

$b \leq a$ **2.** $b < a$ **3.** $a \leq b$ **4.** $a < b$ **5.** $b \leq a$
$a \leq b$ **7.** $b < a$ **8.** $a < b$ **9.** Let n represent the
nber; $n < 10$ **11.** Let t represent the temperature;
-3 **13.** Let d represent the number of years of
ving experience; $d \geq 5$ **15.** Let a represent the age of
altar; $a > 1200$ **17.** Let h represent Tania's hourly
ge; $12 < h < 15$ **19.** Let w represent the wind speed;
> 50 **21.** Let c represent the cost of a room; $c \leq 120$
More than 2.375 hr **25.** At least 2.25 **27.** Scores
ater than or equal to 97 **29.** 8 credits or more
At least 3 plate appearances **33.** Lengths greater than
n **35.** Depths less than 437.5 ft **37.** Blue-book value

is greater than or equal to $10,625 **39.** Lengths less than
55 in. **41.** Temperatures greater than 37°C
43. No more than 3 ft tall **45.** A serving contains at least
16 g of fat. **47.** Dates after September 16 **49.** No more
than 134 text messages **51.** Years after 2012
53. Mileages less than or equal to 225 **55.** ✍ **57.** -14
58. $-\frac{2}{3}$ **59.** -60 **60.** -11.1 **61.** 0 **62.** 5
63. -2 **64.** -1 **65.** ✍ **67.** Temperatures between
-15°C and $-9\frac{4}{9}$°C **69.** Lengths less than or equal to 8 cm
71. They contain at least 7.5 g of fat per serving.
73. At least $42 **75.** ✍

Review Exercises: Chapter 2, pp. 142–143

1. True **2.** False **3.** True **4.** True **5.** True
6. False **7.** True **8.** True **9.** -25 **10.** 7
11. -65 **12.** 3 **13.** -20 **14.** 1.11 **15.** $\frac{1}{2}$ **16.** $-\frac{3}{2}$
17. -8 **18.** -4 **19.** $-\frac{1}{3}$ **20.** 4 **21.** No solution;
contradiction **22.** 4 **23.** 16 **24.** 1 **25.** $-\frac{7}{5}$ **26.** 0
27. All real numbers; identity **28.** $d = \dfrac{C}{\pi}$ **29.** $B = \dfrac{3V}{h}$
30. $y = \frac{5}{2}x - 5$ **31.** $x = \dfrac{b}{t - a}$ **32.** 0.012 **33.** 44%
34. 70% **35.** 140 **36.** No **37.** Yes **38.** No
39. $5x - 6 < 2x + 3$
40. $-2 < x \leq 5$
41. $t > 0$ **42.** $\{t|t \geq -\frac{1}{2}\}$, or $\left[-\frac{1}{2}, \infty\right)$
43. $\{x|x \geq 7\}$, or $[7, \infty)$ **44.** $\{y|y > 3\}$, or $(3, \infty)$
45. $\{y|y \leq -4\}$, or $(-\infty, -4]$
46. $\{x|x < -11\}$, or $(-\infty, -11)$ **47.** $\{y|y > -7\}$, or
$(-7, \infty)$ **48.** $\{x|x > -6\}$, or $(-6, \infty)$
49. $\{x|x > -\frac{9}{11}\}$, or $\left(-\frac{9}{11}, \infty\right)$ **50.** $\{t|t \leq -12\}$, or
$(-\infty, -12]$ **51.** $\{x|x \leq -8\}$, or $(-\infty, -8]$
52. About 48% **53.** 8 ft, 10 ft **54.** Japanese students:
41,000; Chinese students: 62,000 **55.** 57, 59
56. Width: 11 cm; length: 17 cm **57.** $160 **58.** About 109
million subscribers **59.** 35°, 85°, 60° **60.** No more than
55 g of fat **61.** 14 or fewer copies **62.** ✍ Multiplying
both sides of an equation by *any* nonzero number results in
an equivalent equation. When multiplying on both sides of
an inequality, the sign of the number being multiplied by
must be considered. If the number is positive, the direction
of the inequality symbol remains unchanged; if the number
is negative, the direction of the inequality symbol must be
reversed to produce an equivalent inequality. **63.** ✍
The solutions of an equation can usually each be checked.
The solutions of an inequality are normally too numerous
to check. Checking a few numbers from the solution set
found cannot guarantee that the answer is correct, although
if any number does not check, the answer found is
incorrect. **64.** About 1 hr 36 min **65.** Nile: 4160 mi;
Amazon: 4225 mi **66.** $16 **67.** $-23, 23$ **68.** $-20, 20$
69. $a = \dfrac{y - 3}{2 - b}$ **70.** $F = \dfrac{0.3(12w)}{9}$, or $F = 0.4w$

Test: Chapter 2, p. 144

1. [2.1] 9   **2.** [2.1] 15   **3.** [2.1] −3   **4.** [2.1] 49
5. [2.1] −12   **6.** [2.2] 2   **7.** [2.1] −8   **8.** [2.2] $-\frac{23}{67}$
9. [2.2] 7   **10.** [2.2] $\frac{23}{3}$ **11.** [2.2] All real numbers; identity
12. [2.6] $\{x \mid x > -5\}$, or $(-5, \infty)$
13. [2.6] $\{x \mid x > -13\}$, or $(-13, \infty)$
14. [2.6] $\{y \mid y \le -13\}$, or $(-\infty, -13]$
15. [2.6] $\{y \mid y \le -\frac{15}{2}\}$, or $\left(-\infty, -\frac{15}{2}\right]$
16. [2.6] $\{n \mid n < -5\}$, or $(-\infty, -5)$
17. [2.6] $\{x \mid x < -7\}$, or $(-\infty, -7)$
18. [2.6] $\{t \mid t \ge -1\}$, or $[-1, \infty)$
19. [2.6] $\{x \mid x \le -1\}$, or $(-\infty, -1]$
20. [2.3] $r = \dfrac{A}{2\pi h}$ **21.** [2.3] $l = 2w - P$ **22.** [2.4] 2.3
23. [2.4] 0.3%   **24.** [2.4] 14.8   **25.** [2.4] 44%
26. [2.6]

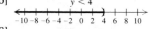
$y < 4$

27. [2.6]

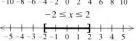
$-2 \le x \le 2$

28. [2.5] Width: 7 cm; length: 11 cm   **29.** [2.5] 525 mi
from Springer Mountain and 1575 mi from Mt. Katahdin
30. [2.5] 81 mm, 83 mm, 85 mm   **31.** [2.4] $65
32. [2.7] More than 36 one-way trips per month
33. [2.3] $d = \dfrac{a}{3}$ **34.** [1.4], [2.2] −15, 15   **35.** [2.7] Let
h = the number of hours of sun each day; $4 \le h \le 6$
36. [2.5] 60 tickets

Cumulative Review: Chapters 1–2, pp. 145–146

1. −12   **2.** $\frac{3}{4}$ **3.** −4.2   **4.** 10   **5.** 134   **6.** 149
7. $2x + 1$ **8.** $-10t + 12$ **9.** $-21n + 36$
10.

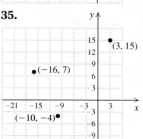

11. 27
12. $6(2x + 3y + 5z)$ **13.** −6   **14.** 16   **15.** 9
16. $\frac{13}{18}$ **17.** 1   **18.** $-\frac{7}{2}$ **19.** $z = \dfrac{x}{4y}$ **20.** $y = \frac{4}{9}x - \frac{1}{9}$
21. $n = \dfrac{p}{a + r}$ **22.** 1.83   **23.** 37.5%
24.

$t > -\frac{5}{2}$
25. $\{t \mid t \le -2\}$, or $(-\infty, -2]$

26. $\{t \mid t < 3\}$, or $(-\infty, 3)$ **27.** $\{x \mid x < 30\}$, or $(-\infty, 30)$
28. $\{n \mid n \ge 2\}$, or $[2, \infty)$ **29.** 48 million   **30.** 3.2 hr
31. $14\frac{1}{3}$ m   **32.** 9 ft, 15 ft   **33.** No more than $52
34. About 194%   **35.** 105°   **36.** For widths greater than
27 cm   **37.** $4t$ **38.** −5, 5   **39.** $1025

CHAPTER 3

Exercise Set 3.1, pp. 154–157

1. (a)   **2.** (c)   **3.** (b)   **4.** (d)   **5.** 2 drinks
7. The person weighs more than 140 lb.   **9.** About $5156

11. $231,856,000   **13.** About 29.2 million tons   **15.** Abo
3.2 million tons   **17.** About $12 billion   **19.** 2001
21.

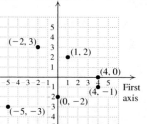

23.

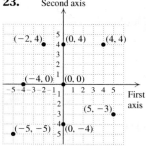

25.

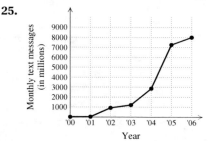

27. $A(-4, 5)$; $B(-3, -3)$; $C(0, 4)$; $D(3, 4)$; $E(3, -4)$
29. $A(4, 1)$; $B(0, -5)$; $C(-4, 0)$; $D(-3, -2)$; $E(3, 0)$
31.

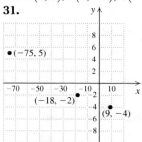

33.

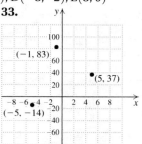

35.

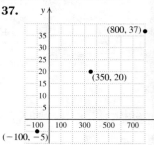

37.

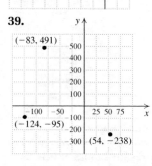

39.

41. IV   **43.** III   **45.** I
47. II   **49.** I and IV
51. I and III   **53.** ✍
55. $y = \dfrac{2x}{5}$, or $y = \frac{2}{5}x$
56. $y = \dfrac{-3x}{2}$, or $y = -\frac{3}{2}x$
57. $y = x - 8$
58. $y = -\frac{2}{5}x + 2$
59. $y = -\frac{2}{3}x + \frac{5}{3}$
60. $y = \frac{5}{8}x - \frac{1}{8}$ **61.** ✍   **63.** II or IV   **65.** $(-1, -5)$

Second axis

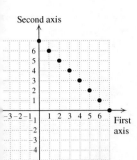

First axis

69. $\frac{65}{2}$ sq units
71. Latitude 27° North; longitude 81° West
73.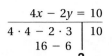

echnology Connection, p. 164

$y = -5x + 6.5$

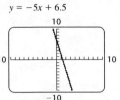

2. $y = 3x + 4.5$

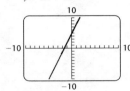

$7y - 4x = 22$, or $y = \frac{4}{7}x + \frac{22}{7}$

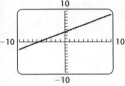

4. $5y + 11x = -20$, or $y = -\frac{11}{5}x - 4$

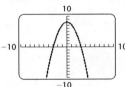

$2y - x^2 = 0$, or $y = 0.5x^2$

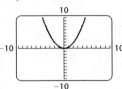

6. $y + x^2 = 8$, or $y = -x^2 + 8$

ercise Set 3.2, pp. 165–167

False **2.** True **3.** True **4.** True **5.** True
False **7.** Yes **9.** No **11.** No

$y = x + 3$
$\begin{array}{c|c} 2 & -1 + 3 \\ \hline 2 \overset{?}{=} 2 & \end{array}$ True
$(2, 5)$; answers may vary

$y = x + 3$
$\begin{array}{c|c} 7 & 4 + 3 \\ \hline 7 \overset{?}{=} 7 & \end{array}$ True

$y = \frac{1}{2}x + 3$
$\begin{array}{c|c} 5 & \frac{1}{2} \cdot 4 + 3 \\ & 2 + 3 \\ \hline 5 \overset{?}{=} 5 & \end{array}$ True
$(0, 3)$; answers may vary

$y = \frac{1}{2}x + 3$
$\begin{array}{c|c} 2 & \frac{1}{2}(-2) + 3 \\ & -1 + 3 \\ \hline 2 \overset{?}{=} 2 & \end{array}$ True

$y + 3x = 7$
$\begin{array}{c|c} 1 + 3 \cdot 2 & 7 \\ 1 + 6 & \\ \hline 7 \overset{?}{=} 7 & \end{array}$ True
$(1, 4)$; answers may vary

$y + 3x = 7$
$\begin{array}{c|c} -5 + 3 \cdot 4 & 7 \\ -5 + 12 & \\ \hline 7 \overset{?}{=} 7 & \end{array}$ True

19.
$4x - 2y = 10$
$\begin{array}{c|c} 4 \cdot 0 - 2(-5) & 10 \\ 0 + 10 & \\ \hline 10 \overset{?}{=} 10 & \end{array}$ True

$4x - 2y = 10$
$\begin{array}{c|c} 4 \cdot 4 - 2 \cdot 3 & 10 \\ 16 - 6 & \\ \hline 10 \overset{?}{=} 10 & \end{array}$ True
$(2, -1)$; answers may vary

21.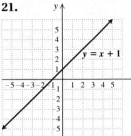

23.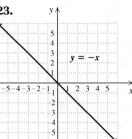

25.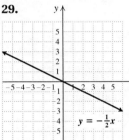

27.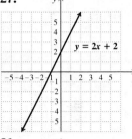

29.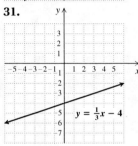

31.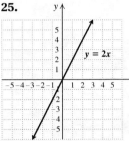

33.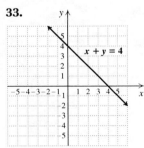

35.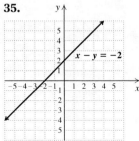

37.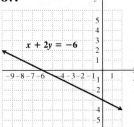

39.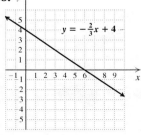

41.

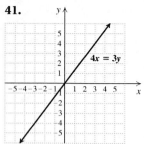

$4x = 3y$

43.

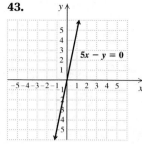

$5x - y = 0$

45.

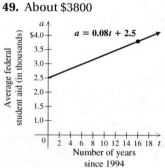

$6x - 3y = 9$

47.

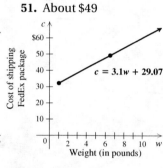

$6y + 2x = 8$

49. About $3800

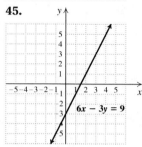

$a = 0.08t + 2.5$

Average federal student aid (in thousands)

Number of years since 1994

51. About $49

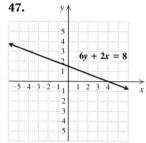

$c = 3.1w + 29.07$

Cost of shipping FedEx package

Weight (in pounds)

53. About $96

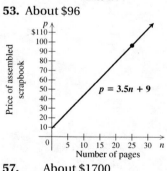

$p = 3.5n + 9$

Price of assembled scrapbook

Number of pages

55. About 33 gal

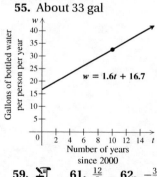

$w = 1.6t + 16.7$

Gallons of bottled water per person per year

Number of years since 2000

57. About $1700

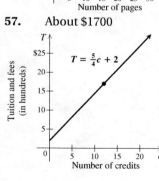

$T = \frac{5}{4}c + 2$

Tuition and fees (in hundreds)

Number of credits

59. 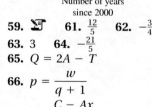 **61.** $\frac{12}{5}$ **62.** $-\frac{3}{4}$

63. 3 **64.** $-\frac{21}{5}$

65. $Q = 2A - T$

66. $p = \dfrac{w}{q + 1}$

67. $y = \dfrac{C - Ax}{B}$

68. $y = m(x - h) + k$

69.

71.

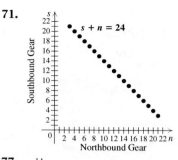

$s + n = 24$

Southbound Gear

Northbound Gear

73. $x + y = 5$, or $y = -x + 5$
75. $y = x + 2$

Answers may vary.
1 dinner, 40 lunches
5 dinners, 20 lunche
8 dinners, 5 lunches

77.

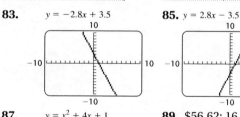

$25d + 5l = 225$

79.

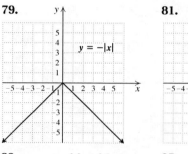

$y = -|x|$

81.

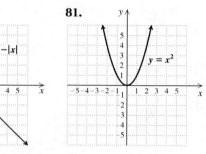

$y = x^2$

83. $y = -2.8x + 3.5$

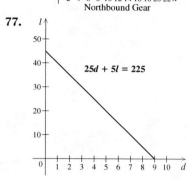

85. $y = 2.8x - 3.5$

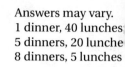

87. $y = x^2 + 4x + 1$

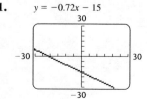

89. $56.62; 16.2 gal

Technology Connection, p. 171

1. $y = -0.72x - 15$

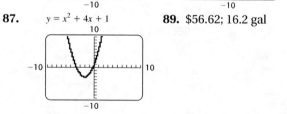

Xscl = 5, Yscl = 5

2. $y - 2.13x = 27$, or $y = 2.13x + 27$

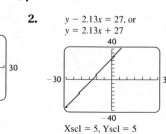

Xscl = 5, Yscl = 5

$5x + 6y = 84$, or
$y = -\frac{5}{6}x + 14$

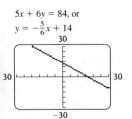

Xscl = 5, Yscl = 5

4. $2x - 7y = 150$, or
$y = \frac{2}{7}x - \frac{150}{7}$

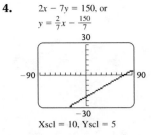

Xscl = 10, Yscl = 5

$19x - 17y = 200$, or
$y = \frac{19}{17}x - \frac{200}{17}$

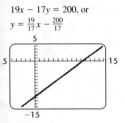

6. $6x + 5y = 159$, or
$y = -\frac{6}{5}x + \frac{159}{5}$

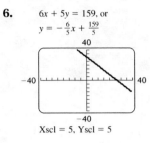

Xscl = 5, Yscl = 5

ercise Set 3.3, pp. 173–175

(f)   2. (e)   **3.** (d)   **4.** (c)   **5.** (b)   **6.** (a)
(a) $(0,5)$; **(b)** $(2,0)$ **9. (a)** $(0,-4)$; **(b)** $(3,0)$
(a) $(0,-2)$; **(b)** $(-3,0),(3,0)$ **13. (a)** $(0,0)$;
$(-2,0),(0,0),(5,0)$ **15. (a)** $(0,3)$; **(b)** $(5,0)$
(a) $(0,-18)$; **(b)** $(4,0)$ **19. (a)** $(0,16)$; **(b)** $(-20,0)$
(a) None; **(b)** $(12,0)$ **23. (a)** $(0,-9)$; **(b)** none

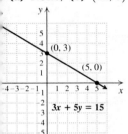

27.

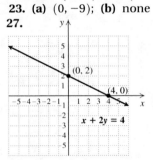

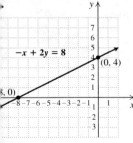

31.

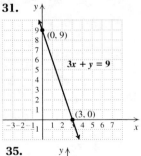

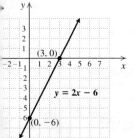

35.

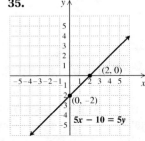

37.

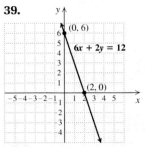

39.

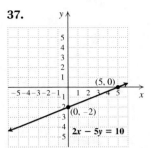

41.

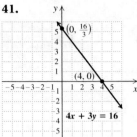

43.

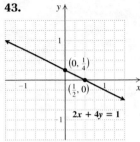

45.

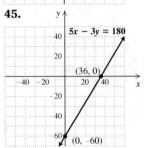

47.

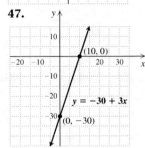

49.

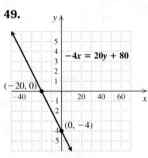

51.

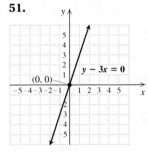

53.

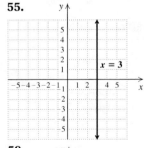

55.

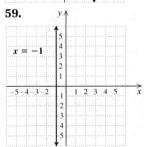

57.

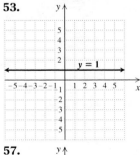

59.

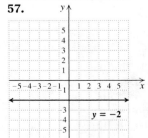

61.

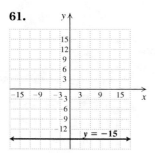

63.

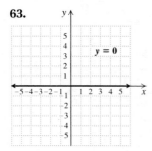

65.

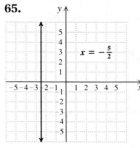

67.

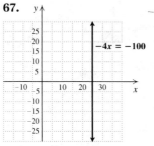

69.

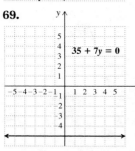

71. $y = -1$ **73.** $x = 4$
75. $x = 0$ **77.** ✍
79. $d - 7$
80. $w + 5$, or $5 + w$
81. Let n represent the number; $7 + 4n$
82. Let n represent the number; $3n$
83. Let x and y represent the numbers; $2(x + y)$
84. Let a and b represent the numbers; $\frac{1}{2}(a + b)$
85. ✍ **87.** $y = 0$ **89.** $x = -2$ **91.** $(-3, 4)$
93. $-5x + 3y = 15$, or $y = \frac{5}{3}x + 5$ **95.** -24
97. $\left(\frac{C - D}{A}, 0\right)$ **99.** $\left(0, -\frac{80}{7}\right)$, or $(0, -11.\overline{428571})$; $(40, 0)$
101. $(0, -9)$; $(45, 0)$ **103.** $\left(0, \frac{1}{25}\right)$, or $(0, 0.04)$; $\left(\frac{1}{50}, 0\right)$, or $(0.02, 0)$

Exercise Set 3.4, pp. 179–184

1. Miles per hour, or $\dfrac{\text{miles}}{\text{hour}}$

2. Hours per chapter, or $\dfrac{\text{hours}}{\text{chapter}}$

3. Dollars per mile, or $\dfrac{\text{dollars}}{\text{mile}}$

4. Petunias per foot, or $\dfrac{\text{petunias}}{\text{foot}}$

5. Minutes per errand, or $\dfrac{\text{minutes}}{\text{errand}}$

6. Cups of flour per cake, or $\dfrac{\text{cups of flour}}{\text{cake}}$

7. (a) 30 mpg; (b) \$39.33/day; (c) 130 mi/day; (d) 30¢/mi
9. (a) 7 mph; (b) \$7.50/hr; (c) \$1.07/mi
11. (a) \$22/hr; (b) 20.6 pages/hr; (c) \$1.07/page
13. \$568.4 billion/yr **15.** (a) 14.5 floors/min;
(b) 4.14 sec/floor **17.** (a) 23.42 ft/min; (b) 0.04 min/ft

19.

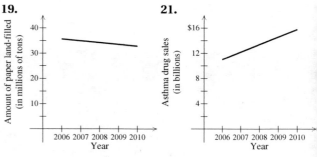

21.

23.

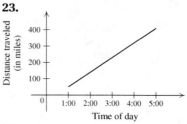

25.

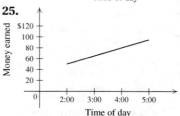

27.

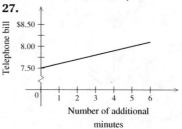

29. 20 calls/hr **31.** 75 mi/hr **33.** 12¢/min
35. -2000 people/yr **37.** 0.02 gal/mi **39.** (e) **41.** (c
43. (b) **45.** ✍ **47.** 5 **48.** -6 **49.** -1 **50.** $-\frac{4}{3}$
51. $-\frac{4}{3}$ **52.** 1 **53.** 0 **54.** Undefined **55.** ✍
57.

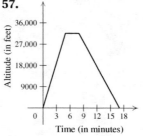

59.

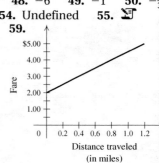

61. 0.45 min/mi **63.** About 41.6 min **65.** 3.6 bu/hr

Exercise Set 3.5, pp. 190–196

1. Positive **2.** Negative **3.** Negative **4.** Positive
5. Positive **6.** Negative **7.** Zero **8.** Positive
9. Negative **10.** Zero **11.** \$60/blog **13.** $-$\$6/month
15. 1 point/\$1000 income **17.** About $-2.1°$/min **19.**
21. $\frac{3}{2}$ **23.** 2 **25.** -1 **27.** 0 **29.** $-\frac{1}{3}$

Undefined   **33.** $-\frac{3}{4}$ **35.** $\frac{1}{4}$ **37.** 0 **39.** $\frac{5}{4}$
$-\frac{4}{5}$ **43.** $\frac{2}{3}$ **45.** -1 **47.** $-\frac{1}{2}$ **49.** 0
1 **53.** Undefined **55.** 0 **57.** Undefined
Undefined **61.** 0 **63.** 15% **65.** 35%
$\frac{29}{98}$, or about 30% **69.** About 5.1%; yes **71.**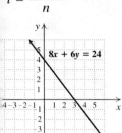
$y = \dfrac{c - ax}{b}$ **74.** $r = \dfrac{p + mn}{x}$ **75.** $y = \dfrac{ax - c}{b}$
$t = \dfrac{q - rs}{n}$

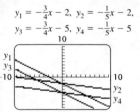

78.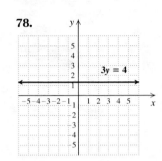

81. 0.364, or 36.4% **83.** $\{m \mid m \geq \frac{5}{2}\}$ **85.** $\frac{1}{2}$

Technology Connection, p. 201

$y_1 = -\frac{3}{4}x - 2,\ y_2 = -\frac{1}{5}x - 2,$
$y_3 = -\frac{3}{4}x - 5,\ y_4 = -\frac{1}{5}x - 5$

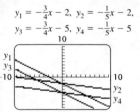

Exercise Set 3.6, pp. 203–205

1. (f) **2.** (b) **3.** (d) **4.** (c) **5.** (e) **6.** (a)
9.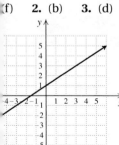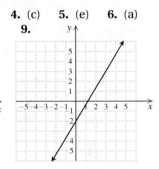

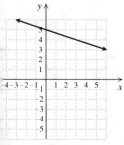 **13.**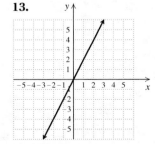

15. 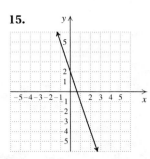 **17.**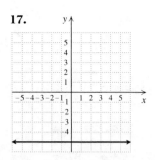

19. $-\frac{2}{7}; (0, 5)$ **21.** $\frac{1}{3}; (0, 7)$ **23.** $\frac{9}{5}; (0, -4)$ **25.** 3; (0, 7)
27. $-2; (0, 4)$ **29.** 0; (0, 3) **31.** $\frac{2}{5}; \left(0, \frac{8}{5}\right)$ **33.** $\frac{9}{8}; (0, 0)$
35. $y = 5x + 7$ **37.** $y = \frac{7}{8}x - 1$ **39.** $y = -\frac{5}{3}x - 8$
41. $y = \frac{1}{3}$ **43.** $y = \frac{3}{2}x + 17$, where y is the number
of gallons per person and x is the number of years since
2000 **45.** $y = \frac{2}{5}x + 15$, where y is the number of jobs, in
millions, and x is the number of years since 2000
47. 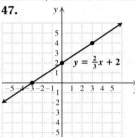 **49.**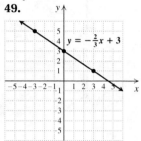

51. 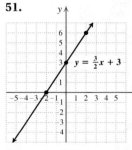 **53.**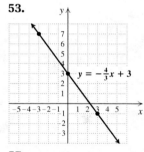

55. 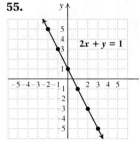 **57.**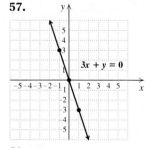

59. 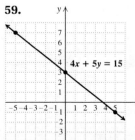 **61.**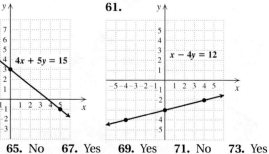

63. Yes **65.** No **67.** Yes **69.** Yes **71.** No **73.** Yes

75. $y = 5x + 11$ **77.** $y = \frac{1}{2}x$ **79.** $y = x + 3$
81. $y = x - 4$ **83.** ✍   **85.** $y = m(x - h) + k$
86. $y = -2(x + 4) + 9$ **87.** -7 **88.** 13   **89.** -9
90. -11 **91.** ✍   **93.** When $x = 0$, $y = b$, so $(0, b)$ is on the line. When $x = 1$, $y = m + b$, so $(1, m + b)$ is on the line. Then

$$\text{slope} = \frac{(m + b) - b}{1 - 0} = m.$$

95. $y = \frac{1}{3}x + 3$ **97.** $y = -\frac{5}{3}x + 3$ **99.** $y = -\frac{2}{3}x$

Connecting the Concepts, p. 206

1. (a) Yes;
(b)
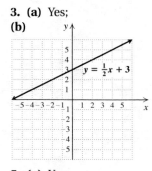

2. (a) Yes;
(b)
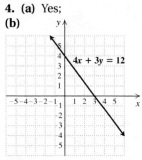

3. (a) Yes;
(b)
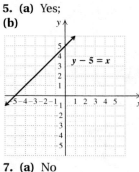

4. (a) Yes;
(b)
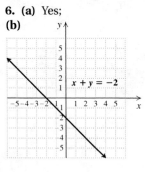

5. (a) Yes;
(b)

6. (a) Yes;
(b)

7. (a) No
8. (a) Yes;
(b)
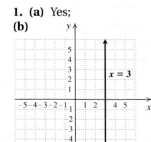

9. (a) Yes;
(b)
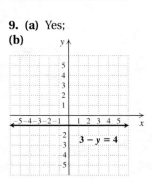

10. (a) No

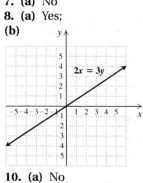
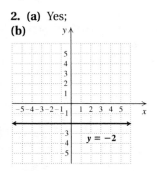

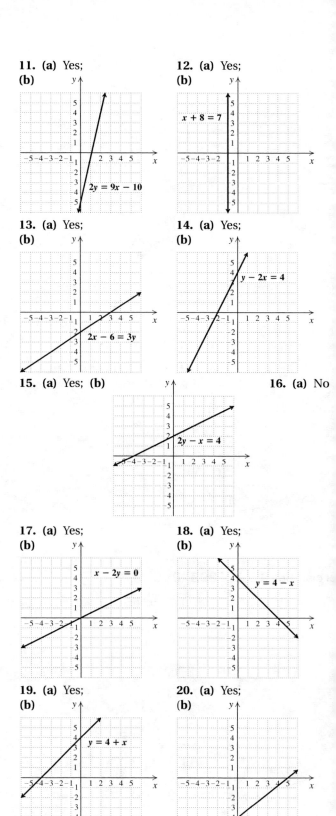

11. (a) Yes;
(b) $2y = 9x - 10$

12. (a) Yes;
(b) $x + 8 = 7$

13. (a) Yes;
(b) $2x - 6 = 3y$

14. (a) Yes;
(b) $y - 2x = 4$

15. (a) Yes; **(b)** $2y - x = 4$ **16. (a)** No

17. (a) Yes;
(b) $x - 2y = 0$

18. (a) Yes;
(b) $y = 4 - x$

19. (a) Yes;
(b) $y = 4 + x$

20. (a) Yes;
(b) $4x - 5y = 20$

chnology Connection, p. 208

$$y_1 = \tfrac{3}{4}x + 2; \ y_2 = -\tfrac{4}{3}x - 1$$ **2.** $$y_1 = -\tfrac{2}{5}x - 4; \ y_2 = \tfrac{5}{2}x + 3$$

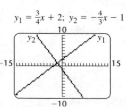   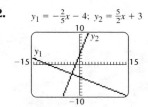

$$y_1 = \tfrac{31}{40}x + 2; \ y_2 = -\tfrac{40}{30}x - 1$$ No: $-\dfrac{40}{30} \neq -\dfrac{1}{\tfrac{31}{40}}$

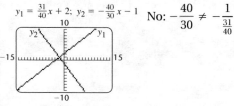

hough the lines appear to be perpendicular, they are not, cause the product of their slopes is not -1:

$$\left(-\frac{40}{30}\right) = -\frac{1240}{1200} \neq -1.$$

sualizing for Success, p. 212

C   **2.** G   **3.** F   **4.** B   **5.** D   **6.** A   **7.** I
H   **9.** J   **10.** E

ercise Set 3.7, pp. 213–216

(g)   **2.** (b)   **3.** (d)   **4.** (h)   **5.** (e)   **6.** (a)
(f)   **8.** (c)   **9.** (c)   **10.** (b)   **11.** (d)   **12.** (a)
$y - 6 = 3(x - 1)$ **15.** $y - 8 = \tfrac{3}{5}(x - 2)$
$y - 1 = -4(x - 3)$ **19.** $y - (-4) = \tfrac{3}{2}(x - 5)$
$y - 6 = -\tfrac{5}{4}(x - (-2))$
$y - (-1) = -2(x - (-4))$
$y - 8 = 1(x - (-2))$ **27.** $y = 4x - 7$
$y = \tfrac{7}{4}x - 9$ **31.** $y = -2x + 1$ **33.** $y = -4x - 9$
$y = \tfrac{2}{3}x + \tfrac{8}{3}$ **37.** $y = -\tfrac{5}{6}x + 4$ **39.** $y = \tfrac{1}{2}x + 4$
$y = 4x - 5$ **43.** $y = -\tfrac{2}{3}x - \tfrac{13}{3}$ **45.** $x = 5$
$y = -\tfrac{3}{2}x + \tfrac{11}{2}$ **49.** $y = x + 6$ **51.** $y = -\tfrac{1}{2}x + 6$
$x = -3$

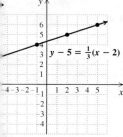   **57.**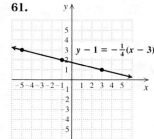

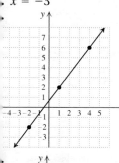   **61.**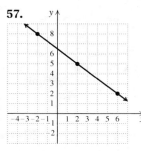

63. 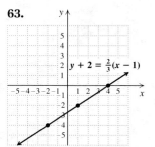   **65.**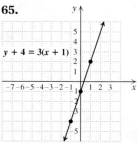

67. 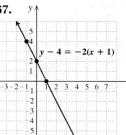   **69.**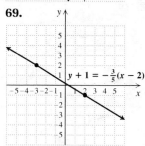

71. **(a)** 51.6 births per 1000 females; **(b)** 39.8 births per 1000 females   **73.** **(a)** About 13.1%; **(b)** 4%
75. **(a)** 16.47 million students; **(b)** 18.95 million students
77. **(a)** 33.65 million residents; **(b)** about 38.6 million residents
79. $y = -x + 5$ **81.** $y = \tfrac{2}{3}x + 3$ **83.** $y = \tfrac{2}{5}x - 2$
85. $y = 2x + 7$ **87.** ⚏   **89.** -125 **90.** 64   **91.** -64
92. 8   **93.** 28   **94.** -4 **95.** ⚏
97.    **99.** $y = 2x - 9$
101. $y = -\tfrac{4}{3}x + \tfrac{23}{3}$
103. $y = -4x + 7$
105. $y = \tfrac{10}{3}x + \tfrac{25}{3}$
107. $(2, 0), (0, 5)$

109. $-\dfrac{x}{4} + \dfrac{y}{3} = 1; (-4, 0), (0, 3)$ **111.** ⚏

Connecting the Concepts, pp. 216–217

1. Slope–intercept form   **2.** Standard form
3. None of these   **4.** Standard form
5. Point–slope form   **6.** None of these
7. $2x - 5y = 10$ **8.** $x - y = 2$
9. $-2x + y = 7$, or $2x - y = -7$ **10.** $\tfrac{1}{2}x + y = 3$
11. $3x - y = -23$, or $-3x + y = 23$ **12.** $x + 0y = 18$
13. $y = \tfrac{2}{7}x - \tfrac{8}{7}$ **14.** $y = -x - 8$ **15.** $y = 8x - 3$
16. $y = -\tfrac{3}{5}x + 3$ **17.** $y = -\tfrac{8}{9}x + \tfrac{5}{9}$ **18.** $y = -x$
19. $y = -\tfrac{1}{2}$ **20.** $y = \tfrac{1}{2}x$

Review Exercises: Chapter 3, pp. 220–222

1. True   **2.** True   **3.** False   **4.** False   **5.** True
6. True   **7.** True   **8.** False   **9.** True   **10.** True
11. About 1.3 billion searches   **12.** About 1137 searches

13.–15.

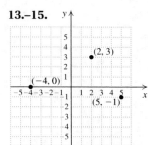

16. III   **17.** IV   **18.** II
19. $(-5, -1)$ **20.** $(-2, 5)$
21. $(3, 0)$

22.

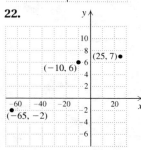

23. (a) No; **(b)** yes

24.

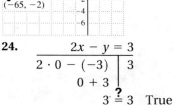

$(-1, -5)$; answers may vary

25.

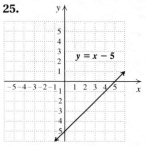

26.

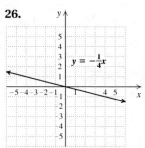

27.

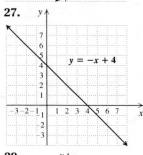

28.

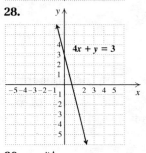

29.

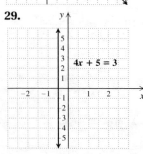

30.

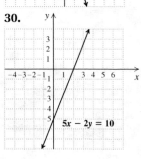

31. About 7 million viewers

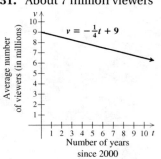

32. (a) $\frac{2}{15}$ mi/min;
(b) 7.5 min/mi
33. 12 mpg   **34.** 0
35. $\frac{7}{3}$ **36.** $-\frac{3}{7}$ **37.** $-\frac{6}{5}$
38. 0   **39.** Undefined
40. 2   **41.** $8.\overline{3}\%$
42. $(16, 0), (0, -10)$
43. $-\frac{3}{5}$; $(0, 9)$
44. Perpendicular
45. Parallel

46. $y = \frac{3}{8}x + 7$ **47.** $y - 9 = -\frac{1}{3}(x - (-2))$
48. (a) \$1725; **(b)** \$2701   **49.** $y = 5x - 25$
50. $y = -\frac{5}{3}x - \frac{5}{3}$

51.

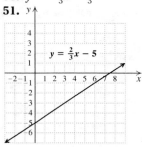

52.

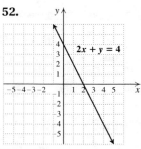

53.

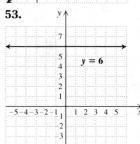

54.

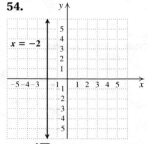

55.

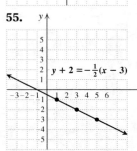

56. ✍ Two perpendicular lines share the same y-intercept if their point of intersection is on the y-axis.
57. ✍ The graph of a vertical line has only an x-intercept. The graph of a horizontal line has only a y-intercept. The graph of a nonvertical, non-horizontal line will have only one intercept if it passes through the origin: $(0, 0)$ is both the x-intercept and the y-intercept.   **58.** -1
59. 19   **60.** Area: 45 sq units; perimeter: 28 units
61. $(0, 4), (1, 3), (-1, 3)$; answers may vary

Test: Chapter 3, pp. 222–223

1. [3.1] About 95 students   **2.** [3.1] About 137 students
3. [3.1] III   **4.** [3.1] II   **5.** [3.1] $(3, 4)$ **6.** [3.1] $(0, -4)$
7. [3.1] $(-5, 2)$

[3.2]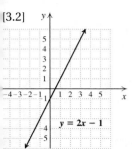

9. [3.3]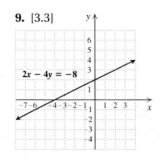

[3.3]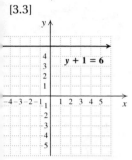

11. [3.2]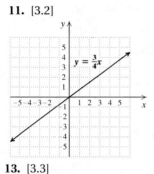

[3.2]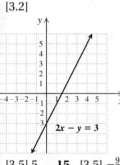

13. [3.3]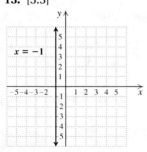

[3.5] 5   **15.** [3.5] $-\frac{9}{4}$ **16.** [3.5] Undefined
[3.4] $\frac{1}{3}$ km/min   **18.** [3.5] 31.5%
[3.3] $(6, 0), (0, -30)$ **20.** [3.6] 8; $(0, 10)$
[3.6] $y = -\frac{1}{3}x - 11$ **22.** [3.6] Parallel
[3.6] Perpendicular   **24.** [3.7] $y = -\frac{5}{2}x - \frac{11}{2}$
[3.7] **(a)**   **(b)** 138 beats per minute

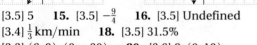

[3.6]   **27.** [3.7]

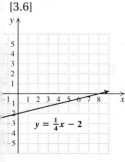   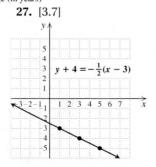

28. [3.6] $y = \frac{2}{5}x + 9$ **29.** [3.1] Area: 25 sq units; perimeter: 20 units   **30.** [3.2], [3.7] $(0, 12), (-3, 15), (5, 7)$

Cumulative Review: Chapters 1–3, pp. 224–225

1. 7   **2.** $12a - 6b + 18$ **3.** $4(2x - y + 1)$ **4.** $2 \cdot 3^3$
5. -0.15 **6.** 37   **7.** $\frac{1}{10}$ **8.** -10 **9.** 0.367   **10.** $\frac{11}{60}$
11. 2.6   **12.** 7.28   **13.** $-\frac{5}{12}$ **14.** -3 **15.** 27
16. $-2y - 7$ **17.** $5x + 11$ **18.** -2.6 **19.** -27
20. 16   **21.** -6 **22.** 2   **23.** $\frac{7}{9}$ **24.** -17 **25.** 2
26. $\{x \mid x < 16\}$, or $(-\infty, 16)$ **27.** $\{x \mid x \le -\frac{11}{8}\}$, or
$(-\infty, -\frac{11}{8}]$ **28.** $h = \dfrac{A - \pi r^2}{2\pi r}$ **29.** IV

30. $-1 < x \le 2$
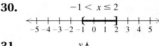

31. 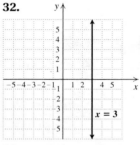   **32.**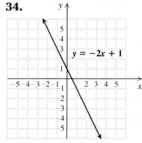

33. 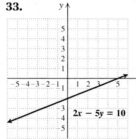   **34.**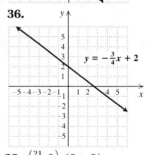

35. 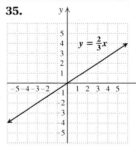   **36.**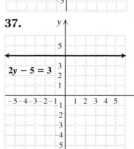

37. 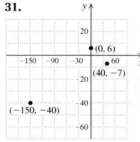   **38.** $\left(\frac{21}{2}, 0\right), (0, -3)$
39. $\left(-\frac{5}{4}, 0\right), (0, 5)$
40. 3; $(0, -2)$ **41.** $-\frac{1}{3}$
42. $y = \frac{2}{7}x - 4$
43. $y - 4 = -\frac{3}{8}(x - (-6))$
44. $y = -\frac{3}{8}x + \frac{7}{4}$
45. $y = 2x + 1$
46. 0.5 million bicycles per year

47. (a)

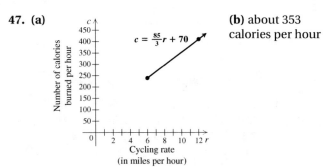

$c = \frac{85}{3}r + 70$

(b) about 353 calories per hour

48. \$210 billion   **49.** \$54,533   **50.** 21 million Americans
51. \$120   **52.** 50 m, 53 m, 40 m   **53.** 4 hr
54. \$25,000   **55.** $-4, 4$ **56.** 2   **57.** -5 **58.** 3
59. No solution   **60.** $Q = \dfrac{2 - pm}{p}$
61. $y = -\frac{7}{3}x + 7;\ y = -\frac{7}{3}x - 7;\ y = \frac{7}{3}x - 7;\ y = \frac{7}{3}x + 7$

CHAPTER 4

Exercise Set 4.1, pp. 234–235

1. (e)   **2.** (f)   **3.** (b)   **4.** (h)   **5.** (g)   **6.** (a)
7. (c)   **8.** (d)   **9.** Base: $2x$; exponent: 5
11. Base: x; exponent: 3   **13.** Base: $\dfrac{4}{y}$; exponent: 7
15. d^{13} **17.** a^7 **19.** 6^{15} **21.** $(3y)^{12}$ **23.** $(8n)^{10}$
25. a^5b^9 **27.** $(x+3)^{13}$ **29.** r^{10} **31.** m^4n^9 **33.** 7^3
35. t^7 **37.** $5a$ **39.** 1   **41.** $(r+s)^8$ **43.** $\frac{4}{5}d^7$
45. $4a^7b^6$ **47.** $x^{12}y^7$ **49.** 1   **51.** 5   **53.** 2   **55.** -4
57. x^{33} **59.** 5^{32} **61.** t^{80} **63.** $100x^2$ **65.** $-8a^3$
67. $25n^{14}$ **69.** $a^{14}b^7$ **71.** $r^{17}t^{11}$ **73.** $24x^{19}$
75. $\dfrac{x^3}{125}$ **77.** $\dfrac{49}{36n^2}$ **79.** $\dfrac{a^{18}}{b^{48}}$ **81.** $\dfrac{x^8y^4}{z^{12}}$ **83.** $\dfrac{a^{12}}{16b^{20}}$
85. $-\dfrac{125x^{21}y^3}{8z^{12}}$ **87.** 1   **89.** ✍   **91.** -24 **92.** -15
93. -11 **94.** 16   **95.** -14 **96.** 4   **97.** ✍
99. ✍   **101.** Let $x = 1$; then $3x^2 = 3$, but $(3x)^2 = 9$.
103. Let $t = -1$; then $\dfrac{t^6}{t^2} = 1$, but $t^3 = -1$.   **105.** y^{6x}
107. x^t **109.** 13   **111.** $<$ **113.** $<$ **115.** $>$
117. 4,000,000; 4,194,304; 194,304   **119.** 2,000,000,000;
2,147,483,648; 147,483,648   **121.** 1,536,000 bytes, or
approximately 1,500,000 bytes

Technology Connection, p. 241

1. 1.71×10^{17} **2.** $5.\overline{370} \times 10^{-15}$ **3.** 3.68×10^{16}

Exercise Set 4.2, pp. 242–244

1. (c)   **2.** (d)   **3.** (a)   **4.** (b)   **5.** $\dfrac{1}{2^3} = \dfrac{1}{8}$
7. $\dfrac{1}{(-2)^6} = \dfrac{1}{64}$ **9.** $\dfrac{1}{t^9}$ **11.** $\dfrac{x}{y^2}$ **13.** $\dfrac{t}{r^5}$ **15.** a^8

17. $\dfrac{1}{7}$ **19.** $\left(\dfrac{5}{3}\right)^2 = \dfrac{25}{9}$ **21.** $\left(\dfrac{2}{x}\right)^5 = \dfrac{32}{x^5}$ **23.** $\left(\dfrac{t}{s}\right)^7 = \dfrac{t}{s}$
25. 9^{-2} **27.** y^{-3} **29.** 5^{-1} **31.** t^{-1} **33.** 2^3, or 8
35. $\dfrac{1}{x^{12}}$ **37.** $\dfrac{1}{t^2}$ **39.** $\dfrac{1}{n^{15}}$ **41.** t^{18} **43.** $\dfrac{1}{t^{12}}$
45. $\dfrac{1}{m^7n^7}$ **47.** $\dfrac{9}{x^8}$ **49.** $\dfrac{25t^6}{r^8}$ **51.** t^{14} **53.** $\dfrac{1}{y^4}$
55. $5y^3$ **57.** $2x^5$ **59.** $\dfrac{-3b^9}{2a^7}$ **61.** 1   **63.** $\dfrac{8y^7z}{x^3}$
65. $3s^2t^4u^4$ **67.** $\dfrac{1}{x^{12}y^{15}}$ **69.** $\dfrac{m^{10}n^6}{9}$ **71.** $\dfrac{b^5c^4}{a^8}$
73. $\dfrac{9}{a^8}$ **75.** $\dfrac{n^{12}}{m^3}$ **77.** $\dfrac{27b^{12}}{8a^6}$ **79.** 1   **81.** $\dfrac{2b^3}{a^4}$
83. $\dfrac{5y^4z^{10}}{4x^{11}}$ **85.** 4920   **87.** 0.00892   **89.** 904,000,000
91. 0.000003497   **93.** 3.6×10^7 **95.** 5.83×10^{-3}
97. 7.8×10^{10} **99.** 5.27×10^{-7} **101.** 1.032×10^{-6}
103. 6×10^{13} **105.** 2.47×10^8 **107.** 3.915×10^{-16}
109. 2.5×10^{13} **111.** 5.0×10^{-6} **113.** 3×10^{-21}
115. ✍   **117.** $8x$ **118.** $-3a - 6b$ **119.** $-2x - 7$
120. $-4t - r - 5$ **121.** 1004   **122.** 9   **123.** ✍
125. 8×10^5 **127.** 2^{-12} **129.** 5   **131.** 5^6
133. $\frac{1}{3} + \frac{1}{4} = \frac{7}{12}$ **135.** 9   **137.** $6.304347826 \times 10^{25}$
139. $1.19140625 \times 10^{-15}$ **141.** 3×10^8 mi
143. \$2.31 \times 10^8$ **145.** 2.277×10^{10} min

Connecting the Concepts, p. 245

1. x^{14} **2.** $\dfrac{1}{x^{14}}$ **3.** $\dfrac{1}{x^{14}}$ **4.** x^{14} **5.** x^{40} **6.** x^{40}
7. c^8 **8.** $\dfrac{1}{c^8}$ **9.** $16x^{12}y^4$ **10.** $\dfrac{1}{16x^{12}y^4}$ **11.** 1
12. a^5 **13.** $\dfrac{a^{15}}{b^{20}}$ **14.** $\dfrac{b^{20}}{a^{15}}$ **15.** $\dfrac{5x^3}{2y^4}$ **16.** $\dfrac{6a^2}{7b^5}$
17. $\dfrac{7t^6}{xp^5}$ **18.** $\dfrac{16a^2}{9b^6}$ **19.** $18p^4q^{14}$ **20.** $\dfrac{9x^3}{2y^5}$

Technology Connection, pp. 249–250

1. 9.8

Exercise Set 4.3, pp. 250–254

1. (b)   **2.** (f)   **3.** (h)   **4.** (d)   **5.** (g)   **6.** (e)
7. (a)   **8.** (c)   **9.** $8x^3, -11x^2, 6x, 1$
11. $-t^6, -3t^3, 9t, -4$ **13.** Coefficients: 8, 2; degrees: 4, 1
15. Coefficients: 9, -3, 4; degrees: 2, 1, 0
17. Coefficients: 6, 9, 1; degrees: 5, 1, 3   **19.** Coefficients:
1, -1, 4, -3; degrees: 4, 3, 1, 0   **21. (a)** 1, 3, 4;   **(b)** $8t^4$, 8;
(c) 4   **23. (a)** 2, 0, 4;   **(b)** $2a^4$, 2;   **(c)** 4
25. (a) 0, 2, 1, 5;   **(b)** $-x^5$, -1;   **(c)** 5

Term	Coefficient	Degree of the Term	Degree of the Polynomial
$8x^5$	8	5	
$-\frac{1}{2}x^4$	$-\frac{1}{2}$	4	
$-4x^3$	-4	3	5
$7x^2$	7	2	
6	6	0	

Trinomial   **31.** Polynomial with no special name
Binomial   **35.** Monomial   **37.** $11n^2 + n$ **39.** $4a^4$
$7x^3 + x^2 - 6x$ **43.** $11b^3 + b^2 - b$ **45.** $-x^4 - x^3$
$\frac{1}{15}x^4 + 10$ **49.** $-1.1a^2 + 5.3a - 7.5$ **51.** $-3; 21$
16; 34   **55.** $-38; 148$ **57.** 159; 165   **59.** $-39; 21$
$1.93 billion   **63.** 1112 ft   **65.** 62.8 cm
153.86 m^2 **69.** About 75 donations
About 9 words   **73.** About 6   **75.** About 16;
out 19   **77.** 〽️   **79.** $x - 3$ **80.** $-2x - 6$
$6a - 3$ **82.** $-t - 1$ **83.** $-t^4 + 17t$
$0.4a^2 - a + 11$ **85.** 〽️
$2x^5 + 4x^4 + 6x^3 + 8$; answers may vary   **89.** $2510
$3x^6$ **93.** 3 and 8   **95.** 85.0

t	$-t^2 + 10t - 18$
3	3
4	6
5	7
6	6
7	3

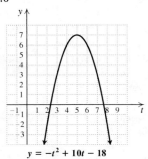

$y = -t^2 + 10t - 18$

chnology Connection, p. 258

In each case, let $y_1 =$ the expression before the addition
subtraction has been performed, $y_2 =$ the simplified
m or difference, and $y_3 = y_2 - y_1$; and note that the
ph of y_3 coincides with the x-axis. That is, $y_3 = 0$.

ercise Set 4.4, pp. 259-261

x^2 **2.** -6 **3.** $-$ **4.** $+$ **5.** $4x + 9$ **7.** $-6t + 8$
$-3x^2 + 6x - 2$ **11.** $9t^2 + t + 3$
$8m^3 - 3m - 7$ **15.** $7 + 13a - a^2 + 7a^3$
$2x^6 + 9x^4 + 2x^3 - 4x^2 + 5x$
$x^4 + \frac{1}{4}x^3 - \frac{3}{4}x^2 - \frac{5}{6}x + 3$
$4.2t^3 + 3.5t^2 - 6.4t - 1.8$ **23.** $-4x^3 + 4x^2 + 6x$
$1.3x^4 + 0.35x^3 + 9.53x^2 + 2x + 0.96$
$-(-3t^3 + 4t^2 - 7); 3t^3 - 4t^2 + 7$
$-(x^4 - 8x^3 + 6x); -x^4 + 8x^3 - 6x$
$-9x + 10$ **33.** $-3a^4 + 5a^2 - 1.2$

35. $4x^4 - 6x^2 - \frac{3}{4}x + 8$ **37.** $-2x - 7$
39. $-t^2 - 12t + 13$ **41.** $8a^3 + 8a^2 + a - 10$
43. $4.6x^3 + 9.2x^2 - 3.8x - 23$ **45.** 0
47. $1 + a + 12a^2 - 3a^3$ **49.** $\frac{9}{8}x^3 - \frac{1}{2}x$
51. $0.05t^3 - 0.07t^2 + 0.01t + 1$ **53.** $2x^2 + 6$
55. $-3x^4 - 8x^3 - 7x^2$ **57.** (a) $5x^2 + 4x$; (b) 145; 273
59. $16y + 26$ **61.** $(r + 11)(r + 9); 9r + 99 + 11r + r^2$
63. $(x + 3)^2; x^2 + 3x + 9 + 3x$ **65.** $m^2 - 40$
67. $\pi r^2 - 49$ **69.** $(x^2 - 12)$ ft^2 **71.** $(z^2 - 36\pi)$ ft^2
73. $\left(144 - \frac{d^2}{4}\pi\right)$ m^2 **75.** 〽️   **77.** $2x^2 - 2x + 6$
78. $-15x^2 + 10x + 35$ **79.** x^8 **80.** y^7 **81.** $2n^3$
82. $-6n^{12}$ **83.** 〽️   **85.** $9t^2 - 20t + 11$
87. $-6x + 14$ **89.** $250.591x^3 + 2.812x$ **91.** $20w + 42$
93. $2x^2 + 20x$ **95.** $8x + 24$ **97.** 〽️

Technology Connection, p. 266

1. Let $y_1 = (5x^4 - 2x^2 + 3x)(x^2 + 2x)$ and
$y_2 = 5x^6 + 10x^5 - 2x^4 - x^3 + 6x^2$. With the table set in
AUTO mode, note that the values in the Y₁- and Y₂-columns
match, regardless of how far we scroll up or down.
2. Use TRACE, a table, or a boldly drawn graph to confirm
that y_3 is always 0.

Exercise Set 4.5, pp. 267-269

1. (c)   **2.** (d)   **3.** (d)   **4.** (a)   **5.** (c)   **6.** (b)
7. $21x^5$ **9.** $-x^7$ **11.** x^8 **13.** $36t^4$ **15.** $-0.12x^9$
17. $-\frac{1}{20}x^{12}$ **19.** $5n^3$ **21.** $-44x^{10}$ **23.** $72y^{10}$
25. $20x^2 + 5x$ **27.** $3a^2 - 27a$ **29.** $x^5 + x^2$
31. $-6n^3 + 24n^2 - 3n$ **33.** $-15t^3 - 30t^2$
35. $4a^9 - 8a^7 - \frac{5}{12}a^4$ **37.** $x^2 + 7x + 12$
39. $t^2 + 4t - 21$ **41.** $a^2 - 1.3a + 0.42$ **43.** $x^2 - 9$
45. $28 - 15x + 2x^2$ **47.** $t^2 + \frac{17}{6}t + 2$
49. $\frac{3}{16}a^2 + \frac{5}{4}a - 2$
51. 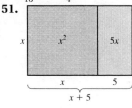   **53.**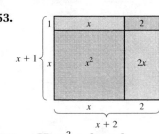
55. 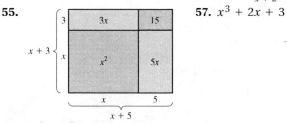   **57.** $x^3 + 2x + 3$
59. $2a^3 - a^2 - 11a + 10$
61. $3y^6 - 21y^4 + y^3 + 2y^2 - 7y - 14$
63. $33x^2 + 25x + 2$ **65.** $x^4 + 4x^3 - 3x^2 + 16x - 3$
67. $10t^4 + 3t^3 - 20t^2 + \frac{9}{2}t - 2$
69. $x^4 + 8x^3 + 12x^2 + 9x + 4$ **71.** 〽️   **73.** 0   **74.** 0
75. 8   **76.** 7   **77.** 32   **78.** 50   **79.** 〽️

81. $75y^2 - 45y$ **83.** 5   **85.** $V = (4x^3 - 48x^2 + 144x)$ in³; $S = (-4x^2 + 144)$ in²   **87.** $(x^3 - 5x^2 + 8x - 4)$ cm³   **89.** 16 ft by 8 ft   **91.** 0   **93.** $x^3 + x^2 - 22x - 40$ **95.** 0

Visualizing for Success, p. 275

1. E, F   **2.** B, O   **3.** S, K   **4.** R, G   **5.** D, M   **6.** J, P
7. C, L   **8.** N, Q   **9.** A, H   **10.** I, T

Exercise Set 4.6, pp. 276–278

1. True   **2.** False   **3.** False   **4.** True
5. $x^3 + 3x^2 + 2x + 6$ **7.** $t^5 + 7t^4 - 2t - 14$
9. $y^2 - y - 6$ **11.** $9x^2 + 21x + 10$
13. $5x^2 + 17x - 12$ **15.** $15 - 13t + 2t^2$
17. $x^4 - 4x^2 - 21$ **19.** $p^2 - \frac{1}{16}$ **21.** $x^2 - 0.6x + 0.09$
23. $-3n^2 - 19n + 14$ **25.** $x^2 + 20x + 100$
27. $1 - 3t + 5t^2 - 15t^3$ **29.** $x^5 + 3x^3 - x^2 - 3$
31. $3x^6 - 2x^4 - 6x^2 + 4$ **33.** $4t^6 + 20t^3 + 25$
35. $8x^5 + 16x^3 + 5x^2 + 10$ **37.** $100x^4 - 9$
39. $x^2 - 64$ **41.** $4x^2 - 1$ **43.** $25m^4 - 16$
45. $81a^6 - 1$ **47.** $x^8 - 0.01$ **49.** $t^2 - \frac{9}{16}$
51. $x^2 + 6x + 9$ **53.** $49x^6 - 14x^3 + 1$
55. $a^2 - \frac{4}{5}a + \frac{4}{25}$ **57.** $t^8 + 6t^4 + 9$
59. $4 - 12x^4 + 9x^8$ **61.** $25 + 60t^2 + 36t^4$
63. $49x^2 - 4.2x + 0.09$ **65.** $14n^5 - 7n^3$
67. $a^3 - a^2 - 10a + 12$ **69.** $49 - 42x^4 + 9x^8$
71. $5x^3 + 30x^2 - 10x$ **73.** $q^{10} - 1$
75. $15t^5 - 3t^4 + 3t^3$ **77.** $36x^8 - 36x^5 + 9x^2$
79. $18a^4 + 0.8a^3 + 4.5a + 0.2$ **81.** $\frac{1}{25} - 36x^8$
83. $a^3 + 1$ **85.** $x^2 + 6x + 9$ **87.** $t^2 + 7t + 12$
89. $a^2 + 10a + 25$ **91.** $x^2 + 10x + 21$
93. $a^2 + 8a + 7$ **95.** $25t^2 + 20t + 4$
97. 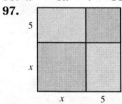   **99.**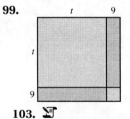

101. 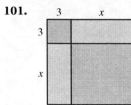   **103.**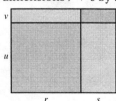

105. Washing machine: 9 kWh/mo; refrigerator: 189 kWh/mo; freezer: 99 kWh/mo   **106.** About $5.8 billion   **107.** $y = \dfrac{8}{5x}$ **108.** $a = \dfrac{c}{3b}$
109. $x = \dfrac{by + c}{a}$ **110.** $y = \dfrac{ax - c}{b}$ **111.** ☜
113. $16x^4 - 81$ **115.** $81t^4 - 72t^2 + 16$
117. $t^{24} - 4t^{18} + 6t^{12} - 4t^6 + 1$ **119.** 396   **121.** -7
123. $17F + 7(F - 17)$, $F^2 - (F - 17)(F - 7)$; other equivalent expressions are possible.   **125.** $(y + 1)(y - 1)$, $y(y + 1) - y - 1$; other equivalent expressions are possible.
127. $y^2 - 4y + 4$ **129.** ◣

Connecting the Concepts, p. 279

1. Addition; $3x^2 + 3x + 3$ **2.** Subtraction; $6x + 13$
3. Multiplication; $48x^5 - 42x^3$ **4.** Multiplication; $6x^2 + x - 2$ **5.** Subtraction; $9x^3 - 5x^2 - 7x + 13$
6. Multiplication; $2x^3 + 3x^2 - 5x - 3$ **7.** Multiplication; $81x^2 - 1$ **8.** Addition; $9x^4 + 2x^3 - 5x$
9. $-6x^2 + 2x - 12$ **10.** $9x^2 + 45x + 56$
11. $40x^9 - 48x^8 + 16x^5$ **12.** $t^9 + 5t^7$
13. $4m^2 - 4m + 1$ **14.** $x^3 - 1$ **15.** $5x^3 + 3$
16. $c^2 - 9$ **17.** $16y^6 + 56y^3 + 49$
18. $3a^4 - 13a^3 - 13a^2 - 4$ **19.** $16t^4 - 25$
20. $a^8 - 5a^4 - 24$

Technology Connection, p. 283

1. 36.22   **2.** 22,312

Exercise Set 4.7, pp. 284–287

1. (a)   **2.** (b)   **3.** (b)   **4.** (a)   **5.** (c)   **6.** (c)
7. (a)   **8.** (a)   **9.** -13 **11.** -68 **13.** 3.51 L
15. 1889 calories   **17.** 73.005 in²   **19.** 66.4 m
21. Coefficients: 3, -5, 2, -11; degrees: 3, 2, 2, 0; 3
23. Coefficients: 7, -1, 1, 9; degrees: 0, 3, 3, 3; 3
25. $2r - 6s$ **27.** $5xy^2 - 2x^2y + x + 3x^2$
29. $9u^2v - 11uv^2 + 11u^2$ **31.** $6a^2c - 7ab^2 + a^2b$
33. $11x^2 - 10xy - y^2$ **35.** $-6a^4 - 8ab + 7ab^2$
37. $-6r^2 - 5rt - t^2$ **39.** $3x^3 - x^2y + xy^2 - 3y^3$
41. $-2y^4x^3 - 3y^3x$ **43.** $-8x + 8y$
45. $12c^2 + 5cd - 2d^2$ **47.** $x^2y^2 + 4xy - 5$
49. $4a^2 - b^2$ **51.** $20r^2t^2 - 23rt + 6$
53. $m^6n^2 + 2m^3n - 48$ **55.** $30x^2 - 28xy + 6y^2$
57. $0.01 - p^2q^2$ **59.** $x^2 + 2xh + h^2$
61. $16a^2 - 40ab + 25b^2$ **63.** $a^2b^2 - c^2d^4$
65. $x^3y^2 + x^2y^3 + 2x^2y^2 + 2xy^3 + 3xy + 3y^2$
67. $a^2 + 2ab + b^2 - c^2$ **69.** $a^2 - b^2 - 2bc - c^2$
71. $x^2 + 2xy + y^2$ **73.** $\frac{1}{2}a^2b^2 - 2$
75. $a^2 + c^2 + ab + 2ac + ad + bc + bd + cd$
77. $m^2 - n^2$
79. We draw a rectangle with dimensions $r + s$ by $u + v$.   **81.**

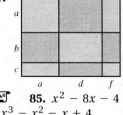

83. ☜   **85.** $x^2 - 8x - 4$
86. $2x^3 - x^2 - x + 4$
87. $-2x + 5$ **88.** $5x^2 + x$ **89.** $13x^2 + 1$
90. $-x - 3$ **91.** ☜   **93.** $4xy - 4y^2$
95. $2\pi ab - \pi b^2$ **97.** $x^3 + 2y^3 + x^2y + xy^2$
99. $2x^2 - 2\pi r^2 + 4xh + 2\pi rh$ **101.** ☜   **103.** 40
105. $P + 2Pr + Pr^2$ **107.** $15,638.03

Exercise Set 4.8, pp. 292–293

1. $8x^6 - 5x^3$ **3.** $1 - 2u + u^6$ **5.** $6t^2 - 8t + 2$
7. $7x^3 - 6x + \frac{3}{2}$ **9.** $-4t^2 - 2t + 1$ **11.** $4x - 5 + \dfrac{1}{2x}$

$x + 2x^3y + 3$ **15.** $-3rs - r + 2s$ **17.** $x - 6$

$t - 5 + \dfrac{-45}{t - 5}$ **21.** $2x - 1 + \dfrac{1}{x + 6}$

$t^2 - 3t + 9$ **25.** $a + 5 + \dfrac{4}{a - 5}$

$x - 3 - \dfrac{3}{5x - 1}$ **29.** $3a + 1 + \dfrac{3}{2a + 5}$

$t^2 - 3t + 1$ **33.** $x^2 + 1$ **35.** $t^2 - 1 + \dfrac{3t - 1}{t^2 + 5}$

$3x^2 - 3 + \dfrac{x - 1}{2x^2 + 1}$ **39.** ✍

42.

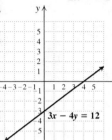

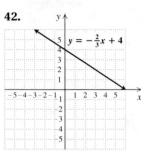

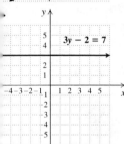

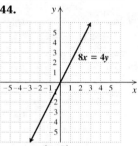

$-\frac{3}{10}$ **46.** Slope: 4; y-intercept: $\left(0, \frac{7}{2}\right)$

$y = -5x - 10$ **48.** $y = \frac{5}{4}x - \frac{9}{2}$ **49.** ✍

$5x^{6k} - 16x^{3k} + 14$ **53.** $3t^{2h} + 2t^h - 5$

$a + 3 + \dfrac{5}{5a^2 - 7a - 2}$ **57.** $2x^2 + x - 3$

3 **61.** -1

Review Exercises: Chapter 4, pp. 297–298

1. True   **2.** True   **3.** True   **4.** False   **5.** False
6. False   **7.** True   **8.** True   **9.** n^{12} **10.** $(7x)^{10}$
11. t^6 **12.** 4^3, or 64   **13.** 1   **14.** $-9c^4d^2$
15. $-8x^3y^6$ **16.** $18x^5$ **17.** a^7b^6 **18.** $\dfrac{4t^{10}}{9s^8}$
19. $\dfrac{1}{8^6}$ **20.** a^{-9} **21.** $\dfrac{1}{4^2}$, or $\dfrac{1}{16}$ **22.** $\dfrac{2b^9}{a^{13}}$ **23.** $\dfrac{1}{w^{15}}$
24. $\dfrac{x^6}{4y^2}$ **25.** $\dfrac{y^3}{8x^3}$ **26.** 470,000,000   **27.** 1.09×10^{-5}
28. 2.09×10^4 **29.** 5.12×10^{-5}
30. $8x^2, -x, \frac{2}{3}$ **31.** $-4y^5, 7y^2, -3y, -2$ **32.** $9, -1, 7$
33. $7, -\frac{5}{6}, -4, 10$ **34. (a)** $2, 0, 5$; **(b)** $15t^5, 15$; **(c)** 5
35. (a) $5, 0, 2, 1$; **(b)** $-2x^5, -2$; **(c)** 5   **36.** Trinomial
37. Polynomial with no special name   **38.** Monomial
39. $-x^2 + 7x$ **40.** $-\frac{1}{4}x^3 + 4x^2 + 7$ **41.** $t - 1$
42. $14a^5 - 2a^2 - a - \frac{2}{3}$ **43.** -24 **44.** 16
45. $x^5 + 8x^4 + 6x^3 - 2x - 9$ **46.** $6a^5 - a^3 - 12a^2$
47. $-3y^2 + 8y + 3$ **48.** $x^5 - 3x^3 - 2x^2 + 8$

49. $\frac{3}{4}x^4 + \frac{1}{4}x^3 - \frac{1}{3}x^2 - \frac{7}{4}x + \frac{3}{8}$
50. $-x^5 + x^4 - 5x^3 - 2x^2 + 2x$ **51. (a)** $4w + 6$;
(b) $w^2 + 3w$ **52.** $-30x^5$ **53.** $49x^2 + 14x + 1$
54. $a^2 - 3a - 28$ **55.** $d^2 - 64$
56. $12x^3 - 23x^2 + 13x - 2$ **57.** $x^2 - 16x + 64$
58. $15t^5 - 6t^4 + 12t^3$ **59.** $4a^2 - 81$
60. $x^2 - 1.3x + 0.4$
61. $x^7 + x^5 - 3x^4 + 3x^3 - 2x^2 + 5x - 3$
62. $16y^6 - 40y^3 + 25$ **63.** $2t^4 - 11t^2 - 21$
64. $a^2 + \frac{1}{6}a - \frac{1}{3}$ **65.** $-49 + 4n^2$ **66.** 49
67. Coefficients: $1, -7, 9, -8$; degrees: $6, 2, 2, 0$; 6
68. Coefficients: $1, -1, 1$; degrees: $13, 22, 15$; 22
69. $-4u + 4v - 7$ **70.** $6m^3 + 4m^2n - mn^2$
71. $2a^2 - 16ab$ **72.** $11x^3y^2 - 8x^2y - 6x^2 - 6x + 6$
73. $2x^2 - xy - 15y^2$ **74.** $25a^2b^2 - 10abcd^2 + c^2d^4$
75. $\frac{1}{2}x^2 - \frac{1}{2}y^2$ **76.** $y^4 - \frac{1}{3}y + 4$
77. $3x^2 - 7x + 4 + \dfrac{1}{2x + 3}$ **78.** $t^3 + 2t - 3$
79. ✍ In the expression $5x^3$, the exponent refers only to the x. In the expression $(5x)^3$, the entire expression $5x$ is the base.   **80.** ✍ It is possible to determine two possibilities for the binomial that was squared by using the equation $(A - B)^2 = A^2 - 2AB + B^2$ in reverse. Since, in $x^2 - 6x + 9$, $A^2 = x^2$ and $B^2 = 9$, or 3^2, the binomial that was squared was $A - B$, or $x - 3$. If the polynomial is written $9 - 6x + x^2$, then $A^2 = 9$ and $B^2 = x^2$, so the binomial that was squared was $3 - x$. We cannot determine without further information whether the binomial squared was $x - 3$ or $3 - x$.   **81. (a)** 9; **(b)** 28   **82.** $64x^{16}$
83. $8x^4 + 4x^3 + 5x - 2$ **84.** $-16x^6 + x^2 - 10x + 25$
85. $\frac{94}{13}$ **86.** 2.28×10^{11} platelets

Test: Chapter 4, p. 299

1. [4.1] x^{13} **2.** [4.1] 3   **3.** [4.1] 1   **4.** [4.1] t^{45}
5. [4.1] $-40x^{19}y^4$ **6.** [4.1] $\frac{6}{5}a^5b^3$ **7.** [4.2] $\dfrac{1}{y^7}$
8. [4.2] 5^{-6} **9.** [4.2] $\dfrac{1}{t^9}$ **10.** [4.2] $\dfrac{3y^5}{x^5}$ **11.** [4.2] $\dfrac{b^4}{16a^{12}}$
12. [4.2] $\dfrac{c^3}{a^3b^3}$ **13.** [4.2] 3.06×10^9 **14.** [4.2] 0.00000005
15. [4.2] 1.75×10^{17} **16.** [4.2] 1.296×10^{22}
17. [4.3] Binomial   **18.** [4.3] $3, -1, \frac{1}{9}$ **19.** [4.3] Degrees of terms: $3, 1, 5, 0$; leading term: $7t^5$; leading coefficient: 7; degree of polynomial: 5   **20.** [4.3] -7 **21.** [4.3] $5a^2 - 6$
22. [4.3] $\frac{7}{4}y^2 - 4y$ **23.** [4.3] $4x^3 + 4x^2 + 3$
24. [4.4] $4x^5 + x^4 + 5x^3 - 8x^2 + 2x - 7$
25. [4.4] $5x^4 + 5x^2 + x + 5$
26. [4.4] $-2a^4 + 3a^3 - a - 7$
27. [4.4] $-t^4 + 2.5t^3 - 0.6t^2 - 9$
28. [4.5] $-6x^4 + 6x^3 + 10x^2$ **29.** [4.6] $x^2 - \frac{2}{3}x + \frac{1}{9}$
30. [4.6] $25t^2 - 49$ **31.** [4.6] $6b^2 + 7b - 5$
32. [4.6] $x^{14} - 4x^8 + 4x^6 - 16$
33. [4.6] $48 + 34y - 5y^2$ **34.** [4.5] $6x^3 - 7x^2 - 11x - 3$
35. [4.6] $64a^6 + 48a^3 + 9$ **36.** [4.7] 24
37. [4.7] $-4x^3y - x^2y^2 + xy^3 - y^3 + 19$
38. [4.7] $8a^2b^2 + 6ab + 6ab^2 + ab^3 - 4b^3$
39. [4.7] $9x^{10} - y^2$ **40.** [4.8] $4x^2 + 3x - 5$

41. [4.8] $2x^2 - 4x - 2 + \dfrac{17}{3x + 2}$ **42.** [4.5], [4.6]

$V = l(l - 2)(l - 1) = l^3 - 3l^2 + 2l$ **43.** [2.2], [4.6] $\frac{100}{21}$

44. [4.2] $\frac{1}{2} - \frac{1}{4} = \frac{1}{4}$ **45.** [4.2] About 1.4×10^7 hr

Cumulative Review: Chapters 1–4, pp. 300–301

1. 6   **2.** −8   **3.** $-\frac{7}{45}$ **4.** 6   **5.** $y + 10$ **6.** t^{12}
7. $-4x^5y^3$ **8.** $50a^4b^7$ **9.** $2(5a - 3b + 6)$ **10.** $\frac{11}{16}$
11. 6   **12.** $\frac{1}{4}t^3 - 5t^2 - 0.35$ **13.** II
14.

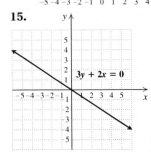

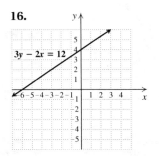

15.

$3y + 2x = 0$

16.

$3y - 2x = 12$

17.

$3y = 2$

18.

$3y = 2x + 9$

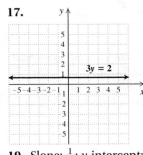

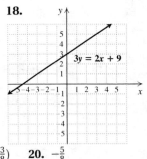

19. Slope: $\frac{1}{10}$; y-intercept: $\left(0, \frac{3}{8}\right)$ **20.** $-\frac{5}{8}$
21. $y = -\frac{2}{3}x - 10$ **22.** x-intercept: $(4, 0)$; y-intercept:
$\left(0, \frac{8}{5}\right)$ **23.** −4   **24.** $\frac{3}{5}$ **25.** $\frac{8}{3}$ **26.** 22   **27.** $\frac{5}{3}$
28. −7   **29.** $\{t \mid t \geq -8\}$, or $[-8, \infty)$ **30.** $\left\{x \mid x < \frac{1}{2}\right\}$, or
$\left(-\infty, \frac{1}{2}\right)$ **31.** $t = \dfrac{5pq}{2c}$ **32.** $7u^2v - 2uv^2 + uv + 3u^2$
33. $3x^3 - 3x^2 + 12x - 7$ **34.** $x^5 - 2x$
35. $20a - 30b + 70$ **36.** $-16x^5 - 48x^4 + 56x^3$
37. $6a^2 + 11a - 7$ **38.** $x^3 - x^2 - 7x + 10$
39. $16t^4 + 24t^2 + 9$ **40.** $\frac{1}{4}x^2 - 1$
41. $6r^4 - 5r^2s - 4s^2$ **42.** $x + \dfrac{3}{x - 1}$ **43.** $\dfrac{1}{7^{10}}$
44. $\dfrac{1}{x^7}$ **45.** $\dfrac{9}{16s^2t^{10}}$ **46.** $\dfrac{x^7y^2}{3}$ **47.** 48 thousand
megawatts   **48.** About 1298 megawatt hours
49. Washer: 20 kWh; dryer: 50 kWh
50. (a)

$w = 60n + 75$

Kilowatt hours of electricity

Number of people in household

(b) 375 kWh

51. No more than 6 hr   **52.** $160 billion   **53.** About 3.(
54. $\$\frac{12}{7}$ billion per year   **55.** 0   **56.** No solution
57. $\frac{22}{9}$ **58.** $y = \frac{1}{2}x + 4$ **59.** $\frac{1}{7} + 1 = \frac{8}{7}$ **60.** $15x^{12}$

CHAPTER 5

Technology Connection, p. 310

1. Correct   **2.** Correct   **3.** Not correct
4. Not correct   **5.** Not correct   **6.** Correct
7. Not correct   **8.** Correct

Exercise Set 5.1, pp. 310–311

1. (h)   **2.** (f)   **3.** (b)   **4.** (e)   **5.** (c)   **6.** (g)
7. (d)   **8.** (a)   **9.** Answers may vary. $(14x)(x^2)$,
$(7x^2)(2x), (-2)(-7x^3)$ **11.** Answers may vary. $(-15)(a^4$
$(-5a)(3a^3), (-3a^2)(5a^2)$ **13.** Answers may vary.
$(5t^2)(5t^3), (25t)(t^4), (-5t)(-5t^4)$
15. $8(x + 3)$ **17.** $6(x - 5)$ **19.** $2(x^2 + x - 4)$
21. $t(3t + 1)$ **23.** $-5y(y + 2)$ **25.** $x^2(x + 6)$
27. $8a^2(2a^2 - 3)$ **29.** $-t^2(6t^4 - 9t^2 + 4)$
31. $6x^2(x^6 + 2x^4 - 4x^2 + 5)$
33. $x^2y^2(x^3y^3 + x^2y + xy - 1)$
35. $-5a^2b^2(7ab^2 - 2b + 3a)$ **37.** $(n - 6)(n + 3)$
39. $(x + 3)(x^2 - 7)$ **41.** $(2y - 9)(y^2 + 1)$
43. $(x + 2)(x^2 + 5)$ **45.** $(a + 3)(5a^2 + 2)$
47. $(3n - 2)(3n^2 + 1)$ **49.** $(t - 5)(4t^2 + 3)$
51. $(7x + 5)(x^2 - 3)$ **53.** $(6a + 7)(a^2 + 1)$
55. $(x + 6)(2x^2 - 5)$ **57.** Not factorable by grouping
59. $(y + 8)(y^2 - 2)$ **61.** $(x - 4)(2x^2 - 9)$ **63.** 🖎
65. $x^2 + 9x + 14$ **66.** $x^2 - 9x + 14$ **67.** $x^2 - 5x -$
68. $x^2 + 5x - 14$ **69.** $a^2 - 4a + 3$ **70.** $t^2 + 8t + 1$
71. $t^2 + 5t - 50$ **72.** $a^2 - 2a - 24$ **73.** 🖎
75. $(2x^3 + 3)(2x^2 + 3)$ **77.** $2x(x + 1)(x^2 - 2)$
79. $(x - 1)(5x^4 + x^2 + 3)$ **81.** Answers may vary.
$8x^4y^3 - 24x^2y^4 + 16x^3y^4$

Exercise Set 5.2, pp. 317–318

1. Positive; positive   **2.** Negative; negative
3. Negative; positive   **4.** Positive; positive
5. Positive   **6.** Negative   **7.** $(x + 4)(x + 4)$
9. $(x + 1)(x + 10)$ **11.** $(x + 3)(x + 7)$
13. $(t - 2)(t - 7)$ **15.** $(b - 4)(b - 1)$
17. $(a - 3)(a - 4)$ **19.** $(d - 2)(d - 5)$
21. $(x - 5)(x + 3)$ **23.** $(x + 5)(x - 3)$
25. $2(x + 2)(x - 9)$ **27.** $-x(x + 2)(x - 8)$
29. $(y - 5)(y + 9)$ **31.** $(x - 6)(x + 12)$
33. $-5(b - 3)(b + 10)$ **35.** $x^3(x - 2)(x + 1)$
37. Prime   **39.** $(t + 4)(t + 8)$ **41.** $(x + 9)(x + 11)$
43. $3x(x - 25)(x + 4)$ **45.** $-2(x - 24)(x + 3)$
47. $(y - 12)(y - 8)$ **49.** $-a^4(a - 6)(a + 15)$
51. $\left(t + \frac{1}{3}\right)^2$ **53.** Prime   **55.** $(p - 5q)(p - 2q)$
57. Prime   **59.** $(s - 6t)(s + 2t)$ **61.** $6a^8(a - 2)(a +$
63. 🖎   **65.** $6x^2 + 17x + 12$ **66.** $6x^2 + x - 12$
67. $6x^2 - x - 12$ **68.** $6x^2 - 17x + 12$

$5x^2 - 36x + 7$ **70.** $3x^2 + 13x - 30$
73. $-5, 5, -23, 23, -49, 49$
$(y + 0.2)(y - 0.4)$ **77.** $-\frac{1}{3}a(a - 3)(a + 2)$
$(x^m + 4)(x^m + 7)$ **81.** $(a + 1)(x + 2)(x + 1)$
$(x + 3)^3$, or $(x^3 + 9x^2 + 27x + 27)$ cubic meters
$x^2\left(\frac{3}{4}\pi + 2\right)$, or $\frac{1}{4}x^2(3\pi + 8)$ **87.** $x^2\left(9 - \frac{1}{2}\pi\right)$
$(x + 4)(x + 5)$

ercise Set 5.3, pp. 327–328

(c)   **2.** (a)   **3.** (d)   **4.** (b)   **5.** $(2x - 1)(x + 4)$
$(3x + 1)(x - 6)$ **9.** $(2t + 1)(2t + 5)$
$(5a - 3)(3a - 1)$ **13.** $(3x + 4)(2x + 3)$
$2(3x + 1)(x - 2)$ **17.** $t(7t + 1)(t + 2)$
$(4x - 5)(3x - 2)$ **21.** $-1(7x + 4)(5x + 2)$, or
$7x + 4)(5x + 2)$ **23.** Prime   **25.** $(5x + 4)^2$
$(20y - 1)(y + 3)$ **29.** $(7x + 5)(2x + 9)$
$-1(x - 3)(2x + 5)$, or $-(x - 3)(2x + 5)$
$-3(2x + 1)(x + 5)$ **35.** $2(a + 1)(5a - 9)$
$4(3x - 1)(x + 6)$ **39.** $(3x + 1)(x + 1)$
$(x + 3)(x - 2)$ **43.** $(4t - 3)(2t - 7)$
$(3x + 2)(2x + 5)$ **47.** $(y + 4)(2y - 1)$
$(3a - 4)(2a - 1)$ **51.** $(16t + 7)(t + 1)$
$-1(3x + 1)(3x + 5)$, or $-(3x + 1)(3x + 5)$
$10(x^2 + 3x - 7)$ **57.** $3x(3x - 1)(2x + 3)$
$(x + 1)(25x + 64)$ **61.** $3x(7x + 1)(8x + 1)$
$-t^2(2t - 3)(7t + 1)$ **65.** $2(2y + 9)(8y - 3)$
$(2a - b)(a - 2b)$ **69.** $2(s + t)(4s + 7t)$
$3(3x - 4y)^2$ **73.** $-2(3a - 2b)(4a - 3b)$
$x^2(2x + 3)(7x - 1)$ **77.** $a^6(3a + 4)(3a + 2)$
81. $x^2 - 4x + 4$ **82.** $x^2 + 4x + 4$
$x^2 - 4$ **84.** $25t^2 - 30t + 9$ **85.** $16a^2 + 8a + 1$
$4n^2 - 49$ **87.** $9c^2 - 60c + 100$
$1 - 10a + 25a^2$ **89.** $64n^2 - 9$ **90.** $81 - y^2$
93. $(3xy + 2)(6xy - 5)$ **95.** Prime
$(4t^5 - 1)^2$ **99.** $-1(5x^m - 2)(3x^m - 4)$, or
$5x^m - 2)(3x^m - 4)$ **101.** $(3a^{3n} + 1)(a^{3n} - 1)$
3. $[7(t - 3)^n - 2][(t - 3)^n + 1]$

nnecting the Concepts, pp. 328–329

$6x^2(x^3 - 3)$ **2.** $(x + 2)(x + 8)$ **3.** $(x + 7)(2x - 1)$
$(x + 3)(x^2 + 2)$ **5.** $5(x - 2)(x + 10)$ **6.** Prime
$7y(x - 4)(x + 1)$ **8.** $3a^2(5a^2 - 9b^2 + 7b)$
$(b - 7)^2$ **10.** $(3x - 1)(4x + 1)$
$(c + 1)(c + 2)(c - 2)$ **12.** $2(x - 5)(x + 20)$
Prime   **14.** $15(d^2 - 2d + 5)$
$(3p + 2q)(5p + 2q)$ **16.** $-2t(t + 2)(t + 3)$
$(x + 11)(x - 7)$ **18.** $10(c + 1)^2$
$-1(2x - 5)(x + 1)$ **20.** $2n(m - 5)(m^2 - 3)$

ercise Set 5.4, pp. 334–335

Prime polynomial   **2.** Difference of squares
Difference of squares   **4.** None of these
Perfect-square trinomial   **6.** Perfect-square trinomial
None of these   **8.** Prime polynomial
Difference of squares   **10.** Perfect-square trinomial

11. Yes   **13.** No   **15.** No   **17.** Yes   **19.** $(x + 8)^2$
21. $(x - 5)^2$ **23.** $5(p + 2)^2$ **25.** $(1 - t)^2$, or $(t - 1)^2$
27. $2(3x + 1)^2$ **29.** $(7 - 4y)^2$, or $(4y - 7)^2$
31. $-x^3(x - 9)^2$ **33.** $2n(n + 10)^2$ **35.** $5(2x + 5)^2$
37. $(7 - 3x)^2$, or $(3x - 7)^2$ **39.** $(4x + 3)^2$
41. $2(1 + 5x)^2$, or $2(5x + 1)^2$ **43.** $(3p + 2q)^2$
45. Prime   **47.** $-1(8m + n)^2$, or $-(8m + n)^2$
49. $-2(4s - 5t)^2$ **51.** Yes   **53.** No   **55.** Yes
57. $(x + 5)(x - 5)$ **59.** $(p + 3)(p - 3)$
61. $(7 + t)(-7 + t)$, or $(t + 7)(t - 7)$
63. $6(a + 2)(a - 2)$ **65.** $(7x - 1)^2$
67. $2(10 + t)(10 - t)$ **69.** $-5(4a + 3)(4a - 3)$
71. $5(t + 4)(t - 4)$ **73.** $2(2x + 9)(2x - 9)$
75. $x(6 + 7x)(6 - 7x)$ **77.** Prime
79. $(t^2 + 1)(t + 1)(t - 1)$ **81.** $-3x(x - 4)^2$
83. $3t(5t + 3)(5t - 3)$ **85.** $a^6(a - 1)^2$
87. $10(a + b)(a - b)$ **89.** $(4x^2 + y^2)(2x + y)(2x - y)$
91. $2(3t + 2s)(3t - 2s)$ **93.**   **95.** $8x^6y^{12}$
96. $-125x^6y^3$ **97.** $x^3 + 3x^2 + 3x + 1$
98. $x^3 - 3x^2 + 3x - 1$ **99.** $p^3 + 3p^2q + 3pq^2 + q^3$
100. $p^3 - 3p^2q + 3pq^2 - q^3$ **101.**
103. $(x^4 + 2^4)(x^2 + 2^2)(x + 2)(x - 2)$, or
$(x^4 + 16)(x^2 + 4)(x + 2)(x - 2)$
105. $2x\left(3x - \frac{2}{5}\right)\left(3x + \frac{2}{5}\right)$
107. $[(y - 5)^2 + z^4][(y - 5) + z^2][(y - 5) - z^2]$, or
$(y^2 - 10y + 25 + z^4)(y - 5 + z^2)(y - 5 - z^2)$
109. $-1(x^2 + 1)(x + 3)(x - 3)$, or $-(x^2 + 1)(x + 3)(x - 3)$
111. $(y + 4)^2$ **113.** $(3p + 5)(3p - 5)^2$
115. $(9 + b^{2k})(3 + b^k)(3 - b^k)$ **117.** $2x^3 - x^2 - 1$
119. $(y + x + 7)(y - x - 1)$ **121.** 16
123. $(x + 1)^2 - x^2 = [(x + 1) + x][(x + 1) - x] = 2x + 1 = (x + 1) + x$

Exercise Set 5.5, p. 339

1. Difference of cubes   **2.** Sum of cubes   **3.** Difference
of squares   **4.** None of these   **5.** Sum of cubes
6. Difference of cubes   **7.** None of these   **8.** Difference
of squares   **9.** Difference of cubes   **10.** None of these
11. $(x - 4)(x^2 + 4x + 16)$ **13.** $(z + 1)(z^2 - z + 1)$
15. $(t - 10)(t^2 + 10t + 100)$
17. $(3x + 1)(9x^2 - 3x + 1)$
19. $(4 - 5x)(16 + 20x + 25x^2)$
21. $(x - y)(x^2 + xy + y^2)$ **23.** $\left(a + \frac{1}{2}\right)\left(a^2 - \frac{1}{2}a + \frac{1}{4}\right)$
25. $8(t - 1)(t^2 + t + 1)$ **27.** $2(3x + 1)(9x^2 - 3x + 1)$
29. $rs(s + 4)(s^2 - 4s + 16)$
31. $5(x - 2z)(x^2 + 2xz + 4z^2)$
33. $\left(y - \frac{1}{10}\right)\left(y^2 + \frac{1}{10}y + \frac{1}{100}\right)$
35. $(x + 0.1)(x^2 - 0.1x + 0.01)$
37. $8(2x^2 - t^2)(4x^4 + 2x^2t^2 + t^4)$
39. $2y(3y - 4)(9y^2 + 12y + 16)$
41. $(z + 1)(z^2 - z + 1)(z - 1)(z^2 + z + 1)$
43. $(t^2 + 4y^2)(t^4 - 4t^2y^2 + 16y^4)$
45. $(x^4 - yz^4)(x^8 + x^4yz^4 + y^2z^8)$ **47.**
49. $-\frac{1}{5}$ **50.** $\frac{1}{4}$

51.

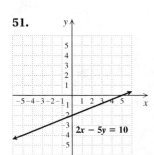

$2x - 5y = 10$

52.

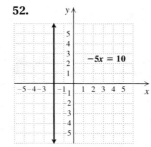

$-5x = 10$

53.

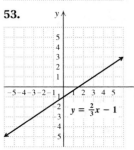

$y = \frac{2}{3}x - 1$

54.

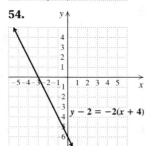

$y - 2 = -2(x + 4)$

55. ⌨ **57.** $(x^{2a} - y^b)(x^{4a} + x^{2a}y^b + y^{2b})$
59. $2x(x^2 + 75)$ **61.** $5\left(xy^2 - \frac{1}{2}\right)\left(x^2y^4 + \frac{1}{2}xy^2 + \frac{1}{4}\right)$
63. $-(3x^{4a} + 3x^{2a} + 1)$ **65.** $(t - 8)(t - 1)(t^2 + t + 1)$

Exercise Set 5.6, pp. 343–344

1. Common factor **2.** Perfect-square trinomial
3. Grouping **4.** Multiplying **5.** $5(a + 5)(a - 5)$
7. $(y - 7)^2$ **9.** $(3t + 7)(t + 3)$ **11.** $x(x + 9)^2$
13. $(x - 5)^2(x + 5)$ **15.** $3t(3t + 1)(3t - 1)$
17. $3x(3x - 5)(x + 3)$ **19.** Prime **21.** $6(y - 5)(y + 8)$
23. $-2a^4(a - 2)^2$ **25.** $5x(x^2 + 4)(x + 2)(x - 2)$
27. $(t^2 + 3)(t^2 - 3)$ **29.** $-x^4(x^2 - 2x + 7)$
31. $(x - y)(x^2 + xy + y^2)$ **33.** $a(x^2 + y^2)$
35. $2\pi r(h + r)$ **37.** $(a + b)(5a + 3b)$
39. $(x + 1)(x + y)$ **41.** $(a - 2)(a - y)$
43. $(3x - 2y)(x + 5y)$ **45.** $8mn(m^2 - 4mn + 3)$
47. $(a - 2b)^2$ **49.** $(4x + 3y)^2$ **51.** Prime
53. $(a^2b^2 + 4)(ab + 2)(ab - 2)$ **55.** $4c(4d - c)(5d - c)$
57. $(2t + 1)(4t^2 - 2t + 1)(2t - 1)(4t^2 + 2t + 1)$
59. $-1(xy + 2)(xy + 6)$, or $-(xy + 2)(xy + 6)$
61. $5(pq + 6)(pq - 1)$
63. $2a(3a + 2b)(9a^2 - 6ab + 4b^2)$
65. $x^4(x + 2y)(x - y)$ **67.** $\left(6a - \frac{5}{4}\right)^2$ **69.** $\left(\frac{1}{9}x - \frac{4}{3}\right)^2$
71. $(1 + 4x^6y^6)(1 + 2x^3y^3)(1 - 2x^3y^3)$ **73.** $(2ab + 3)^2$
75. $z(z + 6)(z^2 - 6)$ **77.** ⌨ **79.** $\frac{9}{8}$ **80.** $-\frac{5}{3}$
81. $-\frac{7}{2}$ **82.** $\frac{1}{4}$ **83.** 3 **84.** 11 **85.** -1 **86.** 3
87. ⌨ **89.** $-x(x^2 + 9)(x^2 - 2)$
91. $-1(x^2 + 2)(x + 3)(x - 3)$, or
$-(x^2 + 2)(x + 3)(x - 3)$ **93.** $(y + 1)(y - 7)(y + 3)$
95. $(y + 4 + x)^2$ **97.** $(a + 3)^2(2a + b + 4)(a - b + 5)$
99. $(7x^2 + 1 + 5x^3)(7x^2 + 1 - 5x^3)$

Technology Connection, p. 351

1. $-4.65, 0.65$ **2.** $-0.37, 5.37$ **3.** $-8.98, -4.56$
4. No solution **5.** $0, 2.76$

Exercise Set 5.7, pp. 351–353

1. (c) **2.** (a) **3.** (d) **4.** (b) **5.** $-9, -2$ **7.** $-6, \frac{3}{2}$
9. $\frac{1}{7}, \frac{3}{10}$ **11.** $0, 7$ **13.** $\frac{1}{21}, \frac{18}{11}$ **15.** $-\frac{8}{3}, 0$ **17.** $50, 70$
19. $-5, \frac{2}{3}, 1$ **21.** $1, 6$ **23.** $-7, 3$ **25.** $-9, -2$ **27.** $0, 1$
29. $-6, 0$ **31.** $-6, 6$ **33.** $-\frac{7}{2}, \frac{7}{2}$ **35.** -5 **37.** 8
39. $0, 2$ **41.** $-\frac{5}{4}, 3$ **43.** 3 **45.** $0, \frac{4}{3}$ **47.** $-\frac{7}{6}, \frac{7}{6}$
49. $-4, -\frac{2}{3}$ **51.** $-3, 1$ **53.** $-1, 0, \frac{3}{2}$ **55.** $-7, -\frac{8}{3}, \frac{5}{2}$
57. $-1, 4$ **59.** $-3, 2$ **61.** $(-2, 0), (3, 0)$ **63.** $(-4, 0),$
$(2, 0)$ **65.** $(-3, 0), \left(\frac{3}{2}, 0\right)$ **67.** ⌨ **69.** Let m and n
represent the numbers; $(m + n)^2$ **70.** Let m and n repre-
sent the numbers; $m^2 + n^2$ **71.** Let x represent the first
integer; then $x + 1$ represents the second integer; $x(x + 1)$
72. Mother's Day: \$13.8 billion; Father's Day: \$9 billion
73. $140°, 35°, 5°$ **74.** Length: 64 in.; width: 32 in.
75. ⌨ **77.** **(a)** $x^2 - x - 20 = 0$; **(b)** $x^2 - 6x - 7 = 0$;
(c) $4x^2 - 13x + 3 = 0$; **(d)** $6x^2 - 5x + 1 = 0$;
(e) $12x^2 - 17x + 6 = 0$; **(f)** $x^3 - 4x^2 + x + 6 = 0$
79. $-5, 4$ **81.** $-\frac{3}{5}, \frac{3}{5}$ **83.** $-4, 2$
85. **(a)** $2x^2 + 20x - 4 = 0$; **(b)** $x^2 - 3x - 18 = 0$;
(c) $(x + 1)(5x - 5) = 0$; **(d)** $(2x + 8)(2x - 5) = 0$;
(e) $4x^2 + 8x + 36 = 0$; **(f)** $9x^2 - 12x + 24 = 0$
87. ⌨ **89.** $2.33, 6.77$ **91.** $-9.15, -4.59$ **93.** $-3.76,$

Connecting the Concepts, p. 354

1. Expression **2.** Equation **3.** Equation
4. Expression **5.** Expression **6.** Equation
7. $2x^3 + x^2 - 8x$ **8.** $-2x^2 - 11$ **9.** $-10, 10$
10. $6a^2 - 19a + 10$ **11.** $(n - 1)(n - 9)$ **12.** $2, 8$
13. $-\frac{5}{2}$ **14.** $7x^3 + 2x - 7$ **15.** $(4x + 9)(4x - 9)$
16. $-3, 8$ **17.** $-4a^2 - a - 11$
18. $2x^2(9x^2 - 12x + 10)$ **19.** $-1, -\frac{2}{3}$
20. $8x^5 - 20x^4 + 12x^2$

Translating for Success, p. 361

1. O **2.** M **3.** K **4.** I **5.** G **6.** E **7.** C
8. A **9.** H **10.** B

Exercise Set 5.8, pp. 362–366

1. $-2, 3$ **3.** 6 m, 8 m, 10 m **5.** 11, 12
7. -14 and -12; 12 and 14 **9.** Length: 30 ft; width: 6 ft
11. Length: 6 cm; width: 4 cm **13.** Base: 12 in.; height: 9 in.
15. Foot: 7 ft; height: 12 ft **17.** 1 min, 3 min **19.** In 2004
21. 16 teams **23.** 66 handshakes **25.** 12 players
27. 9 ft **29.** 32 ft **31.** 300 ft by 400 ft by 500 ft
33. Dining room: 12 ft by 12 ft; kitchen: 12 ft by 10 ft
35. 20 ft **37.** 1 sec, 2 sec **39.** ⌨ **41.** $-\frac{12}{35}$ **42.** $-\frac{2}{2}$
43. -1 **44.** $-\frac{7}{4}$ **45.** $\frac{1}{4}$ **46.** $\frac{4}{5}$ **47.** $\frac{53}{168}$ **48.** $\frac{19}{18}$
49. ⌨ **51.** \$180 **53.** 39 cm **55.** 4 in., 6 in.
57. 35 ft **59.** 2 hr, 4.2 hr **61.** 3 hr

Review Exercises: Chapter 5, pp. 369–371

1. False **2.** True **3.** True **4.** False **5.** False
6. True **7.** True **8.** False **9.** Answers may vary.
$(4x)(5x^2), (-2x^2)(-10x), (x^3)(20)$

Answers may vary. $(-3x^2)(6x^3), (2x^4)(-9x)$,
$18x)(x^4)$ **11.** $6x^3(2x-3)$ **12.** $4a(2a-3)$
$(10t+1)(10t-1)$ **14.** $(x+4)(x-3)$
$(x+7)^2$ **16.** $3x(2x+1)^2$ **17.** $(2x+3)(3x^2+1)$
$(6a-5)(a+1)$ **19.** $(5t-3)^2$
$2(24t^2-14t+3)$ **21.** $(9a^2+1)(3a+1)(3a-1)$
$3x(3x-5)(x+3)$ **23.** $2(x-5)(x^2+5x+25)$
$(x+4)(x^3-2)$ **25.** $(ab^2+8)(ab^2-8)$
$-4x^4(2x^2-8x+1)$ **27.** $3(2x-5)^2$
Prime **29.** $-t(t+6)(t-7)$ **30.** $(2x+5)(2x-5)$
$(n+6)(n-10)$ **32.** $5(z^2-6z+2)$
$(4t+5)(t+2)$ **34.** $(2t+1)(t-4)$
$7x(x+1)(x+4)$ **36.** $(2y+3x^2)(4y^2-6x^2y+9x^4)$
$5(2x-1)^2$ **38.** $-6x(x+5)(x-5)$
$(5-x)(3-x)$ **40.** Prime **41.** $(xy+8)(xy-2)$
$3(2a+7b)^2$ **43.** $(m+5)(m+t)$
$32(x^2+2y^2z^2)(x^2-2y^2z^2)$ **45.** $(2m+n)(3m+n)$
$(3r+5s)(2r-3s)$ **47.** $-11,9$ **48.** $-7,5$
$-\frac{3}{4},\frac{3}{4}$ **50.** $\frac{2}{3},1$ **51.** $-\frac{5}{2},6$ **52.** $-2,3$ **53.** $0,\frac{3}{5}$
1 **55.** $-3,4$ **56.** 10 teams **57.** $(-1,0),\left(\frac{5}{2},0\right)$
Height: 14 ft; base: 14 ft **59.** 10 holes
Answers may vary. Because Celia did not first factor
the largest common factor, 4, her factorization will not be
"complete" until she removes a common factor of 2 from each
nomial. The answer should be $4(x-5)(x+5)$. Awarding 3
7 points would seem reasonable. **61.** The equations
ved in this chapter have an x^2-term (are quadratic),
ereas those solved previously have no x^2-term (are
ear). The principle of zero products is used to solve
adratic equations and is not used to solve linear
uations. **62.** 2.5 cm **63.** 0, 2 **64.** Length: 12 cm;
dth: 6 cm **65.** 100 cm², 225 cm² **66.** $-3,2,\frac{5}{2}$
No real solution

st: Chapter 5, pp. 371–372

[5.1] Answers may vary. $(3x^2)(4x^2),(-2x)(-6x^3)$,
$2x^3)(x)$ **2.** [5.2] $(x-4)(x-9)$ **3.** [5.4] $(x-5)^2$
[5.1] $2y^2(2y^2-4y+3)$ **5.** [5.1] $(x+1)(x^2+2)$
[5.1] $t^5(t^2-3)$ **7.** [5.2] $a(a+4)(a-1)$
[5.3] $2(5x-6)(x+4)$ **9.** [5.4] $(2t+5)(2t-5)$
[5.2] $(x+2)(x-3)$ **11.** [5.3] $-3m(2m+1)(m+1)$
[5.5] $3(r-1)(r^2+r+1)$ **13.** [5.4] $5(3r+2)^2$
[5.4] $3(x^2+4)(x+2)(x-2)$ **15.** [5.4] $(7t+6)^2$
[5.1] $(x+2)(x^3-3)$ **17.** [5.2] Prime
[5.3] $(2x+3)(2x-5)$ **19.** [5.3] $3t(2t+5)(t-1)$
[5.3] $3(m-5n)(m+2n)$ **21.** [5.7] 1, 5
[5.7] $-\frac{3}{2},5$ **23.** [5.7] $0,\frac{2}{5}$ **24.** [5.7] $-\frac{1}{5},\frac{1}{5}$
[5.7] $-4,5$ **26.** [5.7] $(-1,0),\left(\frac{8}{3},0\right)$
[5.8] Length: 10 m; width: 4 m **28.** [5.8] 10 people
[5.8] 5 ft **30.** [5.8] 15 cm by 30 cm
[5.2] $(a-4)(a+8)$ **32.** [5.7] $-\frac{8}{3},0,\frac{2}{5}$

mulative Review: Chapters 1–5, pp. 372–373

$\frac{1}{2}$ **2.** $\frac{9}{32}$ **3.** $\frac{9}{8}$ **4.** 29 **5.** $\frac{1}{9x^4y^6}$ **6.** t^{10}
$3x^4+5x^3+x-10$ **8.** $-3a^2b-ab^2+2b^3$

9. $\frac{t^8}{4s^2}$ **10.** $-\frac{8x^6y^3}{27z^{12}}$ **11.** 8 **12.** -8 **13.** $-x^4$
14. $2x^3-5x^2+\frac{1}{2}x-1$ **15.** $-4t^{11}+8t^9+20t^8$
16. $9x^2-30x+25$ **17.** $100x^{10}-y^2$
18. x^3-2x^2+1 **19.** $(c+1)(c-1)$
20. $5(x+y)(1+2x)$ **21.** $(2r-t)^2$
22. $(2x-5)(3x-2)$ **23.** $10(y^2+4)$
24. $y(x-1)(x-2)$ **25.** $(3x-2y)(4x+y)$
26. $(5a+4b)(25a^2-20ab+16b^2)$ **27.** $\frac{1}{12}$
28. 1 **29.** $-\frac{9}{4}$ **30.** $\{x\mid x\geq 1\}$, or $[1,\infty)$ **31.** $-3,1$
32. $-4,3$ **33.** $-2,2$ **34.** $0,4$ **35.** $c=\dfrac{a}{b+d}$ **36.** 0
37. $-2;(0,5)$ **38.** $y=5x-\frac{1}{3}$ **39.** $y=5x+\frac{5}{3}$

40.

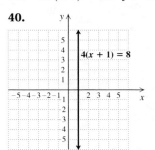

41.

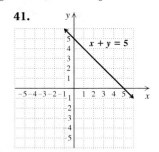

42.

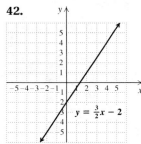

43.

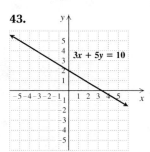

44.

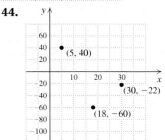

45. 372 min
46. 11,616,000 subscribers per year **47.** 60,000,000 users **48.** 101,180 people
49. Bottom of ladder to building: 5 ft; top of ladder to ground: 12 ft
50. Length: 12 ft; width: 2 ft
51. Scores that are 9 and higher
52. (a)

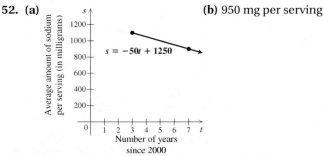

(b) 950 mg per serving
53. $b=\dfrac{2}{a+1}$ **54.** $y=-8$
55. (a) $9y^2+12y+4-x^2$; (b) $(3y+2+x)(3y+2-x)$
56. $-1,0,\frac{1}{3}$

Glossary

solute value [1.4]   The distance that a number is from 0 on the number line.

ditive inverse [1.6]   A number's opposite. Two numbers are additive inverses of each other if their sum is zero.

ebraic expression [1.1]   A collection of numerals and/or variables on which the operations $+$, $-$, $\cdot$, $\div$, $(\ )^n$, or $\sqrt[n]{(\ )}$ are performed.

thmetic sequence [14.2]   A sequence in which the difference between any two successive terms is constant.

thmetic series [14.2]   A series for which the associated sequence is arithmetic.

ending order   A polynomial written with the terms arranged according to degree of one variable, from least to greatest.

ociative law of addition [1.2]   The statement that when three numbers are added, regrouping the addends gives the same sum.

ociative law of multiplication [1.2]   The statement that when three numbers are multiplied, regrouping the factors gives the same product.

mptote [12.2], [13.3]   A line that a graph approaches more and more closely as x increases or as x decreases.

rage [2.7]   Most commonly, the mean of a set of numbers found by adding the numbers and dividing by the number of addends.

s (singular, axis) [3.1]   Two perpendicular number lines used to identify points in a plane.

s of symmetry [11.6]   A line that can be drawn through graph such that the part of the graph on one side of the line is an exact reflection of the part on the opposite side.

graph [3.1]   A graphic display of data using bars proportional in length to the numbers represented.

se [1.8]   In exponential notation, the number or expression being raised to a power. In expressions of the form a^n, a is the base.

omial [4.2]   A polynomial composed of two terms.

nches [13.3]   The two curves that comprise a hyperbola.

ak-even point [8.8]   In business, the point of intersection of the revenue function and the cost function.

C

Circle [13.1]   A set of points in a plane that are a fixed distance r, called the radius, from a fixed point (h, k), called the center.

Circle graph [3.1]   A graphic display of data using sectors of a circle to represent percents.

Circumference [2.3]   The distance around a circle.

Closed interval $[a, b]$ [2.6]   The set of all numbers x for which $a \leq x \leq b$. Thus, $[a, b] = \{x \mid a \leq x \leq b\}$.

Coefficient [2.1]   The numerical multiplier of a variable or variables.

Combined variation [7.5]   A mathematical relationship in which a variable varies directly and/or inversely, at the same time, with more than one other variable.

Common logarithm [12.5]   A logarithm with base 10.

Commutative law of addition [1.2]   The statement that when two numbers are added, changing the order in which the numbers are added does not affect the sum.

Commutative law of multiplication [1.2]   The statement that when two numbers are multiplied, changing the order in which the numbers are multiplied does not affect the product.

Complementary angles [2.5]   A pair of angles, the sum of whose measures is 90°.

Completing the square [11.1]   The procedure in which one adds a particular constant to an expression so that the resulting sum is a perfect square.

Complex number [10.8]   Any number that can be written as $a + bi$, where a and b are real numbers and $i = \sqrt{-1}$.

Complex rational expression [6.5]   A rational expression that has one or more rational expressions within its numerator and/or denominator.

Complex-number system [10.8]   A number system that contains the real-number system and is designed so that negative numbers have defined square roots.

Composite function [12.1]   A function in which a quantity depends on a variable that, in turn, depends on another variable.

Composite number [1.3]   A natural number, other than 1, that is not prime.

Compound inequality [9.2]   A statement in which two or more inequalities are combined using the word *and* or the word *or*.

Compound interest [11.1]   Interest computed on the sum of an original principal and the interest previously accrued by that principal.

Conditional equation [2.2]   An equation that is true for some replacements of a variable(s) and false for others.

Conic section [13.1]   A curve formed by the intersection of a plane and a cone.

Conjugates [10.5], [10.8]   Pairs of radical expressions, like $a\sqrt{b} + c\sqrt{d}$ and $a\sqrt{b} - c\sqrt{d}$, for which the product does not have a radical term or pairs of imaginary numbers, like $a + bi$ and $a - bi$, for which the product is real.

Conjunction [9.2]   A sentence in which two statements are joined by the word *and*.

Consecutive numbers [2.5]   Integers that are one unit apart.

Consistent system of equations [8.1], [8.4]   A system of equations that has at least one solution.

Constant [1.1]   A known number.

Constant function [7.3]   A function given by an equation of the form $f(x) = b$, where b is a real number.

Constant of proportionality [7.5]   The constant in an equation of variation.

Constraint [9.5]   A requirement imposed on a problem.

Contradiction [2.2]   An equation that is never true.

Coordinates [3.1]   The numbers in an ordered pair.

Cube root [10.1]   The number c is called the cube root of a if $c^3 = a$.

D

Data point [11.8]   A given ordered pair of a function, usually found experimentally.

Degree of a polynomial [4.3]   The degree of the term of highest degree in a polynomial.

Degree of a term [4.3]   The number of variable factors in a term.

Demand function [8.8]   A function modeling the relationship between the price of a good and the quantity of that good demanded.

Denominator [1.3], [6.1]   The number below the fraction bar in a fraction or the expression below the fraction bar in a rational expression.

Dependent equations [8.1]   Equations in a system from which one equation can be removed without changing the solution set.

Descending order [4.3]   A polynomial written with the terms arranged according to degree of one variable, from greatest to least.

Determinant [8.7]   A descriptor of a square matrix. The determinant of a two-by-two matrix $\begin{bmatrix} a & c \\ b & d \end{bmatrix}$ is denoted $\begin{vmatrix} a & c \\ b & d \end{vmatrix}$ and represents $ad - bc$.

Difference of squares [4.6], [5.4]   An expression that can be written in the form $A^2 - B^2$.

Direct variation [7.5]   A situation that translates to an equation of the form $y = kx$, with k a nonzero constant.

Discriminant [11.3]   The expression $b^2 - 4ac$ from the quadratic formula.

Disjunction [9.2]   A sentence in which two statements are joined by the word *or*.

Distributive law [1.2]   The statement that multiplying a factor by the sum of two addends gives the same result as multiplying the factor by each of the two addends and then adding.

Domain [7.2]   The set of all first coordinates of the ordered pairs in a function.

Doubling time [12.7]   The time necessary for a population to double in size.

E

e [12.5]   An irrational number that is approximately 2.7182818284, which is used in many applications.

Element [8.6]   An entry in a matrix.

Elimination method [8.2]   An algebraic method that uses the addition principle to solve a system of equations.

Ellipse [13.2]   The set of all points in a plane for which the sum of the distances from two fixed points F_1 and F_2, called foci, is constant.

Equation [1.1]   A number sentence with the verb $=$.

Equation of variation [7.5]   An equation used to represent direct, inverse, or combined variation.

Equilibrium point [8.8]   The point of intersection between the demand function and the supply function.

Equivalent equations [2.1]   Equations with the same solutions.

Equivalent expressions [1.2]   Expressions that have the same value for all allowable replacements.

Equivalent inequalities [2.6]   Inequalities that have the same solution set.

Evaluate [1.1]   To substitute a value for each occurrence of a variable in an expression and calculate the result.

Exponent [1.8]   The power to which a base is raised. In expressions of the form a^n, the number n is an exponent. For n a natural number, a^n represents n factors of a.

Exponential decay [12.7]   A decrease in quantity over time that can be modeled by an exponential equation of the form $P(t) = P_0 e^{-kt}$, $k > 0$.

Exponential equation [12.6]   An equation in which a variable appears in an exponent.

Exponential function [12.2]   A function that can be described by an exponential equation.

Exponential growth [12.7]   An increase in quantity over time that can be modeled by an exponential function of the form $P(t) = P_0 e^{kt}$, $k > 0$.

Exponential notation [1.8]   A representation of a number using a base raised to a power.

Extrapolation [3.7]   The process of predicting a future value on the basis of given data.

F

Factor [1.2]   *Verb*: to write an equivalent expression that is a product. *Noun*: a multiplier.

ite sequence [14.1]   A function having for its domain a
et of natural numbers: $\{1, 2, 3, 4, 5, \ldots, n\}$, for some nat-
ral number n.

ed costs [8.8]   In business, costs that are incurred
egardless of how many items are produced.

cus (plural, foci) [13.2]   One of two fixed points that de-
ermine the points of an ellipse or a hyperbola.

L [4.5]   An acronym for a procedure for multiplying
wo binomials by multiplying the First terms, the Outer
erms, the Inner terms, and the Last terms, and then
dding the results.

rmula [2.3]   An equation that uses numbers and/or let-
ers to represent a relationship between two or more
uantities.

ction notation [1.3]   A number written using a numer-
tor and a denominator.

nction [7.1]   A correspondence that assigns to each
member of a set called the domain exactly one member
f a set called the range.

neral term of a sequence [14.1]   The nth term, denoted a_n.

ometric sequence [14.3]   A sequence in which the ratio
f every pair of successive terms is constant.

ometric series [14.3]   A series for which the associated
equence is geometric.

ade [3.5]   The ratio of the vertical distance a road rises
ver the horizontal distance it runs, expressed as a
percent.

ph [3.1]   A picture or diagram of the data in a table, or
line, a curve, a plane, or collection of points, etc.,
hat represents all the solutions of an equation or an
nequality.

lf-life [12.7]   The amount of time necessary for half of a
uantity to decay.

lf-open interval [2.6]   An interval that includes exactly
ne endpoint.

rizontal-line test [12.1]   The statement that if it is impossible to draw a horizontal line that intersects the
graph of a function more than once, then that function is
ne-to-one.

perbola [13.3]   The set of all points P in the plane such
hat the difference of the distance from P to two fixed
points is constant.

potenuse [5.8]   In a right triangle, the side opposite the
ight angle.

0.8]   The square root of -1. That is, $i = \sqrt{-1}$ and $i^2 = -1$.

ntity [2.2]   An equation that is always true.

ntity property of 0 [1.5]   The statement that the sum of
number and 0 is always the original number.

Identity property of 1 [1.3]   The statement that the
product of a number and 1 is always the original number.

Imaginary number [10.8]   A number that can be written in
the form $a + bi$, where a and b are real numbers and
$b \neq 0$ and $i = \sqrt{-1}$.

Inconsistent system of equations [8.1]   A system of equations for which there is no solution.

Independent equations [8.1]   Equations that are not
dependent.

Index (plural, indices) [10.1]   In the radical $\sqrt[n]{a}$, the number n is called the index.

Inequality [1.4]   A mathematical sentence using
$<, >, \leq, \geq$, or $\neq$.

Infinite geometric series [14.3]   The sum of the terms of
an infinite geometric sequence.

Infinite sequence [14.1]   A function having for its domain
the set of natural numbers: $\{1, 2, 3, 4, 5, \ldots\}$.

Input [7.1]   A member of the domain of a function.

Integers [1.4]   The whole numbers and their opposites.

Interpolation [3.7]   The process of estimating a value between given values.

Intersection of two sets [9.2]   The set of all elements that
are common to both sets.

Interval notation [2.6]   The use of a pair of numbers inside parentheses and/or brackets to represent the set of
all numbers between those two numbers. *See also* Closed,
Open, and Half-open intervals.

Inverse relation [12.1]   The relation formed by inter-
changing the members of the domain and the range of
a relation.

Inverse variation [7.5]   A situation that translates to
an equation of the form $y = k/x$, with k a nonzero
constant.

Irrational number [1.4]   A real number that cannot be
named as a ratio of two integers. In decimal notation, irrational numbers neither terminate nor repeat.

Isosceles right triangle [10.7]   A right triangle in which
both legs have the same length.

J

Joint variation [7.5]   A situation that translates to an equation of the form $y = kxz$, with k a nonzero constant.

L

Largest common factor [5.1]   The common factor of the
terms of a polynomial with the largest possible coefficient and the largest possible exponent(s).

Leading coefficient [4.3]   The coefficient of the term of
highest degree in a polynomial.

Leading term [4.3]   The term of highest degree in a polynomial.

Least common denominator (LCD) [6.3]   The least common multiple of the denominators of two or more
rational expressions.

Least common multiple (LCM) [6.3]   The multiple of all expressions under consideration that has the smallest positive coefficient and the least possible degree.

Legs [5.8]   In a right triangle, the two sides that form the right angle.

Like radicals [10.5]   Radical expressions that have identical indices and radicands.

Like terms [1.5], [4.3]   Terms that have exactly the same variable factors.

Line graph [3.1]   A graph in which quantities are represented as points connected by straight-line segments.

Linear equation [3.2], [8.4]   In two variables, any equation that can be written in the form $y = mx + b$, or $Ax + By = C$, where x and y are variables and m, b, A, B, and C are constants and A and B are not both 0. In three variables, an equation that is equivalent to one of the form $Ax + By + Cz = D$, where x, y, and z are variables, and A, B, and C are constants that are not all 0.

Linear function [7.3]   A function that can be described by an equation of the form $f(x) = mx + b$, where m and b are constants.

Linear inequality [9.4]   An inequality whose related equation is a linear equation.

Linear programming [9.5]   A branch of mathematics involving graphs of inequalities and their constraints.

Logarithmic equation [12.6]   An equation containing a logarithmic expression.

Logarithmic function, base a [12.3]   The inverse of an exponential function with base a.

M

Matrix (plural, matrices) [8.6]   A rectangular array of numbers.

Maximum value [11.6]   The greatest function value (output) achieved by a function.

Mean [2.7]   The sum of a set of numbers divided by the number of addends.

Minimum value [11.6]   The least function value (output) achieved by a function.

Monomial [4.3]   A constant, a variable, or a product of a constant and one or more variables.

Motion problem [6.7]   A problem that deals with distance, speed, and time.

Multiplicative inverses [1.3]   Reciprocals; two numbers whose product is 1.

Multiplicative property of zero [1.7]   The statement that the product of 0 and any real number is 0.

N

Natural logarithm [12.5]   A logarithm with base e.

Natural numbers [1.3]   The counting numbers: 1, 2, 3, 4, 5, ...

Nonlinear function [7.3]   A function whose graph is not a straight line.

Numerator [1.3], [6.1]   The number above the fraction bar in a fraction or the expression above the fraction bar in a rational expression.

O

Objective function [9.5]   In linear programming, the function in which the expression being maximized or minimized appears.

One-to-one function [12.1]   A function for which all different inputs have different outputs.

Open interval (a, b) [2.6]   The set of all numbers x for which $a < x < b$. Thus, $(a, b) = \{x \mid a < x < b\}$.

Opposite [1.6]   The additive inverse of a number. Opposites are the same distance from 0 on the number line but on different sides of 0.

Ordered pair [3.1]   A pair of numbers of the form (h, k) for which the order in which the numbers are listed is important.

Origin [3.1]   The point on a graph in a coordinate plane where the two axes intersect.

Output [7.1]   A member of the range of a function.

P

Parabola [11.6], [13.1]   A graph of a second degree polynomial equation in one variable.

Parallel lines [3.6]   Lines that extend indefinitely without intersecting.

Pascal's triangle [14.4]   A triangular array of coefficients of the expansion $(a + b)^n$ for $n = 0, 1, 2, \ldots$.

Perfect square [10.1]   A rational number for which there exists a number a for which $a^2 = p$.

Perfect-square trinomial [4.6], [5.4]   A trinomial that is the square of a binomial.

Perpendicular lines [3.6]   Lines that intersect at a right angle.

Piecewise function [7.2]   A function that is defined by different equations for various parts of its domain.

Point–slope equation [3.7]   An equation of the type $y - y_1 = m(x - x_1)$, where x and y are variables, and m is the slope of the line and (x_1, y_1) is a point on the line.

Polynomial [4.2]   A monomial or a sum of monomials.

Price [8.8]   The amount a purchaser pays for an item.

Polynomial equation [5.7]   An equation in which two polynomials are set equal to each other.

Polynomial inequality [11.9]   An inequality that is equivalent to an inequality with a polynomial as one side and 0 as the other.

Prime factorization [1.3]   The factorization of a natural number into a product of its prime factors.

Prime number [1.3]   A natural number that has exactly two different natural number factors: the number itself and 1.

Principal square root [10.1]   The nonnegative square root of a number.

portion [6.7] An equation stating that two ratios are equal.

re imaginary number [10.8] A complex number of the form $a + bi$, with $a = 0$ and $b \neq 0$.

thagorean theorem [5.8] The theorem that states that n any right triangle, if a and b are the lengths of the legs nd c is the length of the hypotenuse, then $a^2 + b^2 = c^2$.

adrants [3.1] The four regions into which the axes livide a plane.

adratic equation [5.7] An equation equivalent to one of the form $ax^2 + bx + c = 0$, where $a \neq 0$.

adratic formula [11.2] $x = \dfrac{-b \pm \sqrt{b^2 - 4ac}}{2a}$, which gives the solutions of $ax^2 + bx + c = 0$, where $a \neq 0$.

adratic function [11.1] A second-degree polynomial unction in one variable.

adratic inequality [11.9] A second-degree polynomial nequality in one variable.

dical equation [10.6] An equation in which a variable appears in a radicand.

dical expression [10.1] An algebraic expression in which a radical sign appears.

dical sign [10.1] The symbol $\sqrt{}$ or $\sqrt[n]{}$, where $n > 2$.

dical term [10.5] A term in which a radical sign appears.

dicand [10.1] The expression under a radical sign.

dius (plural, radii) [13.1] The distance from the center of a circle to a point on the circle. Also, a segment connecting the center to a point on the circle.

nge [7.2] The set of all second coordinates of the ordered pairs in a function.

te [3.4] A ratio that indicates how two quantities change with respect to each other.

tio [6.7] The quotient of two quantities. The ratio of a to b is a/b, also written $a : b$.

tional equation [6.6] An equation containing one or more rational expressions.

tional expression [6.1] A quotient of two polynomials.

tional inequality [11.9] An inequality containing a rational expression.

tional number [1.4] A number that can be written in the form $\dfrac{a}{b}$, where a and b are integers and $b \neq 0$. In decimal notation, a rational number repeats or terminates.

tionalizing the denominator [10.4], [10.5] A procedure for finding an equivalent expression without a radical in ts denominator.

tionalizing the numerator [10.4], [10.5] A procedure for finding an equivalent expression without a radical in ts numerator.

Real number [1.4] Any number that is either rational or irrational.

Reciprocal [1.3] A multiplicative inverse. Two numbers are reciprocals if their product is 1.

Reflection [11.6] The mirror image of a graph.

Relation [7.1] A correspondence between two sets, called the domain and the range, such that each member of the domain corresponds to at least one member of the range.

Repeating decimal [1.4] A decimal in which a block of digits repeats indefinitely.

Right triangle [5.8] A triangle that includes a right angle.

Row-equivalent operations [8.6] Operations used to produce equivalent systems of equations.

S

Scientific notation [4.2] A number written in the form $N \times 10^m$, where m is an integer, $1 \leq N < 10$, and N is expressed in decimal notation.

Sequence [14.1] A function for which the domain is a set of consecutive natural numbers beginning with 1.

Series [14.1] The sum of specified terms in a sequence.

Set [1.4] A collection of objects.

Set-builder notation [2.6] The naming of a set by describing basic characteristics of the elements in the set.

Sigma notation [14.1] The naming of a sum using the Greek letter Σ (sigma) as part of an abbreviated form.

Similar triangles [10.7] Triangles in which corresponding sides are proportional and corresponding angles have the same measure.

Simplify To rewrite an expression in an equivalent, abbreviated, form.

Slope [3.5] The ratio of the rise to the run for any two points on a line.

Slope–intercept equation [3.6] An equation of the form $y = mx + b$, where x and y are variables, m is the slope of the line, and $(0, b)$ is its y-intercept.

Solution [1.1], [2.1], [2.6], [8.1] A replacement or substitution that makes an equation, an inequality, or a system of equations or inequalities true.

Solution set [2.1], [2.6], [8.1] The set of all solutions of an equation, an inequality, or a system of equations or inequalities.

Solve [2.1], [2.6], [8.1] To find all solutions of an equation, an inequality, or a system of equations or inequalities; to find the solution(s) of a problem.

Speed [6.7] The ratio of distance traveled to the time required to travel that distance.

Square matrix [8.7] A matrix with the same number of rows and columns.

Square root [10.1] The number c is a square root of a if $c^2 = a$.

Substitute [1.1] To replace a variable with a number or an expression that represents a number.

Substitution method [8.2] An algebraic method for solving systems of equations.

Supplementary angles [2.5]   A pair of angles, the sum of whose measure is 180°.

Supply function [8.8]   A function modeling the relationship between the price of a good and the quantity of that good supplied.

System of equations [8.1]   A set of two or more equations that are to be solved simultaneously.

T

Term [1.2], [4.3]   A number, a variable, or a product or a quotient of numbers and/or variables.

Terminating decimal [1.4]   A number in decimal notation that can be written using a finite number of decimal places.

Total cost [8.8]   The amount spent to produce a product.

Total profit [8.8]   The amount taken in less the amount spent, or total revenue minus total cost.

Total revenue [8.8]   The amount taken in from the sale of a product.

Trinomial [4.3]   A polynomial that is composed of three terms.

U

Union of A and B [9.2]   The set of all elements belonging to either A or B or both.

Undefined [1.7]   An expression that has no meaning attached to it.

V

Value [1.1]   The numerical result after a number has been substituted into an expression.

Variable [1.1]   A letter that represents an unknown number.

Variable costs [8.8]   In business, costs that vary according to the amount produced.

Variable expression [1.1]   An expression containing a variable.

Vertex (plural, vertices) [11.6], [13.1], [13.2], [13.3]   The point at which the graph of a parabola, an ellipse, or a hyperbola crosses its axis of symmetry.

Vertical-line test [7.1]   The statement that a graph represents a function if it is impossible to draw a vertical line that intersects the graph more than once.

W

Whole numbers [1.3]   The natural numbers and 0: 0, 1, 2, 3, . . .

X

x-intercept [3.3]   A point at which a graph crosses the x-axis.

Y

y-intercept [3.3]   A point at which a graph crosses the y-axis.

Z

Zeros [11.9]   The x-values for which $f(x)$ is 0, for any function f.

Index of Applications

Geometric Formulas

Plane Geometry

Rectangle
Area: $A = lw$
Perimeter: $P = 2l + 2w$

Square
Area: $A = s^2$
Perimeter: $P = 4s$

Triangle
Area: $A = \frac{1}{2}bh$

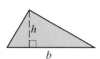

Triangle
Sum of Angle Measures:
$A + B + C = 180°$

Right Triangle
Pythagorean Theorem
(Equation):
$a^2 + b^2 = c^2$

Parallelogram
Area: $A = bh$

Trapezoid
Area: $A = \frac{1}{2}h(b_1 + b_2)$

Circle
Area: $A = \pi r^2$
Circumference:
$C = \pi d = 2\pi r$
$\left(\frac{22}{7}\right.$ and 3.14 are different
approximations for $\left.\pi\right)$

Solid Geometry

Rectangular Solid
Volume: $V = lwh$

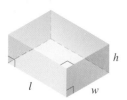

Cube
Volume: $V = s^3$

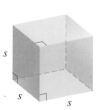

Right Circular Cylinder
Volume: $V = \pi r^2 h$
Total Surface Area:
$S = 2\pi rh + 2\pi r^2$

Right Circular Cone
Volume: $V = \frac{1}{3}\pi r^2 h$
Total Surface Area:
$S = \pi r^2 + \pi rs$
Slant Height:
$s = \sqrt{r^2 + h^2}$

Sphere
Volume: $V = \frac{4}{3}\pi r^3$
Surface Area: $S = 4\pi r^2$

Selected Keys of the Scientific Calculator

This secondary function takes the square root of number displayed.

Squares number displayed.

Activates secondary functions printed above certain keys. Also denoted INV or 2nd.

Used when entering numbers in scientific notation. Also denoted EXP.

Finds reciprocal of number displayed.

Used to raise any base to a power. Also denoted y^x, a^x, or ∧.

Stores number displayed in memory. Also denoted MIN or M.

Recalls number stored in memory. Also denoted MR.

This secondary function raises 10 to any power entered.

Clears all preceding numbers and operations. Also used to turn calculator on.

Used as an approximation for pi.

Used to perform indicated operation.

Used to control order in which certain operations are performed.

Clears last number displayed but not preceding operations.

Used when entering decimal notation.

Used to change sign of number displayed.

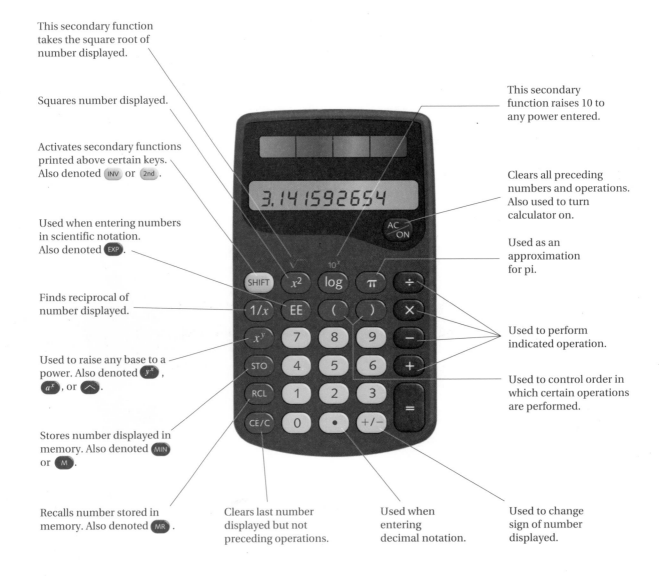